History of

ROCKETRY & SPACE TRAVEL

History of
ROCKETRY & S

Original Illustrations by Harry H-K Lange

Introduction by Frederick C. Durant III

Revised Edition

PACE TRAVEL

WERNHER VON BRAUN

FREDERICK I. ORDWAY III

Thomas Y. Crowell Company / New York / Established 1834

Introduction

The history of astronautics may be thought of as two separate histories—rocketry and space flight. These fascinating stories proceeded in parallel, unrelated fashion for hundreds of years until the last decades of the nineteenth century. At about that time, the first appreciation was gained of the necessity for rocket propulsion to achieve man's ancient, hitherto unattainable dream of flight into space.

The beginnings of rocketry date to the thirteenth century and the use of black-powder rockets. The Chinese are generally given credit for being the first to use the rocket as a propulsive device, although no hard factual reference to this exists. It is accepted by historians, however, that crude rockets were fired as military weapons in the thirteenth century in the Far East, the Near East, and in Europe. "Reaction propulsion" as an effect was known much earlier to the Greeks, but the principles were apparently not fully understood within the framework of the science of that period.

Authors Wernher von Braun and Frederick I. Ordway III are each eminently qualified to present this exciting and still widely unknown story. I have known both men for nearly twenty years, during which period Von Braun has demonstrated his ability as the leading rocket engineer in the Western World. Ordway, through personal interest and initiative, has collected one of the largest private astronautical archives in the world and has been a major contributor to astronautical reference works. The interests of both men are broad—a necessity when studying a worldwide technological history of intermittent and sporadic progress spanning centuries. Both men have had a classic, as well as a scientific, education which enables them to recognize the impact of both the philosophical and technical aspects of the evolution of astronautics. From a historical standpoint, the significance of events and of individual efforts is not always evident, nor the relative impact easily seen in retrospect. In my opinion, this book represents an important contribution by recording the manifold contributions of many individuals from many differ-ent nations. It chronicles events which have led to perhaps man's greatest adventure—the exploration of space.

The history of rocketry and astronautics can, of course, never be completely told at any one time. "New" information and insights into the past will always remain to be discovered. Military archives, long-forgotten writings, and rare graphic presentations are continually coming to light. At the same time, new history is being written almost daily of space accomplishments. Another whole segment of this history has still to be written—that of the social and sociological implications and impact upon man resulting from the fruition of this investment of time, immense effort, money, and materials to achieve space mobility. This is quite apart from the impacts which will be felt from this new knowledge of the cosmos, as well as the new knowledge gained of man, himself.

At this instant, however, I know of no comparable reference work which documents rocket flight in such detail, contains as many references, or presents so many fine photographs and illustrations of past and current events. The authors have endeavored to encompass and present in a lucid fashion the hundreds of elements of this history and have succeeded admirably. Much is presented comprehensively for the first time in a single volume and the work promises to be an important standard reference.

It has always been surprising to me how little of the history of rocketry and space flight is known to the average intelligent person. This includes tens of thousands of persons professionally engaged in space programs. I would suspect that a significant percentage of the rocket engineers whom you might question would not know who Sir William Congreve was, let alone William Hale. Nor would they be likely to know that every major nation in Europe had rocket brigades in the nineteenth century; that rockets were used, albeit not widely, by the United States in the Mexican War in 1846–1847, and by both the Union and Confederate armies during the Civil

War. Why should they know? The only reason, I suppose, is that it can be both interesting and satisfying to know the history of one's profession. There is a cultural aspect, also, in being knowledgeable of the technical ancestry of modern space launch vehicles.

The study of astronautical history is exciting and rewarding because one learns of the prescience and insight of brilliant intellects over the centuries. One learns also that improvements in technology and development of bold ideas were largely the result of study and research by individuals. These individuals, caught up in a dream, were driven relentlessly by the excitement of a concept and the possibility of contributing to its fulfillment. These stories make exciting history. Another aspect is that numerous and varied scientific disciplines and technologies are involved. Interdisciplinary study is required and for this reason it is sometimes difficult to make valid judgments of individual contributions.

Great strides in space accomplishment had to await modern technology and the team effort of thousands of minds simultaneously working on hundreds of problems in a tremendously complex system. Under the leadership of Major General Walter R. Dornberger and Dr. Von Braun, the opening of the German test station at Peenemünde in 1937 signaled the dawning of the systems approach necessary to achieve space flight. We know now that a great cooperative effort led by skilled administrators is required; a partnership of industry and government, and widespread technical communications. These, together with powerful tools such as computers, farflung ground facilities for static-test and launch operations, and worldwide tracking stations make today's space technology possible. It is uniquely different from the individual creative effort, however brilliant, of thirty years ago.

The human mind is still the common denominator of any team effort, however vast. The individual will still be the initiator of new concepts and inventions, and the solver of problems. Thus, the study of this history will reveal the creative mind in peace and in war over the centuries. Oftentimes, the name of the individual is unknown, but he is there and his contribution is evident.

I believe that this book will enlighten all who read it. It is hoped that reading it will encourage further interest and open new avenues of study of one or more of its facets, some of which have been barely touched upon because of space limitations.

Man's ancient drive to explore was limited to the Earth's surface until this century. Now the way to the Solar System is open. This is the story of how it began and how it became possible in our time.

FREDERICK C. DURANT III
Assistant Director, Astronautics
National Air and Space Museum

Smithsonian Institution
Washington, D.C.

Preface

This book is the result of many years of research and writing, and could never have been completed without the aid of scores of persons, libraries, and organizations all over the world. We are particularly grateful to the persons listed below, noting in parentheses the area of assistance rendered. We regret that space did not permit more of their material to be utilized, but it was invariably valuable to us in constructing a balanced picture of events.

David S. Akens, George C. Marshall Space Flight Center, NASA (United States rocketry and documentation); John Alden, Rare Book Collection, Boston Public Library (rare books); Kenneth H. Allen, North American Aviation, Inc. (postwar missiles); M. Almazov, Soviet News, U.S.S.R. Embassy, London (Soviet missile and space programs).

John Barbato, Space Systems Division, United States Air Force Systems Command (carrier vehicles and satellites); Charles Barr, Northrop Corporation (wartime United States rocket airplanes); Ingénieur Général J. J. Barré, Versailles (prewar French rocketry); C. W. Birnbaum, Douglas Missile and Space Systems Division (United States carrier vehicle information); R. Boccarossa, Engins Matra (French satellites, missiles); Aktiebolaget Bofors (Swedish missiles); Professor John A. Boyle, Department of Persian Studies, University of Manchester, England (Persian legends); British Patent Office (rocket patents); British Museum, London (library research and reproductions); Dr. William M. Bryant (translation of Latin texts); Werner Buedeler (German documentation); Francis A. Burnham, United States Air Force Systems Command, Space Systems Division (satellite programs).

L. J. Carter, British Interplanetary Society (documentation on British rocketry); Cinémathèque Française (film stills); A. V. Cleaver, Rolls-Royce, Ltd. (British rocketry); Contraves AG (Swiss missiles); Jean Coulomb, Centre National d'Études Spatiales (French space vehicles); R. Courcelle, Bibliothèque Royale de Belgique (research of French-language works on rocketry); Sir Alwyn D. Crow (British prewar and wartime rocketry); Peter Curtice, Central Office of Information, London (British rocketry).

A. J. Dalkin, Royal Artillery Institution, Rotunda Museum (early British and Indian rockets); Alain Danet, Paris-Match, Paris (French space developments); Melvin S. Day, NASA, Washington (technical documentation); L. Decker, National Army Museum, U.K. (early British rocketry); Kurt H. Debus, John F. Kennedy Space Center, NASA (United States launch facilities); A. P. DeWeese, New York Public Library (support in rare book and general research); Frank L. Dickey, Douglas Aircraft Company (postwar United States rocket and astronautic developments); Colonel John Joffre Driscoll (United States World War II rocketry); F. George Drobka, NASA, Washington (technical documentation); Frederick C. Durant III, National Air and Space Museum, Smithsonian Institution (broad support in information research, location of photographic materials).

Commander Burton I. Edelson, Office of Naval Research, London (space documentation); Krafft A. Ehricke, Autonetics Division, North American Aviation, Inc. (postwar United States space programs); Dr. Eugene M. Emme, NASA, Washington (postwar rocket and space history); Rolf Engel (prewar German rocketry); Colonel Denis Ewart-Evans, School of Artillery, Manorbier, Wales (British World War II rocketry).

Robert R. Finney, United States Army Missile Command (postwar Army missiles); Captain Robert F. Freitag, USN-ret. (United States V-2 firings); Dr. William A. Fowler, California Institute of Technology (United States wartime rocketry); Arnold W. Frutkin, NASA, Washington (postwar United States sounding rocket and international cooperation programs).

Les Gaver, NASA, Washington (spacecraft photography); Colonel Richard Gimbel, USAF-ret., Yale University Library (early space concepts); Colonel T. A. Glasgow, Aerospace Medical Division, Air Force Systems Command (United States space medical programs); Colonel C. V. Glines, Office, Assistant Secretary of Defense, Washington (United States postwar rocketry); Mrs. Robert H. Goddard (activities of Dr. Robert H. Goddard); M. G. J. Gollin (British liquid-fuel rocketry in World War II); Professor L. Carrington Goodrich, Association for Asian Studies, Columbia University (ancient Chinese rocketry); Grumman Aircraft Engineering Corp. (Apollo spaceship).

James W. Harford, American Institute of Aeronautics and Astronautics (early AIS/ARS rocketry); Gordon L. Harris, John F. Kennedy Space Center, NASA (United States launch facilities); Robert Hartwell, Department of Oriental Languages and Civilization, University of Chicago (ancient Chinese rocketry); T. A. Heathcote, National Army Museum, U.K. (early British rocketry); Dr. Heinrich Hertel, Technische Universität Berlin (World War II German rocket airplanes); Dr. C. N. Hickman (NDRC and prewar rocket research in the United States); D. N. Hoare, Bristol-Aerojet Ltd. (British sounding rockets); John M. Hughes, Aberdeen Proving Ground (United States Army missiles).

Imperial War Museum, London (World War I rocketry); George S. James, Aerojet-General Corporation (early United States JATO developments); L. L. Janssens, Société pour la Réalisation d'Engins Balistiques (French missiles); Joseph M. Jones, George C. Marshall Space Flight Center, NASA (carrier vehicle information); Harry C. Jordon, Ballistic Systems Division, Air Force Systems Command (United States Air Force missiles); Jorge Salmon Jordan, *El Comercio*, Lima (Pedro E. Paulet work); Brigadier Leonard Walter Jubb, British Defence Research Staff (prewar and World War II British rocketry).

Professor Väinö Kaukonen, Helsinki University (Finnish legends); Captain Richard K. King, Hq. Air Force Systems Command (United States Air Force ballistic missiles); Ernst Klee (World War II German rocketry); Zdenek Kopal, Department of Astronomy, University of Manchester (early Lunar studies); J. Gary Kornmayer, General Dynamics Convair Division (Atlas missiles and carriers); Professor Edward A. Kracke, Jr., Department of Oriental Languages and Civilizations, University of Chicago (ancient Chinese rocketry); Krausskoff-Flugwelt Verlag (prewar German rocketry).

Fritz Lang (*Frau im Mond*—film); Lily Latté (*Frau im Mond*—film); Dr. Charles C. Lauritsen, California Institute of Technology (wartime United States rocketry); Willy Ley (prewar German activities); Library of Congress, Washington (support in rare book and general research); Robert E. Logan,

American Museum of National History (early space flight concepts); Antonio Lulli, Peruvian Embassy, Washington (Pedro E. Paulet work).

Frank J. Malina, International Academy of Astronautics, Paris (wartime rocketry); Paul Mathias, Paris-Match, New York (French space developments); Metropolitan Museum of Art, New York (ancient astronomical and astronautical concepts); Bernard H. Mollberg (photographic analysis and selection); D. W. Morton, British Aircraft Corp., Ltd. (British missiles); Captain W. P. Murphy, USN, Office of Chief Polaris Executive, U.K. Ministry of Defence (postwar naval rocket experiments); H. J. Murray, Redstone Scientific Information Center (documentation); Professor Herbert Myron, Jr., Boston University (translation of medieval French material).

Brigadier F. S. Napier (British wartime rocketry); T. D. Nicholson, American Museum-Hayden Planetarium (astronomical information); Nord-Aviation (French rocketry); Novosti Press Agency, London (Soviet information, photographs); Colonel Frederick I. Ordway, Jr., USAF-ret. (World War I and War of 1812 research).

Geoffrey K. C. Pardoe, Hawker Siddley Dynamics, Ltd. (British postwar rocketry, carrier vehicles); G. Edward Pendray (AIS/ARS prewar rocketry); Robert L. Perry, Rand Corporation (United States Rand satellite study); Dr. William H. Pickering, Jet Propulsion Laboratory (postwar United States spacecraft developments); M. F. Poffley, Ministry of Aviation, London (British World War II rocketry); George A. Pughe, Aerospace Technology Division, Library of Congress (Soviet translations; analyses of missile and space programs).

William C. Ragsdale (photographic analysis and selection); Donald L. Raymond, American Institute of Aeronautics and Astronautics (early AIS/ARS rocketry); G. Rear, Ministry of Defence—Royal Air Force (British missiles); Major General Ormand J. Ritland, USAF-ret. (United States ballistic missile and space systems); Royal Astronomical Society Library, London (literature research); Dr. Harry O. Ruppe, Technische Hochschule München (prewar German rocketry).

Max Salmon, Office National d'Études et de Recherches Aérospatiales (French space developments); Duncan Sandys, Member of Parliament (British World War II rocketry); Dr. Irene Sänger-Bredt (photographs and information concerning Eugen Sänger's prewar research); Major Francis N. Satterlee, Office of the Assistant Secretary of Defense, Washington (Defense Department missile and space programs); Andrew M. Sea, Manned Spacecraft Center, NASA (manned satellite photography, information); Mitchell R. Sharpe, Jr., George C. Marshall Space Flight Center, NASA (information search, location of sources); Nathan Sivin, Harvard University (ancient Chinese rocketry); John Shesta (early AIS/ARS rocketry); Colonel Leslie A. Skinner, USA-ret. (United States Army Ordnance prewar and wartime rocketry); Bart J. Slattery, Jr., George C. Marshall Space Flight Center, NASA (carrier vehicle information); Brountislav J. Soshinsky (translation of historical Soviet material); Charles L. Stewart (information on surrender of German rocket scientists to American forces at close of World War II); F. D. Storrs, Short Brothers & Harland Ltd. (British missiles); Dr. Ernst Stuhlinger, George C. Marshall Space Flight Center (Saturn-launched satellites; Mars spaceship concept); Sud-Aviation (French rocketry); Svenska Aeroplan AB (Swedish missiles).

Major General H. N. Toftoy, USA-ret. (postwar United States rocket developments); Captain Robert C. Truax, USN-ret., Aerojet General Corporation (Annapolis rocket experiments).

Edward G. Uhl, Fairchild-Stratos Corporation (bazooka developments); United States Intelligence Corps Agency, Office of the Chief (surrender of German rocket scientists to United States forces at end of World War II); University of Manchester Library, Manchester, U.K. (rare book research, reproduction of material).

Ivan Volkoff (ancient and medieval space flight concepts); Ruth von Saurma, George C. Marshall Space Flight Center, NASA (technical documentation).

Ronald C. Wakeford, Research Analysis Corporation (wartime British rocketry); Dr. Hellmuth Walter, Worthington Corp. (prewar and wartime German rocketry); Professor James R. Ware, Harvard University (ancient Chinese rocketry); Richard R. Wilford, Jet Propulsion Laboratory (spacecraft); William L. Worden, Boeing Company (missile and carrier vehicle information). Paul T. H. Yung, Library of Congress, Washington (ancient Chinese rocketry).

Accademia della Scienze di Torino (Italian nineteenth-century rocketry).

Beinecke Rare Book and Manuscript Library, Yale University, New Haven (rare book research); Biblioteca Casanatense, Rome (rare book research); Biblioteca Central, Diputación Provincial de Barcelona (rare book research); Biblioteca Nacional, Madrid (rare book research); Biblioteca Nazionale Centrale, Rome (rare book research); Bibliothèque Cantonale, Lausanne (Swiss military rockets); Bibliothèque de la Musée de l'Armée, Paris (military rockets); Bibliothèque Nationale, Paris (rare book and manuscript research); Bibliothèque Royale de Belgique (rare book research); Boston Public Library (rare book research); Dr. Bodo Bartocha, Office of Planning and Policy Studies, National Science Foundation, Washington (documentation); Gerald H. Bidlack, Communications Satellite Corporation, Washington (communications satellites).

Deutsches Museum, München (prewar and World War II German rocketry); Charles F. Ducander, Science and Astronautics Committee, U. S. House of Representatives, Washington (documentation).

Etablissements Ruggiere, Paris (documentation).

Free Library of Philadelphia (rare book research).

Massachusetts Institute of Technology Libraries, Cambridge (book research); Ministère de la Guerre, Paris (military rockets); Musée de l'Air—Service de Documentation, Paris (military rockets); Musée du Château de Rohan, Strasbourg (old fireworks); Musei Vaticani, Rome (early astronomical texts); Museo del Ejercito, Madrid (Spanish military rocketry); Museo di Armi Antiche della Pusteria di S. Ambrogio, Milano (old military rockets); Museo di Risorgimento, Palazzo Carignano, Torino (early fireworks); Museo Storico Nazionale Artiglieria, Torino (Italian nineteenth-century rocketry); Museu Militar, Lisbon (signal rockets).

National Army Museum, Sandhurst (early British rocketry); National Library of Ireland, Dublin (rare book research), National Maritime Museum, Greenwich (fleet-to-shore bombardment rockets); New York Public Library (rare book research).

Pierre Versins, Prilly, Switzerland (early astronautical concepts).

Royal Artillery Institution Library, London (early British rocketry); Royal Artillery Institution Rotunda Museum, London (early British and Indian rocketry); Rockefeller Library, Brown University, Providence (pyrotechnics).

Servicio Histórico Militar, Biblioteca Central, Madrid (Spanish military rocketry).

J. Gordon Vaeth, National Environmental Satellite Center, ESSA, Washington (meteorological satellites).

Widener Library, Harvard University, Cambridge (rare book research); Glen Wilson, Senate Committee on Aeronautical and Space Sciences, U. S. Senate, Washington (documentation).

WERNHER VON BRAUN
FREDERICK I. ORDWAY III

Huntsville, Alabama, U.S.A.

Contents

INTRODUCTION, *v*

PREFACE, *vii*

1 THE LURE OF OTHER WORLDS, *2*

2 A THOUSAND YEARS OF ROCKETRY, *22*

3 PIONEERS OF SPACE TRAVEL, *40*

4 THE LEGACY OF THE PIONEERS, *60*

5 THE ROCKET RETURNS TO WAR, *86*

6 POSTWAR MILITARY ROCKETRY, *120*

7 PROBING THE FRINGE OF SPACE, *150*

8 THE REMOTE EXPLORERS, *176*

9 MANNED SPACE FLIGHT, *202*

BIBLIOGRAPHY, *255*

INDEX, *271*

To the thousands of dedicated men and women all over the world whose titanic efforts to explore the mysteries of space are inexorably turning into reality the dreams and aspirations of earlier generations.

1 THE LURE OF OT

Before man could think about traveling to other worlds, he had to accept their existence. The idea is unquestioned today, but for thousands of years he thought of himself and the planet on which he lived as unique. The Earth was believed to be an unmatched pocket of life and change in a cold, dead, unalterable universe. From the beginning of thought, attempts were made to grapple with the mystery of the Earth's origin through myth and legend.

Nordic mythology created the giant Ymir, from whose body the land was born and whose sweat created the sea. From his skull was created the firmament, which remained unlighted until the gods brought forth the stars, harnessed the chariot of the Sun to the horse Arwaker, and hitched the Moon to Alswider, another mythical horse.

The Chinese had Tao, the "great original cause" that created a shaggy dwarf, P'an Ku. As the dwarf breathed, the winds began; as he opened his eyes, light was brought forth. When P'an Ku said the word *Sun* seven times, the Sun came into existence, followed by the Moon and stars. After P'an Ku died, his head became the mountains, his blood the rivers, his sweat the rains. His skin and hair turned into plants and trees, while the human race sprang from the insects on his body—perhaps the least flattering origin ever imagined for man.

The first steps toward a scientific view of the universe were taken in Babylonia and Egypt at least five thousand years ago. As early as 3000 B.C., Babylonian astrologer-astronomers were making methodical observations of the heavens. By the second millennium they had fitted the planets to the system of the zodiac, and by 1000 B.C. they apparently were keeping records of the movements of the brighter planets, as well as the Sun and Moon. Tables of the motion of Venus between the years 1921 and 1901 B.C. have been found by archeologists, and data on Mars and Jupiter were reduced for future reference.

In Egypt, astronomer-priests worked out a calendar of twelve 30-day months, with a five-day period to round out the year. Their celestial observations led to a star catalog that listed forty-three constellations by the thirteenth century B.C. The Egyptians knew that Mercury and Venus were closer to the Sun than the Earth, Mars, Jupiter, and Saturn. By 1000 B.C., the Sun-clock was in regular use in Egypt, an added sign of astronomical knowledge.

Great as these achievements were, they were just building blocks for the Greek astronomers in the city-states across the Mediterranean. Early in the sixth century B.C., Thales of Miletus, whom the Greeks credited with founding science, mathematics, and philosophy, traveled to Egypt to learn from its astronomers and returned to found what became known as the Ionian school of Greek astronomy. Thales was able to predict a Solar eclipse—its occurrence on 28 May 585 B.C. frightened the armies of Media and Lydia into making peace—and he measured the angular diameter of the Sun. Despite these advances, Thales clung to the traditional Egyptian view of the Earth as a circular disc floating on a great ocean inside a hemisphere of shining stars.

The members of the Ionian school questioned these traditional beliefs and proposed their own revolutionary theories. Anaximenes suggested that many bodies like the Earth exist in the heavens. Heraclitus, visualizing the sky as filled with pure fire, saw a universe of ceaseless change. Anaxagoras believed that the Moon was like the Earth and could support life. Anaximander pictured the sky as a sphere that revolved around the Earth—an idea that recurred frequently in history—with rings of universal fire burning around the sphere. The Sun, the stars, and the Moon were visualized as traveling within tubes of mist in the sphere. Anaximander knew that the Earth was not flat, but he pictured it as a cylinder, with the flat ends at the east and west.

A rival school, established by Pythagoras of Samos, flourished from the sixth to the fourth centuries B.C. One member of the school, Parmenides of Elea, was a strong proponent of a spherical Earth. He believed that the Earth, which he divided into five zones, was condensed from air, while the stars

2

HER WORLDS

were of compressed fire. He looked upon a finite, motionless, spherical universe—whose apparent motions were illusory. The Sun, Moon, planets, and stars were thought to be arranged in bands around the Earth. Another thinker, Philolaus, went a step further and proposed that the Earth, the Sun, the Moon, the stars, and the planets revolved around a great sphere of fire, the center of the universe.

The Pythagoreans encountered opposition because they maintained that the Earth moved around the central sphere of fire, always keeping the same side toward the fire (Greece was on the shady side). There were two counterarguments: The gods were insulted by the idea of a moving Earth, and there was no evidence that the people who lived on the side of the Earth away from Greece could see the eternal fire.

There was no way of disputing the first argument, but to meet the practical question, the Pythagoreans invented a counter-Earth, or Antikhthon, which was placed so that it always protected our Earth from the eternal fire. They managed to avoid an explanation of why their Antikhthon was not visible from the Earth.

The idea of a spherical Earth became so imbedded in Greek thought that even Plato, an archconservative in political matters, accepted its truth. In the *Phaedo* he wrote:

my persuasion as to the form of the Earth and the regions within it I need not hesitate to tell you . . . . I am convinced, then, that in the first place if the Earth, being a sphere, is in the middle of the heaven, it has no need either of air or of any other such force to keep it from falling, but that the uniformity of the substance of the heaven in all its parts, and the equilibrium of the Earth itself, suffice to hold it.

In Plato's cosmology, the planets moved with the heavenly sphere, with a circular movement in a direction opposite to their daily rotation. The Earth was at the center of the universe, with the Moon, the Sun, Venus, Mercury, Mars, Jupiter, and Saturn at increasing distances from it.

Plato believed that "weakness and sluggishness" prevented man from traveling upward through the air,

for if anyone could reach the tip of it, or could get wings and fly up, then, just as fishes here, when they come up out of the sea, espy the things here, so he, having come up, would likewise descry the things there, and if his strength could endure the sight, would know that there is the true heaven, the true light, and the true Earth . . . the things beyond would appear to surpass even more the things here.

Aristotle, too, accepted the concept of a spherical Earth, writing that the opponents of the theory "fail to take account of the distance of the Sun from the Earth and the size of the Earth's circumference." He disputed the belief that the Earth floated in water, but he was convinced that the Earth was at the center of the universe. The stars, Aristotle said in his *De caelo*, were not only spherical and at a great distance, they were eternal occupants of a perfectly spherical universe centered on the Earth.

Since Plato and Aristotle were not primarily astronomers, their cosmological theories marked no great advances in thought. A lesser figure, Heraclides of Pontus (c. 388–315 B.C.), did produce some strikingly original ideas. He explained the daily rotation of the stars by assuming that the Earth turned on its axis, and he also discovered that Mercury and Venus revolved around the Sun rather than around the Earth.

These two observations paved the way for one of the great intellectual leaps forward in human history. Aristarchus of Samos (c. 310–230 B.C.) went the crucial step beyond Heraclides; he said that the Earth, too, revolved around the Sun. The idea was too revolutionary to be accepted by his contemporaries; indeed, it had to wait nearly two thousand years to be vindicated. Only Seleucus of Seleucia, a Chaldean who lived one hundred years later, accepted Aristarchus's theory as true.

Aristarchus also measured the distance from the Earth to the Sun, using geometrical methods. His

3

In Babylonia, astrologer-priests began making methodical observations of the universe in about 3000 B.C. This ancient seal shows a man about to take off for the Moon, lifted by a great bird. (AMERICAN MUS. OF NATURAL HISTORY)

In Egypt the Sun-clock was in regular use by 1000 B.C. On the balustrade at Amarna figures representing Akh-en-Aton and Nefertiti hold offerings for the Sun god Aton. (METROPOLITAN MUS. OF ART)

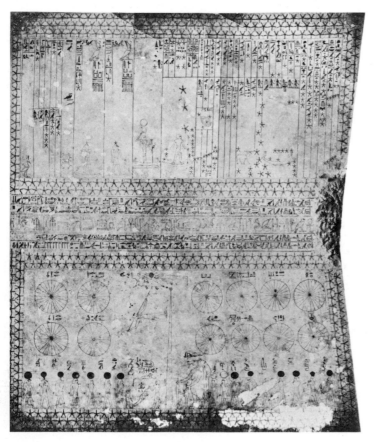

Astronomical ceiling of the tomb of Sen-Mut, Thebes, dates from the Eighteenth Dynasty. (METROPOLITAN MUS. OF ART)

4

figure was 4 to 5 million miles, twenty times too small but much closer to the truth than most contemporary estimates.

Later, a school of astronomers at Alexandria began to fill in blanks in astronomical knowledge. Eratosthenes (276–192 B.C.) made an accurate estimate of the circumference of the Earth, determined the angle of the ecliptic, and prepared a star catalog. Hipparchus, the greatest of all Greek astronomers, worked in Rhodes from 146 to 127 B.C. Hipparchus rejected the idea that the Sun was the center of the Solar System. But he did make accurate measurements of the size of the Sun and Moon, and he worked out a satisfactory theory to explain the motions of the planets. Hipparchus' star catalog, with 850 entries, was unequaled at the time and remained a standard reference for centuries.

The achievements of Greek astronomy were summed up in the work of Ptolemy, who worked in Alexandria from A.D. 127 to 141. Ptolemy's great work was the *Megiste Syntaxis* (*Great Collection*), known to us by its Arab name, *Almagest,* a mathematical and astronomical treatise that summarized all that was known about the universe. Ptolemy was more of a compiler than an original worker. He accepted Hipparchus's picture of the universe: The Earth was at the center, and was immovable, with the Moon, the Sun, and the planets orbiting in perfect circles. Ptolemy's treatise, as well as his tables of the Moon's motion, remained the supreme authority for more than twelve hundred years.

By Ptolemy's time, Greek science was looking backward, not forward. The light of Hellenic culture winked out as the Roman Empire fell. The torch passed, not to the barbarian hordes that swept over the empire, but to the Arabs who followed their Islamic faith in a tidal wave of conquest in the Near East. The Arabs translated the Greek and Latin texts, studied them, and added to their findings. In the ninth century, Muhammad al-Batani calculated the precession of the equinoxes; around 1000, Ibn Junis recorded both Solar and Lunar eclipses. But Arabic culture waned in the thirteenth century, and astronomical knowledge marked time for another three centuries.

A single astronomical textbook, the *Tractatus de sphaera* (*The Sphere*) of Johannes Sacrobosco, contained most of what was taught in Europe during this period. Sacrobosco, who probably wrote in the thirteenth century, offered proofs that the Earth and heaven were spherical; among them were the observations that the Moon rose and set earlier in the east, and that eclipses occurred later in the Orient than in Europe. But Sacrobosco believed firmly that the Earth was the center of the universe, a belief he justified with this argument:

To persons on the Earth's surface the stars appear of the same size whether they are in mid-sky or just rising or about to set, and this is because the Earth is equally distant from them. For if the Earth were nearer to the firmament in one direction than in another, a person at that point of the Earth's surface which was nearer to the firmament would not see half of the heavens. But this is contrary to Ptolemy and all the philosophers, who say that, wherever man lives, six signs rise and six signs set, and half of the heaven is always visible and half hid from him.

The same sort of argument was offered to prove that the Earth did not move.

That the Earth is held immobile in the midst of all, although it is the heaviest, seems explicable thus. Every heavy thing tends toward the center. Now the center is a point in the middle of the firmament. Therefore, the Earth, since it is heaviest, naturally tends toward that point. Also, whatever is moved from the middle toward the circumference ascends. Therefore, if the Earth were moved from the middle toward the circumference, it would be ascending, which is impossible.

Much of the astronomical effort of the time went into the preparation of commentaries on the *Tractatus de sphaera*. One of the better commentaries, written

The Pythagoreans believed in a spherical Earth that revolved around a central sphere of fire. A counter Earth, between the two spheres, protected the Earth from the central fire.

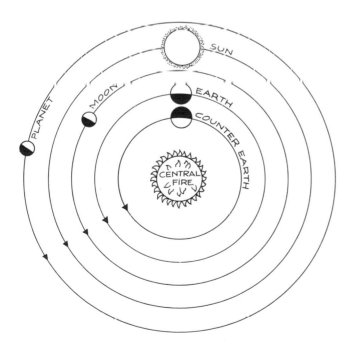

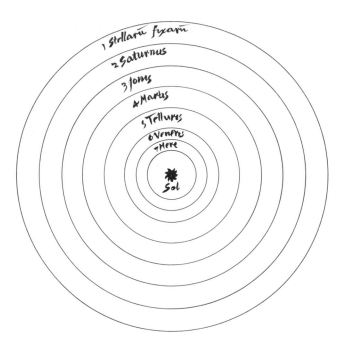

By placing the planets in orbit around the Sun, Nicolaus Copernicus (1473–1543) revolutionized man's picture of the universe.

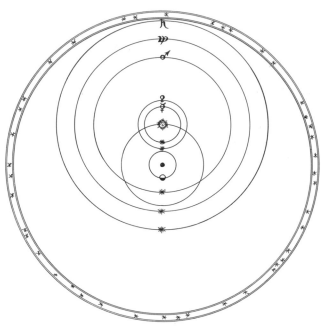

Tycho Brahe (1546-1601) saw the Earth (center) as a stationary body, around which revolved the Sun, itself the center of motion of the known planets.

by Robertus Anglicus in 1271, offered this description of the planets:

Saturn is of cold and dry nature; Jupiter of hot and moist nature; Mars of hot and dry nature which consumes by burning; but the Sun is of a hot and dry nature, which heat is life-giving; Venus of cold and humid nature with aerial humidity; Mercury hot with the hot, cold with the cold, following the nature of the planet with which it is in conjunction, the Moon of cold and humid nature with the humidity of water rather than that of air.

These fantasies dominated astronomical thought until the time of Mikolaj Kopernik (1473–1543), whom we know by the Latinized name of Nicolaus Copernicus. With Copernicus, man's picture of the universe changed irrevocably. In his monumental *De revolutionibus orbium coelestium* (*On the Revolutions of the Celestial Orbs*), published in 1543, Copernicus revived Aristarchus's heliocentric theory and established the true picture of the Solar System: the Sun in the center, with the Earth and the other planets orbiting the Sun. While Copernicus clung to the classical idea that the orbits of the planets were perfect circles, he accurately measured the distances of the planets from the Sun.

Where Copernicus was a towering theoretician, the greatest of his immediate successors, Tycho Brahe (1546–1601) was an outstanding observer, the best since Hipparchus. Brahe was able to measure the positions of the stars and planets with astonishing

precision for pre-telescope times. Too conservative to accept the Copernican theory, he struck a compromise by proposing that all the planets but the Earth orbited the Sun, which orbited the Earth in turn. In 1582 he wrote:

I believe that it is absolutely and undoubtedly necessary to have the Earth fixed at the center of the universe, following the opinion of the ancients and the testimony of

German astronomer Johannes Kepler (1571–1630) showed that the orbit of a planet can be represented by an ellipse, with the Sun at one of the two foci. A planet travels faster when it is nearer the Sun, and areas A and B, swept out during equal periods of time, are equal.

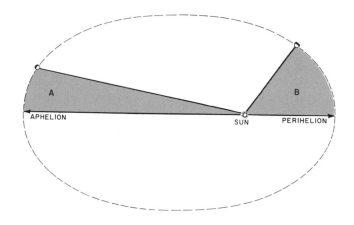

the Scriptures. I do not agree at all with Ptolemy in assuming that the Earth is the center of the orbits of the second mobile sphere; but I believe the celestial motions to be so arranged that only the Moon and the Sun, together with the eighth sphere which is the remotest of all and encloses the others, have the center of their motion in the Earth. The five other planets revolve around the Sun, which acts as their king and master, and the Sun will always be at the center of their orbits, being accompanied by them in its annual motion . . . . Thus the Sun is the regulator and terminus of all these revolutions, and, like Apollo surrounded by the Muses, he governs the harmony of the heavens.

Brahe's careful measurements were used by one of his pupils, Johannes Kepler, to develop a new set of laws about the planetary motions. Ceaselessly, for many years, Kepler tried theory after theory to fit the planetary orbits into a coherent explanation. Kepler finally arrived at his three great laws of planetary motion: The planets orbit the Sun in ellipses, not circles, with the Sun at one focus of the ellipse; lines drawn from the Sun to a planet will sweep over equal areas in equal periods of time; and the period of any planet's orbit is related to the planet's distance from the Sun. Kepler's findings, published in the *Astronomia nova* (*New Astronomy*) of 1609 and the *De harmonice mundi* (*On the Harmony of the World*) of 1619, set the stage for the next great advance.

This came when Galileo Galilei (1564–1642) first used a telescope to observe the skies. Galileo's observations destroyed forever the theory that the heavens were perfect and unchanging, far different from the crude and imperfect Earth. During a lifetime of observation Galileo discovered sunspots, from which he determined the Sun's rotational speed—he nearly ruined his eyesight while gazing at the Sun; he noticed many surface features on the Moon and worked out the height of mountains and the depth of craters; he discovered the four major satellites of Jupiter, which he called the Cosmian or Medicean stars, after Cosmo de' Medici II; he found that Venus, like the Moon, has phases; and he wrote that "the Galaxy is nothing else but a mass of innumerable stars planted together in clusters."

Galileo's discovery of the Cosmian stars proved that the Moon was not the only satellite in the Solar System. He told the world of his discovery in the *Sidereus nuncius* (*Sidereal Messenger*):

On the seventh day of January in the present year, 1610, in the first hour [sunset] of the following night, when I was viewing the constellations of the heavens through a telescope, the planet Jupiter presented itself to my view, and as I had prepared for myself a very excellent instrument, I noticed a circumstance which I had never been able to notice before, namely that three little stars, small but very bright, were near the planet.

He at first thought that they were fixed stars, but "when on January 8th, led by some fatality, I turned again to look at the same part of the heavens, I found a very different state of things . . . . I therefore concluded, and decided unhesitatingly, that there are three stars in the heavens moving about Jupiter, as Venus and Mercury around the Sun." Six days later he discovered the fourth satellite.

In his *Dialogo sopra i due massimi sistemi del mondo* (*Dialogue of the Two Chief Systems of the World*), published in 1632, Galileo defended the Copernican theory with brilliant arguments and biting satire, and brought the wrath of traditionalists on his head. Hauled before the Inquisition, he was forced to recant his views; he died, blind and under house arrest, in 1641.

Galileo's ideas lived on despite the Inquisition, and astronomers expanded his observations. Then, toward the end of the seventeenth century, Sir Isaac Newton tied all the observations together with his law of universal gravitation, which explained in pre-

Isaac Newton (1642–1727) explained in mathematical terms practically every motion in the universe, from the fall of an apple to the orbits of the planets. This diagram illustrates his theory for a satellite: As the muzzle velocity of a cannon on the mountaintop is increased, the range of the shell also increases. If the velocity could be made high enough, the shell would not fall, but rather would remain in orbit.

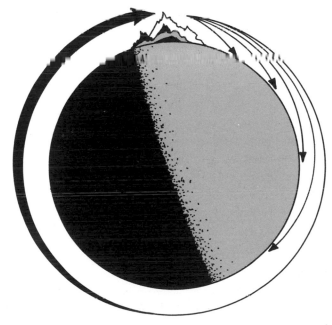

cise mathematical terms almost every motion of the universe, from the fall of an apple to the orbits of the planets.

Newton's great contributions to the dynamical nature of the universe were published in the famed *Philosophiae naturalis principia mathematica* (*Mathematical Principles of Natural Philosophy*) in 1687. He demonstrated in this work that Kepler's laws of planetary motion could be interpreted by his own universal laws of motion. In particular, he showed that the attraction of the Sun on a planet is directly proportional to the product of the Solar and planetary masses and inversely proportional to the square of the distance separating the two bodies.

"Newton was the greatest genius that ever existed and the most fortunate, for we cannot find more than once a system of the world to establish," said Joseph Lagrange (1736–1813). The history of astronomy for the next two centuries was largely the working out

Modern view of the inner and outer Solar system. The outermost planet, Pluto, was not observed until 1930.

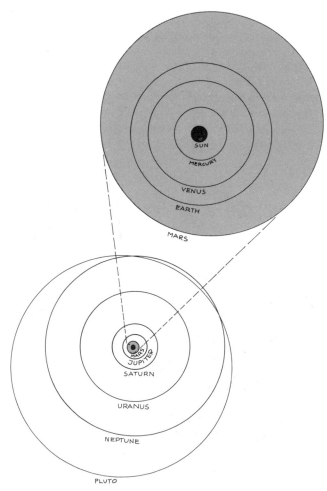

of the "system of the world" along Newtonian lines. A major effort was the *Mécanique céleste* (*Celestial Mechanics*) of Pierre Simon, Marquis de Laplace, a five-volume work published between 1799 and 1825, which worked out Newton's principles in enormous detail. Laplace demonstrated the stability of the Solar System; he and other astronomers made precise predictions of the future orbits of the planets. Variations from those orbits caused by the gravitational attraction of unseen planets led to the discovery of Neptune in 1846 by Urbain Leverrier and Pluto in 1930 by Clyde Tombaugh. Uranus had been discovered by Sir William Herschel in 1781, in the course of one of his methodical surveys of the sky.

Starting in 1801, astronomers discovered that the large gap in the Solar System between the orbits of Mars and Jupiter actually was filled with thousands of small bodies, which they called asteroids. The first of these to be found, Ceres, has a diameter of 480 miles. It is still the largest known asteroid. More planetary satellites have been discovered—the total stands at thirty-one, including the Moon.

Astronomers now divide the planets into two groups. One group is made up of the four planets nearest the Sun: Mercury, Venus, Earth, and Mars, which are called the terrestrial planets because they resemble the Earth in size and density. The other group consists of the next four planets, Jupiter, Saturn, Uranus, and Neptune, which are relatively huge, but not nearly as dense as the Earth. They are believed to consist of metallic and solid hydrogen and helium cores surrounded by a layer of crystalline ammonia and finally by thick, turbulent hydrogen-rich atmospheres. Pluto, the outermost planet, remains in part a mystery; it is so different from the four giant planets that some astronomers believe it to be a satellite that somehow escaped the gravitational hold of Neptune.

The Solar System is over 7½ billion miles across, taking Pluto's orbit as the measure. This enormous distance is dwarfed by the space between the Sun and the nearest stars—a distance so great that light, traveling at 186,000 miles per second, travels for over four years from the nearest star to our Solar System.

It has taken civilized man some five thousand years to accumulate this store of knowledge. A trip to another world could not be imagined in anything approaching realistic terms until astronomy gave a true picture of the universe. As man's astronomical knowledge increased, however, the fictional space voyages devised by his restless imagination became correspondingly more sophisticated. This growing body of cosmic literature served both to express man's innate longing to reach other worlds and to stimulate further his desire to do so. Now that he at last knows the dimensions of the Solar System, he is ready to explore it. And when the first astronaut steps onto the Moon he will owe a debt to such writers as Jules Verne, who helped fire mankind's curiosity, as well as to the scientists like Sir Isaac Newton, who prepared the way for actually getting there.

No work of fiction dealing with cosmic travel predates the Christian era. The classical view of the Earth as a unique body in the center of an uninhabited, changeless universe made such speculations inconceivable. True, some thinkers, such as Plutarch (*c.* A.D. 46–120), believed that the Moon might resemble the Earth—in his *De facie in orbe lunae* (*On the Face on the Moon's Disk*) Plutarch contended that the Moon is a small Earth, inhabited by intelligent beings—but the standard view was given in the *Somnium scipionis* (*Scipio's Dream*) of Marcus Tullius Cicero, in which the dreaming hero realizes the uniqueness of the Earth:

The Universe consists of nine circles, or rather of nine moving globes. The outer sphere is that of the heavens, which embraces all the others and under which the stars are fixed. Underneath this, seven globes rotate in the opposite direction from that of the heavens. The first circle carries the star known to men as Saturn; the second carries Jupiter, benevolent and propitious to humanity; then comes Mars, gleaming red and hateful; below this, occupying the middle region, shines the Sun, the chief, prince and regulator of the other celestial bodies, and the soul of the world which is illuminated and filled by the light of its immense globe. After it, like two companions, come Venus and Mercury. Finally, the lowest orb is occupied by the Moon, which borrows its light from the Sun. Below this last celestial circle there is nothing but what is mortal and perishable except for the minds granted by the gods to the human race. Above the Moon, all things are eternal. Our Earth, placed at the center of the world, and remote from the heavens on all sides, stays motionless and all heavy bodies are impelled towards it by their own weight.

This scheme, according to Cicero, was truly harmonious:

The motion of the spheres creates a harmony formed out of their unequal but well-proportioned intervals, combining various bass and treble notes into a melodious concert. Such tremendous motions cannot take place in silence, and Nature has given a bass note to the lowest and slow orb of the Moon, and a treble note to the topmost and rapid orb of the starry firmament: between these two limits of the octave, the eight moving globes produce seven notes in different modes, and this number is the crux of all things. The ears of men are filled

One of the earliest fictional descriptions of space travel was written by Lucian of Samosata in the second century A.D. *In* Vera Historia, *Lucian describes a sailing vessel that is lifted from the sea by a violent whirlwind and carried to the Moon.*

with this harmony and no longer capable of hearing it just as people living close to the cataracts of the Nile are no longer aware of the noise. The ear-splitting concert of the rapidly spinning Universe is so tremendous that your ears close up to keep its harmony out, just as you cannot bear to look at the fiery Sun because its piercing light dazzles and blinds you.

What is probably the first work of fiction describing what we now call space travel was the *Vera Historia* (*True History*) of Lucian of Samosata, a Greek sophist and satirist who wrote within a half century of Plutarch. Lucian provides all the necessary elements of space-travel fiction: a trip through space, a landing on another world, a description of that world, and a return.

It is unlikely that any other author has taken such pains to assure his readers that he is not telling the truth. Before beginning his tale, Lucian writes, "I shall at least say one thing true, when I tell you that I lie, and shall hope to escape the general censure, by acknowledging that I mean to speak not a word of truth throughout."

With that warning out of the way, Lucian describes a sailing vessel that is returning homeward when a great wind lifts it into the skies.

9

About noon . . . a most violent whirlwind arose, and carried the ship above three thousand stadia, lifting it up above the water, from whence it did not let us down again into the seas but kept us suspended in midair. In this manner we hung for seven days and nights, and on the eighth beheld a large tract of land, like an island, round, shining and remarkably full of light; we got on shore, and found on examination that it was cultivated and full of inhabitants, though we could not then see any of them.

The Lunar inhabitants are called Hippogypi, and they ride on three-headed vultures adorned with feathers "bigger than the mast of a ship."

As Marjorie Nicolson points out in her book *Voyages to the Moon,* "Lucian made his voyage . . . by mere chance; he suggested no previous idea of the possibility, no pondering upon means of conveyance, no plan or design." Nevertheless, the Lunar voyage was made, and the target world was explored, providing a model for tales of later centuries.

Lucian wrote a second story of space travel, the *Icaro-Menippus,* in which the trip to the Moon is carefully planned in advance. The hero, Menippus, uses birds' wings; hence the title, a reference to Icarus's brief flight.

In the story, Menippus strapped on a vulture's wing and an eagle's wing and, after making some test flights, reached the top of Mount Olympus. He then flew to the Moon, but that was not enough for this ambitious explorer, who kept flying to the stars and heaven itself. The trip took only three days. ("It shall be done, said I, and away I set out for heaven . . . in a little time the Earth was invisible, and the Moon appeared very small; and now, leaving the Sun on my right hand, I flew amongst the stars, and on the third day reached my journey's end.") The return trip was less adventuresome; Jupiter, angered by Menippus's intrusion, orders his wings cut off and directs Mercury to bear the mortal back to Earth.

Lucian's tale stood alone for centuries. The next surviving account of cosmic travel is found in the 60,000-verse epic poem *Shāh-Nāma,* published by the Persian poet Firdausī in 1010 following forty years of labor. Although it was written eight centuries after Lucian's *True History,* the Persian epic may contain the record of man's first imaginative venture into space, since it is a retelling of ancient legends.

The hero of the epic is Jamshíd, who reigned for seven hundred years over men, demons, birds, and fairies, and could transport himself on a demon-borne aerial throne into the heavens. The epic also tell of Kai-Kā'ūs, a mythical, headstrong king of Persia who was forever embarking on perilous adventures.

One day, Kai-Kā'ūs was persuaded by a dív, or demon, to attempt the conquest of heaven. After questioning wise men and astrologers, he decided on "crooked and ugly means." He sends men to steal young eagles from their nests, and has the birds fed on meat until they become "as strong as lions so they could pull down a mountain sheep." Then Kai-Kā'ūs builds a throne, with lances attached from which are hung legs of lamb. Binding four young eagles to the throne, he seats himself on it and is borne into the air as the eagles hurl themselves at the meat. The journey ends disastrously; the eagles become tired, fold their wings, and plunge "headlong from the black clouds, dragging down the king's throne and lances out of the air." The passage of the poem, translated for the authors by Professor John A. Boyle of the Department of Persian Studies, University of Manchester, England, follows:

The soul of that king was full of thought as to how he should rise into the air without wings.

He asked many questions of the learned as to how far it was from this Earth to the sphere of the Moon.

The astrologers spoke and the king listened, and he selected crooked and ugly means.

He ordered that during the night men should go to the nests of eagles,

Take a large number of their young ones and place one or two in every house.

He reared them for a year and a month on birds, roast meat and sometimes lambs.

When they had each of them become as strong as lions so that they could pull down a mountain sheep,

He constructed a throne of Qimāri (Cambodian) aloes-wood and strengthened the tops of the planks with gold.

He fastened long lances in the side and so made it ready.

He suspended legs of lamb from the lances, giving his whole mind to the matter.

Then he fetched four vigorous eagles and bound them firmly to the throne.

Kai-Kā'ūs seated himself on the throne having placed a goblet of wine in front of him.

When the swift eagles grew hungry they each of them hastened towards the meat.

They raised up the throne from the face of the Earth; they lifted it up from the plain into the clouds.

To the extent of the strength that was in them they directed their efforts towards the meat.

I have heard that Kai-Kā'ūs ascended to the firmament in order to pass beyond the angels.

Another said that he rose into the heavens in order to fight [them] with bow and arrow.

There are all sorts of traditions about this; only the Wise One knows the secret of it.

[The eagles] flew for a long time and then grew tired. So will be he that is seized by greed.

When no strength was left with the flying birds, they folded their wings according to their custom.

They plunged headlong from the black clouds dragging down the king's throne and lances out of the air.

They came towards such a forest as this; they alighted on the face of the Earth in Āmul.

Animal power is used in part of another great fantasy, the *Orlando Furioso* of Lodovico Ariosto, the first edition of which appeared in 1516. The hero of this tale, Astolpho, voyages to the Moon in a chariot drawn by four red horses in quest of the lost mind of Orlando. The mind turns up in a flask, but that is not all the Moon offers. Not only did the Moon, which was "swell'd like the Earth, and seem'd an Earth in size," possess most of the natural features of this planet, it also had cities, towns, and castles.

One of the most unusual works of early science fiction was written by Johannes Kepler. His *Somnium (Dream)* was not published until 1634, four years after Kepler's death. John Lear, who made a careful study of the work in his book, *Kepler's Dream*, published in 1965, suggested that the great astronomer was forced to present his ideas about the Moon in fictional form to avoid religious and political censure.

"The moon guide was designed for distribution to a restricted audience," Lear wrote. "Phrased in Latin, the international language of the learned, it was cast in the form of an allegory, the hidden meaning of which would be familiar only to scientists. As Kepler explained in a letter to his friend, Matthias Bernegger, the text of the geography had been deliberately strewn with 'almost as many problems as there are lines.'"

The *Somnium* is a fantastic tale, couched in supernatural terms, of a voyage from Earth—called Volva in the book—to the Moon, which Kepler called Levania. Kepler knew that there could be no dense atmosphere between the two worlds, and so he rejected animals and wings as means of transportation. Because he had no acceptable alternative, he dipped into the supernatural and chose demons to make the trip.

Kepler's demons abhor sunlight, but can travel at will during the night. Normally, it is impossible for them to pass between the two worlds, but from time to time when the shadow of the Earth intersects the Moon, they are able to cross. And, under certain rare conditions, they carry with them humans who have been given an anesthetic potion as protection against the ill effects of rarified air.

Kepler described the Moon in terms of the latest astronomical knowledge, but he added bizarre forms of life, vastly different from Earth's creatures. The Lunar beings envisioned by Kepler do not live in cities and towns; in fact, they possess no civilization at all. During the day they come out of caves and crevices to sun themselves briefly, only to seek the lengthening shadows and the coolness of the gloom again.

Kepler was followed by many writers who dealt with the theme of space travel in both poetry and prose. Of these the most famous is doubtless the "Speedy Messenger" by Domingo Gonsales, author of *The Man in the Moon: or a Discourse of a Voyage Thither,* published in 1638.

The name Domingo Gonsales was the pseudonym for an English ecclesiastic, Francis Godwin, Bishop of Hereford. The author mentions the rotation of worlds based on observations of their markings, something unknown before 1612, and he apparently understands that the attraction of a body varies in terms of mass and distance, a fact developed after

In the sixteenth-century fantasy Orlando Furioso, *the hero travels to the Moon in a chariot drawn by four red horses. According to the author, Lodovico Ariosto, the Moon "had most of the natural features of this planet, and cities, towns, and castle, too."*

1620. From these and other considerations, scholars believe the book was completed in 1630, three years before Godwin's death. It became quite popular, with some twenty-five editions in four languages published between 1638 and 1767.

The author states in the preface:

That There should be Antipodes *was once thought as great a* Paradox *as now that the* Moon *Should bee habitable. But the knowledge of this may seeme more properly reserv'd for this our discovering age: In which our Galilaeusses, can by advantage of their spectacles gaze the sunne into spots, & descry mountaines in the* Moon.

Domingo Gonsales, the protagonist and supposed author of the book, is a Spaniard of good but poor family, who has become ill while returning home from the East Indies, where he has made his fortune. Because of his illness, Gonsales and his servant, Diego, are taken off the ship and left on St. Helena Island. Seeking a way off the island, Gonsales trains some wild geese, called *gansas*, to carry a chairlike device ("engine").

I tooke some 30, or 40, young ones of them, and bred them up by hand partly for my recreation, partly also as having in my head some rudiments of that device, which afterward I put into practice . . . [and] began to cast in my head how I might doe to joyne a number of them together in bearing of some great burthen; which if I could bring to passe, I might enable a man to fly and be carried in the ayre, to some certaine place safe and without hurt.

To test his device, Domingo "fastened about every one of [his] *Gansas* a little pulley of Corke, and putting a string through it of meetly length, fastened the one end thereof unto a blocke almost eight Pound weight, unto the other end of the string [he] tied a poyse weighing some two Pound, which being done, and causing the signall to be erected, they presently rose all."

Following this initial success, Domingo sent a lamb aloft. Then came the time for the first manned flight. "I placed my selfe with all my trinckets, upon the top of a rocke at the Rivers mouth, and putting my selfe at full Sea upon an Engine . . . , my Birds presently arose, 25 in number, and carried me lustily to the other rocke on the other side, being about a Quarter of a league."

Gonsales and his birds eventually were picked up by a ship bound for Spain, but they were shipwrecked on one of the Canary Islands. Stranded among savages who continually "warre" against the Spaniards, Gonsales again mounted his "engine" and tried to fly to a nearby city.

But the birds took the "bitt between their teeth" and mounted upward, as if drawn "as the Loadstone draweth Iron." He alit temporarily on a strange land somewhere between Earth and the Moon. Soon the "Gansa's began to bestir themselues, still directing their course toward the Globe or body of the Moone." They sped along at about 85 miles per hour or, as Gonsales stated it, "Fifty Leagues in every hower." Since Godwin estimated the Moon to be about fifty thousand miles distant, at this rate the trip took some eleven days. $(85\,m/hr)(24\,hr/day)(11\,days) = 22,440\ miles$

The traveler found that the Moon was like "another Earth," its surface covered by a "huge and mighty Sea," later revealed to cover "Three parts in Foure (if not more)." The gansas set him down atop a huge hill "where immediately were presented unto [his] eyes many strange and unwonted sights."

The trees were "three times as high as ours, and more then [sic] five times the breadth and thickness." And there were "herbes, Beastes and Birds; although to compare them with ours I know not well how, because I found not any thing there, any *species* either of *Beast* or *Bird* that resembled ours any thing at all, except *Swallowes, Nightingales, Cuckooes, Woodcockes, Batts,* and wild *Fowle.*" The intelligent inhabitants of the Moon were "most divers but for the most part, twice the height of ours. Their colour never seen in an earthly world, and therefore neither to be described unto us by any, nor to be conceived of one that never saw it."

Although his stay on the Moon had been pleasant and instructive, the explorer became homesick, while his gansas grew restless "for want of their wonted migration." He therefore fastened himself to his "engine," signaled the birds, and took off, landing in China "in lesse than nine days." The quicker voyage homeward was explained by the greater attraction of the Earth. During the years that followed, many writers were to imitate Godwin and write about other inhabited worlds.

In 1638, the same year that Godwin's story was published, John Wilkins wrote the *Discovery of a New World; or, A Discourse tending to prove, that 'tis probable there may be another Habitable World in that planet.* Unlike the Godwin story, Wilkins's book was based on facts—at least, on the facts as they were known in the pre-Newtonian era. Wilkins's work inevitably contains many misconceptions and fundamental errors.

Wilkins was convinced—as many people still are, for no cogent reason—that the main problem in Moon travel is to lift the flier to the point between the Earth and the Moon where the Earth's influence ends. That point was believed by Wilkins to be not much farther "than that orb of thick vaporous air, that encompasseth the earth," or about twenty miles.

Once that altitude was attained—and Wilkins believed it could be quite easily—the rest of the voyage would be simple. And since "our bodies will . . . be devoid of gravity" no efforts would be exerted and no food would be required en route.

The next two major works dealing with travel beyond the Earth were written by Savinien de Cyrano de Bergerac, owner of the world's most famous nose. De Bergerac—wit, playwright, author, swordsman, philosopher, satirist, and part-time science-fiction addict—found time somehow to write *Voyage dans la Lune* (*Voyage to the Moon*) and *Histoire des États et Empires du Soleil* (*History of the States and Empires of the Sun*), which were published in 1649 and 1652, respectively. Since their author was well acquainted with the latest scientific studies, both are authoritative—if wildly fanciful—parodies on the theme of travel to other planets.

De Bergerac believed the Moon to be "a World like ours, to which this of ours serves likewise for a Moon." His first scheme for getting to the Moon was perhaps the most original ever devised. "I planted my selfe in the middle of a great many Glasses full of Dew, tied fast about me; upon which the Sun so violently darted his Rays, that the Heat, which attracted them, as it does the thickest Clouds, carried me up so high, that at length I found my selfe about the middle region of the Air."

Unfortunately, De Bergerac came down in Canada, not on the Moon. After a series of adventures in that country, Cyrano made another attempt at flight, this time in a "machine which I fancied might carry me up as high as I pleased . . . from the Top of a Rock [I] threw my self in the Air: But because I had not taken my measures aright, I fell with a sosh in the Valley below."

Returning to his flying machine, Cyrano found a group of soldiers busily tying firecrackers to it. Just as they lit the fuse, he leaped aboard. "Hardly were both my Feet within, when Whip, away went I up in a Cloud." Flames ignited tier after tier of rockets, lifting Cyrano ever higher. When the fireworks were exhausted, the machine fell "down again towards the Earth."

But Cyrano found himself drawn instead toward the Moon. He gives two reasons for this: His body was still greasy with marrow he had anointed himself with previously, and the Moon was "then in the Wain." He goes on to explain that since the Moon in that quarter would "suck up the Marrow of Animals, she drank up that wherewith I was anointed, with so much the more force that her Globe was nearer to me." Once he had landed on the Moon, Cyrano's imagination faltered; his return trip de-

pended on supernatural means, and he came back to Earth as a spirit.

Not satisfied with the Lunar voyage, Cyrano built a new machine that would take him to the Sun and planets. He described it as a box 6 feet high and 3 feet square with holes below and in the cover, containing "a Vessel of Christal . . . made in a Globular Figure." It was "purposely made with many angles, and in the form of an Icosaedron, to the end that every Facet being convex and concave, my Boul might produce the effect of a Burning-Glass." A board within was provided for the pilot.

The operation of this unusual vehicle was somewhat complicated. First, it was necessary for sunlight to shine on the transparent Icosaedron

which through its Facets received the Treasures of the Sun . . . . I foresaw very well, that the Vacuity that would happen in the Icosaedron, by reason of the Sunbeams, united by the concave Glasses, would, to fill up the space, attract a great abundance of Air, whereby my Box would be carried up: and that proportionable as I mounted, the rushing wind that should force it through the Hole, could not rise to the roof, but that furiously penetrating the Machine, it must needs force it on high.

As the machine mounts and the air becomes thinner, the device no longer serves, and Cyrano abandons it, continuing by a vague means of will power.

Most of the science-fiction works of the following years were variations on themes developed by writers like De Bergerac. A major event, in 1686, was the publication by Bernard de Fontenelle of a popular astronomy book called *Entretiens sur la Pluralité des Mondes* (*Discourses on the Plurality of Worlds*). A delightful work, it was read widely throughout Europe, partly because of its style but largely because of its fascinating speculations on the nature and habitability of other planets in the Solar System. Not only did De Fontenelle state that each known planet has its own race of people, but he went into detail about their appearance, civilization, customs, and habits. Oddly enough, De Fontenelle was not convinced of the Moon's habitability, believing that the air there was probably too rarefied. He gave relatively little attention to Mars, compared to such unlikely (to us) abodes of life as Mercury and Jupiter.

Four years later, Gabriel Daniel wrote *Voiage du Monde de Descartes* (*Voyage to the World of Descartes*), a novel that introduced the idea of soul or thought travel. The hero's soul separated from his body and soared out to the "Globe of the Moon" and the universe beyond, finding, among many other mysteries, the great master "Monsieur Descartes."

Fictional space travel was accomplished in many ways. In David Russen's Iter Lunare, *a giant spring was constructed on top of a mountain to catapult a man into space toward the Moon.*

The Moon was described in great detail, and was found to resemble the Earth. "One sees there fields, forests, seas and rivers. I see no animals, but I believe that, if they were transported there, one could nourish them, and perhaps they would multiply."

David Russen's *Iter Lunare: or Voyage to the Moon,* published in 1703, introduced the novel idea of using a spring catapult to propel a man into space from the top of a high mountain.

Since Springiness is a cause of forcible motion, and a Spring will, when bended and let loose, extend itself to its length; could a Spring of well-tempered steel be framed, whose Basis being fastened to the Earth and on the other end placed a frame or Seat, wherein a Man, with other necessaries, could abide with safety, the Spring being with Cords, Pullies or other Engins bent and then let loose by degrees by those who manage the Pullies, the other end would reach the Moon.

Two years after *Iter Lunare* there appeared Daniel Defoe's *The Consolidator,* also a tale of Lunar travel. It tells how ancient peoples mastered the art of flying to and from the Moon, and how Mira-cho-cho-lasmo came to Earth to visit the emperor of China. Defoe reviewed many legends of flights to the Moon and several types of what today would be called spaceships.

Probably the most intriguing of these is the Consolidator, described as an engine "in the shape of a Chariot, on the backs of two vast Bodies with extended Wings, which spread about fifty yards in breadth, composed of feathers so nicely put together, that no air could pass; and as the Bodies were made of lunar Earth, which would bear the Fire, the Cavities were filled with an ambient Flame, which

fed on a certain Spirit, deposited in a proper quantity to last out the Voyage; and this Fire so ordered as to move about such springs and wheels as kept the wings in most exact and regular Motion," described as "always ascendant." The story did not say what sort of propellant Defoe had in mind, but he appears closer to rocketry than most other writers of his time and, indeed, a long period afterward.

A quarter of a century later came Samuel Brunt's satiric *A Voyage to Cacklogallinia,* part of which concerns a Lunar voyage. After many varied adventures, the book's hero, Captain Brunt, was shipwrecked on Cacklogallinia, a strange land inhabited by bird people. The captain, befriended by Volatilio, quickly mastered their language and obtained a position in the government, where he could influence proposals made by the Cacklogallinians to reduce their government's burdensome debt.

One proposal involved an expedition to look for gold on the Moon. Brunt thought little of it and advanced many arguments against it, but to no avail; the idea had captured the imagination of the court, and the people as well. A great commercial enterprise unfolded, with shares sold as an investment in the gold everyone was certain existed on the Moon. Funds were promptly raised to finance the trip. The plan was to send two explorers to the Moon in a kind of palanquin, or streamlined flying chariot, propelled by birds. (The Cacklogallinians were birds themselves, but the palanquin was needed for the captain and Volatilio, who decided he, too, might want to ride in it.)

Before going to the Moon, the travelers investigated the environment away from the Earth and the ability of the birds to fly at high altitudes. The author knew that the air became less dense with increasing altitude, so the birds did not fly rapidly into space; instead, they rose slowly to accustom themselves to the changing atmospheric conditions.

The first test flight was made by Volatilio, who reported, "I ascended into the Mid-space, and found a vast alteration in the Air, which even here was very sensibly rarified." He explained that a "wet Spunge" provided welcome relief to the birds as they accustomed themselves to the thin air.

After several more flights, the time came for the last test before the flight to the Moon. "According to the Orders we receiv'd, *Volatilio* took his flight in an oblique Ascent, without a *Palanquin,* but wrapped up as warm as possible, accompanied by two servants." When Volatilio returned, he reported that he had passed the atmosphere "and, by Experience, had found my Conjecture true; for being out of the magnetick Power of the Earth, we rested in the Air, as on the solid Earth, and in an Air extremely temperate, and less subtle than what we breathe."

After some scheming by the courtiers to increase their profits from the enterprise, the voyage began. Even though it was made "with incredible swiftness," the trip was no overnight affair. "We were about a Month before we came into the Attraction of the Moon, in all which time none of us had the least inclination to Sleep, or Eat, or found our selves any way fatigued, nor, till we reach'd that Planet, did we close our Eyes." They floated in the weightless state until they descended to the Moon to begin their adventures. The Moon turned out to be inhabited by shades who lived quietly and peacefully without material wants or urges. The search for gold came to nothing—there was gold on the Moon, but the Lunarians did not allow the Cacklogallinians to take it.

After all this, Ralph Morris's 1751 novel, *A Narrative of the Life and Astonishing Adventures of John Daniel*, appears rather tame. With his son Jacob, the hero is stranded on a far-off island. They construct a device from materials salvaged from a shipwreck. It is made to fly by pump-operated calico wings supported by iron ribs—as the pump goes up and down, so do the wings. The machine is so efficient that the adventurers are carried not to a civilized country but—of course—to the Moon.

Hardly in the same class as these lightweight works is *Micromégas*, written by Voltaire in 1752 as a satire on man's pretensions to greatness. Voltaire does not start his tale on the Earth, or even in the Solar System, but on the gigantic star Sirius. The Sirians are proportionately large—the hero, Micromégas, is 120,000 royal feet high. A precocious lad, he had mastered geometry when he was only two hundred and fifty years old, and by the time he was four hundred and fifty he was busily studying—and writing about—the possibility of life on other worlds. Convicted of heretic beliefs, he was banished for a mere eight hundred years, a sentence Micromégas put to good use. He decided to explore the universe, using sunbeams, comets, and a sure knowledge of gravitation to make his trip pleasant and easy. Travelling across the Milky Way from star to star, he reaches the Solar System and settles down for a visit on Saturn, a puny planet to his way of thinking, whose inhabitants live only fifteen hundred years.

Micromégas strikes up a warm friendship with the secretary of the grand academy of Saturn, and the two argue about, and philosophize on, all manner of subjects. Finally, they visit the rest of the Solar System, flying first to the rings and moons of Saturn, then to Jupiter and Mars. At last they reach Earth, a tiny world the Sirian and Saturnian are convinced is uninhabited. But, peering idly through a diamond, Micromégas sights a whale swimming in an ocean he had assumed to be a mere puddle. Then a ship bearing explorers comes into view. Reluctantly, Micromégas acknowledges that even so tiny, so insignificant a world as the Earth can harbor rational beings.

Stories about space travel continued to appear at a steady rate. A few were original, but many were derivative, dull, and unimaginative. All underscored the persistent, romantic notion that there must be other worlds, inhabited by some kind of beings, and that somehow man can reach those worlds.

In a mid-eighteenth-century booklet, *Man in the Moon*, the hero, Israel Jobson, reaches the Moon by ladder; in a sequel, *The History of Israel Jobson, the Wandering Jew*, a chariot is used for the trip. Both books are believed to have been written by Miles Wilson, an English curate.

Not all speculative works were fictional. In 1698, Christian Huygens, a renowned scientist, wrote *Cosmotheoros, or Conjectures Concerning the Planetary Worlds*, in which he concluded that the planets were the abodes of rational beings. Emanuel Swedenborg, in 1758, wrote *Earths in our Solar System, which are called Planets, and Earths in the Starry Heavens*, which took much the same approach. In the book, Swedenborg's soul went out into the infinite. In the heavens, he wrote, are stars without end, around myriads of which are "thousands, yea, ten thousands of earths, all full of inhabitants." Swedenborg also gathered information from angels and spirits, which, he wrote, came to him from each of the Solar System's planets. Swedenborg mixed science, religion, and imagination to enrich the growing literature of supernatural voyages into the cosmos.

A 1775 work by Louis Guillaume de La Folie, *Le Philosophe Sans Prétention*, has some earmarks of the modern science-fiction novel. It tells of Ormisais, a Mercurian who arrives on Earth and tells his story to one Nadir, an Oriental. It seems that a Mercurian inventor, Scintilla, had created a marvelous electric flying chariot and had demonstrated it to his fellow scientists despite their scorn and ridicule. Ormisais was so certain that the chariot would not work that he casually vowed to fly it to the Earth. To his surprise, he was carried through space—his adventures are fairly standard—until he crashes on Earth and relates his story.

The fact that the space machine was an electric chariot is indicative of a change in science fiction. Readers now knew enough about science to insist on more realism from their fiction. But their insistence was limited to the means of travel; the wildest details about the nature of the planets and their imaginary inhabitants were still acceptable.

Joseph Atterlay's *A Voyage to the Moon with some Account of the Manners and Customs, Science and Philosophy of the People of Morosofia and other Lunarians*, published in 1827, is a good example of the new wave in science fiction. The author, whose real name was George Tucker, described a quite modern science-fiction device:

"The machine in which we proposed to embark, was a copper vessel, that could have been an exact cube of six feet, if the corners and edges had not been rounded off. It had an opening large enough to receive our bodies, which was closed by double sliding pannels, with quilted cloth between them." A metal called lunarium was used to "overcome the weight of the machine, as well as its contents, and take us to the moon." This antigravity concept became popular during the eighteenth and nineteenth centuries, although it had no more scientific credibility than geese or flying chariots. Still, it had an aura of

In Voyage to the Moon, *published in 1827, author Joseph Atterlay made an attempt at "science" fiction. Atterlay's spaceship, loaded with scientific equipment, rose to the Moon by virtue of an antigravity material called Lunarium.*

science around it, and that was what counted most.

Eight years later, Edgar Allan Poe sent the hero of *Hans Pfaall—A Tale* (republished as *Lunar Discoveries, Extraordinary Aerial Voyage by Baron Hans Pfaall*) on a Lunar trip in a homemade balloon. Pfaall's reason for going to the Moon was hardly romantic; he was broke and heavily in debt, and the only way out was to flee the Earth.

Pfaall built a balloon, not forgetting "an apparatus for the condensation of the atmospheric air" to provide air for breathing as he passed through what he assumed was a rarified atmosphere extending to the Moon. The takeoff from Rotterdam at first seemed uneventful: "[I] was pleased to find that I shot upward with inconceivable rapidity (upon cutting the attachment cord), carrying with all ease one hundred and seventy-five pounds of leaden ballast." Presently, however, he had some trouble with kegs of gunpowder that gave the balloon an unexpectedly great jolt.

a concussion . . . burst abruptly . . . and seemed to rip the very firmament asunder . . . . The balloon at first collapsed, then furiously expanded, then whirled round and round with sickening velocity, and finally, reeling and staggering like a drunken man, hurled over the rim of the car, and left me dangling, at a terrific height, with my head downward, and my face outward, by a piece of slender cord about three feet in length.

But Hans finally managed to pull himself back into the balloon.

As the balloon progressed Moonward, Hans's air condenser failed to work, but after experiencing some bad moments he was able to put it in working order. He averaged about one thousand miles a day, and by the eighth day he was so distant that "not even the outlines of the continents could be seen." Hans settled down to what had become a routine trip.

Seventeen days out of Rotterdam catastrophe struck. The balloon burst. "I was falling, falling with the most impetuous, the most unparalleled velocity!" Convinced he was falling back to Earth, Hans Pfaall braced himself for annihilation. But he found that the Earth "was over my head and completely hidden by the ballon, while the moon . . . the moon itself in all its glory—lay beneath me and at my feet."

Hans dumped all his ballast and even cut the balloon car loose, and presently settled gently down in the middle of a Lunar city populated by vast crowds of "ugly little people." After spending five years with the Lunarians, he sent one of them to Earth in his reconstructed balloon to ask forgiveness of his debts. Alas, the two-foot-high Lunarian was so afraid of the denizens of Earth that he did not wait for an answer. Hans was doomed to remain forever on the Moon, a debtor in exile.

The celebrated "Moon hoax" of 1835 showed just how ready most people were to accept the existence of life on other worlds. The hoax was the work of Richard Adams Locke, who presented a wild tale of Lunar creatures who had purportedly been seen through the telescope of Sir John Herschel. The report, under the imposing title of *Great Astronomical Discoveries Lately Made By Sir John Herschel, LL.D., F.R.S., etc, At the Cape of Good Hope*, appeared as a week-long serial in the New York *Sun* in September 1835. It gained credibility because it purported to record facts submitted by Sir John to the august but (unknown to most) defunct Edinburgh *Journal of Science*. The skill of the author and the tenor of an epoch when the public was ready to believe almost anything reported by science also had something to do with it. Locke's hoax, swallowed hook, line, and sinker at first, was exposed in short order—but not before many people had gorged themselves on descriptions of Lunarian civilization.

The thirty-year period between the Moon hoax and the publication, in 1865, of Jules Verne's immortal *De la terre à la lune (From the Earth to the Moon)* was a glorious era of science fiction. The public believed in the plurality of worlds, in inhabitants whose nature might not be known but who nevertheless existed, and in the certainty that the Moon and planets would soon be visited in reality as well as in the pages of fiction. While waiting for the actual physical contact to occur, many people thought it might be possible to communicate with the other worlds and thus learn more about them. Many schemes were hatched, including building huge fires, planting trees in geometrical patterns, and constructing mammoth mirrors.

Among the many authors of science fiction during this period was the Frenchman Achille Eyraud, whose short book, *Voyage à Venus*, contained a description of a spacecraft powered by the reaction principle. As pointed out by Alexandre Ananoff in his *L'Astronautique*, "If Cyrano first dreamt of using rockets to fly through the air, it is Achille Eyraud to whom goes the honor, in 1863, of having applied this principle to a true spaceship."

Eyraud was followed by Jules Verne, whose dominance in the field of science fiction still endures. The science in *De la terre à la lune* is nearly as accurate as the knowledge at the time permitted. Despite this, the voyage that Verne describes, while spectacular, is not feasible. Verne pictured a nine-hundred-foot-long cannon, pointing straight up into the sky. The cylindrical projectile, or rather the spacecraft

which it fired, weighed some twenty thousand pounds, had a conical nose, and was fitted to accommodate three astronauts. Among the spaceship's interior features were walls "lined with a thick padding of leather," a middle section containing storage cupboards, and a lower area with a large, circumferential seat. Access was by means of a "narrow aperture" in the cone, secured by an aluminum plate. The travelers could look into space through four lens-shaped portholes with heavy metal lids. All manner of provisions were aboard, including chemically supplied air.

It is now known that the acceleration of a projectile fired from a huge cannon would destroy the voyagers, as would the heat generated as the spacecraft rushed through the atmosphere. Verne did not ignore the problems, but the solutions he provided were not adequate. The book ended with the firing of the cannon and the arrival of the spaceship into Lunar space, but the story was picked up again in Verne's *Autour de la lune (Around the Moon)*.

After the takeoff, the travelers lost consciousness briefly because of the terrific acceleration. They survived because of a mechanism that absorbed the re-

Hans Pfaall, hero of a story by Edgar Allan Poe, fled from the Earth in a homemade balloon because he was heavily in debt. He took off from Rotterdam, carrying an air condenser so he could breathe the rarefied air in space.

coil. This consisted of a "bed of water, intended to support a watertight wooden disc, which worked easily within the walls of the projectile. It was upon this kind of raft that the travellers were to take their place. This body of water was divided by horizontal partitions, which the shock of departure would have to break in succession. Then each sheet of water, from the highest to the lowest, running off into escape tubes toward the top of the projectile, supplied with extremely powerful plugs, could not strike the lowest plate except after breaking successively the different partitions."

When they regained consciousness, the space voyagers felt uncomfortably warm. Their leader explained, "This stifling heat, penetrating through the partitions of the projectile, is produced by its friction on the atmospheric strata. It will soon diminish because we are already floating in Space, and after having been nearly stifled, we shall have to suffer intense cold."

Some 4,500 miles from Earth, a large meteor passed close enough to the spacecraft to throw it off course. The astronauts calculated that the ship, instead of landing on the Moon, would orbit it, giving them an excellent view of both sides.

The ship drew closer, until it seemed it might land after all. As a precaution, steps were taken to reduce the craft's velocity by firing "powerful fireworks" placed inside twenty steel-lined guns protruding from the hull. Before they were fired, the astronauts confirmed the earlier predictions that the spaceship would just barely miss the Moon. The closest approach was about twenty-nine miles, over the north polar regions.

A final attempt to land on the Moon was made as the travelers began to pull away, but the spaceship, instead of falling toward the Moon, plunged toward the Earth. It landed in the Pacific, where it was retrieved by an American corvette, the USS *Susquehanna*.

Verne's reasons for not permitting his space travelers to reach the Moon are obscure, but one can surmise what they may have been. Since he had resorted to a cannon to obtain the velocity necessary to depart from Earth, it would be hard for him (1) to arrange for the projectile to land on the Moon; and, just as important, (2) to devise a scheme for it to take off from the Lunar surface and return to Earth. Certainly there would be no cannon on the Moon waiting for the intrepid adventurers—unless they could be expected to construct one themselves once on the Moon (unlikely), or unless they could secure help from the local population (even less likely, since Verne, as opposed to most of his literary predecessors,

postulated that the Moon was barren and lifeless).

Looking back over the hundred years since the appearance of Verne's two Moon tales, the debt modern astronauts owe him is apparent. His prodigious output brought scientific adventure to a reading public all over the world. His very name became a synonym for high adventure. And he was read with great respect by working scientists, so carefully did he do his scientific homework. Towering over the vast majority of later writers, Verne is still deservedly popular today.

As far as is known, the first fictional proposal for a manned space station appeared in Edward Everett Hale's story "The Brick Moon," published originally in *Atlantic Monthly* in 1869–1870 and later collected with other tales in the anthology *His Level Best and Other Stories*. Hale's theory was that a satellite placed in polar orbit would serve as a navigational aid for sailors, permitting them to determine longitude accurately and easily. He explained it thus:

For you see that if, by good luck, there were a ring like Saturn's which stretched around the world, above Greenwich and the meridian of Greenwich, . . . anyone who wanted to measure his longitude or distance from Greenwich would look out of his window and see how high this ring was above his horizon. At New Orleans, which is quarter round the world from Greenwich, it would be just on his horizon . . . . So if we only had a ring like that . . . vertical to the plane of the equator, as the brass ring of an artificial globe goes, only far higher in proportion . . . we could calculate the longitude.

The Brick Moon was suggested as an alternative to this ring. In modern terms, the young Bostonians who are the heroes of the tale planned to put their artificial satellite into a polar orbit, where it would serve the purpose. They planned to use brick because "It must stand fire well, very well." An orbit 4,000 miles high is decided upon so that the Brick Moon can be seen "by a belt of observers six or eight thousand miles in diameter." The size of the Brick Moon is set at 200 feet in diameter, so that it can be seen from 4,000 miles away.

Plans had to be made for orbiting the moon, and, after discussions, the flywheel technique was decided upon. "We would build two huge fly-wheels, the diameter of each should be 'ever so great,' the circumference heavy beyond all precedent, and thundering strong, so that no temptation might burst it. They should revolve, their edges nearly touching, in opposite directions, for years, if it were necessary, to accumulate power, driven by some waterfall now wasted to the world."

At the proper time, the Brick Moon would roll

down "a gigantic groove" until it landed on both flywheels at the same time and was hurtled upward. "Upward; but the heavier wheel would have deflected it a little from the vertical. Upward and northward it would rise, therefore, until it had passed the axis of the world. It would, of course, feel the world's attraction at the time, which would bend its flight gently, but still it would leave the world more and more behind." Once in orbit, the Brick Moon would "forever revolve . . . the blessing of all sea-

The first known proposal for a manned satellite appeared in a story by Edward Everett Hale about a Brick Moon. Its 37 inhabitants signaled the Earth in Morse code by jumping up and down on the outside of the satellite. People on Earth threw them books and other objects, some of which missed the Moon and went into orbit around it.

In Percy Greg's novel Across the Zodiac, *the hero travels to Mars in a huge spaceship, propelled by an antigravity device called "apergy."*

men . . . the second cynosure of all lovers upon the waves, and of all girls left behind them."

The cost of the Brick Moon was calculated at $60,000—small change for modern times, but too much for the tale's heroes. Only after they have made their fortune can they consider the plan again; making further calculations, they come up with a total cost of $214,729, with each additional moon to cost $159,732. The money is raised, the wheels are built and put into operation, and plans are made for the launching.

But the Moon slipped prematurely down "upon these angry fly-wheels, and in an instant, with all our friends [construction workers and their visiting families], it had been hurled into the sky!" A year went by without news. Then a memorandum ap-

Kurd Lasswitz, author of Auf zwei Planeten (On Two Planets) *reasoned that if Martians were more intelligent, they—not Earthmen—would be the first to venture from planet to planet. Consequently, his travelers flew from Mars to Earth, where they set up a base at the North Pole.*

peared in the *Astronomische Nachrichten;* the Brick Moon had been seen by Professor Karl Zitta of Breslau, who has named it Phoebe. Later, it is found to be orbiting 5,000 miles above the Earth's surface. Through opera glasses, it appears about the size and brilliance of Jupiter.

Observations of the wayward satellite showed signs of life. "Something is moving—coming, going. One, two, three, ten; there are more than thirty in all. They are men and women and their children!" The passengers had "survived that giddy flight through the ether, and were going and coming on the surface of their own little world, bound to it by its own attraction and living by its own laws."

It was soon learned that thirty-seven people were living on the Moon. Suspecting that they were being observed, they arranged themselves on the outside of the satellite and "at one moment, as by one signal, all . . . jumped into the air—high jumps. Again they did it, and again." It soon became apparent that they were signaling—short leaps and long leaps, dots and dashes—Morse code.

It turned out that there was plenty of air, food, and friends aboard: "What more can man require?" And it rained regularly, providing drinking water. The climate is good, even tropical, which helped form a soil, making it possible to grow palms, breadfruit, bananas, oats, maize, rice, wheat. Crops were harvested up to ten times a year.

Back on Earth, friends of the marooned space voyagers decide to send presents up to the Brick Moon by carefully wrapping the packages in many-layered wrappings. As the packages flew through the atmosphere, each layer would burn and disintegrate, but the inner portion often reached the Brick Moon unscathed. Some objects do get through and are retrieved, some are lost forever, and some take up orbit with the satellite. ("They had five volumes of the Congressional Globe whirling like bats within a hundred feet of their heads.")

Once the excitement wears off, life gets back to normal, both on Earth and on the Brick Moon. Communications continue back and forth, and occasionally presents are interchanged. Hale takes leave of his contented space heroes wondering if it can be possible that "all human sympathies can thrive, and all human powers be exercised, and all human joys increase, if we live with all our might with the thirty or forty people next to us, telegraphing kindly to all other people, to be sure? Can it be possible that our passion for large cities, and large parties, and large theatres, and large churches, develops no faith nor hope nor love which would not find aliment and exercise in a little 'world of our own?'"

From the latter part of the nineteenth century, fictional accounts of Moon voyages decline in importance and fall outside the mainstream of science fiction. There are relatively few exceptions to this trend. Not only was the Moon becoming recognized as a dead world, but it was just too close to the Earth to offer a sophisticated, science-oriented public the kind of romantic excitement associated with a Domingo Gonsales or a Cyrano de Bergerac. Interest was shifting to the planets.

A sign of the changing times came in 1880 with the appearance of Percy Greg's two-volume novel *Across the Zodiac*. Here a mysterious something called "apergy" is used to negate gravity, providing the means for a voyage to Mars. The spaceship, a huge thing with three-foot-thick walls, "resembled the form of an antique Dutch East-Indiaman." The deck and keel were "absolutely flat, and each one hundred feet in length and fifty in breadth, the height of the vessel being about twenty feet." The apergy receptacle was placed above the generator in the center of the ship. From them "descended right through the floor a conducting bar in an antapergic sheet, so divided that without separating it from the upper portion the lower might revolve in any direction through an angle of twenty minutes." This sheath is used to direct "a stream of repulsive force" against the Sun or any other body.

The most noteworthy fact is that this ship is used to go to Mars, which had finally begun to assume the importance to science-fiction writers that it deserved. This was a result of increasing knowledge about the planet and the development of theories of the origin of the Solar System, which made Mars seem especially interesting. Greg wrote at the time of the discovery of Mars's "canals," and of the planet's two satellites (which he described in his novel). New data made Mars seem like an older Earth, and therefore a potential home for a more advanced race of intelligent beings.

Greg gives a haunting description of the planet. "The seas are not so much blue as grey. Masses of land reflected a light between yellow and orange indicating . . . that orange must be as much the predominant color of vegetation as green on Earth . . . . The sky, instead of the brilliant azure of a similar latitude on Earth, presented to my eye a vault of pale green . . . . The lower slopes [of a mountain] were entirely clothed with yellow or reddish foliage."

Kurd Lasswitz's *Auf zwei Planeten* (*On Two Planets*) carried the Mars theme several notches higher in the literary scale. Published in 1897, Lasswitz's book was based on the logical assumption that if Mars was the abode of a higher intelligence, the first space trip would be made from Mars to Earth. Accordingly, he had travelers from Mars flying to Earth and setting up a base at the North Pole. The method of space travel is a gravity-nullifying device, a material which, when formed into a shell-like structure, prohibits the passage of gravity and becomes weightless when the ports are closed.

H. G. Wells wrote his *War of the Worlds* as a magazine serial in 1897, and the story was published in book form the following year. It is the story of a Martian invasion of our planet in which the invaders score marked successes at first but then are vanquished by terrestrial diseases for which their bodies have no defenses. Some forty years later, a Welles named Orson terrorized the United States with an eerie retelling of the story in a radio program. But tales of an Earth expedition to Mars have not been lacking; Garrett P. Serviss's *Edison's Conquest of Mars*, which appeared soon after Wells's tale, told of a punitive expedition bound for the red planet.

The Moon was not entirely forgotten, however. A few years later, Wells published *The First Men in the Moon*. An antigravity material, Cavorite, was used to transport the spaceship the quarter million miles to the Moon. Wells populated the Moon with insectlike creatures living in underground caves and tunnels.

The appearance of *The First Men in the Moon* marks roughly the end of one era in science fiction and the beginning of another. The discovery was made in the closing years of the nineteenth century that the rocket reaction engine was the solution—the realistic, scientific solution—to the problem of space propulsion. Years of work lay ahead, but at last man knew how to go about the job. He need no longer invent implausible methods; nonfiction could begin to take over from the Cyranos.

The year 1900 did not signal the abrupt end of one epoch in space literature and the beginning of another. It is, however, a convenient point of departure from which to begin a new series of adventures based on science and technology instead of legend and fantasy.

The discovery of the importance of the rocket to space travel did not mark the end of science fiction; instead, it gave it a new and more mature outlook and greater popularity. Excellent works continue to be published, and they will appear long after man has landed on the Moon and the planets. But their role in stimulating the interplanetary venture inevitably declined and the practical work of going into space was stepped up. The debt to great speculators, from Lucian to Verne and Wells, was about to be paid.

2 A THOUSAND YE

While writers of science fiction used geese, bottles of dew, spirits, and chariots to carry their heroes to the Moon, the device that would finally make the trip possible was undergoing a slow but steady evolution, changing from a toy to a weapon, from a crude device to a relatively sophisticated machine. The time was to come when the rocket would take its place as the only possible means of space transportation.

The rocket is a reaction device, which works in accordance with Sir Isaac Newton's Third Law of Motion: For every action there is an equal and opposite reaction. A rocket can be compared to a continuously firing machine gun mounted on the rear of a rowboat. As the gun is fired to the rear, the recoil from the stream of bullets moves the boat forward. A rocket-motor's "bullets" are minute particles that are thrown out through a nozzle as a propellant is burned in a suitable chamber. The reaction to the discharge of these particles makes the rocket fly in the opposite direction.

Although a rocket is a reaction device, not all reaction devices are rockets. A rocket is a special case because it contains all the elements it needs to operate, including both fuel and oxidizer. A jet-airplane engine, by contrast, is a reaction device that uses the oxygen in the air to support the combustion of the fuel carried on board.

The reaction principle was known long before a true rocket was invented. In his *Noctes Atticae* (*Attic Nights*), Aulus Gellius describes the ancient pigeon of Archytas, dating back to about 360 B.C. Hanging from a string, the pigeon was made to move by steam blowing from small exhaust ports.

A more sophisticated device was the reaction wheel, or aeolopile, developed by Hero, a Greek resident of Alexandria. Hero lived at about the time of Christ, but his exact dates are unknown. Some scholars say the first century B.C., others the first century A.D., with the evidence pointing somewhat more strongly in favor of the latter, due to a reference in Hero's *Dioptra* to a Lunar eclipse that would have

been seen in Alexandria in A.D. 62. The aeolopile, described in his *Pneumatica*, was, in effect, a primitive steam turbine, although apparently no practical use was made of the device. It was constructed of a hollow globe, which was pivoted to turn on two central trunnions. One trunnion also was hollow, permitting steam to pass through it into the globe. On opposite sides of the globe and at right angles to the axis of the pivots were two bent tubes, whose open ends were pointed in opposite directions. As the steam escaped through these tubes, the globe revolved.

Centuries later, the reaction to discharging steam was used to propel a model of a car designed by Jacob Willem Gravesande, a Dutch professor best known for his 1720–1721 two-volume *Physices elementa mathematica, experimentis confirmata sive introductio ad philosophiam newtonianam* (a textbook on Newtonian philosophy published in Leyden). Records also are available of schemes to build steam-reaction helicopters and even a man-carrying craft of unusual design.

The precise origin of the rocket itself is lost in the shadow of time. Almost all Western and Oriental histories credit the Chinese with the invention, but sources are seldom given for this claim, making it difficult to accept or reject. Part of the trouble in settling the question is caused by lack of clarity in descriptions of ancient weapons; often, it is difficult to tell from a vague description whether a projectile was powered by a rocket or merely carried powder or other material that burned.

There are many references, for example, to fire-arrows. These arrows were fitted with an inflammable material—pitch, bitumen, or resin. Launched by muscle power, they made flaming rocketlike arcs to their targets. And there was the fire-pot containing naphtha and other ingredients. Shot by hurling devices, the fire-pot spread its burning contents over a fairly wide area. In 305 B.C., in Greece, during the siege of Rhodes by Demetrius, the Rhodians are believed to have employed eight hundred flame-carriers in attempts to destroy the enemy's wooden siege engines. A subsequent innovation was the shooting of fire-arrows and fire-pots by rocket devices, though just when they first were used is unclear (fire-pots themselves date from at least 1000 B.C.). Some scholars conclude from passages in the Byzantine princess Anna Comena's writings that rockets were used to carry fire-pots to the enemy in the ninth and tenth centuries within the Byzantine Empire, but this is generally regarded as unlikely. In 1450, Robertus Valturius, in *De re militari* (*Military Treatise*), wrote of what may have been rockets dating from Emperor Leo VI (886–911). It is said that the Byzantine ruler's warriors made use of "fire that is launched (or hurled)." The description, however, applies just as well to Greek fire slung by ballistas as to rockets.

Most authorities believe the invention of rockets is tied inextricably to the discovery of black powder which served as the first rocket propellant. The best available evidence, including both early Chinese documents and the writings of some of the first Europeans who visited China, indicates the Chinese certainly were the first to use black powder and, therefore, probably the first to use rockets as well.

The ingredients of black powder—technically, it should not be called gunpowder because guns came later, but it usually is—are charcoal, sulphur, and saltpeter. These have been known in China for perhaps two thousand years—charcoal since the very earliest times, and sulphur and saltpeter at least since the sixth century A.D. and probably as far back as the first century B.C. That the ingredient saltpeter is definitely of Chinese origin is indicated by the names given to this material by the Arabs, who called it "Chinese snow," and the Persians, who called it "salt from China." The three ingredients were known in China for many centuries, however, before they were combined into black powder.

The first firecrackers may have appeared in the Chin Dynasty (221–207 B.C.) or during the Han Dynasty (206 B.C.–A.D. 220). According to the Han work *Shen I Ching* (*Classic of Strange Spiritual Manifestations*), what was called Pao Chu, or "burst-

ing bamboo," was "put into the fire," producing a noise that "frightened the spirit of the mountain." Earlier Chin works, *Ching Ch'u Sui Shih Chi* (*Annual Customs of Ching and Ch'u*) and the *Feng Su T'ung I* (*The Meaning of Popular Traditions and Customs*), speak of "bamboo bursting" and the "cracking of bamboo is like the roar of the wild animals." It is not known definitely that the bursting of the bamboo was caused by the explosion of black powder.

Other early Chinese writings also contain references to what was either black powder or a similar substance. A work on medicine written by Sun Saŭ-miso, who died in A.D. 682, describes experiments on *fu huo fa* (calcination), including one in which the author combined equal amounts of saltpeter and sulphur, added some acacia seeds, and lit the resulting powder. Ch'ing Haŭ-Tzu (c. 809), an alchemist, reportedly set fire to saltpeter and sulphur mixed with a substance called *ma tou ling* that resembled black powder. During the Northern Sung Dynasty (A.D. 960–1126) the term Pao Chang was used to describe firecrackers, which are believed to have contained black powder. Another term, Yen Huo, meaning firework, is said to have originated during the reign of Yang Ti (A.D. 605–616). According to a 1947 article in *Isis* by Wang Ling, "On the Invention and Use of Gunpowder and Firearms in China," fireworks became popular during the T'ang Dynasty (A.D. 618–907) and were perfected by the time of the Northern Sung Dynasty.

By 1045, just twenty-one years before William the Conqueror invaded Saxon England, there is no doubt the Chinese were well acquainted with black powder. The *Wu-ching Tsung-yao* (*Complete Compendium of Military Classics*), published that year, contains many references to the subject. Written by a government official named Tseng Kung-Liang at a time when the Sung Dynasty under the Emperor Rjen Tsung was experiencing its first serious military threat, it is largely concerned with strategy. There are some statistics on the disposition of troops, a series of short notices on successful battles, and, most im-

Jacob Willem Gravesande, a Dutch professor who studied Newton's laws of motion, designed a car that moved in reaction to discharging steam (see exhaust pipe, right).

Before William the Conqueror invaded England, the Chinese were experimenting with gunpowder. This fire-arrow, the Huo yao pien chien, *was included in* The Complete Compendium of Military Classics, *published in 1045.*

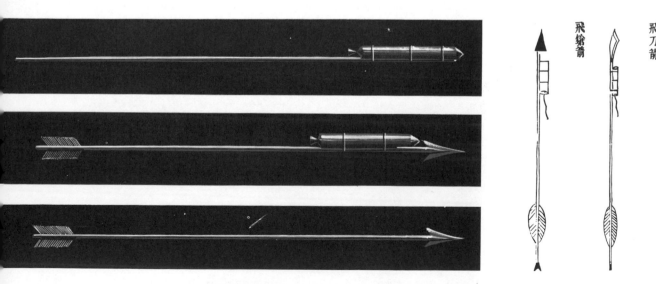

Left, Chinese fire-arrows of the types described in The Complete Compendium of Military Classics. *The two on top have explosives mounted on their sides. Right, actual illustrations from the* Wu Pei Chi. (RIGHT, PROFESSOR JAMES R. WARE)

portant, a section on weapons, including both text and many illustrations.

The *Complete Compendium* indicates that black powder, and possibly black-powder rockets, was used extensively during the Sung Dynasty, a period of brilliant cultural activity lasting from A.D. 960 to 1279. The book gives this formula for making gunpowder:

1 chin 14 ounces of sulphur, together with 2½ chin of saltpeter, 5 ounces of charcoal, 2½ ounces of pitch, and 2½ ounces of dried varnish are powdered and mixed. Next, 2 ounces of dried plant material, 5 ounces of tung oil, and 2½ ounces of wax are also mixed to form a paste. Then these ingredients are all mixed together, and slowly stirred. The mixture is then wrapped in a parcel with five layers of paper, which is fastened with hempen thread, and some melted pitch and wax and is put on the surface.

It is probable that the explosive properties of powder were unknown before the tenth century (unless the ninth-century work of Ch'ing Haü-Tzu is accepted as producing full-fledged explosive powder). Somewhere around the tenth or eleventh centuries, black powder was first compounded from its basic ingredients of saltpeter, charcoal, and sulphur, but this does not mean that it was used to propel rockets at that time. Some historians of technology mention that a rocket called San Kung Ch'uang Tzu Nu is described in the *Complete Compendium*, but close inspection of the eleventh-century handbook indicates the "rocket" is really a ballistalike device. Of course, it could have been used to launch rocket-powered fire-arrows as well as more conventional types, but the text accompanying the picture does not make this clear.

Fire-arrows are mentioned frequently in early Chinese sources, but—as in the case of the Byzantine writings mentioned earlier it is difficult to determine whether the arrows were tipped with fire or whether they were propelled by rockets, which also would give them a fiery appearance.

A French missionary, Father Joseph Marie Amiot, in his *Mémoire concernant l'histoire, les sciences, les arts, etc. des Chinois* (Volume VIII) (*Memoirs on the History, Science, Arts, etc. of the Chinese*), observed that firearms were known in China from the beginning of the Christian era; Koung-Ming is reported to have used them around A.D. 200. But it is not clear what is meant by "firearms." Certainly fire was known, and could have been coupled with a weapon that was neither a gun nor any sort of a rocket.

Father Amiot also described a fire-arrow to which

an early type of rocket may have been attached. According to Amiot: "The tube where the powder is placed must be extremely straight, should be only four inches long, and its end should be two inches from the fire. An arrow thus launched is equivalent to a very powerful gunshot." He does not say, however, when this fire-arrow was introduced.

Another type of fire-arrow was called the *ny-fung-yo*, or "powder that goes against the wind." W. F. Meyers, writing in the *Journal of the North China Branch, Royal Asiatic Society* (1871), described these as burning forward with "a sudden flame—so that no one durst approach them."

Some missionaries, such as Joseph P. G. Pauthier, who in 1821 wrote *Chine, ou description historique, géographique et littéraire de ce vaste empire d'après des documents Chinois* (*China, Historical, Geographic, and Literary Description of this Vast Empire According to Chinese Documents*) believed that the invention of the fire-arrow dated from the eighth century and that by the end of the eleventh century the Tartars had learned about it.

However, the French sinologists Joseph Toussaint Reinaud and Idelphonse Favé, in an indispensable work *Histoire de l'Artillerie: Feu grégeois, des feux de guerre, et des origines de la poudre à canon* (*History of Artillery: Greek Fire, Fireworks, and the Origins of Gunpowder*), published in 1845, and in an article, "Du Feu Grégeois, des Feux de Guerre, et des Origines de la Poudre à Canon chez les Arabes, les Persans, et les Chinois" ("On Greek Fire, Fireworks, and the Origins of Gunpowder by the Arabs, the Persians, and the Chinese"), which appeared in the October 1849 issue of the *Journal Asiatique*, state that, after years of research they discovered no documents leading them to believe that pyrotechnic devices existed prior to the thirteenth century. The French and other missionaries in China had access to vast quantities of documents; but, as Reinaud and Favé admit, the missionaries may not have known enough about weapons to interpret properly all that they read. Their reports, however, do provide additional evidence that incendiary compositions were known in China earlier than in the Arab countries and Western Europe.

The *Sung Shih Ping Chih* (*Military Memoirs of the Sung Dynasty*) refers to a new type of fire-arrow proposed by the general Fêng Chi-shang; it was subsequently made, and tested. Then, in the *Wu Li Hsiao Shih* (*Small Insights into the Principles of Things*), mention is made of a Yo I-Fang who, in A.D. 969, presented an improved fire-arrow to the emperor, T'ai Tsung, brother of the founder of the Sung dynasty, for which he was rewarded with a gift of silk. In 1002, T'ai Tsung's successor, Chen Tsung, used similar devices with ranges up to 1,000 feet.

Still, no direct mention is made during this period of powder being used to *propel* the arrows. But the Huo Yao Pien Chien type of fire-arrow may have been propelled by the force of the exploding black powder, for it is stated that five ounces of powder were placed at its end. And powder may have been used in conjunction with the San Kung Ch'uang Tzu Nu, described in the *Complete Compendium*.

An account of the use of these or very similar weapons is contained in the Sung history, which relates that "in the fifth year of Ch'un Hua [A.D. 994] an army of 100,000 men besieged the city of Tzu T'ung. A fierce attack was made, and the people in the city were greatly alarmed. Chang Yung ordered the hurling of stones by machines, and succeeded in pushing back the invaders. At the same time, fire-arrows were shot off, whereupon the enemy retreated." Other accounts say that fire-arrows were used by the Sung, Yuen, and Chin armies during the 1100's. In 1206, the second year of the K'ai Hsi, a Sung general, Chao Chun, fired the Huo Yao Pien Chien arrows "in order to burn down the wood, straw, and catapults of the enemy."

There is little doubt that powder-propelled fire-arrows were in fairly widespread use by the beginning of the thirteenth century. The Sung Dynasty, under continuous pressure from the north, had to rely more and more on technological developments to maintain its power and protect its civilization. Its ordnance experts introduced and improved incendi-

Probably invented in China, rockets were described by writers as "thunder that shakes the heavens." In the mid and late thirteenth century, the Mongolians used rockets, like those shown below, in battles ranging from Baghdad to Japan.

ary projectiles of many types, explosive grenades, and possibly cannon. They also seem to have made good use of rocket fire-arrows at the battle of K'ai-fung-fu (then called Piang-king) in A.D. 1232, five years after the death of Genghis Khan. A description of the battle appears in Father Antonine Gaubil's *Histoire de Gentchiscan et de toute la dynastie de Mongous, ses successeurs, conquérants de la Chine* (*History of Genghis Khan and of the Mongolian Dynasty, its Successors, Conquerors of China*), published in Paris in 1739.

The town of K'ai-fung-fu, north of the Yellow River, was heavily besieged by Mongol hordes. The town's governor, Kiang-chin, took extraordinary measures which enabled the defenders to resist for many months the onslaught of at least thirty thousand invaders. Against Kiang-chin's defenses, the Mongols could do little; they withdrew, regrouped, changed generals, and unleashed a new offensive, which, according to Father Gaubil, the Chinese met with rockets.

The new weapon was devastating. "When it was lit, it made a noise that resembled thunder and extended 100 li [about five leagues]. The place where it fell was burned, and the fire extended more than two thousand feet (that is to say, it burned a circumference of two thousand feet) . . . . These iron nozzles, the flying powder halberds that were hurled, were what the Mongols feared most," said Gaubil.

Other writers described this weapon as "thunder that shakes the heavens." One source says that "an iron pot was used for that, which was filled with yo [the incendiary mixture]. As soon as it was lit, the pao [fire-projectile] rose and the fire exploded everywhere." This was some sort of explosive grenade, generally launched by catapult, but apparently on occasion by rocket.

The besieged townspeople also used a rocket-type weapon known as the *feï-ho-tsiang*. It was described as an arrow to which combustible material was attached. When lit, the arrow would take off rapidly and fly along a straight trajectory, spreading fire over a distance of ten paces upon landing.

Because of the difficulty of interpreting second- and third-hand reports by untrained observers, some authorities question whether true rockets were used at the siege of K'ai-fung-fu. In an article on "Early Chinese Military Pyrotechnics," which appeared in the November 1947 issue of *The Journal of Chemical Education*, Tenny L. Davis and James R. Ware conclude that the weapons described were flying spears rather than rocket-propelled arrows. These spears were "equipped with [a] fire tube which threw fire forward for a distance of about 30 feet . . . a reasonable distance for fire to be thrown from a small tube, but . . . an unreasonably short trajectory for a rocket and one which would yield but little advantage."

Whether or not rockets played a part in this particular battle, there is substantial evidence that rockets were in general use at about this time. Rockets of one sort or another are mentioned regularly in accounts of battles following the siege of K'ai-fung-fu. For example, Constantine Mouradgea d'Ohsson, in the *Histoire des Mongols* (*History of the Mongolians*), published in 1834, wrote that rockets were used in the siege of Siang-yang-fu in 1271. They saw service in a battle between the Sung and the Yuan in 1274, and again in 1275. At about the same time the Mongols introduced them into Japan. According to the Japanese work *History of Japan's Humiliation*, in 1274, during the battle of Tsu Shima, fire-arrows were launched from Mongolian ships, while on land they were used by the army in attacking Iki Shima. Later, during the second invasion of Japan in 1281, rockets were launched in greater quantities with devastating effects. Once they learned about the properties of gunpowder, the Japanese began to develop fireworks; it is believed that both aerial and daylight types originated in Japan, a country that gave strong impetus to their development. Korea, Java, and India also adapted the Chinese invention by way of the Mongols.

Davis and Ware describe a variety of rocket-propelled arrows, their firing tubes, and several devices from which many arrows could be launched. These include "rocket-basket-arrows," which were fired from a cylinder of bamboo splints 4 feet long. Each cylinder contained from seventeen to twenty arrows on whose tips poison was smeared. Another contraption contained arrows "which will rush out on a solid front like 100 tigers"; they were fired from a frame, all 100 at a time, at targets up to 300 paces distance. There also was the "leopard-herd-rush-transversally" launcher, which could release forty arrows upon command, and the "long-snake-crush-enemy arrows," thirty of which were stored in a wooden box. These arrows were made of bamboo and were about 3 feet long. Each box of thirty weighed between 5 and 6 pounds, making this a highly mobile weapon.

Enemy armies, greatly impressed by the black powder and rockets of the Chinese, adopted them for their own use. Knowledge of these weapons was transmitted quickly to Europe, probably reaching the West by way of the Mongols and the Arabs.

The Mongols, for example, definitely used gunpowder at the Battle of Sejó, which preceded their capture of Budapest on Christmas Day in 1241. Con-

temporary accounts also indicate that this campaign featured what appears to have been the first gas attack on European soil. At the Battle of Sejó River, the Mongols set up on a pole "a long bearded head of horrible appearance" which emitted smoke with such a foul odor that the army of Heinrich von Schlesien was sent fleeing. Although effective as a gas, the real purpose of the smoke apparently was to serve as a screen for a Mongol attack.

Only seventeen years later, the Mongols are known to have used rockets in the Near East. According to the Arab writer Raschid-eddin, the Mongols employed fire-arrows while capturing the city of Baghdad on 15 February 1258. The rockets, containing black powder, were attached near the iron on the lance, with the wick placed on the opposite side. The Arabs subsequently referred to these arrows as "arrows from Cathay."

The exact date the Arabs adopted the rocket is unknown. Instructions for preparing black powder, the necessary propellant, are contained in a number of Arab works that date from the last half of the thirteenth century. Especially important are the writings of a Syrian military historian with the impressive name of al-Hasan al-Rammāh (the Lancer) Nedjm al-din (the star of religion) al-Ahdab (the hunchback). More simply referred to as al-Hasan al-Rammāh, his fame rested on his military writings.

His major work was the *Kitāb al-Furusīya wal munasab al-harbiya*, sometimes transliterated as *Ketab alferoussye ou al menassib alharbye* (*Treatise on Horsemanship and War Stratagems*). It is believed to have been written between 1285 and 1295, the year of al-Hasan al-Rammāh's death. In the foreword, the author announces that he will discuss, among other things, "The mixture of materials, the construction of machines, and sending of fire." He goes on to give a number of pyrotechnic recipes with careful instructions on how to prepare and purify the saltpeter portion.

The Arabs continued to be interested in rockets well after al-Hasan al-Rammāh wrote his book. Ibn Khaldūn (1332–1406) states in his *Kitāb al-'Ibar* (*Book of Wonders*), written in 1384, that the Arabs of North Africa were acquainted with the propulsive force of black powder in 1273. And the French historian Jean, Sire de Joinville, describes an odd, rocket-powered projectile used by the Arabs against the French under Louis IX during the Seventh Crusade.

Writing in 1268 about events that had occurred twenty years previously, De Joinville reports in his *Histoire de roy Saint Louis* (*History of King Saint Louis*) that the French first encountered this rocket while maneuvering along one of the eastern branches of the Nile in an attempt to take Damietta. The Arabs, who were on the other side of the river, launched "a projectile . . . which, when it had fallen on the bank [of the river], *came straight towards them, burning wildly;* it is doubtless *the egg that moves and burns.*" This interesting device was apparently a fairly flat object, filled with black powder and fitted with a tail to stabilize its path. Flames poured from little openings whose fuses were called Ikrikh. It was propelled by three rockets, "combined such that two of these rockets served as a guiding stick for the third."

Knowledge of explosive powder had penetrated Western Europe as far as England by the time De Joinville had come face to face with a rocket on the banks of the Nile. Roger Bacon (*c.* 1214–1220 to *c.* 1292) described the preparation of black powder before the middle of the thirteenth century, probably sometime in the late 1240's. He did not speculate on its use as a propellant for rockets, but he did describe what could have been rockets. The *Epistola Fratris Rog. Baconis, de secretis operibus artis et naturae et nullitate magiae* (*Epistle of Roger Bacon on the Secret Works of Art and of Nature and Also on the Nullity of Magic*) contains numerous references to saltpeter. Wrote Bacon:

We can, with saltpeter and other substances, compose artificially a fire that can be launched over long distances. The light of lightning and the sound of thunder can also be perfectly imitated. By only using a very small quantity of this material much light can be created accompanied by a horrible fracas. It is possible with it to destroy a town or an army . . . . In order to produce this artificial lightning and thunder it is necessary to take saltpeter, sulfur, and *Luru Vopo Vir Can Utriet.*

The words *Luru Vopo Vir Can Utriet* form an anagram which hides the proportion of powdered charcoal to be added to the powder. With this mixture "you will make thunder and flashing, if you know the art."

Bacon's German counterpart, Albertus Magnus (1193–1280) also wrote about black powder and how to make it. In his *De mirabilibus mundi* (*On the Wonders of the World*), he gave this recipe: "*Flying fire:* Take one pound of sulfur, two pounds of coals of willow, six pounds of saltpeter; which three may be ground very finely in marble stone;—afterwards, a little later, at will, some may be placed in a skin of paper for flying or for making thunder."

A more explicit description of a rocket was given by Marchus Graecus, or Marc the Greek, in a work titled *Liber ignium ad comburendos hostes* (*Book of Fires and Burning the Enemy*). Probably written be-

tween 1225 and 1250, but perhaps as late as 1270, the *Liber ignium* goes into considerable length on the subject of gunpowder and provides many recipes of pyrotechnic devices of all ages, including Egyptian, Hellenistic, Byzantine, Arabic, and Latin. It gives instructions on combating enemies at long distances with rockets. The propellant, mixed in a marble mortar, contained 1 pound of sulfur, 2 pounds of charcoal, and 6 pounds of saltpeter. "A certain quantity of this powder" was to be placed in a "long narrow and well pressed casing." In order to "carry the fire the device must fly in the air."

Rather than use the word *rocket,* Marchus Graecus presents the terms *tunica ad volandum* or "casing destined to fly," and *ignis volatilis in aere,* "flying fire." He says that when lit, this rocket will fly immediately towards the desired destination (*evolat ad quemcunque locum volueris*). The casing "must be slender at both ends, wide in the middle, and filled with the powder under consideration. The covering that is to rise in the air can have several foldings [*plicaturas* in Latin]; the type used to produce a detonation can have many of them."

Other types of rockets are described. For example, "flying fire (*ignis volans in aere*) can be made with a mixture of saltpeter, sulfur, and linseed oil. After being mixed and placed in a tube or hollow cane (Latin, *canna*), and then lit, it will rise into the air. Still another type is composed of saltpeter, sulfur, and carbon provided with a wick made of papyrus (*in tenta de papyro facta positis*). Again, upon being lit it soars rapidly skyward.

Other pioneers of medieval rocketry were Muratori, who first used the word rocket in its Italian form, *rocchetta,* in 1379; Konrad Kyser von Eichstadt, whose *Bellifortis* (*War Fortifications*) of 1405 describes several types of rockets; Joanes de Fontana, author of a 1420 sketchbook, *Bellicorum instrumentorum liber* (*Book of War Instruments*), which contains suggestions for military rockets; and Jean Froissart (1338–*c.* 1410), in whose *Chronicles* the use of tube-fired rockets was proposed.

By the sixteenth century many Europeans were writing about, describing, and making proposals for all sorts of rockets, military and nonmilitary. An anonymous book published in Paris in 1561, the *Livre de cannonerie et artifice de feu* (*Book of Cannons and Fireworks*), tells how to make 3½-foot and 4-foot-long rockets. Similar instructions are found in the *Briefve instructions sur le fait de l'artillerie de France* (*Brief Instructions on Matters of French Artillery*) by Daniel Pavelourt (Paris, 1597) and *La Pyrotechnie* (*Pyrotechnics*) by Hanzelet Lorrain (Pont-à-Mousson, 1630).

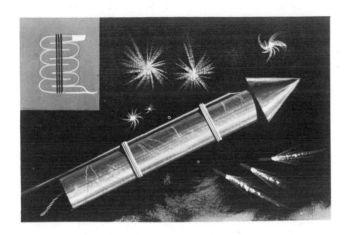

French pyrotechnic expert Jean Appier Hanzelet Lorrain described this rocket in his 1630 treatise La Pyrotechnic.

While rockets remained primarily military weapons, they also were used frequently for fireworks displays, and several books paid special attention to construction of this sort of rocket. The *De la pirotechnia (On Pyrotechnics)* of Vannoccio Biringuccio, published in Venice in 1540, while primarily a book on metallurgy, contains chapters on "Making Fireworks to be used in Warfare and for Festivals."

Nathaneal Nye's *The Art of Gunnery*, published in London in 1647, contains a 43-page section on rockets with the title *A Treatise of Artificial Fire-works for Warre and Recreation; Containing a Description to Make Sundry Kinds of Fire-works, both for Use and Pleasure, with lesse Labour and Cost than any Hath Heretofore been Published.* It includes instructions on how to make various pyrotechnic devices, has numerous illustrations of contemporary rockets, and tells the reader how to handle them. In order to fire a rocket "set your rockets mouth upon the edge of any piece of timber, battlement of a wall, top of the Gunners carriage, wheels, or any dry place whatsoever, where the rod or Twigge may hang perpendicular from it, then lay a Train of powder that may come under the mouth thereof, give fire thereunto, and you have done."

The Italians were the first Europeans to advance significantly the art of firework-making, with the Florentines and Sienese credited as being the first to place fireworks on wooden pedestals. Great fireworks displays were held regularly in many parts of Italy, which reigned supreme in pyrotechnics until the end of the seventeenth century when the French, under the influence of Louis XIV and Louis XV, began to take over the leadership. Frézier's *Traité des Feux d'Artifice* (Paris, 1747) is an excellent compendium of advances made in France by such men as Morel Torré and the brothers Ruggieri, as well as developments in the manufacture and use of fireworks in other countries.

The French military already had a tradition of rocketry. Rockets were used in the defense of Orléans in 1429, and again at the siege of Pont-Andemer in 1449. Rockets were used against Bordeaux in 1452, and a year later they were fired at Gand. The French had no monopoly on the subject; Kazimierz Siemienowicz, in his *Artis magnae artilleriae (Great Art of Artillery)*, published in Amsterdam in 1650, wrote on several types of military rockets. And, in 1668, a German field artillery colonel, Christoph Friedrich von Geissler, experimented with rockets weighing from 55 to 120 pounds. By 1730 a series of successful flights had been made.

Under kings Louis XIV and XV, the French led the world in the development of rockets. Such diverse styles as these were included in Frézier's Traité des feux d'artifice, *published in Paris in 1747.*

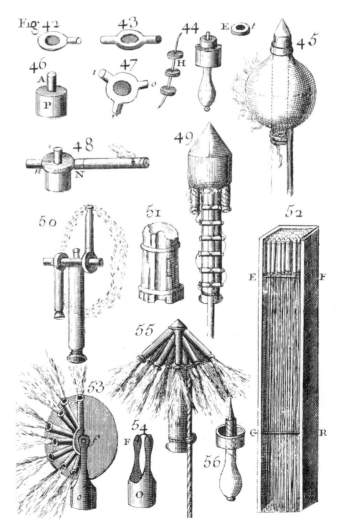

Sir William Congreve (1772–1828) of Woolwich Arsenal, London. In the beginning of the nineteenth century, he developed war rockets that could be fired from land or sea. His rockets were used by the British in such diverse places as Copenhagen, Bologna, and the Potomac River.

The eighteenth century was almost over, however, before Europeans became seriously interested in the military potential of the rocket—and then only because they suddenly found themselves on the receiving end of this weapon. The first major engagements with rockets that involved Europeans took place in India, where troops under Tippoo Sultaun of Mysore, fired them against the British during the two battles of Seringapatam in 1792 and 1799.

Two of Tippoo Sultaun's rockets are displayed in the Rotunda of the Royal Artillery Museum, Woolwich Arsenal, near London. One is a rude tube case, 10 inches long and 2.3 inches in exterior diameter, bound by strips of hide to a straight, 3-foot-4-inch-long sword blade. The iron tube of the second is 7.8 inches long and 1.5 inches in exterior diameter, secured by leather strips to a bamboo stick 6 feet 3 inches long.

Tippoo Sultaun's father, Hyder Ally, had built up a 1,200-man contingent of rocketeers by 1788. Subsequently, Tippoo Sultaun enlarged this corps to about 5,000. It is not known, however, how much of his strength he committed at either of the battles of Seringapatam and the accounts of British officers who took part in the campaigns against him differ as to the effectiveness of the rockets.

In the 1792 battle of Seringapatam, Tippoo Sultaun's army consisted of 36,131 men, including a rocket group of undisclosed size. One rocket unit, commanded by Cummer-dien Khan, had 120 men; another under Purneah, 131 men. On 22 April, twelve days before the main battle, rocketeers worked their way around to the rear of the British encampment, then "threw a great number of rockets at the same instant" to signal the beginning of an assault by 6,000 Indian infantry and a corps of Frenchmen, all directed by Mir Golam Hussain and Mahomed Hulleen Mir Mirans. The rockets had a range of about 1,000 yards. Some burst in the air like shells. Others, called ground rockets, on striking the ground, would rise again and bound along in a serpentine motion until their force was spent. According to one British observer:

The rockets make a great noise, and exceedingly annoy the native cavalry in India, who move in great bodies; but are easily avoided, or seldom take the effect against our [British as opposed to Indian units attached to the British] troops, who are formed in lines of great extent, and no great depth.

The diary of a young English officer named Bayly gives a somewhat different picture of the rockets' effectiveness. "So pestered were we with the rocket boys that there was no moving without danger from the destructive missiles . . . ." He continued:

The rockets and musketry from 20,000 of the enemy were incessant. No hail could be thicker. Every illumination of blue lights was accompanied by a shower of rockets, some of which entered the head of the column, passing through to the rear, causing death, wounds, and dreadful lacerations from the long bamboos of twenty or thirty feet, which are invariably attached to them.

Soon after their Indian experience, the British began developing rockets themselves. At the Royal Laboratory of Woolwich Arsenal, Colonel (later Sir) William Congreve initiated a series of experiments with incendiary barrage rockets. Congreve had been told that the British at Seringapatam had "suffered more from them [the rockets] than from the shells or any other weapon used by the enemy." In at least one instance, an eyewitness told Congreve, a single rocket had killed three men and badly wounded four others. It seemed to him that this might be a good weapon to use against the French. However, the weapon would have to be improved.

"In the year 1804," wrote Congreve in *A Concise Account on the Origin and Progress of the Rocket System*, "it first occurred to me, that, as the projectile force of the rocket is exerted without any re-action upon the point from which it is discharged, it might be successfully applied, both afloat and ashore, as a military engine . . . . I knew that rockets were used for military purposes in India; but that their magnitude was inconsiderable, and their range not exceeding 1000 yards." He then designed and built a 2,000-yard rocket, which he proposed be used in combat, as part of a "plan for the annoyance of Boulogne."

Congreve described his 32-pound rocket in clear, semitechnical terms. Its "carcass is the largest of the kind that has hitherto been constructed for use [apparently he did not know of von Geissler's 120-pounders]; it is completely cased in a stout iron cylinder, terminating in a conical head; it is 3 feet 6 inches in length, 4 inches in diameter, and weighs, when complete, 32 pounds . . . . The stick is 15 feet long, and 1½ inches in diameter, and is so constructed, that it may be firmly attached to the body of the rocket, by a simple and quick operation, at any required time." The rocket contained "about seven pounds of carcass composition," and cost one pound sterling. Congreve spoke of 13,109 rockets having been manufactured up to August 1806, and mentioned briefly of having experimented with 42-pounders with ranges of 4,000 to 5,000 yards.

Congreve's proposal to attack Boulogne was accepted by the British military. Ten launches were fitted with his incendiary rockets and, on 18 November 1805, they assembled off the city. The attack itself was scheduled for 21 November, but a sudden storm came up with such violence that the commander was "compelled to recall the vessels without a rocket having been fired." Five of the launches were swamped before they could retire from the bay.

The next attempt was planned for late spring or early summer of 1806, the flotilla to be outfitted with new 32-pound iron-case rockets capable of 3,000-yard ranges. To insure maximum accuracy, Congreve attached to each a 15-foot guiding stick. The attack was postponed until the fall when, on 8 October, eighteen boats with rockets aboard rowed into the bay. "In about half an hour above 2,000 rockets were discharged. The dismay and astonishment of the enemy were complete—not a shot was returned—and in less than ten minutes after the first discharge, the town was discovered to be on fire."

Even more spectacular than the attack on Boulogne was the barrage of some 25,000 Congreve rockets on Copenhagen in 1807. According to Baron Eben, who was in the city shortly after the bombardment, the "Danes were very much afraid of the rockets, and said they had burnt a great many houses, and besides, warehouses . . . ."

The British also used Congreve's rockets against the island of Aix at about the same time, then in 1809 against Callao, in 1810 against Cadiz, and in 1813 against Leipzig. From 1818 the British Army possessed an official rocket brigade, and other nations began to follow Britain's example. The Austrians formed a similar unit, supplied with rockets from a large factory at Wienerisch-Neustadt. The Russians also were active in war rocketry under the leadership of military engineers Alexander Zasyadko and Konstantin I. Konstantinov. Test fired in St. Petersburg in 1817, Zasyadko's rockets became the equipment of a special army unit. Subsequently, they were put into production at Russia's first rocket manufacturing plant, established in 1826 in St. Petersburg, and were used during the Russo-Turkish war from 1828 to 1829 and later in the Caucasus.

Congreve's rockets were employed frequently in the War of 1812 between Britain and the United States. Their best publicized moment came during a bombardment of Baltimore's Fort McHenry on the night of 13–14 September 1814, when a young lawyer named Francis Scott Key immortalized the spectacle of "the rocket's red glare" in a verse that later became the national anthem of the United States.

In their first large-scale use of military rockets, the British fired 2,000 rockets, invented and built by William Congreve, on the city of Boulogne in 1807. Below are (left to right) 300-, 100-, 42-, 32-, 24-, and 18-pound Congreve rockets. (ROTUNDA MUS. AND NATIONAL AIR AND SPACE MUS.)

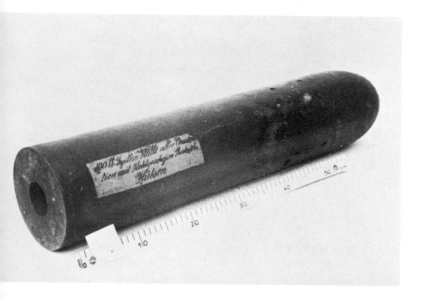

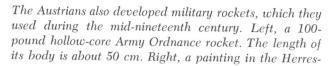

The Austrians also developed military rockets, which they used during the mid-nineteenth century. Left, a 100-pound hollow-core Army Ordnance rocket. The length of its body is about 50 cm. Right, a painting in the Herres-museum, Vienna, shows Austrian troops firing stick rockets during battle. (ROLF ENGEL COLLECTION, NATIONAL AIR AND SPACE MUS.)

Although dramatic, rockets were not particularly effective in this engagement. The bombardment was continued, more or less steadily, for twenty-five hours, but only four Americans were killed and twenty-four wounded.

The rockets witnessed weighed about 30 pounds and carried incendiary charges. They were fired from

Immortalized in verse by Francis Scott Key, the "rocket's red glare" was seen frequently in the War of 1812. In the picture below, the 20-gun sloop Erebus (right), which had been converted by Congreve to a rocket ship, fires on the American Fort Washington on the Potomac River. (NEWPORT NEWS MUS.)

the Erebus, a 20-gun sloop that had been converted under Congreve's direction into a rocket-firing bombardment vessel. The Erebus had some twenty long boxed frames extending from square openings, known as "scuttles," cut in the side of the ship. The boxes protected the interior of the ship from sparks and flames. Within them were large metal rocket-firing tubes. The tubes were fired by pulling lanyards.

Two basic Congreve designs were employed during the War of 1812: (1) case-shot rockets used as a substitute for, or as an auxiliary to, artillery; and (2) rockets loaded with inflammable materials whose purpose was to start fires.

The first, or case-shot, type contained carbine balls, which flew out like shrapnel when a charge of powder exploded. The rockets, when used with infantry, weighed from 3 to 12 pounds and were fired from a prone position. The rockets also could be fired from adjustable tripod stands, mounted on the decks of ships or in their rigging. Often they were fired from small boats, including those propelled solely by oars. They had a range of up to 3,000 yards.

First use of such rockets apparently was made by Rear Admiral Sir George Cockburn in the Chesapeake Bay area. Subsequently Lieutenant (later Sir) James Scott conducted an attack on shore targets from a boat propelled by oars. In describing the launching of the rockets he wrote:

By good luck [for they were an uncertain weapon] in the first flight I let off, one of them fell directly into the block-house and the other alighted in one of the batteries under it. Moving to the remainder of the boats, our gallant leader headed the attack and got possession of the batteries before the enemy could recover from the panic occasioned by the rockets.

Relating what it was like to be under rocket fire, one of the greatest American heroes of the war, Commodore Joshua Barney, wrote:

One of the enemy's rockets . . . fell on board one of our barges and after passing through one of the men, set the barge on fire and a barrel of gun-powder, and another of musket cartridges caught fire and exploded by which several of the men were blown into the water and one man very severely burned.

In another engagement on 8 June 1814, the British fired rockets against Barney's ships on the Patuxent River at the mouth of St. Leonard's Creek. The accuracy of the rockets was poor and they did little damage, but their range was greater than that of cannon and Barney's men were unnerved by the attack. On 10 June, the British did succeed in sinking two of his barges with rockets.

Some two months later, on 24 August 1814, during the Battle of Bladensburg, a seesaw fight between the British 85th Light Infantry Regiment and United States Attorney General William Pinkney's rifle battalion was quickly turned into an American rout when the British put their rockets into action. A special rocket squad, partially concealed in underbrush along the banks of a stream, fired the projectiles and caused such a panic among the Americans that they retreated headlong. "Never did men with arms in their hands make better use of their legs," wrote Lieutenant George R. Gleig, who commanded the British forces.

As the nineteenth century advanced, rocket designers concentrated on improving the weapon's accuracy. The normal way to control the flight direction of the early rockets was by stick. Congreve's incendiary 3.5-inch rockets, for example, were guided by a 15-foot stick attached to the case by hoops. Experiments in Britain, France, and the United States were next aimed at getting rid of the cumbersome stick by introducing a screw-shaped head. An American inventor named Court worked on the idea of constructing rockets so that the exhaust impinged on surfaces inclined to the main axis, producing spin. William Hale, an English inventor, gained fame for his further development of spin-stabilized rockets, which were subsequently used in Europe and Asia, and by the United States during the Mexican War in 1846–1848. Imparting spin to rockets was the first step since the introduction of the stick towards improving their accuracy.

Efforts also were made to increase range, but

Congreve's standard rockets, which flew about 3,000 yards, remained pretty much in a class by themselves. The Swiss developed 6-pound rockets which were fairly accurate at 1,800 to 1,900 yards and, at 1,100 yards, could register three hits out of five attempts. American-made Hale-type rockets flew somewhat over 2,000 yards; 2.25-inch models weighed 6 pounds, while the larger 3.25-inch models weighed 16 pounds.

The American Army made limited use of rockets during the Mexican War.

On 19 November 1846, Major General Winfield Scott was selected to lead the United States expedition to Veracruz and then to Mexico City; his force included, among other elements, a brigade of rocketeers. By 4 December, recruiting posters were out urging "active, brave young men to serve with rocket and mountain howitzer batteries, now preparing by the Ordnance Department for immediate departure." Training took place at Fort Monroe, Virginia.

The battery, which included the rocketeers, was placed under the command of First Lieutenant George H. Talcott. Brevet Second Lieutenant Jesse Lee Reno commanded the rocketeer contingent. Its one hundred and fifty members and their equipment (including fifty 2¼-inch, 6-pound Hale rockets) sailed from Fort Monroe on 1 February 1847, on the bark *Saint Cloud*. It is believed that the rocketeers joined General Scott's forces at the island of Lobos some two hundred miles north of Veracruz toward the end of February. They sailed to Anton Lizardo and then to Sacrificios three miles southeast of Veracruz. On 9 March the landing took place, with sixty-seven surf boats each carrying between seventy and eighty men, among them the rocketeers. The troops quickly advanced to the city, which was placed under siege. Beginning on 24 March rockets were used against Veracruz's fortifications, contributing to their surrender on 29 March.

On 8 April the rocketeers moved inland, having been transferred from General William Scott Worth's to General David Twiggs's division, and advanced along a route discovered by Captain Robert E. Lee. The rocket battery was set up at La Atalaya after its occupation. Under Second Lieutenant Reno, thirty rockets plus forty rounds of spherical case-shot were fired in action, leading to the capture of El Telegrafo Hill on 18 April. Later, in August, rockets were again used in battles around Mexico City, particularly at Churubusco. And, during the storming of Chapultepec on 12 and 13 September, they proved their worth in softening up Mexican positions, keeping the defenders under a steady hail of fire. In 1848, the rocketeers were disbanded. Little is known of Mexican use of rockets during the engagement, though

Ordnance reports list Congreve rockets being in inventory with Santa Anna's forces.

During the period between the Mexican War and World War II Hale and Congreve rockets declined in importance, partly because of storage problems. When the Mexican War rockets were taken out of storage during the Civil War, it was found that their black powder charges had not maintained their bond with the cases. Rockets were used during the Civil War, but only sporadically and indecisively.

The Confederates under Jeb Stuart fired rockets at McClellan's troops at Harrison's Landing on 3 July 1862. Colonel James T. Kirk, 10th Pennsylvania Reserves, recalled that "on Thursday, the 3rd instant, while standing in the line of battle, I had one man wounded by a missile from a rocket fired from a rebel battery." The rockets were later reported to have been fired from "a sort of gun carriage." The Confederates also placed rocket batteries in service in Texas during 1863–1864. Both rockets and launchers were manufactured first at Galveston and later at Houston.

The first Union combat group to be given rockets was the New York Rocket Battalion. Organized by a British officer, Major Thomas W. Lion, it consisted of one hundred and sixty men. Their rockets were from 12 to 20 inches long and 2 to 3 inches in diameter; ranges were from a third of a mile to three miles. Accuracy was poor.

Light carriages with four wrought-iron tubes about 8 feet long could be used; or, alternately, 3¼-inch guiding rods bound together in an open frame-

In 1849, to celebrate the Peace of Aix-la-Chapelle, the British used rockets to light up the Thames.

In 1841, Charles Golightly was caricatured in the saddle of a flying machine that he designed, but never built or tested. He did receive considerable notice in the press—much of it satirical.

work. Sheet-iron launchers with 3-inch hollow tubes were also popular. The payloads of the Union rockets usually contained a highly inflammable compound, but occasionally musket balls were placed in a hollow head and exploded by time fuses. The New York soldiers were issued the equipment in March 1862, but never had the opportunity to use it in combat. However, in 1864, rockets were fired by Union troops under General Alexander Schimmelfennig in South Carolina, who found them "especially practical in driving the enemy's picket boats off the creek and, during the night, out of the harbor."

Congreve's rockets did more than attract and occasionally inspire the military. In 1841, Charles Golightly received a British patent for a flying machine propelled by a steam rocket, a discovery that aroused great interest—much of it satirical. A model of the device was probably never constructed or tested. Like many inventors before him, Golightly was too far ahead of his time: almost ninety years would have to pass before man took to the air in a rocket-powered airplane.

Some modern writers refer to an even earlier "manned-rocket" concept. According to Nicolai A. Rynin (*Mezhplanetyne Soobshcheniya*, Vol. II, Part IV, Chap. 2, p. 10), a Chinese mandarin named Wan-Hoo, in about A.D. 1500, took "two large parallel horizontal stakes, which were tied together by a seat placed between them. Under this apparatus he placed forty-seven rockets which were fired simultaneously by forty-seven servants. However, the rockets under the mandarin's seat exploded irregularly and from the resulting fire unfortunately the inventor was consumed." This story, however, may be just a legend; neither Rynin nor anyone else who has mentioned the experiment has supplied any documentation for it.

Nineteenth-century experimenters also found new nonmilitary uses for rockets. In the early 1800's, rockets were developed to fire lifelines to stranded ships over which breeches buoys could be sent to rescue passengers and crew members. After some fifty years of line-carrying rocket history, Lieutenant Colonel E. M. Boxer of the Royal Laboratory in Britain developed, in 1855, a device consisting of two rocket cases so joined that when the first case had expended its propellant the second ignited. This tandem arrangement gave the rocket a much longer range than earlier models, and made it more effective in mercy missions. The Boxer rocket was kept in inventory by the British Board of Trade until well after World War I. Signal rockets also came to be a standard part of every ship's equipment. And whaling rockets came into use. The "California Whaling Rocket," for example, was made by Fletcher, Suits & Company of San Francisco and is described in the following terms:

Our apparatus consists of a gun metal cylinder, filled with a peculiar composition made only by ourselves, to which is attached, in front, a bomb with a barbed point; inside the bomb is an explosive charge and a chain toggle, which is released by the bursting of the shell on entering the whale; an iron shaft is attached to the rear of the rocket, through which the whale line is spliced. There is absolutely no recoil . . . the hinged flange is thrown up by the rocket passing out, protecting the face from injury.

The manufacturer went on to boast that the device could kill whales at thirty fathoms (attested by a list of ten whaling captains "who recommend them to all parties interested in the whaling business").

Generally speaking, however, interest in rockets declined once the spur of war was removed. By the end of the nineteenth century, rocket research was being carried on by only a few experimenters.

Pedro A. Paulet, a Peruvian chemical engineer, is reported to have conducted experiments in Paris from 1895 to 1897 with a small, 200-pound-thrust rocket motor made of vanadium steel. He was forced to discontinue his work because of economic difficulties and his neighbors' complaints. For some unknown reason, however, Paulet did not report on his work until 7 October 1927, in Lima's *El Comercio*. A Rus-

sian engineer living in Germany, Alexander B. Scherschevsky, learned of the article which he subsequently summarized in his book *Die Rakete für Fahrt und Flug* (*The Rocket for Travel and Flight*), published in Berlin in 1929. According to Scherschevsky, the Paulet rocket's propellants were nitrogen peroxide and gasoline; ignition was by a spark gap in the combustion chamber, and tests were satisfactory. The motor "weighed a little over 5 pounds, producing its 200 pounds of thrust at 300 explosions per minute." Paulet claimed it could be operated for an hour without "suffering appreciable deformation."

If it had not been for Scherschevsky, Paulet would probably have gone unnoticed. As it was, the Peruvian's experiments caught the attentions of later German authors and subsequently those of writers on rocketry all over the world, with the result that he became widely accepted as the pioneer of liquid propellant rocketry. The 7 October 1927 "article" in *El Comercio* was a 2½-column letter written by Paulet from Rome in which he claimed "priority" for his invention. After drawing attention to the many plans for rocket airplanes and spaceships then current in Europe, Paulet said he had conceived such ideas "THIRTY YEARS AGO [sic] when I was a student at the Institute of Applied Chemistry at the University of Paris." He expressed the fear that his claims would not be believed and called upon his former student friends in the Latin Quarter to tell the world of his experiments, which were, nevertheless, "made, truly, without witnesses . . . ." Paulet died on 30 January 1945 with his claims still unconfirmed.

In Austria, Dr. Franz von Hoefft, of Vienna's

An enterprising New Yorker found still another use for the rocket, as advertised in the Whalemen's Shipping List and Merchants' Transcript

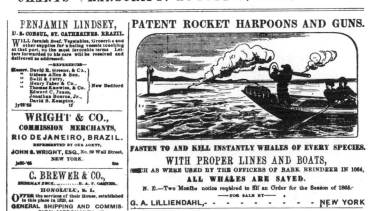

In 1906 Alfred Maul successfully took aerial photographs by attaching a camera to this rocket.

rockets and then took pictures of the Earth below, but his work was discontinued as the airplane arrived on the scene.

The ebb in interest in rockets that had begun in the nineteenth century continued into the first quarter of the twentieth, although the reasons for the decline changed. Lack of war as an incentive to weapons development was no longer a factor. Instead, it just seemed that the rocket had become obsolete. With the advent of radio, rockets lost importance as a method of signaling. Militarily, the rocket could no longer compete with artillery, where rifled barrels, breech loading, and other new techniques led to great increases in range and accuracy.

In the First World War, nevertheless, the Allies did make minor use of rockets, primarily for signaling and illuminating enemy positions. In an article on "The Use of Rockets and Illuminating Shells in the Present War," appearing in the July 1918 issue of the *Journal of Acetylene Lighting*, A. Bergman describes two kinds of rockets in common use at the front. One is the "ordinary, well known type that sails ahead of a tail of fire, and which finally bursts in a brilliant flash, illuminating a large area for a few seconds." The second type of rocket contained in its head a parachute to which a flare was attached. "Through this arrangement it is possible to keep a brilliant burning star suspended in the air for a comparatively long time, which is generally fixed to be about 30 or 35 seconds."

Gesellschaft für Hohenforschung (Society for Altitude Research), proposed plans in 1928 for the development of rocket motors. And, in Germany, Wilhelm Gaedicke performed some preliminary studies of rocket-powered airplanes. At the turn of the century, rockets were being fired into clouds and exploded, hopefully to prevent hailstorms. Alfred Maul successfully lofted cameras to high altitudes with

Both on land and at sea World War I rockets found service in laying smoke screens. As weapons of destruction they saw limited use, mostly in France.

During World War I, Le Prieur rockets were sometimes fired from French and British biplanes or from the ground against German captive balloons. Otherwise, military rockets could not compete in range or accuracy with *artillery of the day. Left, a Le Prieur rocket is fired from a BP12 in a ground test. Right, an H. Farman F40P has five such rockets on each side of the fuselage. (*IMPERIAL WAR MUS.*)*

While the war was going on in Europe, Robert H. Goddard was beginning a long career of rocket research in the United States. As professor of physics at Clark University, Worcester, Mass., he conducted some early experiments on the campus lawn. Left, Professor Goddard beside a 1915 rocket chamber mounting in Worcester. Right, he loads a 1918 bazooka with a 3-inch projectile at the Mount Wilson Observatory, Calif. (ESTHER C. GODDARD)

The French developed Le Prieur rockets (named after Naval Lieutenant Y. P. G. Le Prieur, who invented them) that were fired either from Nieuport (or other) airplanes or from the ground against German observation balloons. Normally, a biplane would carry four or five rockets mounted on each side of the fuselage.

In the United States, some work was done on short-range combat rockets. Dr. Robert H. Goddard, the father of modern rocketry, developed some rockets that were test fired just a few days before the war ended. His work was to bear fruit later, but in the frenzied atmosphere of World War I, it was generally overlooked.

At the same time, the first halting steps were taken toward development of guided missiles. There was no connection yet with rockets; it was something of a daring leap forward just to imagine that airplanes could be guided, without pilots, to a point where they would release their bomb loads on the enemy. The payoff was to come later, when the idea of a guided bombardment drone was wed to the propulsive force of the rocket.

During 1917, under the direction of Charles Kettering, the Delco and Sperry companies began to experiment with what appears certain to have been the first United States guided missile, a pilotless bi-plane known as the "Bug." Made largely of wood, the little plane weighed 600 pounds (including a 300-pound bomb payload) and was powered by a 40-horsepower Ford engine. Takeoff was from a four-wheel carriage running along a portable track. Flight direction was controlled by a small gyro, and altitude by an aneroid barometer. When target distance and wind conditions were determined, the "number of revolutions of the engine required to take the Bug to the target was calculated and a cam was set." Once the engine had propelled the missile the required distance, the cam dropped into position. The bolts that fastened the wings to the fuselage were pulled in and the wings detached, dumping the missile on its target. The Bug was tested successfully in 1918, before Army Air Corps observers in Dayton, Ohio.

A group led by Professor A. M. Low had already started a similar project in the United Kingdom. Low later recalled that the project was dubbed "A.T." so that people would think it was an "Aerial Target." The project was conceived in 1914 when Generals Caddell and Pitcher and Sir David Henderson, then Director-General of Military Aeronautics, proposed that radio could be used to direct a "flying bomb" to its target.

Low put together a team consisting of a captain (Poole) and two lieutenants (Bowen and Whitten).

The first United States guided missile had nothing to do with rocketry. Rather, it was a pilotless plane, built mostly of wood and successfully tested in 1918. Powered by a 40-hp Ford engine, it took off from a four-wheel carriage running along a portable track. After the plane had flown a predetermined distance, the wings dropped off, dumping the missile on the target. (U.S. AIR FORCE)

The British experimented with unmanned airplanes that would be directed by radio to fly bombs to their targets. The plane at right, designed by De Havilland, was powered by a 35-hp engine designed by Granville Bradshaw. It was flight tested on 21 March 1917. (IMPERIAL WAR MUS.)

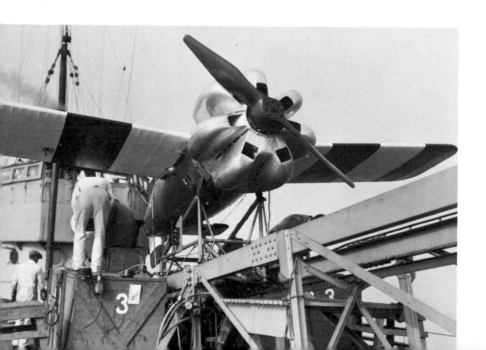

In 1927, the British developed the Larynx, a radio-controlled missile, which they flight tested from the HMS Stronghold. It could carry a 250-pound bomb at 200 mph to a target 100 miles away. (ROYAL AIRCRAFT EST.)

The Queen Bee (left), introduced in 1930, was followed by the Queen Wasp (right). Both were launched by catapult from naval vessels or landing installations. After *completing their missions, they returned and landed on pontoons.* (ROYAL AIRCRAFT ESTABLISHMENT)

Experiments began at Brooklands and continued at Feltham, where the work force increased to forty. After much trial and error the radio equipment was developed and a monoplane constructed by De Havilland powered by "a beautiful opposed engine made by that outstanding designer Granville Bradshaw." Two tests were made in March 1917 at the Royal Flying Corps training school field at Upavon but "the first machine had engine failure on the runway and flopped ungracefully into the mud," according to a 1952 article by Low in *Flight*. (Major Gordon Bell, an observer of the "flight," was heard to say, "I could throw my bloody umbrella farther than that!") The next trial turned out better, Low continues, "for the machine took off, flew under control for a short time until, after a loop, the engine failed . . , [then] and with an appalling crash, the A.T. landed about three yards from where I was sitting and buried most of our beautiful work in the ground. But it had flown and it had worked."

Although work on the A.T. project terminated, British interest in missiles persisted until, in 1927, engineers at the Royal Aircraft Establishment developed a radio-controlled missile called the Larynx. A monoplane, it was flight tested both from the HMS *Stronghold* and from a testing ground in Egypt. At a speed of up to 200 miles per hour, it could carry its 250-pound bomb to targets as far as 100 miles away. In 1930, the Queen Bee was introduced, followed by the Queen Wasp, both launched by catapult from naval vessels or from landing installations. After undertaking their missions they would return, landing on pontoons.

During the Spanish Civil War, 1936–1939, the rocket staged a brief, and somewhat unusual, appearance. Converted sea-rescue rockets were placed into service for the purpose of transporting propaganda materials behind enemy lines. The nosecone was especially constructed so that it would burst open at a predetermined time and release its payload of propaganda leaflets, which were printed on very thin paper.

Although the Spanish Civil War was regarded as a testing ground for a coming world war, the peripheral role given to rockets provided a poor indication of the important role they were to play in the next few years. While practical use of rockets languished after World War I, a few men, working in obscurity and with limited funds, had laid the foundation for a theoretical and technical revolution. The pioneers of rocketry were about to receive the credit due them.

3 PIONEERS OF SPA

The idea gradually dawned around the turn of the twentieth century that the rocket was the key to space travel. Only a few individuals grasped this concept, and no one paid much attention to them at first. But this discovery was a landmark in human thought. At last man had the answer to a problem that had intrigued and baffled him for centuries. The discovery opened the universe to human exploration.

With the benefit of hindsight, it seems strange that the discovery did not come sooner. Men had known about military rockets for centuries, and the reaction principle was commonly employed in fireworks. But the fiction writers who dealt with space travel gave no indication, even on the rare occasions that they mentioned rockets in their tales, that there was a scientific basis for their use. The scientists, meanwhile, simply ignored the problem.

The potential of the rocket was realized independently by three different men, born in widely separated countries, who never even saw each other. Yet these men—Konstantin Eduardovitch Tsiolkovsky of Russia, Robert Hutchings Goddard of the United States, and Hermann Oberth, a Hungarian-born (Transylvanian) German—each came to the same conclusions about the future of space travel, conclusions that have become the basic working formulas of the space age.

Toward the end of the nineteenth century many technical advances were made that were destined to help translate the theories of Tsiolkovsky, Goddard, and Oberth into reality. Industrialization proceeded at a rapid pace. Enormous progress was recorded in metallurgy. Improved explosives became available and smokeless powder was invented. Scientists began to undertake searching investigations into heat engines (of which the rocket is an example) and learned how to liquefy gases that one day would be used as space vehicle propellants. Perhaps most important of all, the excitement of rapidly advancing frontiers of science and technology began to pervade the atmosphere, causing more and more young people to choose scientific and engineering careers, and lead-

ing universities to expand their scientific curricula.

The Russian scientist-schoolteacher Konstantin Eduardovitch Tsiolkovsky was the first to understand and develop the use of rockets in space travel. In his biography of the great pioneer, A. Kosmodemyansky writes that Tsiolkovsky "grasped the principle of obtaining motion by means of the reaction of ejected particles as early as 1883, but he created the mathematically precise theory of rocket propulsion only at the close of the century."

Tsiolkovsky really has only two potential rivals for the honor of being first—Nikolai Ivanovitch Kibalchich and Hermann Ganswindt. Considered more as historical sidelights, because neither contributed significantly to astronautical theory, these two men nevertheless deserve recognition for seeing an essential truth that others—including even Jules Verne—did not.

Kibalchich, born in 1853, became active in his twenties in anti-czarist circles, took part in the successful assassination plot in 1881 against Emperor Alexander II, was arrested shortly after the assassination, and sentenced to death. While spending his final days in jail, Kibalchich developed a scheme to propel a platform by rocket power. As the device flew, gunpowder cartridges would be fed continuously to the motor chamber. By changing the direction of the rocket motor's axis, the platform would change its flight path. Following the discovery of his proposal in police archives, excerpts were published in *Bylove* (*The Post*), 10 and 11, in 1918. Kibalchich wrote, "I am writing this project in prison, a few days before death. I believe in the practicability of my idea and this faith supports me in my desperate plight." This is the extent of his contribution. There are not even any indications, let alone records, of other studies Kibalchich may have carried out on rocketry and astronautics.

A little more is known about Ganswindt. He was a basement inventor who might be considered a German counterpart of Kibalchich. Around 1890, more than a decade before Tsiolkovsky's theories were published, Ganswindt proposed a reaction-powered spaceship. Somehow he had stumbled across the idea that a reaction device would operate in space as well as on Earth; he could not explain why this should be, since he had no mathematical training. Ganswindt suggested that the spaceship be propelled by steel cartridges charged with dynamite (he failed to realize that combusting gases would have enough power). Each cartridge would be placed in a reaction chamber, one half being ejected by the force of the explosion and the other half striking against the top of the chamber to provide the reaction force. Below the chamber, suspended on springs, was the part of the spaceship that housed the crew. It had a center hole through which the "exhaust" of the motor passed.

Despite the credit given to Kibalchich and Ganswindt, Tsiolkovsky is universally regarded as the true pioneer of astronautical theory. As he himself expressed the development of his thoughts:

For a long time I thought of the rocket as everybody else did—just as a means of diversion and of petty everyday uses. I do not remember exactly what prompted me to make calculations of its motions. Probably the first seeds of the idea were sown by that great fantastic author Jules Verne—he directed my thought along certain channels, then came a desire, and after that, the work of the mind.

Tsiolkovsky was born in September 1857 in the town of Izhevskoye, Spassk District, Ryazan Gubernia. Of humble origin, he showed an early great talent for science and invention and dedicated himself to the study of mathematics and physics. He read everything he could lay his hands on, and by his early teens, the germ of the idea of interplanetary travel had entered his restless mind. One day he conceived an admittedly impractical plan to send a vehicle into space which left him so "agitated, nay, shaken, that I could not sleep that night . . . . By morning I understood its futility, and the disillusionment was as great as the illusion had been."

But he persisted. He continued to read, teaching himself virtually everything he ever learned. In 1878 he became a "people's school teacher" and moved to Borovsk, in Kaluga Province. There he began to experiment in a home laboratory and to write reports on his findings. On the basis of his papers he soon was elected to the Society of Physics and Chemistry in St. Petersburg. And then, in 1883, he made the discovery that was to lead the world into the age of space flight.

An entry in his diary for 28 March 1883 shows a basic understanding of reaction flight.

Consider a cask filled with a highly compressed gas. If we open one of its taps the gas will escape through it in a continuous flow, the elasticity of the gas pushing its particles into space will also continuously push the cask itself. The result will be a continuous change in the motion of the cask. Given a sufficient number of taps (say, six), we would be able to regulate the outflow of the gas we liked and the cask (or sphere) would describe any curved line in accordance with any law of velocities . . . . As a general rule, uniform motion along a curved line or rectilinear non-uniform motion in free space involves continuous loss of matter.

In the years that followed, he worked out the implications of his idea, refining it and putting it into scientifically acceptable form. "The old sheet of paper with the final formulae of a rocket device bears the date of 25 August 1898," he wrote long afterward. Five years later, in the journal *Nauotchnoye Obozreniye* (*Scientific Review*) his first article on rocketry appeared. It was titled "Exploration of Space with Reactive Devices" ("Issledovanie Mirovykh Prostransty Reaktivnymi Priborami"). It had taken about two hundred years from the time Sir Isaac Newton expressed his law of action and reaction to the realization that a reaction device could enable man to escape from the planet Earth.

Tsiolkovsky worked alone with meager equipment and virtually no funds. His only assistance in pre-revolutionary times was in the form of a grant, totaling just 470 rubles, received in 1899 from the Academy of Science's Physics and Mathematics Department. He attempted no rocket-motor testing, concentrating on the theoretical aspects of reaction

Tsiolkovsky's first rocket design, the 1903 spaceship, was powered by liquid hydrogen (H) and liquid oxygen (O). The explosives mix at A, producing heated gases, which expand and cool as they travel back through the tube, finally escaping at B.

Russian scientist Konstantin Tsiolkovsky was the first to understand the use of rockets in space travel. Although he never built a rocket, he designed several and solved theoretically how reaction engines could escape from and re-enter the Earth's atmosphere.

motion and interplanetary flight. He always kept his feet to the ground, despite his soaring thoughts. "I could never proceed without calculation. It was calculation that directed my thought and my imagination," he wrote.

Konstantin Tsiolkovsky (left) in his home laboratory in Borovsk, Kaluga Province, Russia.

Tsiolkovsky not only solved theoretically such age-old questions as how to escape from the Earth's atmosphere and gravitational field, but he also described several rockets. The first, conceived in 1903, was to be powered by liquid oxygen and liquid hydrogen—a very modern propellant combination. "In a narrow part of the tube," he wrote, "the explosives mix, producing condensed and heated gases. At the other, wide, end of the tube the gases, rarefied and, consequently, cooled, escape through the nozzle with a very high relative velocity."

The Russian schoolteacher made another discovery—the *multistage rocket*, which he called the "rocket-train." Actually, this concept was not as new as Tsiolkovsky, who discovered it independently, thought; firework-makers had used the principle for at least 200 years. But Tsiolkovsky was the first to analyze the idea in a sophisticated manner. The multistage technique, he concluded, was the only feasible means by which a space vehicle could attain the velocity necessary to escape from the Earth's gravitational hold. His design for a "passenger rocket train of 2017" consisted of twenty single rockets, each with its own engines and propellants. More than 300 feet long, it was over 12 feet in diameter and was built in three layers of metal with quartz windows, a refractory material, and finally a highly refractory

Tsiolkovsky's 1914 rocket spaceship was a further development of the 1903 model. The long curved tube led to the combustion chamber, which burned gaseous oxygen and liquid hydrogen.

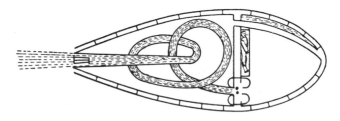

metal to protect the vehicle from the heat produced as it sped through the atmosphere. As each stage consumed its propellants it would be discarded, to keep the weight of the vehicle as low as possible. The next stage would take over the job of accelerating the spaceship, taking advantage of the velocity already given to it by the discarded first stage.

Tsiolkovsky described this important principle of rocketry in these words:

If a single-stage rocket is to attain cosmic velocity it must carry an immense store of fuel. Thus, to reach the first cosmic velocity [his term for *orbital velocity*], 8 km/sec, the weight of the fuel must exceed that of the whole rocket (payload included) by at least four times. This will present considerable difficulties. The stage principle, on the other hand, enables us either to obtain high cosmic velocities, or to employ comparatively small amounts of propellant components.

Once he had worked out the basic principles of rocket dynamics, Tsiolkovsky devoted more and more time to speculations on space flight itself. It became very clear to him "that the device for moving in a void must be a kind of rocket, *i.e.*, be self-sufficient as regards both energy and the mass to thrust away from." He foresaw that a rocket could "navigate interplanetary space, interstellar space, visit planets or their satellites, rings, or any other celestial bodies, and then return to the Earth." He spent a great deal of time analyzing the components of rocket engines and calculating the energy contents of various propellant combinations, including liquid hydrogen, alcohol, kerosene, methane, and liquid oxygen.

As Tsiolkovsky's daring, yet carefully calculated, plans matured he was given increasing recognition. He was elected to the Socialist Academy (predecessor of the U.S.S.R. Academy of Science) in 1919, and later was granted a pension by the Soviet government. His writing continued unabated; from 1925 to 1932 alone some sixty works on astronautics, astronomy, mechanics, physics, and philosophy appeared. Tsiolkovsky died in Kaluga on 19 September 1935, two days after his seventy-eighth birthday.

Although Tsiolkovsky's life spanned the entire period of the evolution of basic astronautical theory, he was not responsible for, and did not witness, the major practical developments in liquid-propellant rocket engines that took place in America and Germany in the 1920's and 1930's. There are many reasons why Russia did not capitalize on Tsiolkovsky's work, including political instability, lack of economic and technical resources, and failure of the military to appreciate the significance of his discoveries.

Tsiolkovsky's brilliant mind conceived theories and developed them, but did not lead him to perform

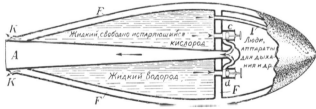

Tsiolkovsky foresaw that rockets could "visit planets or their satellites, and then return to Earth." His book on Lunar travel, On the Moon, *was published in Moscow in 1935. Shown here are the book's jacket (top) and the spaceship he described for interplanetary travel (bottom).*

practical experimental work. Ganswindt and Kibalchich also conceived an idea, but did virtually nothing to demonstrate its technical feasibility. But Robert H. Goddard combined theory and practice during an extraordinary, though often lonely, career that finally earned him the justified title "Father of Modern Rocketry."

Goddard clearly recognized that the entire sci-

43

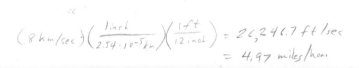

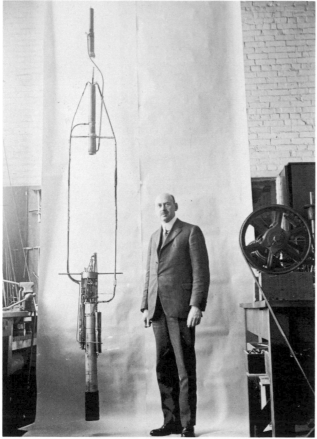

Robert H. Goddard combined theory and practice in a long career of building and testing rockets. Here he is shown (top) with steel combustion chamber and nozzle for a 1915 rocket, and (bottom) standing beside a 1925 double-acting rocket in his experiment center in Worcester, Mass. (ESTHER C. GODDARD)

ence of astronautics rested on the rocket propulsion system. Until the rocket was perfected there would be no trips through outer space, no landings on alien worlds. Goddard dedicated himself first and foremost to the rocket, although he never lost sight of its ultimate purpose.

Goddard was born almost exactly twenty-five years after Tsiolkovsky, on 5 October 1882, in Worcester, Massachusetts. He lived, studied, worked, and was buried there. During his life he was little known and less appreciated, yet his efforts had incalculable influence on the course of history. Only after his death did his country take notice of his genius.

As a boy Goddard showed an aptitude for science and engineering, with his interests channeled particularly into mathematics and physics. Along with science he found time to read such science-fiction classics as Wells's *War of the Worlds* and Verne's *From the Earth to the Moon;* and, like Tsiolkovsky, was inspired by them. In an autobiography written in 1927 (but only published in 1959 in the journal *Astronautics*), he acknowledged his debt to Wells and other science-fiction writers by recalling that they "gripped my imagination tremendously. Wells' wonderful true psychology made the thing very vivid, and possible ways and means of accomplishing the physical marvels set forth kept me busy thinking."

In 1902, while a student at South High School in Worcester, he submitted to *Popular Science News* an article titled "The Navigation of Space." It was not published. In a second article, he developed the scheme, as had Tsiolkovsky before him, of multistage spaceships. This article ended with the statement: "We may safely infer that space navigation is an impossibility at the present time. Yet it is difficult to predict the achievements of science in this direction in the distant future."

Cautious notes like this were to characterize Goddard's writings and statements on rocketry all his life. He had no doubt that the reaction principle underlying rocket motion eventually would permit man to explore the Solar System, "I began to realize that there might be something after all to Newton's Laws," he wrote. "[The Third Law] made me realize that if a way to navigate space were to be discovered or invented, it would be the result of a knowledge of physics and mathematics . . . ." But he was reluctant, as Tsiolkovsky and other European thinkers were not, to apply his full energies to the task of promoting space flight.

Meanwhile, Goddard's education continued. After graduation from Worcester Polytechnic Institute in 1908, he went on to Worcester's Clark University. He received a doctorate in 1911 and subsequently became professor of physics there. While a student and professor at Clark, Goddard accomplished an important portion of his work on rocketry. He began, in 1909, to make detailed studies and calculations of liquid-propellant engines, coming to the conclusion (again, like Tsiolkovsky) that liquid hydrogen and liquid oxygen would be an ideal combination. During a year at Princeton (1912–1913) he continued to work on the theory of rocket motion, further convincing himself that he was following a path that would one day reach to the stars.

Goddard kept detailed diaries of his activities, so that it is possible to follow closely the development of his rockets and to appreciate his method of thinking. His experiments and theories resulted in a succession of patents, most of which are basic to the operation of all modern rocket engines. For example, during July 1914, he was granted patents covering combustion chambers, nozzles, propellant feed systems, and multistage rockets ("a primary rocket, comprising a combustion chamber and a firing tube, a secondary rocket mounted in said firing tube, and means for firing said secondary rocket when the explosive in the primary rocket is substantially consumed").

As World War I approached, Goddard was involved in flight testing simple powder rockets near Worcester, some of which attained altitudes up to 500 feet; these tests soon suggested more elaborate experiments, ones that would remain out of the question unless he could find suitable financial support.

Attempting to obtain such support in September 1916, he wrote to the Smithsonian Institution outlining his work and his minimum financial requirements. After being requested to supply additional material to bolster his proposal, which involved a plan for making scientific measurements at high altitudes by means of rockets, he received on 5 January 1917 a grant of $5,000. Hardly a large sum, it was enough to allow him to begin in earnest his lifelong work. Soon, however, World War I caused a temporary change in his plans.

Instead of continuing with his high-altitude research, Goddard went to California to work on military rockets, including a forerunner of the World War II bazooka. In September 1918, Goddard showed two Signal Corps officers several rockets that were ready for production. One of them could be fired by a doughboy in the trenches; the largest could carry an 8-pound payload three quarters of a mile. Goddard's rockets were demonstrated at Aberdeen, Maryland, on 7 November 1918, just a few days before the Armistice. He had models weighing 5,

7½, and 50 pounds, which were fired from 2-inch and 3-inch tubes, 5½ feet long.

The end of the war meant an end of military interest in rockets; Goddard returned to Clark soon after the Armistice.

In 1919, and again in 1936, Goddard published two basic monographs, both appearing as Smithsonian Miscellaneous Collections. The first, titled *A Method of Attaining Extreme Altitude*, was essentially the study Goddard had submitted to support his request for his first grant; the second, called *Liquid-Propellant Rocket Development*, was a report to the Daniel and Florence Guggenheim Foundation, which continued his financial support. His final major work, published posthumously in 1948, was entitled *Rocket Development: Liquid-Fuel Rocket Research, 1929–1941*.

The most famous of these three works is the first, a sober, learned exposition of the fundamentals of rocketry whose sections carry such titles as "Reduction of Equation to the Simplest Form," "Efficiency of Ordinary Rocket," "Calculations Based on Theory and Experiment," and "Calculation of Minimum Mass to Raise One Pound to Various Altitudes in the Atmosphere." It would have doubtless gone unnoticed by all but a tiny segment of the academic community were it not for the inclusion, at the end of the report, of the section: "Calculation of Minimum Mass Required to Raise One Pound to an 'Infinite' Altitude."

"Infinite altitude" meant space flight—escape from the Earth, a subject never far from Goddard's mind. And space flight in his day meant the Moon, a subject which he got around to after several paragraphs of preliminaries. Goddard broached the subject

From this 7-foot frame (small structure, right, next to ladder) on a farm in Auburn, Mass., Goddard successfully tested the world's first liquid-fuel rocket on 16 March 1926. The rocket, which stood 10 feet tall, accelerated to a speed of 60 mph and flew 184 feet. The wooden frame at the left is a wind breaker. (ESTHER C. GODDARD)

SMITHSONIAN MISCELLANEOUS COLLECTIONS
VOLUME 71, NUMBER 2

A METHOD OF REACHING EXTREME ALTITUDES

(WITH 10 PLATES)

BY
ROBERT H. GODDARD
Clark College, Worcester, Mass.

(PUBLICATION 2540)

CITY OF WASHINGTON
PUBLISHED BY THE SMITHSONIAN INSTITUTION
1919

Goddard's most famous work was probably his least understood. A scholarly treatise on the fundamentals of rocketry, it contained a final section on how rockets could get to the Moon. The contents of the final section were sensationalized by newspaper reporters, who referred to Goddard as the "Moon man."

obliquely, first noting that it would be interesting "to speculate upon the possibility of proving that such extreme altitudes had been reached even if they actually were attained." He realized that proving it would be "a difficult matter," even if a mass of flash powder were ignited at the peak of the trajectory, for "it would be difficult to foretell, even approximately, the direction in which it would be most likely to appear."

Then he came to his point: "The only reliable procedure would be to send the smallest mass of flash powder possible to the dark surface of the moon when in conjunction [*i.e.*, the 'new' moon], in such a way that it would be ignited on impact. The light would then be visible in a powerful telescope." He went on to calculate the amount of flash powder

needed to be "just visible" and "strikingly visible" to a one-foot aperture telescope and to work out the total initial mass of the launching rocket.

Characteristically, he closed his report with words of caution:

This plan of sending a mass of flash powder to the surface of the moon, although a matter of much general interest, is not of obvious scientific importance. There are, however, *developments of the general method under discussion, which involve a number of important features not herein mentioned,* which could lead to results of much scientific interest. These developments involve many experimental difficulties, to be sure; but they depend upon nothing that is really impossible.

Goddard, so used to working quietly and alone, was completely unprepared for what occurred next. Newspaper editors seized on the statements in the paper's last section and sensationalized them, turning the professor from Massachusetts into the "moon man." Goddard, who had sought only the attention of fellow scientists, was profoundly irritated by the wave of publicity, some of which made him a butt of jokes. He finally decided that all he could do was remain silent until the newspapers lost interest, which they inevitably did.

The initial Smithsonian grant was used up by the summer of 1920, but Goddard's request for continued support brought the promise of another $3,500. At about the same time, arrangements were made for him to work for the United States Navy's Bureau of Ordnance-Indian Head Powder Factory in Maryland, where he remained from 1920 to 1923. There emphasis was placed on rocket depth-charges and rocket-boosted armor-piercing projectiles. Returning to Worcester, he carried out serious studies of liquid and solid propellants as well as of stabilization and guidance. From 1925 he concentrated on these all-important phases of rocket technology.

On 23 November 1929, occurred one of the most important events in Goddard's life—an unexpected visit from Colonel Charles A. Lindbergh, who had read of Goddard's work and was fascinated with its potentialities. Lindbergh, the world-famous aviator, subsequently arranged for a $50,000 grant to the rocket pioneer from the Guggenheim Fund for the Promotion of Aeronautics, to be paid through Clark University. A smaller grant from the Carnegie Institution was earmarked for test facilities.

Realizing that Massachusetts was too crowded for him to conduct the type of flights he now envisioned, Goddard went west to search for a suitable location—and found one at the Mescalero Ranch near Roswell, New Mexico. He, his wife, and four assistants set up shop there in 1930. From then until 1941, except for a break in 1932–1934, Goddard undertook one of the most amazing "lone-wolf" development programs in the history of technology.

To demonstrate the extent of his experimental efforts, a chronology of Goddard's major static and flight tests has been prepared. The material is derived from his second monograph, *Liquid-Propellant Rocket Development*, which covers activities from the time of his 1919 Smithsonian report to September 1935; *Rocket Development*, which brings his work up to 1941; and other sources. Mrs. Robert H. Goddard was kind enough to review this material and write a few paragraphs explaining it:

Despite the fact that the data for the accompanying list of milestones in the Goddard rocket researches were checked against several sources, all the figures may not be quite accurate. The measurement of pressures, flows, temperatures, and altitudes in the experiments of the early years was difficult. For example, the weight of liquid oxygen used in each test was hard to define, especially for flight tests, for some oxygen was used to cool the parts before the test, some evaporated in the tank during the final flight preparations, and occasionally some was left in the tank after the test. Further, the rocket was so small that it was not always possible, in the wide New Mexico sky, to ascertain its maximum height, with either the recording telescope or the moving picture camera.

Reliability of propulsion, stability in flight, and recovery were the primary aims in these early tests, rather than the attainment of high altitudes. Heights of one-half to one mile served our purposes. It should be borne in mind that no telemetering or other electronic instruments were then commercially available; our early measuring instruments, including barographs and recording telescopes, had to be made in our own shop. By July 17, 1941, however, the instruments had been sufficiently developed to give the details shown. My husband felt that his altitudes, speeds, and jet velocities were consistently on the low side in most of the tests, especially in the K series.

A few summaries of the number of static and flight tests have been made at points where the tests seemed to culminate, in order that the ratio of proving-stand tests to flight tests might be made clear; the addition of the average intervals between tests has been made because of frequent inquiries as to how often my husband ran his tests in New Mexico.

Descriptions of the pre-Roswell tests, and of the government work after we left Roswell, have been kept at a minimum. Only the New Mexico liquid-propellant period is fully tabulated, because only this Roswell work represents his full-time, self-directed experimental work.

This Goddard rocket, tested in 1927, was equipped with a turntable for launching and a parachute for descending. (ESTHER C. GODDARD)

In this experiment, conducted in 1928, the test rocket was caught at the top of the tower. (ESTHER C. GODDARD)

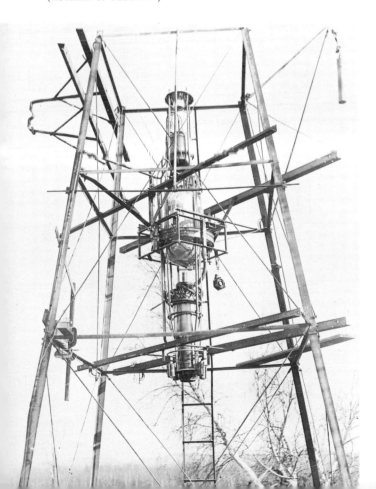

Tests at Worcester, Massachusetts, 1915–1929

1915–1922	Many tests were conducted with rockets using black and smokeless powders at Clark University and, during World War I, for the United States Signal Corps in California. In 1918, Goddard developed a prototype of the World War II bazooka rocket. Other work with solid-propellant rockets was undertaken for the United States Navy in 1920–1923.
1920–1922	Finding that solid propellants were inadequate for reaching the altitudes his theoretical studies had indicated were possible, Goddard turned to liquid oxygen and gasoline (he had mentioned using these liquids in his 1919 paper "A Method of Reaching Extreme Altitudes").
1923–1924	A liquid-oxygen pump and engine were developed that, although they worked, were too small to be satisfactory.
1924–1925	Work progressed on a displacement cylinder model, two pumps and two engines, a powder igniter, and refractory-lined combustion chambers and nozzles.
6 December 1925	In order to reduce weight, Goddard returned to the simple pressure feeding of the liquids. At the Clark University physics laboratories he performed a 24-second test (thrust was great enough to raise the rocket during the last half of the run).
30 December 1925	Rocket trembled in its support for 8 seconds.
3 January 1926	Rocket again quivered for 17 seconds.
20 January 1926	The thrust produced raised the rocket motor the full distance it could travel; outdoor tests with a flight model commenced on 8 March 1926.
16 March 1926	*First flight* of a liquid-propellant rocket. Altitude: 41 feet; average velocity: 60 miles per hour; in air: 2.5 seconds.
3 April 1926	*Second flight* of a liquid-propellant rocket. Landed 50 feet from test stand after being in air 4.2 seconds.
5 May 1926	After several tests indicating the model was too small to permit refinements, it was decided to build a rocket twenty times larger. During 1926 a new tower was built and flow regulators, multiple liquid injection into large combustion chambers, means for measurement of pressure and lifting force, electrically fired igniter, and turntable for rotation were developed.
18 January 1927	The new large rocket was placed into the test tower for the first time. Rocket and turntable were lifted several times in the following months, but no flights took place with the large model.
3 September 1927	Construction began on a rocket one fifth the size of the previous one, *i.e.* four times larger than the 1926 flight models. Few, simple, easily replaced parts were used, and the fuel-injection system was improved greatly.
18 July, 29 September, 10 and 20 October 1928	Rocket started to rise, but it tipped and caught in the tower.
26 December 1928	*Third flight* of a liquid-propellant rocket. Rocket rose out of tower rapidly and tipped passing over observation shelter. Range was 204.5 feet, velocity over 60 miles per hour. This flight was followed by a series of static tests to develop liquid "curtain cooling" for inside of combustion-chamber wall, a regenerative cooling system, and better in-flight stability.
17 July 1929	*Fourth flight* of a liquid-propellant rocket. Started to lift at 13 seconds, rose at 14.5 seconds, reached top of trajectory at 17 seconds, hit ground at 18.5 seconds, landing 171 feet away. Flight was bright and noisy, attracting much public attention.

Tests at Camp Devens, Massachusetts, 1929–1930

3 December 1929–30 June 1930	Tests were carried out at an artillery range at Camp Devens, 25 miles from Worcester. Their object was to improve liquid-propellant rocket motor efficiencies, particularly the "curtain cooling" aspect. Sixteen static tests were made, but no flights. A few special tests were conducted with rocket-operated propellers.

Tests at Roswell, New Mexico, 1930–1932

1930–1932	In July 1930 the project was moved to New Mexico under the auspices of Daniel Guggenheim of New York City, permitting Goddard to devote full time to rocket work. A series of thorough static tests in which the operating conditions were varied was first undertaken. For flight testing, a 5.75-inch diameter, 5-pound combustion chamber was used. In static testing, it produced a maximum thrust of 289 pounds over more than 20 seconds. Thrust was steady, exhaust velocity was over 5,000 feet per second. Owing to the Depression, the Guggenheim financial support ended in June 1932.
30 December 1930	*Fifth flight* of a liquid-propellant rocket. Vehicle was 11 feet long, weighed (empty) 33.5 pounds. It rose to an altitude of 2,000 feet and a speed of 500 miles per hour. A gas pressure tank was employed to force the liquid oxygen and gasoline propellants into the combustion chamber.
29 September 1931	Flight took place with jacket, streamline casing, and remote control. Rocket length was 9 feet 11 inches; diameter 12 inches; loaded weight 87.2 pounds, and empty weight 37 pounds. The rocket was in the air for 9.6 seconds, reached 180 feet, followed a trajectory described as "like a fish swimming."
13 October 1931	Flight effected with simplified combustion chamber, parachute releasing. The 7.75-foot-long, 12-inch-diameter rocket reached more than 1,700-feet altitude, gave loud whistling noise on descent.
27 October 1931	Flight took place with rocket using new gasoline shut-off valve. The dimensions of the rocket were similar to above, altitude was 1,330 feet, range 930 feet, total flight time 8.6 seconds.
23 November 1931	Static test with modified oxygen-injection system used. Thrust was 270 pounds for 11 seconds; exhaust velocity 5,088 feet per second.
19 April 1932	This flight rocket had pressure generated by liquid nitrogen, stabilization effected by gyro-controlled vanes. Length was 10 feet 9.5 inches; empty weight 19.5 pounds; altitude 135 feet; in air for 5 seconds.

Tests at Clark University, Worcester, Massachusetts, 1932–1934

September 1932	A grant from the Smithsonian Institution enabled Goddard, who resumed his full-time teaching at Clark University that fall, to carry out experiments that did not require flight testing.
September 1933	A more extensive program was made possible in 1933–1934 by a grant from the newly founded Daniel and Florence Guggenheim Foundation. During these years, studies were made of insulators, welding methods for light metals, gyroscopic balancers, reciprocating and centrifugal pumps, jet pumps, and rocket chambers.

Resumption of Tests at Roswell, New Mexico, 1934–1941

	A-series tests
	From September 1934 through October 1935 an A-series of tests was made with rockets using simple pressure-feed systems and stabilized by gyro-controlled blast vanes. The rockets were between 13.5 feet and 15 feet 3.25 inches long. Their empty weight varied from 58 to 85 pounds.
16 February 1935	Flight test accomplished without automatic guiding device. Flight was short, rapid; parachute was released, checking the fall.
8 March 1935	Flight test with equalizer (to prevent liquid-oxygen tank pressure from exceeding gasoline tank pressure), pendulum stabilizer, and 10-foot parachute. The motor fired for 12 seconds, producing small white flame; velocity of more than 700 miles per hour achieved (may have been supersonic). Rocket tilted to horizontal, landed 9,000 1.7 miles feet from tower.
28 March 1935	Flight with improved gyro stabilization; rocket was 14 feet 9.75 inches long, weighed (empty) 78.5 pounds, reached altitude of 4,800 feet, range of 13,000 feet. Rocket corrected its path perfectly several times during 20-second flight, which was made at an average speed of 550 miles per hour.

31 May 1935 — Flight effected with new lift-indicator. Rocket length, 15 feet 1.5 inches; weight, 84 pounds; altitude, 7,500 feet; range, 5,500 feet. Stabilization excellent. Loud whistle produced on descent; rocket made 10-inch-deep hole on impact.

25 June 1935 — Flight test with new timing device for parachute and a cushioned gyro. Day was windy. Flight lasted 10 seconds. Rocket reached 120-foot altitude, tipping into wind as it left the launching tower.

12 July 1935 — Flight, with stronger and thicker air vanes. Motor fired 14 seconds; rocket reached 6,600-foot altitude with excellent correction up to 3,000 feet. Parachute was torn off.

29 October 1935 — New gasoline orifices used in this flight. Duration of thrust was 12 seconds, altitude reached was 4,000 feet, velocity was high. Rocket shot produced a wave of dirt, resembling a water wave, when it landed. Resulting hole was 6 inches deep.

K-series tests

From 22 November 1935 to 12 February 1936, Goddard worked on the K-series of tests, which consisted of ten proving-stand experiments designed to lead to the development of a more powerful 10-inch-diameter motor. Two of the most outstanding tests are listed below:

17 December 1935 — Rocket produced a thrust of 496 pounds for 14 seconds, with exhaust velocity of 4,470 feet per second. The liquid oxygen weighed 31 pounds, gasoline weighed 24 pounds, and the rocket weight was 225 pounds.

12 February 1936 — Attained thrust of 623.5 pounds for 4 seconds. Exhaust velocity was 4,340 feet per second. Liquid oxygen weighed 25.5 pounds; gasoline weighed 13.5 pounds.

↳ .8 miles/sec = 49 miles/min = 2,959 miles/hr

L-series tests

This series involved thirty tests, divided into sections A, B, and C. The experiments were conducted from 11 May 1936 to 9 August 1938 and used nitrogen-pressurized rockets with 10-inch-diameter motors.

Section A tests

From 11 May 1936 to 7 November 1936, nitrogen-pressurized flight rockets were developed based on the 10-inch motors employed during the K-series of experiments. Rockets numbered L-1–L-7 were used, with lengths varying from 10 feet 11 inches to 13 feet 6.5 inches, diameters 18 inches, empty weight 120 to 202 pounds, loaded weights 295 to 360 pounds, liquid-oxygen weight about 78 pounds, gasoline 84 pounds, nitrogen 4 pounds.

31 July 1936 — Flight test. Altitude attained was 280 feet, duration 5 seconds, range 300 feet.

3 October 1936 — Flight rocket reached 200-foot altitude vertically in 5 seconds, at which time chamber burned through. Weight of liquid oxygen, 40 pounds; of gasoline, 46 pounds; and of nitrogen, 4 pounds.

7 November 1936 — Flight effected with cluster of four combustion chambers, each 5.75 inches in diameter. Rocket length: 13 feet 6.5 inches. It climbed to about 200 feet, fell to Earth near tower.

Section B tests

From 24 May 1936 to 19 May 1937; rockets L-8–L-15 were used in these tests. Experiments were made on 5.75-inch-diameter chambers with propellants of various volatilities. Other experiments involved the development of tilting cap parachute release, tests of various forms of exposed movable air vanes, tests of retractable air vanes, and tests of parachutes with heavy shroud lines.

18 December 1936 — Flight test with pressure storage tank used. Duration and altitude not recorded, but range was 2,000 feet, rocket landing with axis horizontal. Noise heard up to eight miles away, parts scattered over 300-foot area, most being recovered undamaged.

1 February 1937 — Flight with gyro, air, and blast vanes. Rocket was 16 feet 7.63 inches long; diameter was 9 inches. Firing time 20.5 seconds. Rocket reached altitude of 1,870 feet and corrected well. The ground behind the flame deflector turned green and was glazed by heat.

27 February 1937	Rocket flight with new parachute release operated by gyro. It reached 1,500-foot altitude, and landed 3,000 feet from tower. Flight duration was 20 seconds, speed very high.
26 March 1937	Larger, movable air vanes used in this flight. Rocket soared to 8,000–9,000 feet (duration 22.3 seconds), corrected while propulsion lasted, then tilted.
22 April 1937	Flight test with larger movable air vanes; reinforced parachute. Rocket length: 17.75 feet; diameter: 9 inches; duration: 21.5 seconds. Rocket could not be followed to top of trajectory as it was nearly overhead. It landed about a mile from tower.
19 May 1937	Flight rocket had streamlined, retractable air vanes, wire-wound pressure storage tank (to reduce weight). Length was 17.67 feet; diameter, 9 inches; altitude achieved, 3,250 feet; and duration, 29.5 seconds. Stabilization was much improved.

Section C tests

From 28 July 1937 to 9 August 1938, rockets L-16–L-30 featured light tank construction, movable tailpiece (*i.e.* gimbal) steering, catapult launching, and further developed liquid nitrogen tank-pressurization technique. The lengths of the rockets in this series varied from 17 feet 4.25 inches to 18 feet 5.75 inches, while diameters were 9 inches. Loaded weights were 170 pounds or more, empty weights 80 to 109 pounds. Static-test thrusts ranged from 228 to 477 pounds, exhaust velocities from 3,960 to 5,340 feet per second. The tests indicated extremely high temperatures for the exhaust. Pebbles of the cement gas deflector were fused and thrown out, starting fires more than 50 feet from the tower.

28 July 1937	Flight of rocket with movable tailpiece steering. Wire-wound tanks used, barograph carried. Rocket length was 18 feet 5.5 inches, diameter 9 inches, loaded weight 162 pounds 5 ounces, empty weight 95 pounds 5 ounces. Carried 39 pounds of liquid oxygen, 28 pounds of gasoline. Flight lasted 28 seconds, rocket reached 2,055 feet. The parachute opened near the ground, checked speed. Rocket coasted ⅛ of ascent, landed 1,000 feet from tower.
26 August 1937	Flight had movable tailpiece steering; catapult launching. Length was 18 feet 5.5 inches, diameter 9 inches, loaded weight 162 pounds. Corrected well and strongly seven times during the flight, which took rocket to an altitude of more than 2,000 feet.
24 November 1937	In a short flight, rocket leaned after leaving tower, fell 100 feet away. Thrust was low
6 March 1938	Rocket quickly left tower, producing little smoke; reached 500 feet before starting its coasting period.
17 March 1938	Rocket reached 2,170 feet in 15-second flight. Went vertical to 800 feet, then leaned to right, landing 3,000 feet from tower. Little smoke produced.
20 April 1938	Flight resulted in 4,215-foot altitude; duration of propulsion 25.3 seconds, landed 6,960 feet from tower. Rocket carried official barograph. Weight of liquid oxygen, 21.5 pounds; of gasoline, 34 pounds.
26 May 1938	Altitude of only 140 feet reached; on leaving tower rocket veered to right, landed 500–600 feet away.
9 August 1938	An altitude of 4,920 feet was recorded by telescopic observations, but according to the barograph carried in rocket only 3,294 feet reached. Rocket corrected well, and parachute opened at top of trajectory. Ground and telescope observers felt that rocket went considerably higher than indicated by the barograph.

Experiments leading towards development of propellant pumps

From 17 October 1938 to 28 February 1939, models PT1–8 and P1–4 are associated with Goddard's developmental work on propellant pumps. After the successful flights of 9 August, Goddard turned again to the problem of pumps. He believed pumps were essential if very high altitudes were to be attained. Beginning on 17 October 1938 he made a thorough study (more than 20 proving-stand tests) of five models of small, high-speed centrifugal pumps, which had radically new features. This initial phase ended on 17 November 1938. Then, from 6 January through 28 February 1939 two pumps, called A and D, were selected for use in four proving-stand tests. From these tests it was concluded that a small chamber or gas generator, producing warm oxygen gas, should be developed to operate the turbines. Of these tests the following was the best:

51

Resumption of Tests at Roswell, New Mexico, 1934–1941 (continued)

7 February 1939	With 29 pounds of liquid oxygen and 45 pounds of gasoline, a thrust of 671 pounds was produced for 12 seconds with an exhaust velocity of 4,820 feet per second. The liquid oxygen flowed at 2.15 pounds per second, the gasoline at 2.28 pounds per second; the mixture ratio was .94.

Gas Generator tests

From 24 March to 28 April 1939, 11 static tests were made near the shop of a new gas generator to drive turbines (models P5a–k). The best generator developed ran steadily for 10 seconds at 180 pounds per square inch pressure at greater than 250 pounds per square inch tank pressure, with liquid oxygen flow rate at 0.49 pounds per second. Later, from 18 May to 4 August 1939, this generator was used in eight static tests (P5–12) at the desert launching tower. The best two tests were:

17 July and 4 August 1939	These runs gave thrusts of 700 pounds for about 15 seconds, with oxygen flow rates at 4 pounds per second and gasoline flow rates at 3 pounds per second. The exhaust velocities achieved were in excess of 3,200 feet per second.

Static and flight tests with pump-driven rockets

During the period 18 November 1939 to 10 October 1941, a series of 24 static and flight tests was made with rockets offering a large fuel capacity (models P13–P36). These vehicles used the rocket motors, pumps, and turbines that had been developed previously. They averaged 22 feet in length, were 18 inches in diameter, and weighed (empty) from 190 to 240 pounds. They carried some 140 pounds of liquid oxygen and 112 pounds of gasoline.

2 December 1939	Static test at flight tower, steady 40-second run with thrust of 760 pounds.
15 May 1940	Another static test, flame hot, thrust apparently high. Ground behind the flame deflector seemed to have melted.
11 June 1940	A steady run of 43.5 seconds achieved in this static test, making it longest to date; red-hot stones seen to fly up out of cement gas deflector.
9 August 1940	*First rocket flight with pumps:* rocket reached 300-foot altitude at very low velocity (10 to 15 miles per hour).
6 January 1941	A static test made recording highest thrust to date: 985 pounds.
8 May 1941	*Second rocket flight with pumps:* rocket reached 250 feet, then heeled away from tower.
17 July 1941	In this static test, duration was 34 seconds; average thrust 825-plus pounds; exhaust velocity 4,060 feet per second; average thrust per pound of propellant per second 128; mechanical horsepower 3,040; weight of liquid oxygen, 131.7 pounds; weight of gasoline, 91.5 pounds; and ratio of oxidizer to fuel, 1:43.

Summary of Goddard Static and Flight Tests

Series and period	Static tests (number)	Flight tests (number)	Average interval between tests (days)
First New Mexico series, 1930–1932	21	8 (5 left tower)	20
A-series, September 1934–October 1935	1	14 (7 left tower)	28
K-series, November 1935–February 1936	10	0	8
L-series			
Section A, May–November 1936	4	3 (all left tower)	25
Section B, November 1936–May 1937	2	6 (all left tower)	22
Section C, July 1937–August 1938	7	8 (all left tower)	25
Pump tests, October 1938–February 1939	> 24	0	5.5
Gas generator tests, March–August 1939	19	0	7
Pump-turbine tests, November 1939–October 1941	15	9 (2 left tower)	28

I[...]
1937, [...]
with l[...]
the ol[...]
describ[...]
betwee[...]
lant, an[...]
ent thru[...]
large ch[...]
about 8[...]
lbs, whic[...]
noted tha[...]
four men, [...] He added that "It is, as you can imagine, a fascinating life. The drawback is that until there has been a great and spectacular height reached, no layman, and not many scientists, will concede that you have accomplished anything, and of course there is a vast amount of spade work, of much importance, that must be done first."

Several years later, in response to requests from L. T. E. Thompson of the Naval Proving Ground, Dahlgren, Virginia, Goddard addressed himself to the problem of rocket-accelerated all-purpose bombs. In a letter to Thompson on 24 February 1940 he described a combustion chamber operating under 350

[...]nds per square inch pressure that produced 700 [...]nds of thrust. The maximum diameter was 6 [...]es and length 2½ feet. Weight was but 6¾ [...]ds. Two high-speed centrifugal pumps supplied [...]ropellants to the chamber from the liquid oxy-[...]nd gasoline tanks. He said that rapid starting [...]t needed, for flight tests. Nevertheless even with [...]ign we are using at present, the rise to full working [...]e is not much over a second. The appearance is [...]triking. One moment everything is quiet and no [...]s visible. The next moment there is a blast of [...]e and the entire tower shakes, which continues un-diminished as long as the rocket is in the tower.

On 5 June 1940 Hickman wrote Goddard saying that he felt it his duty "to call the attention of our government to the possibilities of your rocket for defensive purposes." Goddard promptly replied, "Go ahead, and God bless you!" explaining that on a "recent trip East," the Guggenheim Foundation's attitude had changed and that he and Harry G. Guggenheim had met with a joint committee of Army and Navy officials in Washington on 28 May. Goddard presented information on both solid- and liquid-fuel rockets. The Army was "unsympathetic towards any long-range projectile," while the Navy had sev-

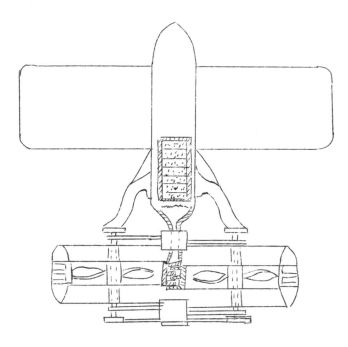

A rocket-propelled airplane designed by Goddard and patented by him on 9 June 1931.

eral ideas for applications of liquid rockets. The general attitude toward rocket research in Washington, however, seemed negative.

"Frankly," Goddard wrote, "I have been filled with disgust at the fact that no intensive fundamental work appears possible, and I suspect I have been hard to live with since my return. I am, however, endeavoring to make a few more attacks to see if it is not possible to carry on the work on the liquid fuel rockets, at least, on an intensive scale."

Following the meeting on 28 May, Goddard and Guggenheim met with Brigadier General George H. Brett, of the Air Corps Materiel Division. This session resulted in a proposal by Goddard on 27 July 1940 that his rocket technology be applied to the problem of assisted takeoff for bombers and other airplanes. A little over three months later, on 26 September, General Brett wrote that, while the Air Corps was "deeply interested in the research work being carried out by your organization under the auspices of the Guggenheim Foundation, it does not, at this time, feel justified in obligating further funds for basic jet propulsion research and experimentation." He added that when Goddard's experiments had "reached a point which indicates the probability of successful reduction to practice of a device, capable of being incorporated in or attached to an airplane to assist in accelerating takeoff and upon which an evaluation can be made in order to determine the feasibility and practicability of military application, the Air Corps will then entertain further proposals involving the actual construction, installation, and test of such device." Goddard was to produce on his own; then the Air Corps would become interested. Goddard later commented that "after trying to do a good piece of work over a period of years and actually getting flights before anyone else, it is discouraging to have the implication made that nothing of value has been accomplished."

In 1941, however, the mood of the government

Goddard's later experiments, at a research center near Roswell, N.M., became increasingly more sophisticated. At left is a four-motor L-7 rocket that flew to a 200-foot altitude on 7 November 1936. Above, a pump-driven rocket tested on 1 August 1940. (ESTHER C. GODDARD)

changed. Goddard's group began work in September under contracts with the Navy's Bureau of Aeronautics and with the previously uninterested Army Air Corps. In July 1942 the personnel and equipment were moved to the Naval Engineering Experiment Station at Annapolis, Maryland, where they continued until July 1945. During this period a liquid-propellant, jet-assisted takeoff unit for flying boats was developed and flight tested. A still more important assignment was the development of variable-thrust rocket motors, which required hundreds of proving-stand tests before a successful motor was finally achieved.

Recognition came late to Goddard, much of it after he had died in Baltimore on 10 August 1945. In 1959 he was honored by the United States Congress and received the first Louis W. Hill Space

The first published work of German pioneer Hermann Oberth, The Rocket into Planetary Space, *appeared in Munich in 1923. Scarcely larger than a pamphlet, the 92-page text explained theoretically how rockets can launch payloads into orbit around the Earth. The book's cover is shown here.*

Transportation Award of the now defunct Institute of Aeronautical Sciences. A year later the Smithsonian Institution, under whose auspices he had worked for so many years, bestowed on him the coveted Langley Medal. One of the National Aeronautics and Space Administration's major facilities, the Goddard Space Flight Center, was named after him on 1 May 1959. And in 1960 the United States government awarded the Guggenheim Foundation and Mrs. Goddard $1,000,000 in settlement for government use of more than two hundred of the pioneer's patents.

The third great pioneer of rocketry and astronautics, Hermann Oberth, was born in the town of Hermannstadt, Transylvania (which had been incorporated into Hungary), on 25 June 1894. The son of a German-speaking family, Hermann Oberth is considered German rather than Hungarian; he studied in German, writes in German, later moved to Germany, and in his adult life became a German citizen.

At the time of Oberth's birth, Tsiolkovsky was in his middle thirties while Goddard had not yet reached his teens. For a long time the three remained ignorant of one another, partly because of differences in age, partly because of the distances between them, partly because they wrote in different languages.

Like his predecessors, Oberth's interest in space flight received its initial stimulus from the great science-fiction writers of the nineteenth century, particularly Verne. In his autobiography, he wrote that "At the age of eleven, I received from my mother as a gift the famous [Lunar] books . . . by Jules Verne, which I had read at least five or six times, and, finally, knew by heart." Even at this age he realized that Verne's scheme of firing the astronauts to the Moon by cannon was not feasible, for "the travelers inside the missile would have been crushed without pity by the enormous acceleration." He started to look for alternative means of reaching the satellite.

Oberth's first ideas were far-fetched—a magnetic acceleration device in a long tunnel from which the air had been evacuated, an airplane with silk propellers, a large wheel developing high centrifugal forces —but he persisted until he came upon the reaction principle. Again, he acknowledged a debt to Jules Verne, who in *Around the Moon* had suggested using rockets to reduce the fall of the spaceship toward the Moon and to permit maneuvering in space. But he wrote, "I should tell a lie in stating that I was delighted at this discovery. I was not pleased at all with the enormous fuel consumption, the hazards of rockets containing solid fuels, the difficulty of handling liquid fuels, the high costs of the chemicals, etc."

Shortly before World War I, Oberth became interested in combat rockets. In 1917, he proposed to the German War Department the development of a liquid-propelled, long-range bombardment missile. After the war, in 1922, he made similar proposals and added speculations on the feasibility of space flight.

Oberth learned of the publication of Goddard's 1919 report through newspaper accounts. Unable to obtain a copy in Germany, he wrote Goddard for one in 1922, adding, "I think that only by the common work of scholars of all nations can be solved this great problem . . . to pass over the atmosphere of our earth by means of a rocket."

Oberth's first book, the now-celebrated *Die Rakete zu den Planetenräumen* (*The Rocket into Planetary Space*), was published in Munich the following year. Oberth added a three-page supplement to assure his readers that if they compared Goddard's 1919 publication with his own "one can easily see that I have worked completely independently." More than thirty-five years later, Oberth was still bothered by the thought that he might be accused of having been inspired by Goddard, emphasizing in a 1959 article that "I had carried on my investigations completely independently of Goddard's work."

Die Rakete zu den Planetenräumen is a small book—with but 92 pages of text, scarcely larger than a pamphlet. But it is a thorough discussion of almost every phase of rocket travel, including the abnormal effects of pressure on the human body.

Oberth's little book demonstrated many of the truths that today are taken for granted—that a rocket can operate in the void, and that it can move faster than the velocity of its own exhaust gases. He realized that it would be possible for a rocket to launch a payload into orbit around the Earth if the required velocity could be generated, a thought which led him, like Goddard and Tsiolkovsky, to investigate many propellant combinations. He also described in detail the design of a rocket, which he called the Modell B, that he felt could be used to explore the upper atmosphere; discussed the merits of alcohol and hydrogen as rocket propellants; and included a section on applications of rocket techniques.

The book rapidly went through its first edition, and Oberth began work on his *Wege zur Raumschiffahrt* (*The Road to Space Travel*), a 423-page expansion of the first book which was published in Munich in 1929. These two books were important not only for the many genuinely new thoughts they contained about the problems of space flight, but also for the inspiration they gave other scientists to work on rockets, a drive that has led directly to today's space achievements.

Unlike Goddard, Oberth did everything he could

Above, a scene from Fritz Lang's film Frau in Mond *showing the arrival of the spaceship on the Moon.* (ARFOR ARCHIVES)

Below, an interior scene of the spaceship en route to the Moon, showing the effect of weightlessness. (CINÉMATHEQUE FRANCAISE)

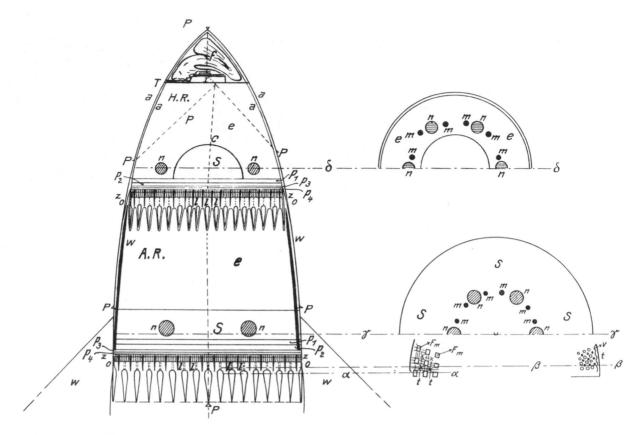

Oberth's Modell E rocket

to publicize rocketry in general and his own work in particular. He became a technical advisor to the Ufa Film Company and director Fritz Lang, who was filming a movie called *Frau im Mond* (*Girl in the Moon*). As a stunt dreamed up by publicity agents, Oberth, with Rudolf Nebel and Alexander B. Scherschevsky as his assistants, was to design, build, and fly a rocket. More a theoretician than an engineer, Oberth had little success. The rocket was actually designed and constructed, but it quickly became apparent that many basic component changes would have to be made if the rocket were ever to fly. A small test motor built by Oberth, the Kegeldüse, was successfully static-tested on 23 July 1930 in a suburb of Berlin. In September, Ufa's test funds ran out and Oberth returned to Transylvania to teach again.

Oberth was always active in movements to forward the use of rockets, and encouraged others to work, to lecture, and to write on rocket and space flight. He joined (and in 1929 became president of) the Verein für Raumschiffahrt, Germany's Society for Space Travel. Although to many almost a legend, he is still alive; since World War II he has written additional books, worked for a few years in the United States with his erstwhile student and helper Von Braun at the Army Ballistic Missile Agency, and returned to West Germany where he now lives in semiretirement, still consulting and writing on space flight.

The period spanned by the lives of the three great pioneers, two in Europe and one in America, is over one hundred years—from Tsiolkovsky's birth in 1857 to the present. Their significant contributions cluster between the mid-1880's, when Tsiolkovsky first developed the relationship between rocketry and astronautics, and the 1930's and the early 1940's—a period exceeding half a century. By the time he was in his early twenties, each man had made his basic discoveries and had laid down the foundations of his future activities—the two Europeans concentrating to varying extents on theoretical astronautics and the American on the practical development of liquid-propellant rocket motors.

What these three pioneers started, others were eager to finish. The impetus provided by their discoveries attracted dozens of eager engineers and scientists into rocketry and astronautical research. Major technical barriers still had to be overcome, but for the first time a sizable group of men had begun to take space travel seriously.

Professor Oberth entzündet die Kaltgas-Düse.

Mit mehr als 3 m hoher Flamme zischt die Riesenfackel der Düse gen Himmel, um ihre Kräfte auf den Hebel des Meßinstrumentes wirken zu lassen

Die Spaltdüse wird montiert, um die beim Brennen entstehenden Kräfte zu messen

Vorarbeiten für die Weltraumrakete
Neue Versuche Professor Oberth's

Der Raketenforscher Professor Oberth hat jetzt gemeinsam mit dem Verein für Raumschiffahrt Flüssigkeitsraketen konstruiert, die sich auf dem Versuchsstand der Chemisch-Technischen Reichsanstalt bereits recht gut bewährt haben. Allerdings sind bisher lediglich Düsenbrennversuche durchgeführt worden, bei denen der durch den Rückstoß der mit einer Geschwindigkeit von 1700 bis 2000 m in der Sekunde ausströmenden Gase entstehende Druck experimentell gemessen wurde. Die aus der Düse ausströmenden Gase werden durch die Verbrennung von Benzin in reinem Sauerstoff erzeugt. Der Vorteil der Flüssigkeitsraketen besteht darin, daß sie längere Zeit betrieben werden können, während die bisher benutzten Pulverraketen schon nach wenigen Sekunden abgebrannt waren. Gleichzeitig kann man die Brennstoffzufuhr bei den Flüssigkeitsraketen in gewissen Grenzen regulieren. Bei den Versuchen in der Chemisch-Technischen Reichsanstalt wurden vorgeführt eine Kaltgas-Düse und eine Spaltdüse.

Oberth failed in his attempt to construct a rocket for the German movie Frau im Mond, *but he did build a motor, which he tested in a Berlin suburb. The above report on the test appeared in the newspaper* Boten aus den Riesengebirge *on 10 August 1930. At left, Klaus Riedel and Rudolf Nebel watch Oberth make last-minute adjustments. Lower right: 18-year-old Wernher von Braun tightens fuel connections on the rocket motor.*

Hermann Oberth at the Ufa Film Company working on demonstration rocket motor for the movie Frau im Mond.

Hermann Oberth as he appeared in 1958 while living in the United States. He has since returned to Germany, where he consults and writes on space flight.

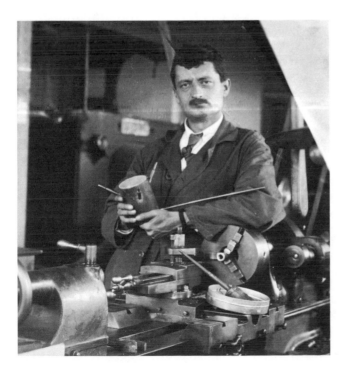

4 THE LEGACY OF T

The modern rocket took shape during the two decades that followed World War I. As the writings of Tsiolkovsky, Goddard, and Oberth attained wider circulation, a growing number of rocket enthusiasts began the work that led directly to space flight. By the end of the 1930's, on the eve of another war, military work on rockets was being carried on vigorously in several nations.

Public interest in rocketry and support of rocket development varied immensely. In Germany and Russia, and to a lesser degree in Great Britain and the United States, popularizers digested the concepts of the pioneers and transmitted to the public not only their spirit but the more easily understood—and often more spectacular—proposals they had made. The Americans seemed to be the least receptive, remaining skeptical about space flight right up to the orbiting of the first artificial satellites in the late 1950's. Outside of a dedicated handful of experimenters, talk of rockets and space travel was viewed as crackpot by the public and as unscientific by most scientists.

The first flight of a liquid-propellant rocket in Europe took place on 14 March 1931, when an 11-pound methane-oxygen rocket soared to an altitude of nearly 1,000 feet near Dessau, in Germany. This achievement was symbolic of German leadership in rocket flight between the two wars, but it did not mean that Germany stood alone. Significant work was performed in the United States, Russia, Britain, France, and—to a lesser extent—in Italy, and there was ample cross-fertilization between rocket researchers of different nations.

During the 1920's and 1930's, rocket and interplanetary societies were established in the major western European nations and in the United States. Most of the theoretical and experimental work was conducted in these nations and—with the notable exception of Goddard's—was reported regularly in rocket and space journals that were distributed to society members and to selected subscribers.

Communications between the early rocket and space societies were frequent during these years. Letters and reports circulated among the European nations and crossed the Atlantic, and the rocketeers themselves visited each other. In January 1931, France's pioneer space-flight scientist Robert Esnault-Pelterie came to the United States to deliver a lecture to the American Interplanetary Society. And, in the same year, G. Edward Pendray, vice-president of the American society, traveled to Berlin to meet members of the German space-flight society and observe tests at their proving grounds. Nikolai Alexsevitch Rynin of the Soviet Union regularly sent out communications on Russian activities, and from Germany Willy Ley and others provided a constant stream of information.

To further cement the camaraderie among the early rocketeers, most of the inner circle became members of several societies. To give one example, in 1934 alone the British Interplanetary Society named as fellows Guido von Pirquet of Austria, Robert Esnault-Pelterie of France, Jakov Isidorovitch Perelman of Russia, Willy Ley and Ilse Kühnel of Germany, and Edward Pendray and Ernst Loebell of the United States.

Virtually all of the civilian experimenters and promoters were much more interested in what the rocket could do, theoretically at least, to further their dreams of visiting the Moon and planets, than in rocketry itself. For the first time in history, they believed, man was in a position to do something about his ingrained desire to visit other worlds. He possessed the rocket, primitive though it might be, and a technological base that made the future appear infinitely "promising."

In Russia, Tsiolkovsky's work provided impetus for additional rocket research. In 1924, the Soviets created a Central Bureau for the Study of the Problems of Rockets (TsBIRP) and an All-Union Society for the Study of Interplanetary Flight (OIMS), both of which staged an exhibition on rocket technology in 1927. These two groups were responsible for the "second generation" of Soviet rocket re-

HE PIONEERS

search, in which the work started by Tsiolkovsky in the early 1900's was brought up to date and expanded.

The leading exponent of rocketry in this second generation was Fridrikh Arturovitch Tsander, who began to develop liquid-propelled rocket engines during the 1920's. By 1930, tests were possible. His two rocket motors, called OR-1 and OR-2, were propelled, respectively, by gasoline and air and gasoline and liquid oxygen. Successful static tests were conducted in 1930 and again in 1933, the first developing over 10 pounds of thrust and the second over 100 pounds of thrust. In the same period Valentin Petrovitch Glushko developed rocket engines at the Gas Dynamics Laboratory in Leningrad and later at the Reaction Scientific Research Institute. In 1932, the year before Tsander's death, he published a significant book entitled *Problems of Flight by Means of Reactive Devices* (sometimes translated as *Problems of Reactive Flight*), while Glushko, with G. E. Langemak, wrote *Rockets, Their Construction and Utilization* in 1935.

After Joseph Stalin became master of the country, the rocket groups created in 1924 were replaced by the better known Len-GIRD, or Group for the Study of Reaction Motion (Gruppa Isutcheniya Reaktivnovo Dvisheniya) in Leningrad, and Mos-GIRD, a similar organization in Moscow. These eventually became the State Reaction Scientific Research Institute.

There is some confusion as to when these organizations were formed. G. A. Tokaty, former chief of the Aerodynamics Laboratory of the Zhukovsky Academy of Aerodynamics of the Soviet Air Force, has said that Len-GIRD was established in 1931, but most other sources give the year as 1929. It may have been set up unofficially in 1929 and not recognized officially until two years later. Whatever the date, the Leningrad group was founded by Nikolai Alexsevitch Rynin and Jakov Isidorovitch Perelman, while the Moscow branch was founded by I. P. Fortikov. These GIRD groups were affiliated with the larger Society for the Promotion of Defense and Aero-Chemical Development (Osoaviakhim).

The members of these groups published scientific reports of their own, translated foreign literature —particularly German—and organized several congresses. One example was the All-Union Conference on the Study of the Stratosphere held March–April 1934, whose proceedings were published by the U.S.S.R. Academy of Sciences in 1935. Special conference papers on *Rocket Technology* and *Jet Propulsion* were released by the Union of Scientific Technical Publishing Houses in 1935–1936.

Beginning as early as 1928 and extending through 1932, an even more monumental publishing effort had taken place: Rynin's great *Mezhplanetyne Soobshcheniya* (*Interplanetary Communications*). (The Soviets used *interplanetary communications* to mean "space travel" or "space flight." Their term *cosmonautics* is equivalent to the preferred Western term astronautics.)

Interplanetary Communications was a nine-volume encyclopedia that offered abundant proof of Soviet interest and activity in astronautics. All but the last two volumes were published before a single book on interplanetary flight had appeared in the United States or Great Britain. During the 1930's only three English-language books were published, compared with several dozen in Russia. Perelman's *Mezhplanetyne Puteshestviya* (*Interplanetary Travels*) went through ten editions and sold 150,000 copies, far more than similar books in any language. Rynin's work was printed in a much smaller edition. Only 1,000 to 2,000 copies of most of the volumes were run off, although the third volume had a printing of 15,000 copies.

The first two volumes of the encyclopedia were a history of science fiction, starting with legends and early fantasies and running up to the works of Verne and Wells. The third volume was a study of proposals for communicating with other worlds; it gave special attention to the energy sources needed for interplanetary signaling, including some far-out

Some Early Russian Liquid-Propellant Rocket Engines

Engine Designation[a]	Thrust (pounds)	Propellant combination	Organization	Designer	Year	Remarks
OR-1	11	gasoline and gaseous air	TsGIRD[b]	Tsander	1929–1932	Combustion tests, of which over 50 were made, proved basic design concept, led to OR-2.
ORM-1	44	toluene and nitrogen tetroxide	GDL[c]	Glushko	1930–1931	Basic combustion and ignition research.
ORM-4 thru ORM-23	varied	toluene and nitrogen tetroxide	GDL	Glushko	1932	Gradual upgrading of performance.
OR-2	110	gasoline and liquid oxygen	MosGIRD[d]	Tsander	1931–1933	Combustion chamber cooled by the oxidizer, nozzle cooled by water circulating through closed-circuit system. An all-wood glider made by C. I. Cheranovskii designed to be powered by engine. Uprated to 150 pounds of thrust to power GIRD-X rocket.
ORM-24 thru ORM-49	—	kerosene and nitric acid	GDL	Glushko	1933	Water-cooled, extended duration testing.
ORM-50	330	kerosene and nitric acid	GDL	Glushko	1933	Built to power antiaircraft missile designed by M. K. Tikhonravov.
ORM-52	660	kerosene and nitric acid	RNII[e]	Glushko	1933	Regenerative cooling by fuel introduced.
ORM-53 thru ORM-64	1300	kerosene and nitric acid	RNII	Glushko	1934–1936	Further testing of engine parameters at higher thrust.
ORM-65	110–390	kerosene and nitric acid	RNII	Glushko	1936	For use in flying bomb and in rocket airplane designed by S. P. Korolev.
ORM-67 thru ORM-70	660	kerosene and nitric acid	RNII	Glushko	1937	Engine testing; no known application.
ORM-101	175	kerosene and tetranitromethane	RNII	Glushko	1937	Combustion research with new combination.
ORM-102	220	kerosene and tetranitromethane	RNII	Glushko	1937	Combustion research and engine performance at higher thrust rating.

[a] The OR designations refer to *opytnaya raketa*, or experimental rocket. The addition of the *M* for motor used by Glushko. Occasionally, the designation *OP* is given, taken from the first two letters of the word *opytnaya* alone.

[b] Group for the Study of Reaction Motion under Tsander within the Central Council of the Osoaviakhim.

[c] The Gas Dynamics Laboratory in Leningrad.

[d] In April 1932, the GIRD group under Tsander was established in Moscow and became known as MosGIRD; it was also under the Osoaviakhim.

[e] State Reaction Scientific Research Institute, resulting from a merger in 1934 of MosGIRD and GDL.

---

ideas such as altering the paths of comets and planets.

The next three books were a history of rocketry into the twentieth century, a mathematical study of jet propulsion, and a volume on airplanes and long-range artillery. Tsiolkovsky got a volume to himself, including an autobiographical sketch.

The eighth volume, whose 350 pages made it the longest in the series, examined the astronautical writings of the major world figures—Oberth, Goddard (whose *A Method of Reaching Extreme Altitudes* was translated in full), Esnault-Pelterie, Scherschevsky, Ley, and many others.

The final volume, entitled *Astronavigation*, gave descriptions and photographs of the Moon and planets and their orbits. It included an exceptionally detailed chronological bibliography of work on space flight, both fiction and nonfiction.

As *Interplanetary Communications* and a host of other books were published, the Russians continued their experimental work. Groups led by Tsander, M. K. Tikhonravov, and Glushko built and flight tested liquid-propellant rockets during the early and mid 1930's. One, the GIRD-X, weighed 65 pounds, was about 8½ feet in length, and slightly more than 6 inches in diameter. It reached an altitude of more than 3 miles on 25 November 1933. Another was fired

Cover for volume 3 of Rynin's Interplanetary Communications, a nine-volume encyclopedia published between 1928 and 1932. Volume 3, the biggest seller, was a study on communications with other worlds.

the next year and by 1936 an Aviavnito sounding rocket had exceeded an altitude of 3.5 miles. It was over 10 feet long, just under a foot in diameter, and weighed 213 pounds.

During the mid-1930's work began on solid-propellant military rockets. This effort eventually resulted in the Katyusha rockets that were fired in great quantities on the German troops in World War II. Another group developed rocket engines for airplanes. The Russians also developed plans for a guided missile; this advanced research project had to be canceled, however, when Germany invaded Russia at the beginning of World War II.

Great as was the progress in Russia, the German rocket effort far outstripped it. The quick sale of the

The Aviavnito sounding rocket was one of several liquid-propellant rockets built in the Soviet Union in the mid-1930's. Ten feet in length, it reached an altitude of 3.5 miles in a 1936 test. (U.S.S.R. ACADEMY OF SCIENCES)

Breslau   Januar-Juni   1927
Ergänzungsheft

Cover of a January-June 1927 summary issue of the monthly journal Die Rakete, *published by the German Society for Space Travel.*

first edition of Oberth's *Die Rakete zu den Planetenräumen* (*The Rocket into Planetary Space*) was an indication of how much Germans in the early 1920's were fascinated with the idea of space flight.

In early June 1927, rocket and space enthusiasts in Germany founded the Verein für Raumschiffahrt (Society for Space Travel). Its membership rose rapidly to around five hundred, enough to support a journal, *Die Rakete* (*The Rocket*). Between the time Oberth's first book was published in 1923 and the appearance of his *Wege zur Raumschiffahrt* (*Road to Space Travel*) in 1929, a number of other works appeared, including Walter Hohmann's *Die Erreichbarkeit der Himmelskörper* (*The Attainability of Celestial Bodies*) in 1925, Willy Ley's *Die Fahrt ins Weltall* (*The Flight into Space*) and *Die Möglichkeit der Weltraumfahrt* (*The Possibility of Space Travel*)

in 1928, and Max Valier's *Der Vorstoss in den Weltenraum* (*The Advance into Space*) in 1924, which, in 1930 (after five printings), was enlarged and retitled *Raketenfahrt* (*Rocket Flight*). Of these, Hohmann's mathematical treatment of orbital and interplanetary flight mechanics was the most advanced. The book is still referred to today.

The VfR circle did more than write books. In early 1928, space flight popularizer Max Valier, who wanted to publicize the capabilities of the rocket, got together with automobile tycoon Fritz von Opel, who wanted publicity for his automobile, and a manufacturer of powder rockets named Friedrich Wilhelm Sander. Their combined talents produced the world's first rocket-powered automobile.

The car's first test—corresponding to a flight test of a more conventional rocket—took place on 15 March 1928 at Opel's track near Rüsselsheim, with Kurt C. Volkhart at the wheel. The results were not spectacular, though the little Opel car did move. The next test was not much better; the car got up to just 45 miles per hour. The experimenters then decided to replace the standard car they had been using with a vehicle specially designed for 400-pound Sander rockets.

The new car, called the Opel-Rak 1, was a converted racer whose conventional engine was replaced first by six Sander rockets and then by eight. On 12 April 1928 successful runs were made at speeds up to 55 miles per hour over 2,000- to 3,000-foot distances at Rüsselsheim. Then a twelve-rocket experiment was made and, though five rockets failed to ignite, the little car reached more than 70 miles per hour. The

The second generation of rocketry was international in spirit. Goddard's 17 July 1929 firing in Worcester, Mass., was reported in the July 1929 issue of Die Rakete *(incorrectly stated as 18 July).* (ARFOR ARCHIVES)

Extra-Blatt

der Zeitschrift „DIE RAKETE"   ::   Breslau, Juli 1929
Offizielles Organ des Vereins für Raumschiffahrt E.V. in Deutschland

In letzter Minute geht die Nachricht ein, daß Professor Goddard in Worcester, Massachusets, am 18. Juli 1929 eine Versuchsrakete von 3 m Länge und 70 cm Durchmesser abgeschossen hat, die eine enorme Höhe erreichen sollte. Die Rakete startete ordnungsgemäß, explodierte jedoch bereits in geringer Höhe mit mächtigem Knall, so daß die Fensterscheiben in der Umgegend zertrümmert wurden.

Es ist dies seit längerer Zeit ein neues Lebenszeichen von Goddard, das deutlich zeigt, wie auch drüben am Raumfahrtproblem intensiv gearbeitet wird.

Opel-Rak 1 was followed by the more streamlined Opel-Rak 2, which was fitted with short, inverse wings to hold it to the ground as it sped along. Opel-Rak 2, outfitted with twenty-four rockets and with Opel himself at the wheel, sped down a track in Berlin on 23 May 1928 at a maximum speed of nearly 125 miles per hour.

These tests were followed by railway-car experiments in June and October 1928. The first, conducted between Celle and Burgwedel, were powered by twenty-four large powder rockets that accelerated the car to well over 100 miles per hour. The second series of tests was held between Blankenburg and Halberstadt. A brief résumé in the VfR journal, *Die Rakete*, of 15 October 1928 said that the car was built jointly by Valier and the J. F. Eisfeld firm. One run was successful; the other, with a larger and heavier payload, was not.

Rocket-sled experiments were also made; and, on 30 September 1928, a rocket-glider flight took place at Rebstock, near Frankfurt. Often mistakenly hailed as the first rocket airplane, the glider was powered by sixteen Sander rockets, each producing 50 pounds of thrust. Piloted by Fritz von Opel, it reached 95 miles per hour.

The first rocket-powered airplane had been flown just three months earlier at the Wasserkuppe mountain by the Rhön-Rossitten Gesellschaft, a glider group. On 11 June 1928, a sailplane named *Ente* (Duck) powered by two Sander slow-burning rockets, covered just over three quarters of a mile in slightly more than sixty seconds. These pioneering flights were ahead of their time, and soon were discontinued.

At about this time, Oberth had his brief adventure with the Ufa Film Company—probably the oddest source of research and development funds in history. When Oberth went back to teaching, some of his helpers and fellow VfR members, among them Rudolf Nebel, Klaus Riedel, Willy Ley, and Wernher von Braun (then a young student), obtained permission to use an abandoned military ammunitions dump in Reinickendorf, a suburb of Berlin, to test their rockets. Dubbed *Raketenflugplatz*, or rocket airfield, it became famous as the site of the early experiments of several of the men who later played major roles in the German army's V-2 missile. The engineering genius of the group was Riedel, an exceptionally talented, self-made man with no formal technical education. He had been involved in rocketry since the early VfR days and participated in many experiments. He died in an automobile accident toward the end of World War II.

Opel-Rak 1, the first successful rocket car, was a converted racer whose engine was replaced by commercial sea-rescue rockets. In tests at Opel's track near Russelsheim, it reached speeds of more than 70 mph. Above, Opel-Rak 1, with its driver, Kurt C. Volkhart. (ROLF ENGEL)

Max Valier, a member of the German VfR (Society for Space Travel), became interested in rocket cars as a means of publicizing the capabilities of the rocket. He is shown here in his liquid-propellant rocket car.

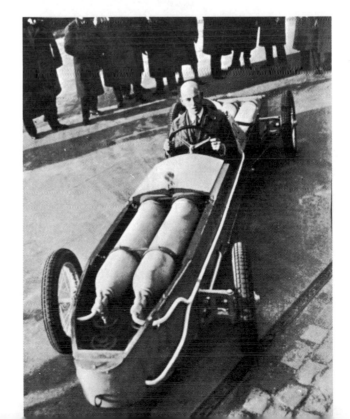

Valier's rocket sled, RS-1, glided along the snow on pontoons. In tests on 22 January 1929 it reached 65 mph.

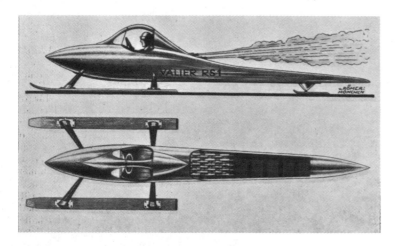

The first rocket-powered airplane was a sailplane named "Ente" (Duck). Powered by two slow-burning Sander rockets, it traveled three quarters of a mile in slightly more than 60 seconds in tests on 11 June 1928.

Automobile manufacturer Fritz von Opel piloted his own rocket glider in tests near Frankfurt on 30 September 1928. Its 16 rockets, each producing 50 pounds of thrust, were built by Friedrich Sander. (THOMPSON RAMO WOOLDRIDGE)

In 1929 Hermann Oberth, shown here with moustache and necktie, attempted to build a spaceship for the Ufa Film Company movie Frau im Mond. Flanking him are co-workers at Ufa.

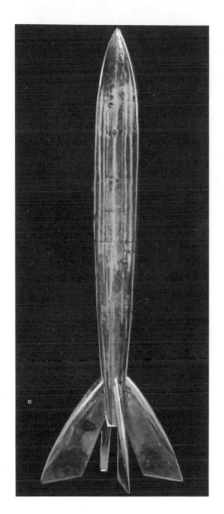

Demonstration rocket developed by Oberth for Frau im Mond.

After Oberth left the film studios, some of his helpers moved their testing equipment into an abandoned ammunitions dump near Berlin. Their "Raketenflugplatz" (rocket airfield) became famous as the site of the early experiments of several of the men who later developed the German war missiles. The above picture shows (left to right) Rudolf Nebel, Wernher von Braun, and Kurt Heinisch at the Raketenflugplatz.

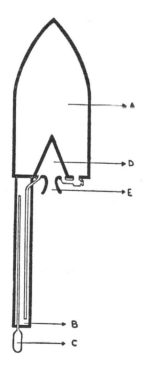

At left, Mirak 1, a rocket developed by the Raketenflugplatz group, had a 1-foot-long body and a 3-foot tail section. Liquid oxygen was stored in the head (A); gasoline, in the tail (B). The carbon dioxide charger was at (C), combustion chamber at (D), and exhaust at (E).

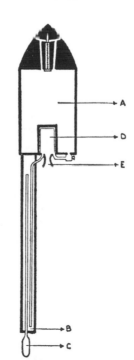

Mirak 2, built with a modified cooling system, developed 70-pound thrusts during the spring of 1931. The letters in the diagram are the same as for Mirak 1.

67

For more than four thousand years, man's mind has slowly opened to the universe around him. From the beginning he saw stars and planets, the Sun and Moon, and an occasional comet and meteor. But what the heavens meant to precivilized man, how he interpreted the lights in the sky, and his first glimmerings of understanding remain largely unknown to us.

To the ancient Babylonians, astronomy was inextricably tied up with astrology and magic. As early as 3000 B.C. they were observing the motions of Venus, and by 2000 B.C. they had recognized the movement of the planets across the zodiac. Astrologer-astronomers developed the notion of a 360-day year composed of twelve 30-day months, and could calculate in advance the positions of the Sun, Moon, and planets.

The Egyptians added five days to the year, for a total of 365. They developed sun clocks, refined the concept of the zodiac, and by 1300 B.C. identified at least forty-three constellations and the five planets visible to the naked eye: Mercury, Venus, Mars, Jupiter, and Saturn.

Neither the Babylonians nor the Egyptians understood the nature and form of heaven and earth. Egyptian papyri relate that in the beginning the universe contained a mass of water called Nu. From it germinated the Sun, a flat Earth, and, floating in the waters above, the stars—many if not all of which were thought to be gods. Babylonian ideas were quite similar, as were those of the early Hebrews. According to the Bible, God said: "Let there be a firmament in the midst of the waters . . . and let the waters under the heaven be gathered together unto one place, and let the dry land appear."

Across the Mediterranean, Thales of Miletus, who lived approximately 624 to 547 B.C., integrated elements of Babylonian and Egyptian astronomy into a culture destined to dominate Western thought for centuries. Thales and his followers envisioned a disklike Earth floating on water.

Later Greek astronomers improved upon this. Pythagoras, born in 572 B.C., correctly believed in a spherical Earth, and implied that the universe might be spherical too—an idea that appeals to many modern astronomers. Anaxagoras theorized that the Moon does not itself shine, but rather reflects sunlight. And Heraclides of Pontus (c. 388–315 B.C.) hypothesized, accurately, that the Earth rotates on its axis and that Mercury and Venus revolve around the Sun. But only Aristarchus of Samos, who died in 230 B.C., placed this planet in its proper orbit around the Sun. That the Earth was the center of the universe remained the accepted view until the time of Copernicus (1473–1543).

As man's knowledge expanded, his imagination also began to encompass new worlds. In the second century A.D., author Lucian of Samosata wrote two tales describing voyages to the Moon. From then until the appearance of the *Shāh-Nāmā* in Persia in the eleventh century and of *Orlando Furioso* in the early sixteenth century, the "space-travel" theme lay dormant in the minds of men. (If it did occur to someone, there is no surviving reference to it.) Only following the discoveries of Nicolaus Copernicus in the sixteenth century was the approximate character of the worlds beyond the Earth finally explained. It took another three and a half centuries for man to figure out scientifically how he could voyage to the Moon and planets.

The key to space travel was the rocket, the only known propulsion system that will operate in a vacuum. Invented by the Chinese in the thirteenth century (and perhaps even earlier), it was used alternately for war and for amusement over a period of hundreds of years. Powder rockets of many shapes and sizes were fired with varying degrees of success by the Chinese, Mongolians, Arabs, Indians, Italians, British, French, Austrians, Americans, Russians, and others. So slow was their development that, as late as World War I, rockets could hardly be considered more than minor adjuncts to the conventional weapons then in use.

LEFT: *A Babylonian astronomer-priest observing the skies. As early as 1921 B.C. the Babylonians had compiled tables of the motions of the brightest of planets, Venus.*

BELOW: *Egyptian Sun and Moon gods. The ancient Egyptians, who developed Sun clocks and Solar calendars, were never able to distinguish the gods from the planets, the stars, the Moon, and the Sun. Amon-Ra, the all-powerful Sun god, was widely revered.*

ABOVE: *In the sixth century* B.C., *Ionian philosopher Thales predicted a Solar eclipse and measured the angular diameter of the Sun. In spite of these advances, he clung to the traditional view of a flat, disk-like Earth, floating in a great ocean.*

RIGHT: *When Kai-Kā'ūs, mythical king of Persia, wanted to conquer the heavens, four specially trained eagles lifted him on his elaborate throne into the firmament. According to Firdausi's epic Shāh-Nāma* (A.D. *1010), the eagles "raised up the throne from the face of the earth, they lifted it up from the plain into the clouds."*

RIGHT: *The first device known to have operated on the reaction principle was developed by Archytas of Tarentum during the first half of the fourth century* B.C. *A founder of theoretical mechanics, he built a pigeonlike device that hung by string and moved from one position to another in reaction to the force produced by jets of discharging steam. Behind the pigeon is the aeolopile, a steam-driven wheel described by Hero of Alexandria in the first century* A.D.—*the second known application of the reaction principle.*

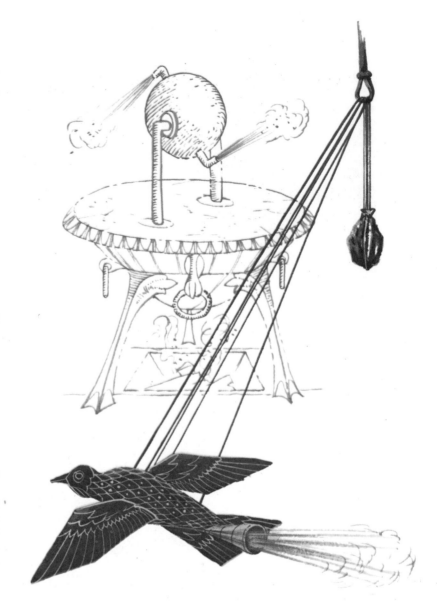

BELOW: *Rockets, probably invented in China, spread quickly to other countries. The Arabs used the rocket-powered "egg that moves and burns" against French invaders in the Seventh Crusade. It was described by Syrian historian al-Hasan al-Rammāh in a late-thirteenth-century* Treatise on Horsemanship and War Stratagems.

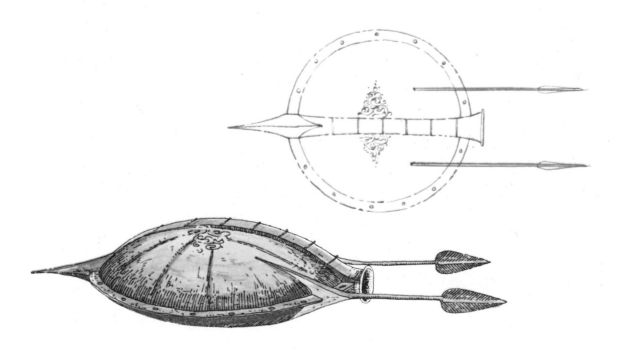

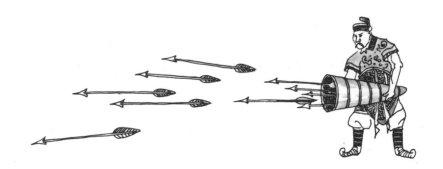

Chinese armies in the thirteenth and fourteenth centuries employed a variety of rocket-type devices against the Mongolians. Carrying such descriptions as "long snake crush enemy" and "leopard herd rush transversally," these "fire-arrows" were fired over ranges of hundreds of feet. But their accuracy was not great, and consequently they were not very effective.

Domingo Gonsales, hero of Bishop Francis Godwin's The Man in the Moone (1638), had no intentions of going to the Moon in this novel device driven by goose-power; he only wanted to escape from an uninhabited island on which he was stranded. To do this he trained a flock of birds to fly him back to civilization. But by the time they were trained their migrating season had begun. And, to Domingo's dismay, their other home was not on our fair planet but—where else?—on the Moon. Thus, a Lunar voyage was made quite by accident.

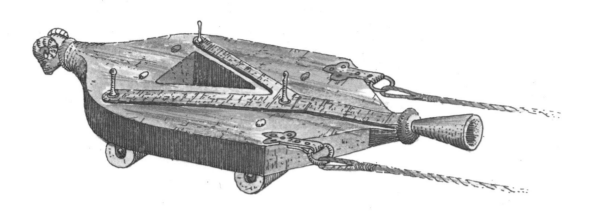

In his Bellicorum instrumentorum liber, Joanes de Fontana described such novel devices as a rocket-propelled cart designed to break through enemy strongpoints, and a rocket-propelled torpedo made of wood.

Fiery as they may have been, nineteenth-century rockets were so inaccurate that they were all but replaced by new and improved artillery. With a few exceptions, such as the Civil War rocket launcher, above, they virtually disappeared by the second half of the century. In the First World War, French Le Prieur rockets (below, about to be launched against a German observation balloon) were occasionally fired from Nieuport biplanes. Still, they were indecisive. Another great war had to come and go before the rocket finally became an important military weapon.

Beginning in August 1930 the VfR-Raketenflug-platz experimenters tested a series of rockets called *Mirak,* a contraction of "Minimum Rakete." Mirak had a body about a foot long and a tail section about 3 feet long. The tail held the tank for the gasoline that fueled the rocket, while the oxidizer (liquid oxygen, or LOX) was stored in the head. The tiny copper motor resembled Oberth's Kegeldüse, but it was immersed in the liquid oxygen, which was expected to furnish more than enough cooling. Mirak 1 had a successful, if brief, stationary test in August in Bernstadt, Saxony. But during the next test, held in September, the oxygen tank burst and the rocket was destroyed. Mirak 2 was built and tested, with a substantially modified cooling system. By the spring of 1931, Mirak 2 was regularly developing thrusts of around 70 pounds in 10-second tests. Finally, it too exploded. The theory was sound, but the technology was just too primitive.

Most of the early difficulties stemmed from cooling, or rather the lack of it. The combustion chambers usually burned through after a short firing period. Their materials were unable to withstand the heat of the burning gases, and the heat transfer to the coolant was inadequate. Clearly the experimenters had to develop better means of cooling their rockets before they could proceed to flight testing.

A motor was finally built that had aluminum walls cooled by water, rather than the liquid oxygen of the earlier Miraks. The motor was incorporated not in Mirak 3 but in a new rocket that Willy Ley nick-named "Repulsor." Repulsor 1 soared to a height of about 200 feet on 14 May 1931; Repulsor 2 reached about the same altitude and achieved a long range for that time of 2,000 feet on 23 May. The third Repulsor did better; in early June 1931 it reached an altitude of at least 2,000 feet and crash-landed a similar distance away. The experimenters had hoped to recover it by parachute, which, to their annoyance, was torn off during the ascent.

Several more No. 3 models were flown before a redesign that resulted in Repulsor 4, a rocket that used a single stick for stability. On its maiden flight in August 1931, Repulsor 4 flew up approximately 3,300 feet, where its parachute opened and floated it gently back to Earth. Other flights of Repulsor-4 models attained altitudes of one mile—no mean accomplishment in those days.

But the Repulsors had just missed out on the honor of being the first successful European rockets. A few months earlier, Johannes Winkler, with the financial support of Hugo A. Hückel, had built a 2-foot-long, 12-inch-diameter rocket fueled by liquid oxygen and liquid methane. Near Dessau, at Gross

Kühnau, the Hückel-Winkler 1 was launched on 14 March 1931, to an altitude of perhaps 1,000 feet. The next in the series, Hückel-Winkler 2, did not do as well. After taking off near Pillau in East Prussia on 6 October 1932, it caught fire and crashed to the ground. Maximum altitude: 10 feet.

The day before the first Hückel-Winkler shot, Karl Poggensee, in a test near Berlin, had fired an experimental solid-fuel rocket to a 1,500-foot altitude. Fitted with an altimeter, cameras, and a device to measure velocity, it was recovered by parachute at the end of the flight. Other rocket pioneers active at about this time included Reinhold Tiling, Gerhard Zucker, and, in Austria, Friedrich Schmiedl.

Reinhold Tiling built six solid-propellant rockets, four of which he fired from Osnabrück in April 1931. One exploded at 500 feet, two climbed to from 1,500 to 2,500 feet, and one reached 6,600 feet, burning for 11 seconds and reaching a maximum speed of 700 miles per hour. Tiling launched his last two rockets, of more advanced design, from Wangerooge, one of the East Frisian Islands. One of them may have climbed as high as 32,000 feet. About 5 feet long, they consumed 14.3 pounds of propellant and carried a payload of 11 pounds.

Starting in February 1931, Friedrich Schmiedl of Austria fired solid-propellant rockets with mail payloads, mostly between Schöckel and Radegund and Schöckel and Kumberg, for several years. The rockets delivered hundreds of letters. Tiling tried the same idea in 1931; a few years later, so did Gerhard Zucker, who envisioned regular rocket mail service across the English Channel. Like Schmiedl and Tiling, Zucker used powder rockets, but his attempts were spectacular only for the explosions they produced. The longest shot he attempted was from Harris to Scarp, in the Western Isles of Scotland, on 31 July 1934. The rocket destroyed itself in an explosion.

Another sidelight to prewar rocketry was the so-called Magdeburg project. Rudolf Nebel had conceived the idea of building a manned rocket, but before embarking on such an ambitious project, first set out to accumulate needed flight data with a small test rocket. Accordingly, with the help of Herbert Schaefer, he built a rocket which was subsequently fired on 9 June 1933, at Wolmirstedt near Magdeburg. The initial test met with scant success: the motor did not provide enough thrust to permit the rocket even to fly free of the 30-foot launching tower. Several later attempts produced the same results until, on 29 June, one finally managed to leave the tower, fly horizontally about 1,000 feet, and land only slightly damaged. It was later rebuilt into

Mirak 2 at the Raketenflugplatz. Liquid oxygen is in large tank at left; fuel, in long, thin tank at right.

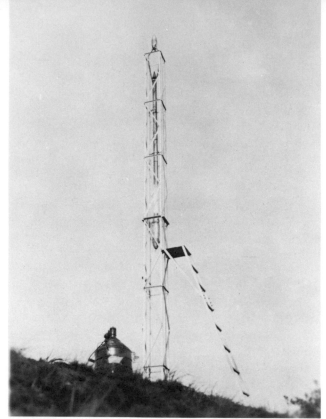

The VfR experimenters designed an improved cooling system, aluminum cooled by water, for the Repulsor series. Repulsor 2, shown here on the test stand at Raketenflugplatz, was fired 2,000 feet on 23 May 1931.

a Repulsor-type rocket and launched from Lindwerder Island in Tegeler Lake near Berlin, reaching an altitude of some 3,000 feet before crashing 300 feet from its tower. Additional tests were conducted from a boat on Schwielow Lake in August 1933 before the project was abandoned altogether.

The early successes of the VfR experimenters were not enough to sustain it during the economic

Shortly after this picture was taken of its launching in August 1931, Repulsor 4 rose to a height of 3,300 feet, where its parachute opened and floated it back to Earth.

depression that gripped Germany. The VfR program fell on hard times, along with the rest of the world, during the 1930's. By 1932, membership in the rocket society began to drop severely. The problems of the rocket pioneers were compounded by increasing objections of the Berlin police to rocket flights within the city limits. In desperation, the VfR group sought support from the German army. After a demonstration flight of a Repulsor at the army proving grounds at nearby Kummersdorf in the summer of 1932, the army invited Wernher von Braun to do the experimental work for his doctor's thesis on rocket combustion phenomena at Kummersdorf.

Work at the Raketenflugplatz ended during the winter of 1933–1934. The VfR was in shaky financial condition and could not pay its accumulated bills. In January 1934, a year after Hitler's rise to power, the Raketenflugplatz was turned back into an ammunition dump by the military. The international ties of the VfR and the Raketenflugplatz irritated the new regime, and it was not long before the Gestapo would make its presence felt. In this stifling atmosphere private interest in rocketry all but vanished.

At Kummersdorf, meanwhile, the army continued experiments under the direction of Captain Walter Dornberger and Von Braun. The Heereswaffenamt-Prüfwesen (Army Ordnance Research and Development Department) gradually developed the Versuchsstelle Kummersdorf–West as a site for developing and static-testing rockets. Between November 1932, when Von Braun began work on his doctor's thesis with the help of a single mechanic, and 1937, when the Kummersdorf–West staff had grown to about eighty, the group worked on several small rockets. This work laid the groundwork for the V-2.

The main source of support within the army for the Kummersdorf project was Artillery General Karl Becker, who, with his mentor Carl Cranz of the Prussian Academy for Military Engineering, had long championed the rocket as an artillery weapon. The Cranz-Becker textbook, *Ballistics*, contained a chapter on the subject, ample evidence of the authors' thinking on the potential of the rocket. It was Becker who encouraged and sponsored Von Braun's doctoral thesis and, after his graduation, put him to work in the army under Major von Horstig and his assistant, Captain Dornberger. And it was Becker who, in 1935, proposed in vain to Hitler a program to develop a long-range bombardment rocket.

The first new rocket to be developed at Kummersdorf was the A-1, an abbreviation for Aggregate 1. Powered by an alcohol–liquid oxygen regeneratively cooled engine developing 660 pounds of thrust, the A-1 was a relatively simple rocket. The alcohol-cooled engine was in the bottom bulkhead of the single pressurized metal tank which was half filled with alcohol. While the alcohol fuel filled the lower half of the metal tank, liquid oxygen was loaded into a thin-walled, open fiberglass container inserted into the upper half of the metal tank. A small compressed-nitrogen flask, pressurizing the single metal tank, thus provided identical feed pressure for both propellants. The payload was a 70-pound gyroscopic flywheel in the rocket's nose, which provided stability during the 16-second powered flight.

After a few successful static tests, the first A-1 was destroyed by an explosion caused by delayed ignition. Model tests had shown, meanwhile, that the flywheel had to be closer to the rocket's center to be effective. Since the location of the open oxygen container within the fuel tank posed the danger of a flashback explosion after a powered flight, the arrangement was changed. The fuel tank was shortened, a separate metal tank was provided for the liquid oxygen, and the gyrowheel was placed between the two tanks. The new configuration was called A-2. In December 1934 on the North Sea island of Borkum, two A-2 rockets, "Max" and "Moritz"—named after characters in a humorous German book —made two successful straight-up flights to altitudes of about 6,500 feet.

The Borkum success was a shot in the arm for

Above, Reinhold Tiling (left, with side to camera) standing beside black-powder rocket he launched from Osnabrück in April 1931. Below, the Tiling rocket, in flight. It rose to a height of 2.5 miles.

Gerhard Zucker envisioned rocket mail service across the English Channel. The longest shot he attempted was from Harris to Scarp, in western Scotland, on 31 July 1934. But the rocket blew up before takeoff.

The Nazis, who disliked the VfR's international ties, turned the Raketenflugplatz back into an ammunitions dump. Rocket research was brought under the army's control at Kummersdorf. Below, Hitler watches a Kummersdorf demonstration in March 1939.

Kummersdorf. The staff was increased and allotted more funds. The Dornberger–Von Braun organization grew, as did the power of the rocket engines. Soon both were too large for the restricted confines of Kummersdorf. A move to another location became necessary in April of 1937. The site chosen was Peenemünde on the Baltic coast, not far from the small town of Wolgast. The first task of the Heeresversuchsstelle Peenemünde (Army Experimental Station Peenemünde), of which Von Braun became technical director, was to develop a new liquid-fuel rocket with adequate growth potential. The second assignment: Prepare the A-3, now virtually complete, for a test firing out over the Baltic Sea.

While the move into the vast new experimental station was accomplished easily, the launching in the fall of 1937 of three A-3's was a different matter. All three test models of the 21-foot-long, 1,650-pound rocket failed. The 3,300-pound-thrust alcohol–liquid oxygen engines behaved well enough, but a new and quite sophisticated inertial guidance system did not. The problem was solved—but only after nearly two years of labor. Meanwhile, larger, more powerful, longer range rockets were on the drawing boards.

The pace of activity at Peenemünde quickened as war drew nearer. In March 1938, German troops invaded Austria. At the end of September, the Munich pact won the Sudetenland for Hitler. Only six months later all of Czechoslovakia capitulated. As these events unfolded, the Ordnance Department demanded with new urgency that the experimenters at Peenemünde prove their worth by developing practical weapons.

The Ordnance Department wanted a long-range missile, capable of flying 150 to perhaps 200 miles with a one-ton warhead. The rocket had to be transportable by railroad and truck, and hence of a size compatible with Germany's existing rail and road network—tunnel widths and heights, road curves, and the like. Above all the rocket had to be reliable.

The response to these criteria was the A-4 rocket, which became known as the V-2, or second weapon of retaliation, when it was used near the end of the war. But the jump from the problem-beset A-3 to a reliable A-4 could not be made without an interim vehicle to test the guidance system, which may have been a luxury for the A-3 but would be a vital necessity for the larger missile. Hence, the A-5 was born.

The A-5 used the same propulsion system as the A-3 and was outwardly identical to the new A-4, although much smaller in size. The A-5 had a greatly improved structure and an improved, yet simplified, guidance and control system. Its first flight, in the fall of 1938 from the nearby Greifswalder Oie island—without the new guidance system—proved the soundness of the A-5's mechanical design. A second series of launches, this time with the new guidance, came off perfectly. The first vertical flight, in the summer of 1939, reached an altitude of 7.5 miles. Other flight models did as well. Some were launched vertically, others along slanting trajectories to simulate the operational trajectory of the forthcoming A-4. Several A-5's were recovered by parachute and flown again.

While most of the work on military rockets in Germany was performed by the Dornberger–Von Braun team at Peenemünde and its associated industrial and university contractors, there were other efforts before and during the war, particularly those sponsored by the Luftwaffe. In 1936 the Luftwaffe had invited the Austrian Dr. Eugen Sänger to build a rocket research establishment at Trauen near Hannover. It was ready when the war started. Sänger's experience had been gained in liquid-propellant rocket engine testing at the University of Vienna, where he had fired Diesel oil–oxygen gas motors developing a little over 50 pounds of thrust for 20 or 30 *minutes*, incredibly long burning times. Sänger visualized many applications for his rocket engines, some of which were designed to use liquid oxygen and conventional fuels, others liquid ozone and metallic fuels (aluminum powder suspended in fuel oil). But his work at Trauen was ended in 1942, and Sänger was transferred to another research institute, where he turned his interest to air-breathing jet engines and worked on conceptional studies of an intercontinental rocket-boosted bomber.

Other German research workers had been trying to mate rockets and airplanes. Early in the 1930's, Hellmuth Walter, a research chemist at the Hanseatische Apparatebau Gesellschaft in Kiel, suggested the use of hydrogen peroxide for propelling torpedos. When the idea failed to work out, Walter turned to aeronautical applications. At the Chemical State Institute in Berlin he developed a rocket engine operating on 80-percent-strength hydrogen peroxide. It was so successful that in 1935 he established his own firm, Hellmuth Walter Kommanditgesellschaft.

The Air Ministry became interested in a proposal to install a Walter rocket engine on a Heinkel Kadett airplane, which was done in February 1937. Although the rocket produced only 220 pounds of thrust, the test was successful. It was the first rocket-assisted takeoff in history. According to Walter "later in that year and during 1938, a great number of flight tests were made with ATO's [assisted takeoff units] at 300 to 500 kg thrust with land and sea planes without any accidents whatsoever." Rocket-powered depth

The 21-foot A-3 on the test stand at Peenemünde, 1937. A-3's engine, which ran on a combination of alcohol and liquid oxygen, was the basis for the wartime V-2.

In Vienna, Dr. Eugen Sänger developed liquid-propellant rockets that burned for 20 to 30 minutes. Here Dr. Sänger (right) is shown pouring liquid oxygen into a container at his test station in 1934.

charges and mines designed to be dropped from aircraft were also developed. Walter engines had many wartime applications.

The Bayrische Motoren Werke (Bavarian Motors Works) at Munich also developed liquid rockets for airplanes. Starting in 1938, under the direction of Helmut von Zborowsky, the company investigated a myriad of propellant combinations before settling on nitric acid doped with 10 percent sulfuric acid to reduce corrosion and a "visol" fuel that consisted of vinyl isobutyl ether and aniline. Rheinmetall-Borsig in Berlin also worked with nitric acid at about this time, while Schmidding und Dynamit A.G. in Bodenbach developed solid-propellant rockets to assist airplane takeoffs.

Peenemünde also had done some work on rocket engines for airplanes. In January 1935 Major von Richthofen, head of Luftwaffe airplane development, visited Von Braun at Kummersdorf to inquire about the feasibility of adapting a liquid-propellant rocket engine to power military aircraft. An engine developing 2,200 pounds of thrust on liquid oxygen and alcohol propellants was soon available. With the help of the airplane manufacturer Ernst Heinkel, it was installed by Von Braun and his associates in a Heinkel He-112. Static testing began during the summer of 1935 and flight testing in the spring of 1937, at about

the same time the Kummersdorf group had transferred to Peenemünde. While the He-112 never became operational, it did provide a stepping stone to later rocket airplane developments and helped inspire Heinkel's work on JATO (jet assisted takeoff) devices.

In neighboring France the rise of rocketry was less spectacular than in Germany. Like Germany, Russia, and the United States, France had a leading pioneer, Robert Esnault-Pelterie. Though his contributions to astronautical knowledge were less important than those of Tsiolkovsky, Goddard, and Oberth, he was a well-known airplane inventor, a brilliant individual, and a member of the French Academy of Sciences. As early as 1907 he began thinking seriously about astronautics. Like Tsiolkovsky and Oberth, he was a highly effective publicist for the idea of interplanetary travel and rocketry.

Esnault-Pelterie launched his public campaign in February 1912 when he delivered a major lecture in St. Petersburg, repeated back home in Paris to the Société Française de Physique in November. The Société was the most prestigious organization to provide a forum up to that time for what many people still considered to be a fantastic subject. Only Esnault-Pelterie's reputation in other fields permitted him to lecture, albeit cautiously, on the "Considera-

Hellmuth Walter, a research chemist from Kiel, built rocket engines fueled by hydrogen peroxide. The peroxide was manufactured in a plant in Lautenberg in the Harz Mountains.

Robert Esnault-Pelterie began theorizing on space flight as early as 1907, and subsequently published basic works on the subject. This picture was taken in 1929. (ARFOR ARCHIVES)

tions sur les résultats d'un allègement indéfini des moteurs" ("Considerations on the Results of an Unlimited Lightening of Motors"—a title referring to the fact that as a rocket uses up its propellants it becomes progressively lighter).

Fifteen years later, on 8 June 1927, he appeared before the Société Astronomique de France to tell astronomers about the results of his further theoretical research in astronautics. The Society subsequently published the written text as a 98-page book, *L'exploration par fusées de la très haute atmosphère et la possibilité des voyages interplanétaires* (*Rocket Explosion of the Very High Atmosphere and the Possibility of Interplanetary Travel*). This title, more audacious than the 1912 delivery, combines Goddard's conservatism and Oberth's optimism. At the same meeting Esnault-Pelterie revealed that he and a banker friend, André Louis-Hirsch, had established a 5,000-franc prize to be awarded annually to the author of the most outstanding work on astronautics. Called the Prix REP-Hirsch (REP-Hirsch Award), it was awarded by the Astronautical Committee of the Société Astronomique de France. The first recipient in 1928 was Hermann Oberth, who was so highly esteemed that the prize was doubled to 10,000 francs.

Esnault-Pelterie's greatest contribution was the publication in 1930 of a book entitled *L'Astronautique* (*Astronautics*), which, together with its 1934 supplement, *L'Astronautique-Complément*, covered virtually all that was then known of rocketry and space flight.

Although Esnault-Pelterie's major interest was theoretical astronautics, he was well aware of the military implications of rocketry. On 20 May 1928, he proposed to French army general Ferrié a plan for the development of ballistic bombardment missiles against which he could imagine no defense. He wrote that such weapons could deliver "over several hundreds of kilometers . . . thousands of tons" of destructive payload, all within a few hours. (He was obviously thinking in terms of salvo firings like the World War II V-1 and V-2 offensives.) "Moreover," he added, "the necessary ground installations would not entail great expense and would doubtless be infinitely less burdensome than if it were a question of delivering the same load by aeroplanes."

His proposal resulted in the appointment of ingénieur général J. J. Barré to his laboratories in 1931, which in turn led to work approved by the Commission des Poudres de Guerre at Versailles first on liquid-oxygen–gasoline motors, then on nitrogen peroxide–benzene motors, and one powered by liquid oxygen and tetranitromethane. In October 1931 tests

French rocketeer J. J. Barré with the experimental EA-41 launched near Toulon.

of the last, an accident occurred, causing Esnault-Pelterie to lose four fingers.

In 1934 a study contract was let to Esnault-Pelterie by the Direction des Études et Fabrications d'Armement under the general supervision of ingénieur général Desmazières. There, in addition to liquid rocket work, 80-mm solid-fuel rockets were developed whose application was to have been to accelerate bombs. Elsewhere, the Services de l'Armement Français studied, in 1939, the use of 1,000-pound-thrust JATO units for assisting heavy bombers to take off. Air Liquide, a private concern, worked for a short period on a 100-pound-thrust test motor under Air Ministry contract at Champigny and at Seyne. French rocketry continued sporadically, and without conclusive results, until the outbreak of war.

Experimental work in rocketry also was conducted by Henri F. Melot who, beginning in 1916, spent nearly three decades developing airplane boost motors at the Institut des Arts et Métiers in Paris. Black-powder rockets were studied from 1932 to 1935 by Louis Damblanc, a civil engineer, at the Institut Aérotechnique at Saint Cyr and some tests were made —the aim being to realize more reliable signal, Coast

Guard, and anti-hail devices. Similar experiments were made at the Établissements Ruggieri and at the École Centrale de Pyrotechnie in Bourges. In the field of astronautics, the great 1937 Paris exhibition at the Palais de la Découverte featured an impressive space-flight exhibit, including contributions from other European countries and from America.

Incredible as it may seem, there was some independent French rocket activity during the German occupation. According to Barré, General Arnaud and Colonel Gentil of the Sous-direction du Service de l'Artillerie directed that the Section Technique de l'Artillerie should secretly operate, in Lyon, under the completely false name Service Central des Marchés et de Surveillance des Approvisionnements (Central Market Service and Supplies Supervision)! Directed by Colonel (later General) Joseph Dubouloz, studies were initiated by Barré to develop an experimental motor operating on liquid oxygen and gasoline ether called the EA-1941 (or EA-41). Static tests began on 15 November 1941 at Larzac, and within a year, seven tests had been successfully conducted at both Larzac and at Vancia near Lyon—"unknown to the occupiers, of course." Barré describes the rocket as the first conceived and built in France, that is, the first airframe powered by a liquid-propellant rocket motor—previously only motors alone had been constructed. The EA-41 motor could be regulated in terms of its propellant consumption, was cooled by its own fuel, and was pressurized by nitrogen gas.

The clandestine group planned to fire their test rockets in 1942 from a field at Beni-Ounif de Figuig in Algeria, but the Allied landings prevented them from doing so. They awaited the Liberation; and, in March 1945, at the Etablissement d'Expériences Techniques at La Renardière near Toulon, the long-awaited firings began. During the course of the first set of two firings in March 1941 all went relatively well, but during the second set, one rocket landed about 20 miles from La Renardière and could never be located.

Across the Channel in Great Britain, prewar rocketry suffered from two crippling handicaps. The British had no great man similar to Oberth or Tsiolkovsky to rally around. And the British government was stubbornly hostile to rocketry. The Explosives Act of 1875 forbade rocket testing, and the government enforced the law to the letter. Rocketry in Britain literally never got off the ground.

British rocket enthusiasts got around these two barriers as best they could, concentrating on public education and on providing a literary forum for astronautical scientists and engineers. In these endeavors, they were more successful.

In 1933 the British Interplanetary Society was founded. Unlike other rocket societies, this group has kept its name and original objectives intact to the present. Apparently the only attempt to make the BIS adopt a more conservative name occurred in 1934, a year after it was founded, when it was suggested that the word "Interplanetary" be dropped from the society's name. The society's president scorned the proposal:

Are we to pander to public opinion . . . an opinion which held to ridicule the votaries of heavier-than-air flight, and which refused to credit the marvel of wireless telegraphy to such good effect that the inventor died heartbroken, deserted even by his friends, who also deemed him mad? . . . it seems to me that a change in name, regardless of the reason for it, would be universally misconstrued as an admission of doubt, as a confession that the interplanetary idea only belongs to the realm of extravagant fiction.

In 1934 the first issue of the BIS *Journal* appeared. It became universally recognized as the most distinguished publication devoted to space flight in the world. The importance the British attach to their *Journal* was evident from its very beginning. P. E. Cleator, the first president of the BIS, editorialized in the *Journal's* second issue, published in April 1934:

The tremendous importance of a substantial and interesting Journal was brought home to me during my conversations with the German experimenters. In the year 1929, the old Germany rocket society . . . ceased the publication of their Journal, *Die Rakete*. The immediate result was the loss of over 600 members! It happened like this: there came a time when the Society had to choose between publishing the Journal and carrying out certain important and costly experiments. Eventually, it was decided to sacrifice the Journal. Now the new programme was all very well for those members who happened to live in Berlin, for they could take part in, or witness, the experiments. But not so for the majority of members, who were scattered throughout the country. With the loss of the Journal, they were deprived of their only real link with the Society. The moral is clear. The Journal of a Society constitutes a vital connecting link . . . . The Journal must come before experimental work.

But the British knew the importance of experimental work. As Cleator later said, "No one is more eager than I am to organize and to begin our share of actual experimental work," but until finances were more secure and conditions more propitious he was unwilling to promote testing. Attempts to get government support were completely unsuccessful. As late as 1934 the Air Ministry was reported to have "evinced not the slightest interest" in liquid-propellant rockets, though engineers at the Royal Aircraft

Establishment had done some investigations of rocket motors in the mid-1920's.

The first British book on astronautics was Cleator's *Rockets Through Space: The Dawn of Interplanetary Travel*, which appeared in 1936. Written at a popular level, it did not contain any profound insights into the new science. What Cleator set out to do, however, he did well. His volume is the best written of the first group of books on rocketry. Since he was close to the center of communication provided by the *Journal*, Cleator was able to include reports on the many activities taking place on both sides of the Atlantic.

In December 1934 Alwyn Douglas Crow (later Sir), Director of Ballistic Research at the Woolwich Royal Arsenal, proposed to Sir Hugh Elles, Master of General Ordnance, that the British begin to investigate the possibilities of developing rocket weapons powered by smokeless cordite powder of the unrestricted burning type. Crow later wrote that

in April 1935 the Research Department at Woolwich Arsenal was asked to put forward a program for the specific investigation of the possibility of developing rockets, utilizing cordite as the propelling agency. Preliminary work was started . . . in May 1935, and by the summer of 1936 encouraging advances in technique had been achieved.

With this encouragement, the Committee of Imperial Defense's Subcommittee on Air Defense Research directed Crow and his team to investigate the use of rockets for antiaircraft defense, long-range attack, air-to-air combat, and assisted takeoff for heavy aircraft. During 1936 and 1937, small motors based on 2-inch- and 3-inch-diameter solid cordite charges were perfected. Larger motors with 11 cordite sticks were also studied. Test firings were conducted in a covered range in England during July and August 1936, outdoors in November, and again during the second half of 1937, before they were transferred to the more favorable climate of Jamaica. Some 2,500 3-inch rockets were fired in Jamaica during the first few months of 1939 under the direction of Brigadier Allan Younger. According to Brigadier Leonard Walter Jubb, a participant, the Jamaica trials were devised "primarily to obtain information on the external ballistics of the rockets." Simultaneous tests were conducted in Britain to prove out the design of a launcher. Both single and twin launchers ultimately were developed for Army and Navy deployment.

Crow, who was responsible for starting this series of tests, ultimately headed Britain's wartime rocket program. In 1938 he left his post as Director of Ballistic Research at the Woolwich Royal Arsenal, a position he had held since 1919, and moved his rocket research team to Fort Halstead, Kent, where he set up what was to be known as the Projectile Development Establishment for the U.P. (unrotated projectile) under the War Office. In 1939, Sir Alwyn became Chief Superintendent of Projectile Development. Shortly after Britain entered the war, his title became Controller of Projectile Development in the Ministry of Supply.

Some notable prewar rocket research also was performed by individual scientists and engineers in Italy, although a strong national development program never was sustained.

The Italian General Staff sponsored a rocket research program beginning in 1927 under the direction of General G. A. Crocco with the assistance of his son Luigi and the collaboration of the Bombrini Parodi Delfino chemical firm. According to an article by Crocco on "Instruction and Research in Jet Propulsion" (*Journal of the American Rocket Society*, March 1950), tests first were conducted with powder rockets with some success, but by 1929 the Italian General Staff canceled the program because dispersion was too great and velocity too low (rockets launched during the experiments had reached a velocity of only about 1,000 feet per second).

Beginning in 1929 Crocco and his associates then began to investigate liquid propellants, selecting gasoline as the fuel and nitrogen dioxide as the

British rockets being prepared for launch at Port Royal, Jamaica, in February 1939. (BRIG. LEONARD WALTER JUBB)

oxidizer. Assisting in this work were Corrado Lani of the Establishment of Constructions, Italian Air Ministry; scientists at the Chemical Institute of the University of Rome; and Riccardo M. Corelli. By 1930 a combustion chamber had been developed which operated for up to ten minutes at 140-pounds-per-square-inch pressures. Crocco later reported that "By the end of 1930, the available funds were exhausted, and despite the promising results obtained, the General Staff did not renew its contract." A familiar end to many early government-sponsored rocket research programs.

Two years later Crocco and Corelli obtained support from the Aviation Ministry for a study of propellants, concentrating first on a mixture of 70 percent trinitroglycerin and 30 percent methyl alcohol, and later on, nitromethane. Again, although preliminary results warranted continuing the study, the program was phased out in 1935.

In the United States, the most crucial influence was the aloofness of Robert H. Goddard from other American rocketeers. Goddard did not join in when rocket enthusiasts met in New York City on 21 March 1930 to found the American Interplanetary Society. He did not publicize his advanced ideas, nor did he help other rocket researchers. Intent on his own work, he allowed others to make the public speeches. The great American rocket pioneer did very little to nurture a climate in which large-scale rocket research might flourish.

The society's announced aims were to promote "interest in and the experimentation toward interplanetary expeditions and travel . . . and the raising of funds for research and experimentation." David Lasser, the first president, was a technically trained individual then serving as editor of *Wonder Stories,* a science-fiction magazine. Other founders included a chemist, William Lemkin; several writers and newspapermen, C. W. van Devander, G. Edward Pendray, C. P. Mason, Laurence Manning, Fletcher Pratt, and Nathan Schachner; and an engineer, Clyde J. Fitch. The society's first activity was a ceremony in which explorer Sir Hubert Wilkins presented it with a copy of *Discovery of a New World,* a volume published in 1638 by John Wilkins, Bishop of Chester, Sir Hubert's ancestor.

The AIS attracted a number of engineers and scientists into its ranks. The four-page first issue of its *Bulletin,* which appeared in June 1930, reported news of the society and events in the United States and abroad. It maintained fairly regular publication, though it probably changed its name more frequently than any other journal in history.

The society itself remained almost continually on the defensive in its dealings with the public. Interplanetary travel was the target of such ridicule in the United States that in 1934 the American Interplanetary Society changed its name to the less frightening American Rocket Society. It kept this name until 1963 when, after merging with the Institute of Aerospace Sciences, it became the American Institute of Aeronautics and Astronautics.

Goddard, while not a member, did contact the society occasionally, if only to correct an error. In the June–July 1931 *Bulletin* he provided an accurate account of his 17 July 1929 rocket firing, which had been reported incorrectly in the preceding issue. He ended his letter with these words:

The article in the *Bulletin* also speaks of my reticence in giving my results to the public. It happens, as I have explained to Mr. Lasser, that so many of my ideas and suggestions have been copied abroad without the acknowledgment usual in scientific circles that I have been forced to take this attitude. Further, I do not think it desirable to publish results of the long series of experiments I have undertaken until I feel that I have made a significant further contribution to the problem.

About a year after the founding of the American Interplanetary Society, Pendray traveled to Europe, visiting the German experimenters at the Raketenflugplatz in April 1931. In an article on "The German Rockets" in the May 1931 issue of the *Bulletin,* he reviewed his trip and supplied details and drawings of the Mirak series of rockets. Pendray's trip helped stimulate experimenters in the United States to conduct tests themselves. A research committee quickly was established by the society, and in the summer of 1931, plans for testing were drawn up. The projected tests were described in the September issue of the *Bulletin* as providing a means "of studying the operating qualities of rocket motors, in order to determine what power they might develop under various conditions."

The first of the society's rocket designs, according to a report in the March 1932 *Bulletin,* was "patterned . . . in general after one of the successful German liquid-fuel rockets . . . the type known as the two-stick Repulsor but containing . . . so many changes and inventions of our own that it must stand or fall upon its own merits." It was to use gasoline and liquid oxygen and be constructed largely of a special aluminum alloy "cast by the Aluminum Company of America from a pattern made upon specifications designed by ourselves."

The motor of the test rocket developed by AIS members (under the direction of H. Franklin Pierce) was somewhat larger and heavier than the German Mirak motors and boasted a number of apparent propellant-feed improvements. Mounted on a shackle at the front end of two 5.5-foot-long, 1.5-inch-diameter cylindrical tanks, containing the liquid oxygen and gasoline propellants, the water-cooled, 6-inch-long, 3-inch-diameter motor was made of cast aluminum. At the rear were four aluminum guiding fins, and at the opposite end, a cone-shaped nose bay with parachute.

Although Rocket No. 1 was completed in January of 1932, tests could not begin until a suitable firing location was found. This turned out to be a New Jersey farm near Stockton, some one hundred miles from New York City. Work began there in August 1932 to prepare two dugouts, one for close observation and the other for controls. A proving stand was built which, according to Pendray,

consisted of two rounded up-right members of wood, held in place by a stout framework of planks. The up-right members, constructed to guide the rocket in the event of an actual flight, were fourteen feet high. The span of the supporting framework was a little under twelve feet. The whole apparatus stood on the ground as an independent unit, the lower parts protected from flame by sandbags, flat stones and banks of earth.

In order to engage the upright members of the proving stand, guides were placed along the sides of the rocket; the uprights were "copiously soaped" to in-

sure movement of the guides. During static tests a 12-foot-long pole held down the rocket; it was "pivoted to an upright post at its outer end, and held down at its inner end by a coil spring which was in turn fastened to the proving stand."

Many difficulties faced the early experimenters. They found it exceedingly uncomfortable to load liquid oxygen into the relatively long, narrow oxidizer tanks ("it requires sometimes as long as fifteen minutes to empty a quart, most of which either evaporates from the furiously boiling supply in the funnel, or spatters down the sleeves of the operator, inflicting innumerable tiny frostbites, like little scalded spots"). The valves, which had to be activated by fuse-wire connections from the dugout, gave them trouble. And the remote firing control was "a complete failure," leading the rocketeers to consider going forth with a "box of matches and a gasoline soaked torch . . . and light the fuse between the tanks of the rocket."

The first static test, held on 12 November 1932, was a success. Recalling the event a short while afterward, Pendray, still in a state of near euphoria, said:

It is impossible adequately to describe that sight, or to convey the feeling it gave us. I suppose we were excited; but there was a certain majesty about the sound and sight which made it impossible for the moment to feel excite-

The American Interplanetary Society static tested its first rocket between two upright "guides" on a New Jersey farm in 1932. At right, AIS president David Lasser, fore-

ground, crouches with Laurence Manning behind a pile of sandbags to watch the experiment.

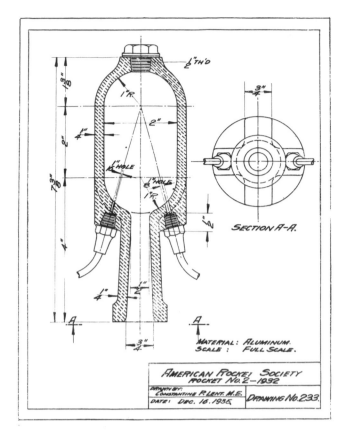

MATERIAL: ALUMINUM.
SCALE: FULL SCALE.

AMERICAN ROCKET SOCIETY
ROCKET No. 2-1932
DRAWN BY: CONSTANTINE P. LENT, M.E.
DATE: DEC. 16. 1935.
DRAWING No. 233.

Rocket No. 2, an improved version of the first rocket, was flight tested in May 1933 on Staten Island, N.Y. The motor shut down after two seconds and the rocket landed some 400 feet offshore. Above, details for the rocket's motor.

ment as such. We forgot to remain behind the shelter of our earthworks. Moreover, we forgot to count the seconds as they passed in that downward pouring cascade of fire.

The exhaust pattern was "clear and clean, of a bluish-white color, and quite steady." About the only flaw in the test was the depletion of the oxidizer before the fuel, with the result that the excess gasoline "came spurting out, throwing a shower of fire all around the foot of the rocket and proving stand."

A flight test of Rocket No. 1, planned for the next morning, had to be canceled because of bad weather. Based on the 60 pounds of thrust developed during the test, the experimenters calculated that the 15-pound rocket might have attained an altitude of 6 miles.

The rocket was overhauled, and became the society's Rocket No. 2. The tanks were placed closer together, the parachute bay was removed, valving was improved, and balsa-wood vanes replaced the aluminum fins. A new streamlined nosecone had a hole to admit cooling air, instead of the cooling jacket

of Rocket No. 1. The launching rack, designed by Laurence Manning and Alfred H. Best, was made of two 2-inch pine poles, 15 feet long, supported below by 4-by-4 timber and above by wooden shackles. It was tilted 5 degrees to insure that the rocket would fly out over the water, where it would do no damage upon landing and could be recovered for post-flight inspection.

At 11:20 in the morning of 14 May 1933, the flight was made from a new testing grounds at Great Kills, Staten Island, under the direction of Pendray and his assistants, who included Manning, Best, Bernard Smith, Carl Ahrens, and Alfred Africano. The motor, instead of burning for 20 to 30 seconds as it had in the November 1932 static test, shut down at an altitude of about 250 feet after burning only 2 seconds; the liquid-oxygen tank had burst, the fins separated from the tanks and the motor, which continued in flight, landing about 400 feet offshore (where they were recovered). The heat of the motor's

ARS Rocket No. 3 being prepared for static tests on Staten Island in September 1934. Shown here are (left to right) John Shesta, G. Edward Pendray, and Bernard Smith. (G. EDWARD PENDRAY)

exhaust caused a rapid pressure buildup that ruptured the tank.

During the rest of 1933 the society continued to hold lectures, publish its journal (now called *Astronautics*), and develop rockets. Three different designs were produced almost simultaneously—Rockets No. 3, 4, and 5. The first of these, designed by Africano, Pendray, and Smith, was about 5.5. feet high and 8 inches in diameter, operated on one quart of gasoline and four quarts of liquid oxygen, and weighed 20 pounds. Rocket No. 3's 60-pound-thrust motors produced a 2-g acceleration.

Rocket No. 4 was somewhat longer (7.5 feet over-all) and narrower (3 inches), and had a smaller propellant capacity—only a pint of gasoline and a quart of liquid oxygen. It was shaped to keep air resistance to a minimum and to permit the motor to ride above the main body, with the exhaust gases deflected outwards by four canted nozzles. Four blades were in the rocket's nose "so arranged that during flight they were held in a collapsed position along the axis of the rocket by air resistance. When the speed slackens away, the blades are opened by springs, and the rocket descends tail-foremost, revolving as the whirling blades break the speed of fall" (*Astronautics,* March 1934). The inventors probably had an eye on Reinhold Tiling's activities in Germany when they devised this scheme. Designed by Ahrens, Best, Manning, and project leader John Shesta, No. 4 had its first static firing, on 10 June 1934, at Staten Island. The test ended with a motor burnout.

The motor was replaced, and changes were made in the rocket. Larger exhaust nozzles were installed, a water-cooling jacket was added, wider propellant inlets were substituted, and the rotor blades were removed in favor of a parachute recovery system. These modifications occupied the design team during July and August of 1934; by September the rocket was ready for another test. Early in the morning of 9 September, again at Great Kills, the flight took place. This time the results were good. After takeoff from the society's new steel launching rack, the motor burned for approximately fifteen seconds, enough to lift the rocket along a trajectory that was described as "excellent." The maximum altitude was 382 feet, the range 1,338 feet. Although not accurately measurable, the velocity appeared to exceed 600 miles per hour, possibly approaching 700 miles per hour. The only disappointment was the failure of the chute to open.

After the flight of Rocket No. 4, the experimenters decided not to attempt to fly Rocket No. 3 because of its motor inadequacies. Attention shifted

from flight testing of liquid rockets toward development and static testing of more reliable and more powerful rocket engines. Rocket No. 5, because of its radical design, was never built, though some of its components were developed and used in subsequent models.

The results of the new rocket motor tests, conducted on 21 April, were reported by John Shesta a few months later in the June 1935 issue of *Astronautics*. Short and long nozzles were used, both operating alternately at pressures of 150 and 300 pounds per square inch. At the high pressures the motors with short nozzles developed 59 pounds of thrust at 430 seconds total impulse, compared with 46 pounds at 380 seconds for those with long nozzles. Thrusts and total impulses at the lower pressure were, respectively, 25 and 17, and 280 and 180. These tests were conducted on a special new proving stand at Crestwood, New Jersey.

Rocket No. 4, only three inches wide, was shaped to minimize air resistance. Exhaust gases were deflected outward through four nozzles.

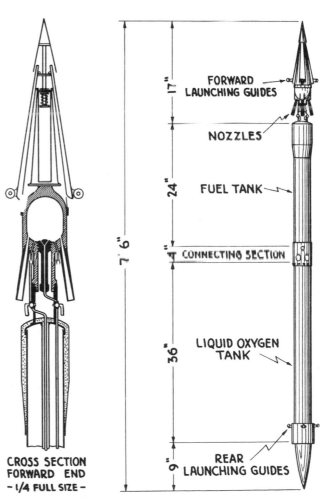

CROSS SECTION
FORWARD END
– 1/4 FULL SIZE –

FORWARD LAUNCHING GUIDES

NOZZLES

FUEL TANK

CONNECTING SECTION

LIQUID OXYGEN TANK

REAR LAUNCHING GUIDES

Additional tests were undertaken in July and August and again in October 1935. These continued into 1939, conclusively demonstrating that cooling combustion chambers with water was not a satisfactory solution to the problem of dissipating excess heat, a finding that opened the way for important advances in the development of cooling techniques.

The idea of using the fuel instead of water or air to cool the combustion chamber—regenerative cooling—had been considered previously by experimenters in both Europe and America. Eugen Sänger had achieved successful test results in 1933 with a Diesel fuel oil–oxygen gas engine. And Harry W. Bull had done preliminary work in the same year at Syracuse University, cooling the nozzle area only. But it was not until James H. Wyld built what he called a "self-cooled tubular regenerative motor" in 1938 that sustained work began in the United States on full regenerative cooling. The fuel was circulated in a cooling jacket surrounding the combustion chamber and nozzle, not only keeping the motor cool, but preheating the fuel and thus improving its combustion characteristics. The first tests of the 2-pound motor were made under the direction of the American Rocket Society's Experimental Committee on 10 December 1938, with satisfactory results.

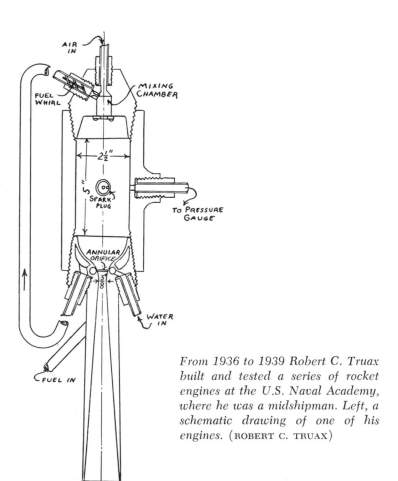

From 1936 to 1939 Robert C. Truax built and tested a series of rocket engines at the U.S. Naval Academy, where he was a midshipman. Left, a schematic drawing of one of his engines. (ROBERT C. TRUAX)

Other organizations were active in rocketry in the United States during the 1930's. The Cleveland Rocket Society had a rocket-testing site some 12 miles east of the city. The site included a 12-foot rocket-motor test stand, a roofed-over control trench, and a laboratory. Members built two types of motor: one made of chrome-nickel steel with water cooling and the other of a light alloy cooled by its liquid-oxygen and gasoline propellants. Experiments were under the technical direction of Ernst Loebell.

At Syracuse, Bull carried out a series of detailed investigations on the key component of the rocket motor, the combustion chamber, with the aim of bringing the reliability of the rocket up to that of more conventional motors. He and his associates varied every element of the chamber, including length, diameter, fuel-injection system, nozzle diameter, cooling system, and more. Most of the experimental chambers consisted of four sections of 2-inch tool-steel stock, produced about 2 pounds of thrust, operated on gasoline and liquid oxygen, and fired from around 20 seconds to over 100 seconds. The final design resulting from these studies, which were carried out in the early 1930's, had four gasoline and eight liquid-oxygen inlets. It was made of tool steel, and had what Bull termed "cooling fins" welded to the sides.

During the mid-1930's, some experiments with small rocket planes also took place in the United States. At Greenwood Lake, New York, F. W. Kessler sponsored the flight of two 15-foot-wingspan, aluminum airplanes powered by liquid oxygen–alcohol rocket motors developing between 40 and 65 pounds of thrust for up to 35 seconds. The two planes, carrying cargoes of mail (4,323 covers and 1,823 postcards), took off from the frozen lake on 23 February 1936, after 10-second takeoff runs. One reached an altitude of about 1,000 feet before the combustion chamber burned out, producing a side thrust that sent it spinning to the ground. The wings of the second plane tore off at about 15 seconds. The airplanes and motors were built by Nathan Carver, and flight operations were supervised by Willy Ley.

From 1936 until 1939 Robert C. Truax, a midshipman at the United States Naval Academy, developed, built, and tested small liquid-propellant rocket engines. Truax's work was to lead to the wartime Navy-sponsored rocket research program at Annapolis. Truax was a spare-time experimenter who had to scrounge help—a trait common to most amateur rocketeers, past and present. He later recalled: "I selected as the main body of the thrust chamber a nickel steel pinion gear. The hub of this gear appeared to be of proper thickness and quality to withstand almost any pressures which might be generated." He spent eight months at a lathe, working on his first test combustion chamber. As he put it, "When my masterpiece was completed, I took it to the head of the Marine Engineering Department and requested permission to set it up in the foundry and fire it. In perhaps justifiable concern over the future of Isherwood Hall [where the foundry was located], permission was denied." Truax persisted, and finally persuaded officials at the Experiment Station across the Severn River to allow him to test his rocket engine and to furnish him with additional working materials.

With the help of a welder, he built a test stand and propellant tanks, the latter from old pipe. "We then made closures for the tanks by burning circles out of boiler plates, welding them in, and providing them with gussets which appeared . . . to be about adequate in thickness and strength." Three tanks were built, one each for the oxidizer and fuel and one for cooling water.

Instrumentation was characteristically simple and direct, involving the use of the Bourdon tube pressure gages, an Eastman Kodak timer, and best of all, a stock room scale on which the thrust chamber was mounted in a nozzle-up position . . . . The instruments were then photographed with a Boy Scout camera at intervals determined primarily by the time required to wind the film . . . . The fuel consumption was measured by means of a boiler gage glass.

Since liquid oxygen was not available, he chose compressed air as the oxidizer; gasoline served as the fuel. "The first tests were run during lunch hours when the workmen from the shop would . . . gather around the rocket and amuse themselves by throwing stones into the jet to see how high they would be hurled." Some 25 pounds of thrust was generated by the engine in a December 1937 test. At first Truax reported, the motor ran "like a motorcycle engine." Then, "with extremely careful adjustment of valves, there came a short, smooth roar, and then again an infernal popping." Despite some success, the motor was redesigned with a fuel-cooled nozzle and chamber and reverse fuel injection.

By September 1938 several new chambers were ready, using refractory-lined nozzles in place of the earlier water-cooled ones. Among the materials that Truax tried were silicon dioxide, silicon carbide, aluminum oxide, and tungsten carbide. The new engine operated satisfactorily under constant chamber-pressure conditions for 10 to 45 seconds; thrust varied from 6 to 25 pounds in a series of seven runs. In December 1938 Truax obtained permission from the Annapolis authorities—who had kept an eye on his

activities—for tests using oxygen in place of air. In the February 1939 *Astronautics* he was able to report on the motor, which was constructed of stainless steel, and was 14 inches long, 3 inches in diameter, and weighed slightly more than 2 pounds.

Between 1932 and 1938 the United States Army Ordnance Department conducted sporadic research on rockets, principally under the direction and impetus of Captain (later Colonel) Leslie A. Skinner at the Aberdeen Proving Ground in Maryland. A variety of single- and double-base powders were static-tested until a double-base powder of German manufacture was selected for continued develop-

The Army Ordnance Department, under the direction of Leslie A. Skinner, concentrated on air-to-air rockets that could be fired from one plane to another. Below, Skinner's diagram for a liquid-propellant engine operating on gasoline and nitrous oxide.

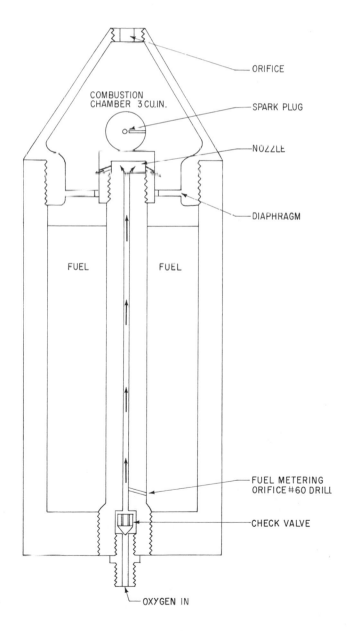

ment. Skinner's primary goal was to develop a rocket that could be fired from one airplane against another —in modern terminology, an air-to-air rocket. Skinner modified 81-mm trench mortar ammunition, loaded the new propellant, and fired the resulting rocket from a simple pipe launcher. The rocket's range was fairly good, but Skinner described its accuracy as "extremely poor."

When Skinner was transferred to Hawaii in 1938, rocket work was stopped at Aberdeen. He returned to the United States in 1940 and was assigned to the Bomb and Pyrotechnic Section of the Chief of Ordnance. His official title was Director of Army Projects of the newly formed Rocket Ordnance Section (Section H) of the National Defense Research Committee. NDRC's rocket group was under the direction of Clarence N. Hickman, who had worked with Goddard in California during World War I, and later became a research director at Bell Telephone Laboratories. A letter written by Hickman in June 1940 to Frank B. Jewett, president of the National Academy of Sciences, was instrumental in calling the government's attention to the importance of Goddard's work. Supporting Skinner and his associates from his position within NDRC, Hickman was able to push the Navy into developing rocket-accelerated bombs and the Army into developing both the antitank weapon that became the bazooka, and the 4.5-inch aircraft and artillery rockets.

The ARS and other groups of experimenters in America and in Europe concentrated on liquid-propellant motors during the 1930's, primarily because liquids contained greater energy than solids; that is, they produced more pounds of thrust per pound of propellant burned per second. Being more powerful, they appeared more attractive for eventual space-flight applications. But liquid fuels were difficult to handle, and being relatively new, little was known about them.

Solid propellants also had both advantages and disadvantages. Since they had been used for centuries, much more was known about them. Solid propellants could be stored for relatively long periods of time; they were comparatively simple to work with, being less hazardous and corrosive than many liquids; they formed an integral part of the motor case, eliminating the need for complicated loading procedures, "plumbing" hardware, and injection apparatus to feed the fuel into a combustion chamber. Finally, the solid propellants were more reliable and less expensive than the liquids.

On the minus side, the solid propellants were less powerful. Once a solid propellant had begun to burn, it could not be shut off and then restarted by closing

and opening a valve. And since the solid propellant was part of the motor case, it could not provide the directional control obtained by swiveling the combustion chambers of a liquid-propellant rocket. When such factors as thrust control, noise, vibration, and acceleration were considered, solid propellants also were at a disadvantage.

Many of the problems inherent in both solids and liquids eventually were solved by the early rocketeers, who continued experiments on both types of fuel. While researchers in the United States spent most of their time developing liquid propellants, the solid-propellant motor was not ignored.

Beginning in September 1937 in Pawling, New York, the ARS Experimental Committee test-fired seven small rockets powered by dry-fuel cartridges, including a two-stage model looking something like the German Repulsors, and designs developed by ARS experimenters Shesta, Pierce, Africano, Goodman, and Wyld. They ranged in weight from 1.19 to 2.28 pounds, took from 3 to 7 seconds to make their ascents, and reached altitudes of 100 to 1,500 feet. More solid-fuel rocket tests were conducted by Peter van Dresser and Alfred Africano during the summer of 1935 in Danbury, Connecticut, the main purpose being to determine where the motor should be placed in the rocket.

In September 1939, the ARS Experimental Committee conducted another series of flights at Mountainville, New Jersey. The maximum altitude achieved in 23 shots was 1,930 feet, reached during a 24-second flight of a 39-pound rocket; none of the other rockets got as high as 800 feet. A set of twelve firings was made on 19 November 1939 at the same location, using Unexcelled Fireworks Company 2-, 3-, 4-, and 6-pound commercial powder rockets. While none reached the peak altitude of the September series, they averaged considerably higher—none under 500 feet, five over 800 feet, and one over 1,000 feet.

A considerable amount of amateur rocketry during the 1930's was organized by university groups under the supervision of professors of mechanical and other branches of engineering. Scattered nonuniversity experimenters were active, some forming local rocket clubs. Most of these closed down when World War II started, but they did serve as training grounds for many rocketeers.

One group that stayed in business after Pearl Harbor was the Galcit Rocket Research Group in California. The Guggenheim Aeronautical Laboratory of the California Institute of Technology (hence the name Galcit), had started a program of rocket research and development in 1936. Operating under a fund established by Weld Arnold, the group made thorough studies of reaction-engine technology in general and rockets in particular, both liquid- and solid-propellant based. The experimental group consisted of Arnold himself, Frank J. Malina, Hsue-shen Tsien, Edward S. Forman, John W. Parsons, and A. M. O. Smith. Theodore von Kármán, Galcit's director, became more and more active as the project matured. With the help of data gathered by ARS experimenters, Galcit progressed rapidly to the rocket-motor test phase. A variable-pressure combustion chamber (100 to 1,000 pounds per square inch) was developed, operating on methyl alcohol and gaseous oxygen. By 1938 the Army Air Corps took notice of Galcit; in a modest way, what had happened in Germany was about to take place in the United States. That December General Henry H. Arnold, commanding the Air Corps, asked the National Academy of Sciences' Committee for Air Corps Research to sponsor a development program for rocket units to help heavily loaded planes take off from short runways. On 1 July 1939, the Academy sponsored the establishment of the Jet Propulsion Research Project at the California Institute of Technology. Von Kármán was the director, and three members of the Galcit group, Malina, Forman, and Parsons, were his assistants. A year later the Army Air Corps took over the project.

The rocket-boosted takeoff project, which became known as JATO, built on experience accumulated since 1936. Both liquid- and solid-propellant motors were studied. The final production units, firing for 10 to 30 seconds, could lift an airplane high enough to continue its flight unassisted. Since only rapid-burning solid propellants were known then, much time was spent on developing slow, or restricted, burning propellants that would provide a constant thrust. By 1941, Galcit 27, which delivered 28 pounds of thrust for 12 seconds, was developed. Tests of motors burning this solid propellant began

a few months before the United States entered World War II.

Scientists and engineers working on liquid-propellant JATO units discarded liquid oxygen, the conventional oxidizer, because JATO units had to be mobile. Liquid oxygen was ruled out because it cannot be stored for long periods and is not easy to transport for long distances. As an alternative, the experimenters began investigating the possibility of using red fuming nitric acid usually referred to as RFNA. Although corrosive and poisonous, RFNA can be stored under certain conditions. Whether it would decompose efficiently with a fuel was not known, but tests during the fall of 1939 showed that it mixed with, and supported the combustion of, gasoline and benzene. A test stand was constructed and an experimental motor was built. In May 1940 the first tests were held, and in July the program was given additional support by the Army Air Corps. The immediate objective was development of a 1,000-pound-thrust motor, which was to become the prototype of a new type of rocket widely used during World War II.

As World War II approached, the future of rocketry had begun to take definite shape. Germany, which had recognized more clearly than other countries the military potential of the rocket, was clearly ahead in the field, but no nation was without its group of rocketeers who would be given their opportunity when military needs for weapons arose. The rocket would soon be placed into combat on a large scale—simple, unguided weapons at first, then complex and terrifying missiles. Although they would not be decisive, they would herald the dawn of a new concept of war.

Rocketry had struggled through its infancy. Just ahead was an accelerated adolescence. The transition between the struggling experimenters on the vacant lot and the massive missile complexes of today was about to be made.

5 THE ROCKET RE[T

World War II abruptly changed the course of rocket history. Until then there had been little continuity of development throughout the world. During the 1920's and 1930's progress was made by fits and starts and goals were unclear. But, with the coming of war, rocketry suddenly flowered.

Every major combatant nation had a rocket program. Under the impetus of war, rockets increased dramatically in size, range, and accuracy. Many types of rockets proliferated. A basic distinction was made between the rocket *per se,* which traveled over a preordained and fixed trajectory, and the missile, a device which could be guided while in flight toward its target. Separate families of rockets and missiles also evolved. Depending upon their primary missions, the weapons were grouped under such headings as surface-to-surface, surface-to-air, air-to-air, and air-to-surface. The war saw the development of every basic type of rocket and missile used today.

A tight curtain of secrecy was wrapped around rocket development during hostilities. When peace came, information about the research programs of the Western allies and the Axis powers became public knowledge. The Soviet Union, however, has maintained its policy of secrecy until this day. Some technical and manufacturing details of rockets twenty or more years old still are not available.

What is known about Soviet World War II rockets has been gleaned painstakingly from the few official articles that have been published. The best known of all Russian rockets was the Katyusha, a solid-propellant infantry support weapon that was manufactured and fired in enormous quantities. The standard model was 6 feet long, 5.1 inches in diameter, and weighed 92.5 pounds, of which more than half—48.2 pounds—was payload. Katyusha was fired from ground- or truck-mounted racks, and had a range of over 3 miles. Much of the double-base powder that propelled Katyusha came from the United States through lend-lease.

Other versions of the rocket were fired from the "Stalin Organ," a mobile launcher that could fire a broadside of 30 to 48 rockets. The smallest rocket was 3.3 inches in diameter, weighed 17.5 pounds, and had a range of less than 3 miles. A 30-pound model had twice this range.

The unguided solid-propellant rockets used against airplanes by the Russians are believed to have been variations of the Katyusha, but details about them have not been revealed. Russian air-to-surface rockets, fired by airplanes against troops and vehicles, were introduced late in 1941. The most widely used model carried an explosive charge of 2.2 pounds, which slammed into the target at up to 1,150 miles per hour. The rocket had a solid propellant, was nearly 2 feet long and 3.2 inches in diameter, and weighed a total of 13.2 pounds.

"Rocket bombs" weighing 56 and 220 pounds were used against tanks and other armored vehicles. A Stormovik I1-2 fighter would carry eight 56-pounders on special wing racks; the German troops had a healthy respect for these weapons.

Little can be said about the Soviet World War II rocket program because of Russian reticence. The story of the Japanese rocket effort is almost as brief, but for another reason. With little interest in rocketry, the Japanese military had the most backward rocket program of all the major belligerents. The barrage and close-support rockets used by Japanese troops during the war were often improvised at the front. The weapons varied widely in description, with diameters ranging from 3.2 to 18 inches and weights from 12 to 1,500 pounds. Typically, ranges were short—from 300 to 500 feet. The Japanese did introduce a bazooka-type antitank rocket, but this was more or less a copy of captured American specimens.

The Japanese also experimented with some more sophisticated rockets and missiles. In an effort to combat United States air attacks, the Japanese Naval Technical Research Institute developed solid-propelled surface-to-air barrage rockets weighing from 13 to 53 pounds and began research on a series of four Funryu guided missiles. Airframes for the Funryu series were built at the naval dockyard at Yokosuka and the engines at the Naval Powder Arsenal and at Mitsubishi Heavy Industries, Ltd. The two completed missiles in this series, Funryu 2 powered by solid propellant, and Funryu 4 powered by liquids, could reach altitudes of 3 to 20 miles, respectively, and were guided by radio commands from the ground. Funryu 1, which never left the experimental stage, was to have been command-guided and directed against surface vessels, while Funryu 3 was to have been a liquid version of Funryu 2.

In the air-to-surface category, two unguided rocket-propelled bombs, weighing 224 and 815 pounds and each with a range of 3 miles, were introduced during the war, while three guided missiles were still being tested when the war ended. The air-to-surface missiles, developed by the Army Bureau of Aeronautics, were models 1A, 1B, and 1C of the I go series. 1A and 1B, made of wood and powered by hydrogen-peroxide motors, were manufactured by Mitsubishi Heavy Industries and the Kawasaki Aircraft Industry Company. 1A's motor, firing for 75 seconds at a maximum thrust of 530 pounds, was to be guided to the target by radio command. The 1B model had a slightly more powerful motor that gave it a 5-mile range. The 1C model, designed to home on the shock waves produced by naval guns, was canceled in 1945.

One sinister curiosity of the Japanese rocket program was a wooden, rocket-powered suicide plane that saw action in 1945. The Japanese had a fling with their own version of the German Me-163, but the only one of the two rocket planes built that ever flew cracked up on its maiden flight from Oppama on 7 July 1945. Their Ohka (sometimes called Marudai) Kamikaze plane was more successful—unfortunately for its pilots.

Ohka was conceived in the spring of 1943 and developed in the following year. The standard model was a wooden monoplane with two fins attached to a 2,645-pound bomb, which accounted for more than half the plane's total weight. Ohka was 20 feet long, with a 16.4-foot wingspread. It was carried to the vicinity of its target by a mother plane. The suicide pilot would then glide for about 50 miles, making a beautiful target at the rather slow speed of 230 miles per hour, before igniting the craft's three 1,700-pound rocket engines. These propelled the plane into its target—or the sea—at a speed of 600 miles per hour after their 10-second burn. The Ohka was first used in combat in April 1945. The American nickname for the airplane was Baka, the Japanese word for "fool."

Unlike the Russians, who have not told much about their wartime rockets, and unlike the Japanese, who did not have much to talk about, the British have released information about a wide range of effective surface-to-air antiaircraft rockets which were developed to protect troops and ships.

Appreciating the threat of German air raids to her cities, Britain began work on these defensive weapons before the war and initial tests were highly encouraging. The first surface-to-air rocket placed in production was a 2-inch barrage model whose per-

Funryu Surface-to-Air Missiles

Missile	Length (feet)	Diameter (inches)	Weight (pounds)	Altitude (miles)	Velocity (mph)	Propulsion
Funryu 2	7.9	12	815	3	525	solid
Funryu 4	13.1	24	4,190	20	650	liquid

I-go Air-to-Surface Missiles

Missile	Length (feet)	Span (feet)	Weight (pounds)	Range (miles)	Velocity (mph)	Propulsion
I-go (1A)	18.9	11.8	3,085	6–7	340	liquid
I-go (1B)	13.4	8.5	1,500	5	340	liquid

formance paralleled that of the British 3-inch anti-aircraft gun. The 2-incher was propelled by a tube of cordite, which was placed in the low-carbon sheet-steel case in such a way that all the exposed surfaces burned when the electrical ignition signal was given. The motor walls were protected from the high-combustion temperatures by a spray composed of sodium silicate solution containing a suspension of finely ground alumina. A shell ring, secured by spring pins, enclosed the motor at the front end. The motor burned for 2.8 seconds and produced 17 pounds of thrust.

The 2-incher was designed for defense against low-flying bombers. Soon a more powerful 3-incher was demanded. Most of the technical problems of producing the bigger rocket were overcome by the summer of 1940, and by the end of the year, the 3-incher was being used to supplement heavy gun defenses. A salvo of up to 128 rockets could be fired from a battery of twin-barreled launchers (which the British called "projectors").

The development of these projectors was spurred

During World War II, the Soviet Union fired Katyusha rockets from the ground or truck mounted racks. The standard Katyushas were 6 feet long, weighed 92.5 pounds, and had a range of 3 miles. Below, they are being fired against the Germans in the battle for Sevastopol. (U.S.S.R. ACAD. OF SCIENCES)

by a meeting held on 20 May 1940 in the private room of a small hotel in Wales, near the Aberporth test grounds, at the request of the Director of Naval Ordnance. The War Cabinet had directed that rocket weapons should be used "forthwith" to protect ships, factories, and other targets against air attack.

By July, the firm of G. A. Harbey of Greenwich had designed and manufactured the first ten projector units; by September, one thousand had come off the assembly line. In October, Major Duncan Sandys took command of the experimental Z-rocket battery. The following March, Sandys, by then a lieutenant colonel, organized a regiment of 3-inch rocket batteries to defend Cardiff. The unit downed its first German plane on 7 April 1941.

Sandys, who had been evacuated in June from the British Norwegian expedition, had at first been given orders to take the existing Z batteries from East Hamstead Park in Berkshire to combat German dive bombers in Malta, but quickly found the units inadequately trained, poorly officered, and without sufficient reserves of rocket ammunition. Accordingly, he took immediate steps to select a new group of officers, including Captain (now Colonel) Kenneth Post as his second in command, and request additional time to bring the batteries up to combat proficiency.

In September he moved to Aberporth in Wales, persuading Sir William R. Cook, Crow's number 2 man, that the UP-3 projectile was as applicable against high-flying enemy bombers as against Stuka dive bombers—which were only rarely employed against British targets. Sandys and Post tested the UP-3's with new fuzes against Queen Bee drones with such success that they were able to convince General Sir Frederick Pile, head of the AA Command, that three Z batteries could promptly be activated, one to be kept at Aberporth for training and development and two to be placed into operational combat service in Cardiff, also in Wales. Sandys set up the various radar elements, projector batteries, and command equipment (including the bomber order-of-battle predictor from which individual batteries received information as to bearing, elevation, and fuze settings) in Cardiff's Penarth Golf Course.

From January 1941 into the spring Sandys literally commuted between Cardiff and Aberporth, remaining in the former city until midnight or 0100 when the German raids would normally terminate, then driving to the test and training center where he would supervise the next day's activities. On Good Friday his chauffeur fell asleep at the wheel during the trip, causing an accident that so injured Sandys that he had to leave active military service. Subsequently, he became Junior Minister in the War Office, heading up an intelligence investigation on the capabilities of German long-range bombardment rocketry.

Both rocket and projector were refined later. Two types of 3-inchers were used, a finned version and the UP-3 unrotating projectile model. The finned version was 6 feet long and weighed 56 pounds; the UP-3 was 4 feet long and weighed 110 pounds. Time fuzes were used for targets at altitudes up to 4 miles and photoelectric fuzes above that height. The UP-3 had a lethal radius of 65 feet.

The single-rocket projectors were replaced by twin "Pillar Box" types, which more than doubled firing rates, and about 100 3-inch antiaircraft gun mountings were adapted into 9-barrel projectors, which were used in Great Britain and North Africa.

By December 1942, 91 batteries, each with 64 twin-barrel projectors, had fired a total of 65,000 3-inch rockets against enemy aircraft. The use of rockets would have been even greater if the factory that produced their fuzes had not been destroyed twice in air raids.

Since the rockets were always used with conventional antiaircraft weapons, their effect is difficult to assess. However, an official report dated 2 November 1944 said: "There is no doubt that the deterrent effect of rockets is considerable. Few pilots will fly straight if they believe their aircraft to be the target for a rocket salvo. AA [antiaircraft] rocket fire, therefore, fulfills the important function of discouraging accurate bombing." The report said that pilots were able to see and avoid the rockets, but that their evasive action disrupted bombing runs.

A tribute came from eyewitness Captain H. Spencer, whose rocket-armed ship, *City of Lincoln*, was attacked by German planes in June 1942. "I had many opportunities for using my P.A.C.'s [the rockets] during the action and have the highest opinion of their value," Spencer wrote. "[They] kept the aircraft up all the time and on several occasions I saw them swerve violently just before dropping their bombs. It did not strike me that this was due to any-

The Japanese Funryu 2, a solid-fuel guided missile, could reach altitudes of 20 miles and was guided by radio commands from the ground. The midsection of the Funryu is shown here. (MITSUBISHI INDUSTRIES)

thing but the P.A.C. rocket. Personally I should never like to be without my P.A.C.'s in any aircraft action."

In a typical combat operation in North Africa, Z Battery 124, under air attack near Bône, fired 800 rockets in 10 salvos, hitting a number of the 50 raiding airplanes. The battery itself suffered no damage from the enemy.

An interesting variation on this theme was the

Japan's famous suicide plane, the Ohka Kamikaze, was propelled by three 1,700 pound rockets and carried a 2,645-pound bomb. The Kamikaze plane shown here was found on an airfield in Okinawa two days after the American landing. (U.S. ARMY)

Sir Alwyn D. Crow (right), head of the British missile effort, shows Prime Minister Winston Churchill a 2-inch rocket in Shoeburyness, Essex, in 1941. The 2-incher was the first in a series of surface-to-air rockets developed by the British to protect their cities from low-flying German bombers.

Snare project, designed to down low-flying enemy planes by entangling their propellers in wires. Officially called Antiaircraft Parachute and Cable Rocket Projector, the Snare was generally installed on the flying bridge of a ship. A lanyard fired a 3-inch rocket, which released a parachute at 550 feet. Connected to the parachute was a 200-foot wire with another parachute at its opposite end. A 90-foot trip wire, attached to the ship, opened the second parachute. As the two parachutes floated down, the wire provided a nasty obstacle for enemy bombers. Snares were generally fired when the enemy airplane was 2,000 feet from the ship at a height of 500 feet or less. The first kill, a German dive-bomber, was chalked up in July 1940.

Toward the end of the war, the British produced a new winged antiaircraft missile to combat Kamikaze attacks. The missile, called the Stooge, was 10.5 feet long and weighed 740 pounds, of which 220 pounds was warhead. It was launched from an adjustable ramp by four solid-propellant rockets that fired for 1.6 seconds and developed 5,600 pounds of thrust; then a 760-pound-thrust sustainer engine

boosted the Stooge to its top speed of 500 miles per hour. With a range of 8 miles, the Stooge was guided by radio commands.

British air-to-surface missiles got off to a later start. Not until July 1941 did the Ordnance Board establish a requirement for a preliminary feasibility study. In August, General Mason MacFarlane saw Russian airplanes launch their rockets; the next month Sir Alwyn D. Crow, head of the British rocket effort, met with officials at the Ministry of Aircraft Production to outline a development program.

The first test took place in October, when a Hurricane fighter fired a 3-inch rocket at a ground target. By May 1942, flight trials had progressed to the point where Hurricanes were carrying eight rockets, four under each wing, firing them from rail launchers.

However, it was decided that tanks were too small and maneuverable to serve as targets for air-launched 3-inchers. The belief that airplanes would have to fly dangerously close to the ground to use the rockets led to the decision to fly rocket missions only against naval targets, including submarines.

After the Air Ministry published in December 1942 a detailed report on air-to-surface rocket trials at the Pendine Range and the Boscombe Down Experimental Aircraft Station, the Fleet Air Arm accepted the 3-incher. In April 1943, a Swordfish from HMS *Archer* sank a German U-boat with rockets—a first in sea warfare. The rocket could punch through a submarine's hull after traveling 50 feet underwater, and was equally effective against surface ships; rockets later sank the Italian liner *Rex*.

The Air Ministry had second thoughts about the

Toward the end of the war, the British produced the Stooge missile to combat Kamikaze attacks. Stooge had a range of 8 miles and was guided by radio control. (MINISTRY OF AVIATION, LONDON)

3-inchers, which were eventually used against tanks. The airborne version, called the RP-3, was a spin-stabilized rotating projectile. It was 5.35 feet long, weighed 60 pounds, had a range of about a mile and traveled at a top speed of 1,000 miles per hour. The rockets were usually fired in pairs from airplanes.

The surface-to-surface missile entered the British inventory even later. While consideration had been given to development of a 60-pound, 3,500-yard-range missile for use by demolition troops and sappers (engineers) as early as 1939, and a prototype was ready by June 1940, progress was made slowly.

By January 1943, a 5-inch-diameter rocket was virtually ready for production. It was to be launched either from a two-legged, two-rail launcher that was 6 feet long, weighed 40 pounds, and could be handled by a single soldier, or from a truck-mounted launcher with six pairs of rails.

But at the last minute the Army decided against using the weapon. The reasons boiled down to doubts about the rocket's range and reliability, a belief that it was not needed in the field, and a shortage of sapper personnel to handle the weapon.

If the Army didn't want the 5-incher, the Navy did. A few months before the 1943 Army turndown, a review of the Dieppe Commando raid, conducted at Combined Operations Headquarters, had concluded that more firepower should have been brought to bear on the landing area before the assault. The 5-inch rocket was suggested as an ideal weapon to make up the lack in future amphibious assaults, especially if it could be fired in heavy salvos from specially designed landing craft.

That led to the outfitting of a Landing Craft Tank (Rocket) with sextuple "Mattress" projectors a short time later. The 5-incher itself was equipped with a new high-explosive shell and an improved cordite motor. The end result was a craft that could fire a devastating salvo of from 800 to 1,000 rockets in less than 45 seconds at ranges up to 3,000 yards. After trials early in 1943, six LCT(R)'s were dispatched to the Mediterranean to support the landings in Sicily and Italy that were to take place during July.

After the Sicily landing, an eyewitness, Lieutenant Commander M. Mulleneux, wrote, "Whatever the destructive effect of the barrage, the effect on morale is shattering . . . ." C. F. Bruce, a headquarters operations planner who also witnessed the landings, said that

all officers to whom I spoke out there were unanimous in their praise of these craft. On the sea when the LCT(R) is firing it presents a most impressive spectacle with its sheets of flame followed by the rushing of rockets over-

A Beaufighter MK-1 launches two 3-inch rockets against a German ship off Norway. Britain's first air-to-surface weapon, the 3-incher was used primarily against naval targets, including submarines. (SIR ALWYN D. CROW)

head and the colossal "clumps" as they land on the target. One LCT(R) fired quite close to the craft I was in, and the sight and sound of it greatly cheered all the soldiers and helped to make them forget how cold and wet they were.

The Navy's success caused the Army to take a new look at land applications for the weapon that it originally developed. Demonstrations for War Office experts, held at the Army's Sennybridge Range in Wales, produced no immediate results, but development work continued. By the end of the year,

British troops load rocket launcher near Reichwald, Germany. This "Land Mattress" launcher could be mounted on truck-trailers or self-propelled vehicles.

Crow's Projectile Development Establishment offered the Army a spiral rail launcher that gave the 5-incher better accuracy, smaller fins, less weight, and a warhead of larger diameter. A proposal by Lieutenant Colonel Michael Wardell in March 1944 led to the development of a "Land Mattress" launcher that could be mounted on truck-trailers or self-propelled vehicles. A prototype, with 32 spiral rail barrels, was ready in May, and was demonstrated to observers from the War Office and Canadian Army Headquarters in June and again in July. The Canadians were impressed enough to order a dozen 30-barrel projectors, which they used that fall when their troops crossed the Rhine and Scheldt rivers.

While the 5-incher was relatively accurate at long ranges, it ran into difficulties at shorter distances. Brigadier A. F. S. Napier, military advisor to Crow, wrote that "at low angles of elevation the range dispersion is very great so a new method of varying range had to be devised; this consisted in placing over the nose of the shell flat discs of varying diameter known as spoilers; these have the effect of increasing air resistance at high angles of elevation."

The 5-incher had a quick-burning, multiple-stick cordite propellant. Eleven sticks of cordite were in a space between two tubular walls, with perforations allowing a free flow of gas.

The British undertook no major wartime programs involving liquid rocket motors. A. V. Cleaver, chief engineer for rocket propulsion at the Aero Engine Division of Rolls-Royce Ltd., one of Britain's leading postwar liquid-propellant rocket researchers, made this comment to the authors:

I can assure you that British developments on liquid propulsion were quite negligible up to the end of the Second World War. In fact, literally the only work of this nature which was undertaken here was the project to develop a liquid oxygen–petrol rocket engine during the closing years of the war. This was done by a man [now dead] called Dr. Isaac Lubbock, who worked for the British Shell organisation, and is quite well known for his other work on developing fuel injectors for the early gas turbine jet engines. . . . The work was generally done in association with the Royal Aircraft Establishment at Farnborough, and eventually developed into a project for a small vehicle called "LOP/GAP." This stood for "Liquid Oxygen Petrol/Ground-to-Air Projectile," and this in turn evolved into an improved vehicle known as RTV.1 [Rocket Test Vehicle 1] which was used in some quantities during the early post-war years at Woomera [Australia] for research on early British anti-aircraft guided weapon systems.

Lubbock's wartime research on liquid-propellant rockets was done under a cooperative contract between the Asiatic Petroleum Company (which later became Shell Petroleum Company, Ltd.) and the Ministry of Supply, whereby the government paid for materials and the company underwrote labor costs. Lubbock had served during World War I in France, had graduated from Cambridge University in mathematics and engineering, and had lectured at the Royal Military Academy at Woolwich prior to becoming head of the company's fuel oil department in 1926. Following the evacuation of British forces at Dunkirk in the Second World War, he began considering the possibility of bombarding the Germans from England across the channel by rocket-powered weapons.

He first investigated solid-propellant rockets, submitting proposals to both Lord Cherwell (Professor F. A. Lindemann, Churchill's scientific advisor) and Sir Alwyn D. Crow in January 1941. Crow replied that solid-propellant work was well in hand but suggested that Lubbock look into the feasibility of using liquid-propellant rockets to assist heavily loaded Wellington bombers to become airborne. With virtually no information on liquids available to them, Lubbock, M. G. J. Gollin, and a few associates started theoretical investigations of the performance of gasoline with liquid oxygen before embarking on experimental research. According to Gollin, among the unknowns they had to deal with were:

how to insulate a liquid oxygen vessel, how to purge the propellant lines and chamber, how to reduce nitrogen gas pressure, how to handle the excess heat produced during combustion, how to initiate combustion, how to measure thrust, how to calculate the specific impulse of the engine, and how to cool the nozzle.

The solutions to these and many other problems had to be worked out from scratch since Lubbock's group did not have access to German prewar work and was not aware of the liquid-propellant rocket experiments of Goddard and the American Rocket Society across the ocean. During the first year, Lubbock's staff totalled eight, including one boy, and his budget a mere £10,000.

The first cold flow tests were made during February and March 1941 at the Fuel Oil Technical Experimental Station at Fulham, followed by hot combustion tests between May and September at Cox Lane, Chessington. In a series of pilot runs codenamed Plow (for petrol–liquid oxygen with water as a temperature moderator), a thrust level of 60 pounds was achieved. Later, full-scale engine tests developing 1,600 to 1,900 pounds of thrust for 20- to 35-seconds duration were made at the Langhurst Flame Warfare Station near Horsham in Sussex. The first run was made on 15 August 1942 for 5 seconds; at the end of September, the experimenters fired for 23 seconds at a maximum thrust of 1,750 pounds.

Lubbock was important to the British in more

ways than one. British Intelligence found his knowledge of liquid propellants extremely useful, and he was called in frequently to help interpret the probable characteristics of German liquid-propellant rocket weapons. Lubbock was unquestionably Britain's leading authority on the subject.

Despite Lubbock's work on liquid-propelled ATO units, the major British effort in this area was with solid-fueled rockets. Some creditable, if not spectacular, progress was made, with solid-propellant motors for lifting airplanes from ships. The first model to be developed, called CRC for cordite rocket catapult, was used on merchant ships. It consisted of a trolley to which were attached two solid-propellant rockets. When enemy planes attacked, the rockets would be ignited and the trolley would hurl the attached airplanes aloft. When escort carriers were attached to convoys, an ATO system was developed to insure that many airplanes would get into the air quickly. The ATO unit was dropped by the airplane after burnout.

The United States drew on British rocket knowledge after Pearl Harbor. The United States had very little experience in high-energy solid propellants of the type neeeded for extended-range, high-speed weapons. The only commercially available product was ballistite, a double-base smokeless powder derived from British trench mortar powder. A visit by Sir Henry Tizard to the United States as the head of a British scientific mission, a trip by Charles C. Lauritsen of the National Defense Research Committee to Great Britain in the summer of 1941 to study their production facilities, and a demonstration of British antiaircraft rockets at the Aberdeen Proving Ground early in the war helped bring British know how to bear on the problem. A pilot plant was obtained from Britain, and Lauritsen and William Fowler at the California Institute of Technology led the effort that ended with a practical production technique. Within a few years, suitable solid propellants were being produced at the Army's Radford Ordnance Works, the Navy's Indian Head Powder Factory, and the Sunflower Ordnance Works, operated by the Hercules Powder Company.

This effort was part of an over-all United States rocket program which, although modest in comparison to German wartime development, was much larger than commonly believed. The United States conducted some experiments with virtually every type of rocket and missile. While relatively few kinds of rockets actually were used by United States combat forces during the war, those that were produced were made in huge quantities. By 1945, the Army was spending $150 million a year on rockets, and the Navy was spending $1.2 billion. The Navy alone had

1,200 plants making rockets or their components.

The United States rocket program was under the direction of Division A (later 3) of the National Defense Research Committee, a coordinating agency established by President Franklin D. Roosevelt on 27 June 1940. The head of NDRC was Vannevar Bush. Its Division A (Armor and Ordnance) was directed by Richard C. Tolman and was divided in turn into two sections of civilian scientists and engineers who worked on rockets and missiles. Section H (named for its leader, Clarence N. Hickman, whose letter urging a rocket development program was a seminal event in American rocket history), and Section L (for Lauritsen, who also was vice-chairman of Division A).

Hickman described in detail to the authors the genesis of Section H, which was to play a vital role in the development of United States rocketry during World War II. In 1917–1918, while studying for his master's degree under A. G. Webster at Clark University, Hickman had met Goddard—at the time working under a small Smithsonian grant to develop a multiple-charge rocket. Acting upon the suggestion of L. T. E. Thompson, Webster's assistant, Goddard sought Hickman's aid in solving some mechanical problems, with the result that the two worked together during the First World War in California, and later at the Aberdeen Proving Ground in Maryland. After the war Goddard, Thompson, and Hickman continued their association. By the time NDRC was created, Thompson was in charge of research at the Navy's Dahlgren Proving Ground, so it was rather easily arranged for Hickman's Section H to begin its testing program at that Virginia site. According to Hickman:

It was not long before Dahlgren became crowded with other work and they wanted to get rid of my testing there. Dr. Thompson suggested that I could use the old valley part of Indian Head [Naval Powder Factory, Indian Head, Maryland] where the Navy had done the testing of big guns. . . . Dr. Tolman, Dr. Thompson, and I paid a visit to Indian Head and decided that it would be a good move, so the Indian Head Propulsion Laboratory was organized with me as director. I still retained my position as chairman of Section H, Division A.

As work expanded, a contract was made with the George Washington University for personnel and services. A team of consultants, including Goddard, was built up, and before long much of the administrative work was taken over by R. E. Gibson, appointed vice-chairman of Section H. Much of the manufacturing work was handled by the Budd Wheel Company of Detroit.

As expansion continued, Hickman again had to look for new research and testing facilities. "Dr. Van Evera, who was head of the George Washington con-

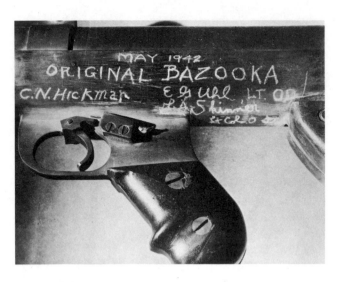

The bazooka, one of the most popular and effective weapons of World War II, was developed late in 1941 by an Army team of Leslie Skinner, C. N. Hickman, and Edward G. Uhl. Above, the original bazooka, autographed by its developers. (C. N. HICKMAN)

tract, and I paid a visit to Cumberland [in early 1944] to see an Army Ordnance factory that had been built for manufacturing small arms ammunition. They had closed the plant because they found they did not need it. We thought it was just the place for us so we took it over." Still later, the Section H group moved to the Allegany Ballistics Laboratory at nearby Pinto, West Virginia, where they worked closely with Army Ordnance, the Chemical Warfare Service, and the Air Corps.

On the West Coast, meanwhile, Hickman assisted in the establishment of Section L under Lauritsen, which "took over the work at Cal Tech on rockets." Outlining the role of his section in Pasadena, Lauritsen told the authors:

During the years 1941 to 1945, we designed and developed all the rockets that were used by the U.S. Navy during the war. We established and operated the Naval Ordnance Test Station, China Lake, California, for testing rockets, training Navy personnel, and for pilot production.

There were many facilities involved in the overall rocket program, both Army and Navy: the Picatinny Arsenal, the Aberdeen Proving Ground, Wright Field in Ohio, the Dover (Delaware) Army Air Force Base, the Navy Proving Ground at Dahlgren (Virginia), and the Naval Ordnance Test Station at Inyokern (California). Many of these activities and those under NDRC were coordinated by an *ad hoc* Committee on Controlled Missiles established in June 1942 by the Joint Committee on New Weapons

and Equipment. This was replaced in January 1945 by the Guided Missiles Subcommittee, which was organized by the Joint Chiefs of Staff, placed under the chairmanship of Bradley Dewar, and kept under the control of the same Joint Committee. Still later, the subcommittee's functions were taken over by the Joint Research and Development Board.

The first company created solely to produce rockets was Reaction Motors, Inc., of Pompton Plains, New Jersey, which is now a division of the Thiokol Chemical Company. Reaction Motors was founded in late 1941 by members of the American Rocket Society. Their work on regeneratively cooled liquid-propellant rocket engines eventually led to development of JATO units and test missiles during the war.

A second pioneering company, Aerojet Engineering Corporation, was organized in Azusa, California, by a group associated with the California Institute of Technology and interested in producing the JATO units developed by Galcit. Aerojet JATO units were used in large numbers during the war; the company was absorbed by the General Tire and Rubber Company in 1944.

Of the various American rocket weapons developed during the war, undoubtedly the best known was the bazooka, a rocket-propelled grenade that was employed with great success on all fronts, European, African, and Pacific.

The basic idea for this weapon was not new; Goddard had done work along the same line during World War I. The events that led to the development of the bazooka started in December 1940, when Colonel Leslie Skinner of Army Ordnance presented to Ordnance Colonel Gregory J. Kessenich a tentative design for a bazookalike weapon. At about the same time, Henry H. Mohaupt, a Swiss engineer, offered the Army Ordnance Technical Staff a concept for an armor-piercing projectile. A grenade fitted with "the special Mohaupt head" was tested and found to be satisfactory—except that it could not be fired from the shoulder, a basic requirement, because of its recoil.

Skinner then applied the techniques of rocketry to solve the recoil problem. Technical advice made available by Hickman during the early research and development program helped lead to a quick solution. Skinner, with the help of Lieutenant Edward G. Uhl, soon had his one-man tank killer close to production.

Under the supervision of Lieutenant Colonel W. T. Moore, the first launcher and rocket parts were produced at the Frankford Arsenal in the spring of 1942. Uhl, now a captain, fired the first bazookas from the shoulder, initially at NDRC's test ground, then

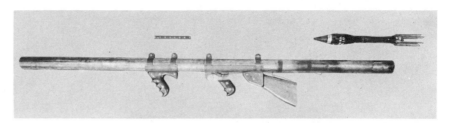

Built to be fired from the shoulder, the original bazooka was 2.36 inches in diameter and about 7 feet long. Its rocket grenade, right, was a converted mortar shell with added fins, nozzle, and method for holding the rocket propellant. (COL. LESLIE A. SKINNER)

at the Aberdeen Proving Ground. According to Hickman, during one of the earliest tests of the tube at Aberdeen, no sight for the weapon was available. So,

when one of the officers asked him [Lieutenant Uhl] to demonstrate the recoilless gun, he improvised a rear and front sight using wire. He hit a moving tank nine times out of ten shots and they said, "This is what we want." A major, who was present, asked what that thing was. They told him it was a recoilless gun. He said: "It looks like Bob Burns' Bazooka to me." Then and there the name Bazooka was born and stuck with it to this day.

A formal demonstration for Army, Navy, and NDRC officials was held at Camp Sims in June 1942, with a medium tank as the target. The bazooka entered into action during the North Africa landings that November, and was standard infantry equipment afterward.

There were two principal elements to the weapon: a tube launcher and the projectile. The tube, outfitted with shoulder stock, grip, trigger, sights, and safety switch, was 4.5 feet long, 3 inches in diameter, and weighed only 13.3 pounds. The rocket was 2.36 inches in diameter, 1.8 feet long, weighed 3.4 pounds (of which 1.57 was payload), and was fired by an electric squib igniter.

The bazooka could knock out a moving tank at 200 yards and was effective at up to 700 yards against bunkers and other stationary targets. It was one of the GI's favorite weapons; under the right circumstances, it made a foot soldier equal to a tank.

The combination of Skinner and Hickman also was effective in developing the most widely used barrage rocket of the war, the 4.5-incher that eventually was used in great numbers by every service.

The rocket started out to be an air-to-surface missile. In 1941, Skinner submitted to Hickman several sketches of rockets that would be suitable for use by airplanes. Hickman selected the 4.5-incher as the smallest that could carry a reasonable warhead and enough propellant to give it a velocity of 1,000 feet per second. Skinner then designed the rockets, improvising the first few working models from fire extinguisher cylinders. Twenty-four rockets were made at the Naval Gun Factory in Washington, and were fired satisfactorily at Indian Head.

Skinner and Uhl then designed the production model of the rocket, modifying their design to include features suggested by Hickman. In 1942, an order for 500 4.5-inchers and 500 3.25-inchers was placed with the Dresser Manufacturing Company; the smaller rocket was to serve as a test vehicle for proximity fuze development.

The rocket had been conceived as an air-to-surface weapon; but, as Skinner informed the authors:

The reluctance of the Air Corps to try out rockets prior to their demonstrated use on aircraft by the British led the NDRC and me to approach the ground forces to see if there was any interest in that quarter. As a result of this contact the ground forces placed the first order for the production of rockets, which was shortly thereafter followed by an order from the Air Corps . . . .

The original order was to have been for 780,000 but had been reduced by the time it had reached the Ordnance Department to 15,000. The ground forces order, which was for a large number (as near as I can remem-

The bazooka became standard infantry equipment on all fronts. Below, a member of a bazooka team fires on a Japanese pillbox on Corregidor, the Philippines, in February 1945. (U.S. ARMY AND EDWARD G. UHL)

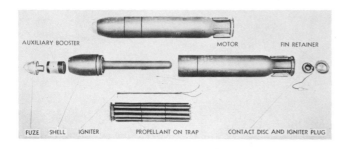

AUXILIARY BOOSTER   MOTOR   FIN RETAINER

FUZE   SHELL   IGNITER   PROPELLANT ON TRAP   CONTACT DISC AND IGNITER PLUG

The 4.5-incher was the most widely used barrage rocket of the war. Its component parts are shown here. (C. N. HICKMAN)

ber, about 500,000), enabled the Propellant Section of the Industrial Division to begin planning . . . to produce solvent double-base powder strictly for rocket purposes.

The 4.5-incher eventually was made in a variety of models. There was the M-8, which was fired from truck- and tank-mounted 8-tube Xylophone and 60-tube Calliope launchers and from many different jeep-mounted launchers; for jungle fighting, the M-8 could be fired from single-shot expendable tubes. The improved M-12 had collapsible fins and was fired from plastic tripods. The M-16 was fired from 24-tube Honeycomb and 60-tube Hornet's Nest launchers, and from Navy rocket ships that softened up fortifications before Marine amphibious assaults. One model of the 4.5-incher, known as Old Faithful, was slightly shorter than the other types, and was fired from landing craft as they neared the beaches. It could carry either fragmentation or antipersonnel charges, and it helped fill the time gap between the

end of long-range naval and air bombardment and the moment when the troops actually hit the beach.

The air-launched version of the M-8 was basically the same as the ground-launched rocket. It was 2.75 feet long, weighed 38.2 pounds, had a payload varying from 4.3 to 5.1 pounds, fired for .03 seconds, and achieved a speed of 600 miles per hour. This version was first used in the winter of 1943–1944 in raids on Japanese installations in Burma—the first combat employment of American-made rockets by airplanes.

A Super 4.5-incher, also launched from the air, was available by December 1944, but did not enter operations service. Designed to knock out targets that resisted the regular model, it weighed 103 pounds, including a 40-pound payload containing 8.5 pounds of high explosives. It was 6 feet long, had a range of between 3 and 4 miles, reached a speed of 900 miles per hour, and was stabilized by four large fixed fins.

Other calibers of surface-to-surface rockets were developed during the war. The 3.5-inch Spinner, developed for the Marines, had a speed of 435 miles per hour and a range of over 2 miles. It never saw combat. The Navy used a 5-inch Spinner Beach-Barrage Rocket to reach targets out of the range of the 4.5-incher. The 5-inch rocket had interchangeable warheads with high-capacity, smoke, chemical warfare, semi-armor-piercing, and pyrotechnic capabilities.

For even longer ranges—up to 5 miles—the 5-inch HVSR (high-velocity, spin-stabilized rocket) was developed. It saw action on PT boats in ship-to-ship engagements, on several types of landing craft,

The 4.5-incher was originally designed as an air-to-surface rocket, but it was also adapted to models that could be fired from the ground or from ships. Shown here are 4.5-   *inch rockets in flight after being fired from a spinning launcher (left) and from projectors mounted on a 2½-ton truck (right).* (C. N. HICKMAN; U.S. ARMY)

and on the submarine *Barp*, which fired more than 70 rockets against targets on the Japanese home island of Honshu from a deck-mounted automatic launcher. This rocket was also used, and spectacularly, in ship-to-shore bombardment at Iwo Jima and Okinawa.

Some United States rocket-launching ships could fire 300 rockets a minute; the rockets carried payloads of from 1.7 to 2.8 pounds. At the end of the war, forty-eight "super" rocket ships had been developed, each of them with ten launchers that gave the capability of firing five hundred 5-inchers a minute, with loading, aiming, and firing carried on by remote control. Some of these ships were en route to combat zones when the Japanese surrendered.

NDRC Section L scientists at Cal Tech developed a short-range (.2 miles) low-velocity (120 miles per hour) 7.2-inch demolition rocket for use against bunkers and other heavily fortified positions. The Army launched them from 20-tube Whiz Bang and 24-tube Grand Slam launchers, both mounted on tanks. The Navy used Woofus 120-tube launchers, fitted to LCM(3) landing craft, to fire the 7.2-inchers.

The Navy turned to rockets to help in the fight against submarines. At the beginning of the war, it asked the NDRC–Cal Tech team to develop a weapon that could supplement the standard ship-launched depth bomb. The Navy wanted a bomb similar to the British Hedgehog, which was fired ahead of the sub-hunting vessel, but one that would not produce the Hedgehog's forbidding recoil. The scientists started work in the fall of 1941; the first rocket-propelled bombs were ready for sea firing off San Diego by 30 March 1942. The tests were successful, and in mid-April, dummy bombs were tested against an American submarine off Key West. The bombs and their launchers (called Mousetraps) were installed on many United States sub-chasers and Coast Guard vessels, starting in October 1942 in the Atlantic and April 1943 in the Pacific. Many kills of Japanese and German subs were credited to them.

One antisubmarine weapon that never saw combat was the Hydrobomb, developed at Cal Tech in response to an Air Corps request for a missile that could be launched from an airplane and would be propelled underwater to its target by a rocket motor. Two Hydrobomb prototypes were built, one by the Westinghouse Manufacturing Company, the other by the United Shoe Machinery Company. Tests of a model with a solid-propellant motor that burned for 30 seconds with 2,200-pound thrust were carried out at the Torpedo Launching Range developed by Cal Tech at Morris Dam, California, in 1943 before the project was abandoned.

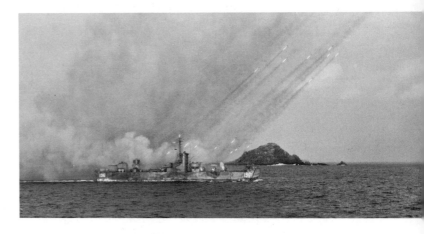

The LSM-196 sends volleys of rockets to the shores of Tokishiki Shima, 1945. This 5-inch rocket with interchangeable warheads was fired on targets out of range of the 4.5-incher. (U.S. NAVY)

Another Air Corps idea that washed out was a 14-inch rocket-boosted, armor-piercing bomb developed in 1941–1942 by the NDRC. The idea had been that the rocket would increase the bomb's penetrating power, but by the time the weapon was ready, the Air Corps had lost interest. But the experience was put to good use, however, when the Navy asked for a rocket that could slow down a bomb; Navy patrol bombers were overshooting submarines too frequently because, sighting their targets at the last minute, their bombs would be released too late to do any harm. What the Navy needed was a rocket that would cancel the plane's momentum and permit the bomb to fall straight down.

Beginning in October 1942, rocket launchers, called "Mousetraps," were installed on United States sub chasers and Coast Guard vessels. They proved highly effective against German and Japanese subs. (U.S. NAVY)

United States Guided Surface-to-Air Missiles

Missile	Length (feet)	Diameter (inches)	Weight (pounds)	Altitude (miles)	Velocity (mph)	Propulsion
Little Joe	11.34	22.7	1,210	1.5	400	solid sustainer and booster
Lark	18.5	18	2,000	4	600	liquid sustainer, solid booster

The result was a retro-firing bomb whose rocket motor permitted a nearly vertical fall. It was tested on 3 July 1942 on a lumbering PBY5A Catalina that immediately took its place in history—it was the first American airplane to fire a rocket. The weapon was 7.2 inches in diameter, carried 35 pounds of explosives, and had a maximum velocity of 200 miles per hour. Among the many kills credited to the bomb was the last German sub reported sunk in the war, on 30 April 1945 in the Bay of Biscay.

The United States was much more interested at the start of the war in firing rockets *from* planes rather than *at* them for one very basic reason: no one was bombing American cities. When the danger of Kamikaze attacks on United States ships arose, the situation changed and two surface-to-air missile programs were begun, Little Joe and Lark.

Kamikaze attacks on United States ships intensified the need for a surface-to-air missile. The Navy began work on the rocket-powered Lark in 1944, but did not get it ready for service before the war ended. (REACTION MOTORS)

Little Joe was gyro-stabilized and controlled by radio command through optical tracking. Its warhead was to detonate by proximity fuze as it reached its target. Several missiles were produced under the direction of the Naval Air Materiel Unit, but the long lead-time necessary before Little Joe could be used caused the program's cancellation.

Like the Little Joe program, the Lark missile effort began in 1944. By 6 February, Lark was given the go-ahead for accelerated development by the Navy Jet-Propelled Missile Board because of Little Joe's troubles. Lark was launched by two solid boosters and had an unusual two-chamber liquid-fuel rocket engine. The larger chamber, which produced 400 pounds of thrust, would be in use only when the 220-pound-thrust smaller chamber failed to keep the missile moving at a preset velocity. Lark had a command mid-course control system, with a semiactive homing device for terminal guidance; it had four wings and four fins, positioned octagonally. Lark was not ready for service when the war ended, but tests continued, first at the Naval Ordnance Test Station at Inyokern, California, and later at the Naval Air Missile Test Station at Point Mugu.

One weakness in both these weapons was guidance, a problem that American technology barely came to grips with during World War II. Air-to-surface missile development was much easier because the airplanes were shooting at targets that were either standing still or moving relatively slowly.

In addition to the 4.5-inch air-to-surface rocket, several other models saw action during the war. Many of them, like the 4.5-incher, were modified ground-to-ground weapons. The first of these was the 3.5-inch FFAR (forward-firing aircraft rocket), which was based directly on the British rocket of nearly the same diameter. The Cal Tech group, supported by the Navy, began development work in the spring of 1941. In August 1943, a rocket 4.58 feet long, weighing 54.5 pounds, and with a range of slightly less than a mile was tested. The rocket first went into action against U-boats in January, with a special head that doubled its underwater lethal range; later the first model was used against surface ships.

A 5-inch FFAR was developed by replacing the 3.5-incher's 20-pound solid head with a 5-inch, 50-pound explosive shell. The rocket, 5.4 feet long and weighing 80 pounds, was popular with the Navy for action against shore- and ship-based antiaircraft guns.

Slightly longer and considerably heavier at 134 pounds, the 5-inch HVAR (high-velocity aircraft rocket) went into action in July 1944. The Holy Moses, as it was called, was developed by an NDRC–Cal Tech–Navy Bureau of Ordnance team, but was first used by the Air Corps near St. Lô in France. About one million Holy Moses rockets had been made when the war ended.

The largest airplane-launched, forward-firing rocket developed during the war was inappropriately called the Tiny Tim. It was 10.25 feet long, 11.75 inches in diameter, and weighed 1,284 pounds. It was created primarily for use against the fortified pill-boxes and bunkers that would have to be knocked out in an invasion of Japan's home islands. Tiny Tim's specifications were laid down in February 1944 by Cal Tech scientists and engineers; the first test round was fired just two months later. Its range was short—just one mile—and 30,000 pounds of thrust gave it a speed of only 550 miles per hour, but the 150 pounds of TNT in Tiny Tim's payload gave it the wallop of a 12-inch naval shell.

Tiny Tim was carried on modified bomb racks and released by standard mechanisms; it was ignited by a lanyard when it dropped several feet from the aircraft. The first test produced a catastrophic accident that destroyed the aircraft, but the ignition mechanism was redesigned and F6F squadrons on the carriers *Franklin* and *Intrepid* were outfitted with Tiny Tims by the fall of 1944, in time for the battle of Okinawa.

The United States also experimented with an assortment of guided bombs—fifteen models in all—as air-to-surface weapons. Most of them were unpowered. One of them, the GB-1, was developed starting in March 1941, entered production in May 1943, and was first used against Cologne in May 1944. GB-1 was basically a 2,000-pound bomb which had been given wings and a television-radio guidance system to increase its accuracy. About one thousand were used against targets in Germany and Austria.

The VB, or vertical bomb, series, consisted of free-fall bombs guided by bombardiers via controls in their tail fins. Azon, or VB-1, could be guided in clusters of five by one bombardier—if the weather was clear and the airplane was flying steadily. VB-3,

The largest airplane-launched rocket of World War II was inappropriately called Tiny Tim. This 10-foot rocket, loaded with 150 pounds of TNT, was created for use against pillboxes and bunkers. (U.S. NAVY)

or Razon, developed by NDRC and the Air Technical Service Command, had a controllable range. VB-6 homed in on the heat given off by the target. VB-10 (called Roc, as were VB's 11 and 12) had a television-radio guidance system. VB-13, last of the series, weighed 12,000 pounds, had a 54-inch-diameter lift shroud, and was more than 20 feet long. Called Tarzon, it was used against enemy battleships and heavy fortifications.

The Bat was a longer-range, radar-guided air-to-surface missile whose development won Hugh L. Dryden the Presidential Certificate of Merit. Bat was nearly 12 feet long, carried a 1,000-pound payload, and traveled at a maximum speed of 300 miles per hour. In April 1945 a Bat sank a Japanese destroyer 20 miles from the launching aircraft, which was the weapon's maximum range.

Another missile, Gargoyle, started life in November 1943 as a glide bomb, but was given a liquid-propellant rocket engine in March 1944 at the Navy's request. The McDonnell Aircraft Company delivered the first Gargoyle in December 1944; four more were delivered the next month. Production authorization was given in May 1945. When the war ended, Gargoyle became a test vehicle without ever having seen action.

One interesting weapon was an alteration of the 4.5-inch rocket into an air-to-air defense rocket.

Myths and stories suggesting different schemes for traveling to other worlds were told for nearly two thousand years, and rockets were used in war and for entertainment for at least six hundred years before men gradually began to link the two ideas. The discovery that the rocket is the key to space travel was made independently toward the end of the nineteenth century in Russia, the United States, and Germany.

The first man to really understand and develop the principles of rocketry and their application to space travel was a Russian schoolteacher, Konstantin Eduardovitch Tsiolkovsky. He stumbled on the concept of rocket flight in 1883—probably, as he later wrote, as a result of Jules Verne's influence—spent some twenty years refining his theories, and published them in 1903. On the basis of his calculations, Tsiolkovsky proposed the use of such modern rocket-propellant combinations as liquid oxygen and liquid hydrogen, and explained in detail the advantages of multistage rockets.

While Tsiolkovsky is universally recognized today as the leading pioneer of astronautical theory, his American counterpart, Robert H. Goddard, combined theory and practice in a long and extraordinary research career. Born in 1883 in Worcester, Massachusetts, Goddard developed a plan for multistage spaceships while still in high school. As a professor at Clark University, he continued to explore the theoretical implications of space flight. Although frequently hampered by lack of sufficient funds, he constructed and tested a series of progressively more sophisticated rockets at sites in Massachusetts and Roswell, New Mexico.

The third great pioneer of rocketry and astronautics, Hermann Oberth, born in 1894 in Transylvania, has been a citizen of Germany for most of his life. Primarily interested in the theory of space travel and in spaceship design, Oberth explained his ideas in two influential books. Published in 1923 and 1929, they helped inspire other rocket enthusiasts in Germany to conduct practical tests of rockets, rocket-powered planes, and even a rocket-powered car. Out of these experiments came the technical know-how that enabled Germany to produce the V-1 and V-2 missiles used during the Second World War.

The V-2, the largest and most advanced of these weapons, was developed at Peenemünde, an Army experimental test station on the Baltic coast, by a team of scientists and engineers under the direction of General Walter Dornberger and Wernher von Braun. More than four thousand of these missiles were fired during 1944 and early 1945 against targets in southern England and on the Continent.

The United States, Russia, Great Britain, and Japan also used rockets and missiles of varying sizes and effect during the war. The German V-2, however, became the direct ancestor of all major postwar military missiles and space carrier vehicles as a result of the capture of German rocket experts and many V-2 components by American and Russian armies.

Each of the military services in the United States continued to develop missiles and rockets following the war. Not until the early 1950's, however, did the United States, which had hired 127 of the German scientists, start emphasizing these programs. The Army developed the first of the larger missiles. Working at Fort Bliss, Texas, and later at Redstone Arsenal in Huntsville, Alabama, a team under Wernher von Braun developed the short-range Redstone missile, first tested in 1953. Then, by adding two special stages to an uprated Redstone, the Huntsville group built Jupiter C, America's first missile to fly an intercontinental range.

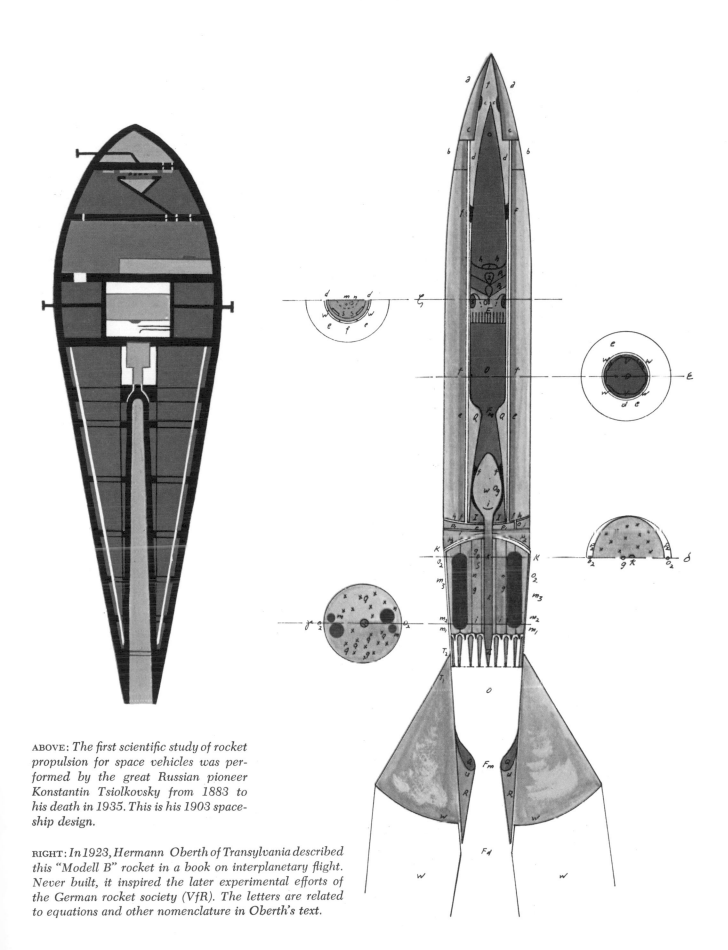

ABOVE: *The first scientific study of rocket propulsion for space vehicles was performed by the great Russian pioneer Konstantin Tsiolkovsky from 1883 to his death in 1935. This is his 1903 spaceship design.*

RIGHT: *In 1923, Hermann Oberth of Transylvania described this "Modell B" rocket in a book on interplanetary flight. Never built, it inspired the later experimental efforts of the German rocket society (VfR). The letters are related to equations and other nomenclature in Oberth's text.*

ABOVE: *Among the precursors of the German V-2 was the A-3 test rocket, shown here in its static test rig. First flight tested in 1937, it was 21 feet tall, 2 feet in diameter, and produced 3,300 pounds of thrust.*

RIGHT: *While Tsiolkovsky and Oberth developed the theory of astronautics, an American, Robert H. Goddard, constructed, tested, and fired rockets. Here, we see one of his research rockets on the test stand near Roswell, New Mexico.*

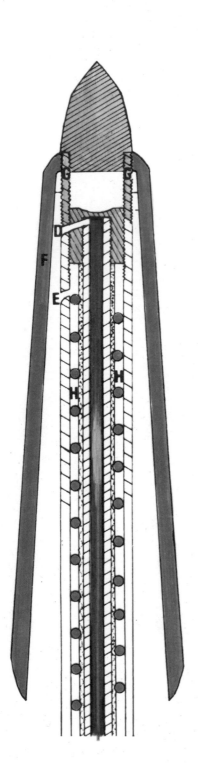

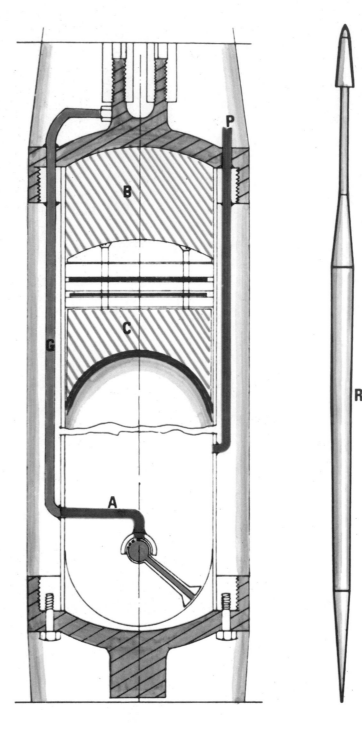

In the mid-1930's the most advanced design of the American Rocket Society was Rocket No. 5, shown here from the outside (R) and in cutaway views. The propellants, liquid oxygen (A) and gasoline (B), were stored in the same cylindrical structure and were separated by a movable pressure piston (C). The propellants were introduced through inlets (D and E) to the motor, which consisted of a cone (F) that served as both combustion chamber and nozzle. Liquid oxygen was fed through one duct (G) and gasoline through another (H). Oxygen pressure was regulated by a safety valve (P).

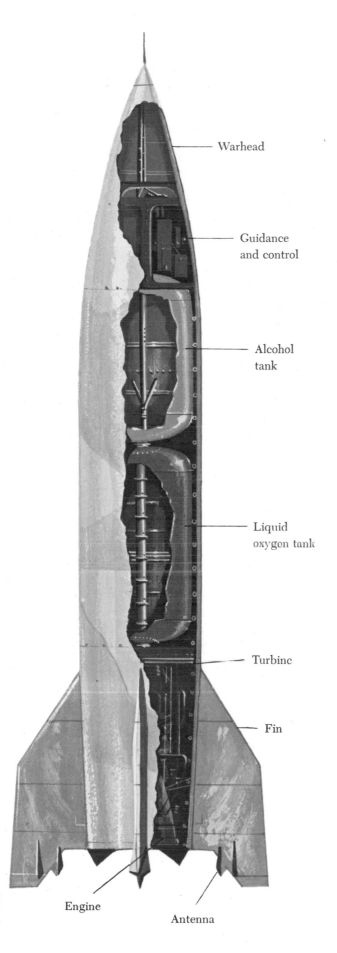

Warhead

Guidance
and control

Alcohol
tank

Liquid
oxygen tank

Turbine

Fin

Engine

Antenna

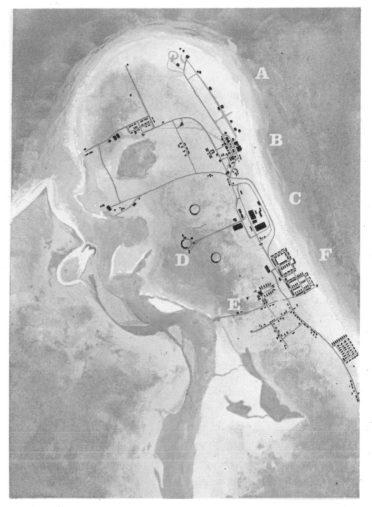

A   Ordnance test area   D   Production test stands
B   Ordnance engineering center E   Military camp
C   Production plant   F   Residential communities

ABOVE: *The V-2 was designed, built, and tested at Peene-münde, the German experimental center on the Baltic coast. Launching facilities were at the northeast corner, near the sea.*

LEFT: *Developed by the Germans during World War II, the V-2 was the largest and most advanced missile of its time. Shown here in cross section, it was 46.1 feet long, 65 inches in diameter, and weighed 27,000 pounds. It became the prototype of postwar American and Russian missiles and space carrier vehicles.*

By 1946, both the United States Navy and the United States Air Force were studying and designing artificial carriers. Had these programs been approved, America might have been able to launch satellites in the early 1950's. The Navy proposal (left) was a single-stage carrier 86 feet long with a 16-inch diameter, designed to orbit itself. The Air Force proposed a three-stage carrier (right) for orbiting a 500-pound satellite.

Offspring of the V-2, the three-stage Jupiter C was designed primarily to test nosecone materials for re-entry into the Earth's atmosphere. This night exposure at Cape Kennedy, Florida, shows the upper staging and the re-entry vehicle, built to withstand frictional heat.

Experience gained in the Jupiter C program was applied directly to the Army's Jupiter—America's first successful intermediate-range ballistic missile. An accurate weapon with a range of 1,500 miles, it was later converted to a space carrier vehicle.

Used against enemy planes, its history has almost been forgotten—its records were burned as a matter of routine. One early attempt had been made to adapt the 4.5-incher to use by fighters, but by the time the final version, called the T-22, was developed, American control of the skies was so complete that the weapon was not needed.

In 1945, the Second Air Division of the 8th Air Force came up with a version of the 4.5-incher as a bomber defense weapon. It was to be loaded and adjusted by a bomber's waist gunner and fired by the tail gunner. Colonel John J. Driscoll, who was active in the development program, described for the authors the reticle that was used to fire the air-to-air rocket:

The distances between the corresponding portions of the sight reticle were spaced to equal the wingspan of an average German (fighter) aircraft . . . there were normally two opportunities to fire at a tail-attacker (e.g., a tail attack level might be opposed at either 850 yards or 300 yards, firing taking place when the wingspan touched the sides of the reticle or was roughly equal to the space between the reticle lines at the corresponding level of attack).

Unfortunately, as with most wartime secret devices (particularly combat experiments), the reports were destroyed in accordance with U.S. Army regulations.

One of the most successful United States rocket programs of the war had nothing to do with missiles. It was the JATO program, aimed at getting heavily loaded aircraft off the ground quickly. It was notable on several accounts.

The Galcit group at Cal Tech had started work on solid-propellant JATO units before the war, developing its Galcit 27 propellant by the summer of 1941. Galcit 27, using an amide powder developed from commercial ingredients to produce 28 pounds of thrust for 12 seconds, was tested on a 753-pound Ercoupe monoplane at March Field, near Riverside, California, from 6 August to 23 August 1941. The aircraft, piloted by Captain (now General) Homer A. Boushey, Jr., took off in 7.5 seconds using 300 feet of runway, compared to its ordinary 580-foot, 13.1-second takeoff. The six JATO rocket units did not disturb the aircraft's stability or controllability.

This line of development was continued, with the Galcit group finally settling on a solid propellant whose oxidizer was a potassium perchlorate compound and whose fuel was a new type of asphalt to which was added a small amount of oil with an asphalt base. The Aerojet Engineering Corporation built motors that produced thrusts of 200, 500, and 1,000 pounds using this propellant.

At about the same time, Robert C. Truax, having completed his two years' sea duty after his graduation from the Naval Academy, went to work on JATO at the Engineering Experiment Station at Annapolis. By then, he was a lieutenant commander in the Bureau of Aeronautics Ship Installations Division under Commander C. A. Bolster. His project, known as TED ESS 3401, was staffed by ensigns R. C. Stiff, J. F. Patton, and W. Schubert, and a civilian from MIT, Robertson Youngquist.

Truax's small staff concentrated on developing a liquid-fuel rocket motor that could produce 3,000 pounds of thrust to get the underpowered PBY seaplane into the air after a relatively short run. By June 1942, a 1,500-pound-thrust engine was tested, but a lag in ignition permitted propellants to accumulate in the thrust chamber. The result was an explosion that wrecked the test stand.

Pressing ahead during the course of conducting gas-generator tests, Ensign Stiff discovered that aniline and red fuming nitric acid would ignite on contact, without needing special ignition equipment. Aniline was more difficult to come by than gasoline and it was harder to handle and store, but it eliminated so many ignition problems that it was immediately adopted as a fuel. In the spring of 1943, Truax's group tested a 1,500-pound-thrust JATO unit that weighed 325 pounds empty and 655 pounds fueled. Two units provided the thrust Truax was after.

Meanwhile, this discovery had gotten the Galcit researchers out of a hole. They too had been working on liquid-fuel rocket motors, and had also run into ignition difficulties; an October 1941 test of a 1,000-pound-thrust engine ran into ignition trouble. Galcit immediately switched to nitric acid and aniline.

The Army provided an A20-A medium bomber for flight testing, and during the winter of 1941–1942 mockups of the 1,000-pound-thrust unit were installed on the 14,000-pound aircraft. The first flight tests of the liquid JATO units were held between 7 April and 24 April 1942 at the Army Air Corps Bombing and Gunnery Range, Muroc, California, with Major P. H. Dane flying 44 test runs.

The JATO effort was further distinguished by the presence of Robert H. Goddard. Under a contract signed with the Navy in December 1941, Goddard and his crew came from New Mexico to Annapolis in July 1942, and developed a liquid oxygen–gasoline JATO. The unit, tested on a PBY-2 on 23 September 1942, was the first JATO to power the takeoff of a Navy aircraft.

The development of liquid oxygen–gasoline JATO's was continued by Reaction Motors. Thrust was raised to 3,000 pounds, and duration of firing to 60 seconds. An engine using liquid oxygen and a

The "Bat" radar-guided missile was nearly 12 feet long and traveled at a maximum speed of 300 miles per hour. Its maximum range was 20 miles, a distance from which a Bat sank a Japanese destroyer in April 1945. (U.S. NAVY)

Combustion chamber developed by Robert C. Truax for the JATO (jet-assisted takeoff) program at Annapolis. Its purpose was to aid overloaded planes in taking off from short runways.

gasoline-water mixture was successfully tested on Martin PBM3C's during 1943.

Not all American rocket work was aimed at immediate applications. Several programs of relatively pure research in rocketry were carried on during the war. They bore within them the germ of future rocket and missile programs.

The Navy's Gorgon program was conceived as early as 1937, with the aim of developing an air-to-air missile. The first designs were laid down in 1941. In May 1943, reconsidering plans for powering their missiles only with jet engines, the Naval Bureau of Ordnance decided to test a 350-pound-thrust two-chamber nitric acid–aniline rocket engine developed by Truax's group. In October 1943, two airframes were selected, one conventional and the other canard. Twenty-five of each—Gorgon 2A and 2B respectively—were ordered, although Gorgon 2B was canceled when the turbojet for which it was designed failed to become available. Other models— 2C, powered by pulsejet; 3A, rocket powered, Gorgon 4, propelled by a ramjet; Gorgon 5, an enlarged model of the 4 vehicle—were used as test vehicles after the war, providing valuable information for the Navy missile program.

Characteristics of Private A Rocket

Length (feet)	8
Span (feet)	2.8
Weight (pounds)	> 500
Payload (pounds)	60
Sustainer thrust (pounds)	1,000
Booster thrust (pounds)	> 21,500

In the first jet-assisted takeoff, the Ercoupe rises rapidly under rocket power. (GEN. H. A. BOUSHEY, JR.)

The second major wartime test-vehicle program was the Private, undertaken by Ordcit (Ordnance Project—California Institute of Technology) at the Jet Propulsion Laboratory. This program, begun in 1944, was designed to develop the technology of long-range, rocket-powered missiles.

Private A was propelled by an Aerojet solid engine, with booster thrust provided by four 4.5-inch aircraft rockets attached by a steel casing. The vehicle had four guiding fins at the rear and a tapered nose. It was launched from a rectangular steel boom with four guide rails. Twenty-four test vehicles were fired between 1 December and 16 December 1944; one achieved a range of 11.3 miles.

The following spring, Private F was fired at Fort Bliss, Texas. It had a single guiding fin and two horizontal lifting surfaces aft, with two stubby wings forward; its purpose was to test the effect of lifting surfaces on guided missiles. A total of seventeen vehicles were launched between 1 April and 13 April 1945.

The United States' only wartime effort in rocket airplanes was hardly a great success. The MX-324 was originally considered as a prototype for an advanced "flying wing" fighter, the XP-79, with an Aerojet 2,000-pound-thrust nitric acid–aniline rocket engine providing the power. During 1943 it became

evident that the rocket engine would not be available, and two Westinghouse turbojet engines were substituted. They didn't work out, the first airplane powered by them crashing during a test.

Eventually, three MX-324's were built. After some glide tests, the first flight with an Aerojet XCAL-200 rocket engine was held at Harper's Lake on 5 July 1944; soon afterward, the airplane was taking off and landing on skids. The MX-324 was flown for some time with these results: One plane was completely destroyed in an accident, a second was severely damaged, and the third was disposed of. For the record, the MX-324 was 14 feet long, had a wingspan of 38 feet, a range of nearly 1,000 miles,

The MX-324, built in 1944, was America's first experimental military rocket airplane. It had a 36-foot wingspan and a "prone" cockpit in which the pilot lay flat in order to withstand higher accelerations. (NORTHROP CORP.)

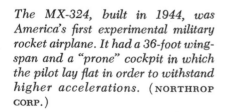

Characteristics of Wac Corporal

Length (feet)	21
Diameter (inches)	12
Weight (pounds)	665 (plus 546 for booster)
Payload (pounds)	25
Velocity (mph)	2,800
Altitude (miles)	< 45

cruised at 480 miles per hour, and was designed to attain 550 miles per hour at top speed.

The first real step into pure rocket research was the Wac Corporal, which was developed by Ordcit. The program began in 1944 in response to an Ordnance Department request for a research rocket that could carry a 25-pound payload to 100,000 feet; the Signal Corps wanted the rocket.

The final design called for the vehicle to be launched by a solid booster from a tower, with a liquid-propellant rocket then taking over to sustain the flight. A one-fifth scale model was built to study the booster-sustainer combination and determine the optimum number of fins (which turned out to be three). The model, known as the Baby Wac, was flown between 3 July and 5 July at California's Goldstone Range.

The Wac Corporal managed to achieve altitudes considerably higher than had been asked, thanks to the uprated 50,000-pound-thrust Tiny Tim booster

and the 1,500-pound-thrust Aerojet nitric acid–aniline sustainer; in addition, the vehicle's weight was kept below early estimates. The booster fired for .6 seconds, the sustainer for 45 seconds. Firings were conducted at the newly opened White Sands Proving Ground between 25 September and 25 October 1945; the maximum altitude achieved was 43.5 miles.

While the Wac Corporal program as such did not continue into the postwar years, it provided invaluable experience for the fledgling United States rocket industry. Even more important, however, was the know-how that was literally captured when the majority of German rocket scientists and engineers surrendered to American soldiers in 1945. For the Germans were dominant in every field of missiles and rockets during World War II. In a very real sense, they created modern military rocket technology. Virtually all postwar missile developments were based, in varying degrees, on what went on in Germany.

The major thrust of German rocket development was, of course, in the *Vergeltungswaffen*—the weapons of retaliation. The V-1, while revolutionary enough, was the more conventional of the two retaliation weapons. A winged subsonic missile developed and controlled by the technical department of the Reichsluftfahrtministerium, the V-1 used an Argus Motoren Gesellschaft pulse-jet engine that operated on gasoline and developed 1,100 pounds of thrust.

The basic concept of the engine can be traced

The German Army rocket center was located at Peenemünde, on the Baltic Coast. Left, the engineering offices at Peenemünde-East. Wernher von Braun's office was on

the second floor, above the small balcony. Right, the rocket engine research and development center as it appeared in 1942.

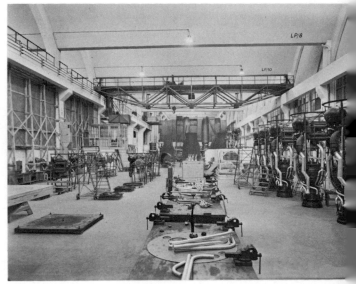

back to a man named Paul Schmidt, of Munich, whose early research was funded jointly by the research departments of the German Air Force and Army. The vehicle itself was designed by Robert Lusser, chief engineer of Fieseler Flugzeugbau, Kassel. The V-1 weighed 4,858 pounds, including its 1,988-pound payload of Amatol, a mixture of trinitrotoluol and ammonium nitrate. The missile was 27 feet long and 33 inches in diameter. It was launched from a ramp and directed to its target by a pre-set guidance system.

The first test firing of the V-1, which was then called the Fieseler Fi-103, took place in December 1941 over the Peenemünde range which had the necessary tracking equipment. By then, the idea of the V-2, a rocket that was to be launched across the Channel at Great Britain, was also well developed. There was a considerable dispute over which of the two weapons should be put in mass production and deployed operationally, since both had about the same range and payload. After a Commission for Long Range Weapons had made an exhaustive study of the two missiles in 1943, Hitler decided to accelerate the development of both weapons for an aerial offensive against southern England. From then on, both the V-1 and the V-2 were given a top priority in the German war effort.

The British intelligence service had been watching Peenemünde, with no clear idea at first of what was happening there. But the British were alarmed enough to raid the station with hundreds of Lancaster and Halifax heavy bombers on the night of 17 August 1943. The raid killed about 800 people, including Dr. Walter Thiel, who was in charge of V-2 engine development, but it did not delay either V-program seriously.

By June 1944, enough V-1's had been produced to start the attack on southern England. More than 8,000 "buzz bombs," as the British called them, were launched against London alone, and thousands of others were launched against Allied-held targets on the Continent.

While the V-1 did provide a severe nervous strain for Londoners, who were always on the alert for the sudden cut-out of the engine that meant the missile was falling, it failed to fulfill its goals. For one thing, it was too slow—with a speed of only 350 miles per hour—and could be shot down. For another, the missiles were none too reliable; only 211 of the 5,000 V-1's fired against Antwerp ever detonated on target. About one quarter of the V-1's aimed at Britain failed because of their inherent unreliability. About half were destroyed by countermeasures—barrage balloons, airplanes, and antiaircraft

The British raided Peenemünde on 17 August 1943, killing 800 people including Dr. Walter Thiel, who was in charge of the V-2 engine development. But the bombs only slightly damaged the Guidance Control building, where the most vital work on the V-2 was being carried out.

fire. About a quarter reached the target, and some of those did not explode.

A historical curiosity that ranks with the Japanese Baka was the piloted V-1, called the V-1e. The 27-foot-long missile was outfitted with a cockpit and instruments by the Luftwaffe experimental station at Rechlin during 1944, with the aim of establishing a German Kamikaze organization, code-named Project Reichenberg. The V-1e was flown several times by a woman test pilot, Hanna Reitsch, who discovered that the 25-percent V-1 failure rate was due to engine vibrations that caused the wing skin to peel off.

Even less successful than the V-1 was a little-known rocket developed by Rheinmetall-Borsig, tested in Poland, and used operationally starting in November 1944. This rocket, called the Rheinbote, was a four-stage contraption that carried a payload of 88 pounds, only half of which was explosive. Its four stages weighed a total of 3,773 pounds, varying in thrust from the 84,000 pounds of the first stage to the more than 7,500 pounds of the fourth. The Rheinbote was unguided and used solid propellants. In one engagement sixty rockets were fired against Antwerp in January 1945 without producing significant results.

The first successful V-2 being readied for launch, October 1942. Developed at Peenemünde, it was the largest and most advanced rocket in the world. More than 5,000 were built before the war was over.

2,200-pound payload from 180 to 210 miles, propelled by an engine using turbopump-fed liquid oxygen and alcohol, and generating an average sea-level thrust of 56,000 pounds. The V-2 had an inertial-guidance system with two free LEV-3 gyroscopes, leveling pendulums, and an integrating gyro-accelerometer.

The original design for the missile, then called the A-4, had been prepared before the war by the Dornberger–Von Braun team at the Army Experimental Station at Peenemünde. During 1938 and 1939, a smaller version of the missile, the A-5, was fired with considerable success. The launches totaled at least 25 by 1940.

While the A-5 flights went ahead, components were designed and developed for the much larger A-4. By the spring of 1939, some A-4 components were actually in production, and the rocket's design had been frozen, with Walter Riedel in charge of the design offices. Manufacturing and assembly techniques were being developed under the direction of Eberhard Rees. Rudolf Hermann had supervised the construction of a supersonic wind tunnel in 1936–1937, and vitally needed aerodynamic data had been obtained from it. Guidance and other related electronics problems were being solved under the scientific supervision of Hermann Steuding and the engineering direction of Ernst Steinhoff.

During 1940 and 1941, all these and other staff members, together with scientists and engineers at universities and in industry, worked day and night under the over-all supervision of Von Braun. By 1942, the first missiles were coming out of the Peenemünde model shops.

The first firing was on 13 June 1942, but it was a failure. Immediately after launch, the propellant feed system failed, and the huge A-4 went out of control and crashed. A second, not entirely successful, test on 16 August chalked up one notable achievement: A-4 No. 2 was the first guided missile to exceed the speed of sound.

The third launching, on 3 October 1942, was a complete success. The engine burned for nearly one minute, giving the A-4 a range of just under 120 miles and a maximum altitude of over 50 miles. Hitler, who had not seemed impressed with the potential of rockets when he viewed test-firings of two engines at Kummersdorf in 1939, suddenly became interested in what was happening at Peenemünde. A V-2 production committee was established in the Ministry of Armaments and War Production, with Gerhard Degenkolb as director. It was not entirely a blessing. As Von Braun wrote later: "The committee immediately began issuing high-handed direc-

The Rheinbote was launched from a V-2 transport car. It had in large degree the four weaknesses that made the V-weapons something less than the terrors for which Hitler had hoped. All were introduced before they were fully developed, lacked accuracy, carried too-small payloads for their purposes, and could not be produced in the vast numbers that would make them effective.

This should not detract from the impressive technical feat produced by the Peenemünde group in making a V-2. Without a doubt, the V-2 was the largest and most advanced missile in the world. It was 46.1 feet long, 65 inches in diameter, and weighed more than 27,000 pounds. It carried its

tives and setting up a mighty production organization. Mainly composed of men of little scientific judgment, although of vast energy, this committee was a thorn in the side to Peenemünde."

Despite this interference, hundreds of V-2's were manufactured and fired over the next two years to prove out systems, train troops, and acquaint the military with the operational characteristics of the weapon.

Production of the V-2 began in a new plant built a few miles south of the Peenemünde Experimental Center. After the August 1943 air raid, which damaged this assembly plant badly, production was shifted to the underground Mittelwerk facility, a converted oil depot, near Nordhausen in the Harz Mountains. Nearly 900 V-2's a month were being produced there near the end of the war. Assembly plants under preparation near Vienna, Berlin, and Friedrichshafen were also closed and their equipment shifted to the Mittelwerk plant when it became evident that the secret was out. (The British got hold of a V-2 that had strayed from its course and landed near Kalmar, Sweden, in June 1944. As chance would have it, that particular shot was intended to test the radio-guidance system of a Wasserfall surface-to-air missile, and the British were misled into believing that the V-2 was radio-guided.)

V-2 components were produced in many parts of Germany. For example, the steam generator was made at the Heinkel factory in Jenbach, Tyrol; the guidance system at Kreiselgeräte G.m.b.H. in Berlin; propellant containers at Zeppelin Luftschiffbau, Friedrichshafen. Many universities cooperated with Peenemünde during the program. Missile training was given at a school near Koeslin in Pomerania, and military proficiency firing took place on a former Polish Army reservation near Blizna.

A program of this magnitude inevitably had political aspects. General Dornberger and his military subordinates took care of most of the contacts Peenemünde had with Nazi party officials, but Von Braun and his technical staff had to handle some of them. Until the end of 1943, the motivation for most of these contacts was curiosity on the part of the Nazi leaders, who had known little about Peenemünde's activities because of military security. But when it became obvious that the V-2 was going to be a spectacular new weapon, the SS began trying to take over the Peenemünde operation.

SS General Hans Kammler made the first attempt to take command of the Peenemünde base from Army General Leo Zanssen, but Dornberger stopped this effectively. The SS, however, kept trying. In February 1944, Von Braun was called to

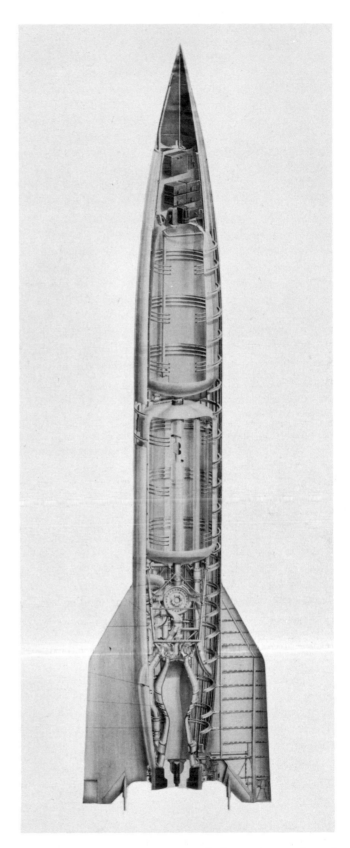

The V-2 was 46.1 feet long, weighed 27,000 pounds, and had a range of 200 miles. It zoomed down on its target just five minutes after taking off.

Gestapo headquarters in East Prussia, where Heinrich Himmler tried to coerce him into deserting the army and working for him. Von Braun turned down the proposal and left. A few days later, at 2 A.M., he was arrested by three Gestapo agents. After two weeks in a Stettin prison, he was charged by an SS court. The accusations: He was not really interested in war rockets, but was working on space exploration; he was opposed to the use of V-2's against England; and he was about to escape to Britain in a small plane, taking vital rocket secrets with him. Dornberger went directly to Hitler and said that without Von Braun there would be no V-2. Von Braun was released.

One problem that had to be solved was whether the V-2 should be a mobile weapon. The technical people preferred a fixed launch site where loading, repairing, servicing, and last-minute adjustments could be handled under near-laboratory conditions. But the military experts realized that any fixed site near the English Channel, no matter how well protected, would be an easy target for the thousands of Allied bombers stationed within easy reach. So the V-2 was made transportable and launchable from

Since it was impossible to protect fixed sites from enemy attack, the V-2 was launched from rail or road equipment. Below, a launching platform mounted on a railroad car.

road or rail equipment. A typical trailer-mounted missile was supported by about thirty vehicles, including transportation trailer, launching platform trailer, propellant vehicles, and command and control trucks. A missile could be fired in four to six hours after a launch site was occupied.

The V-2 assault got off to an inauspicious start on 6 September 1944, when two missiles were fired unsuccessfully against Paris. Two days later the V-2 offensive against southern England began. The first combat missiles were launched from a site near The Hague in the Netherlands at the rate of two a day.

More than 5,000 V-2's were built before the war was over. Some 600 of them were used for training and tests, and a good part of the rest were fired against Great Britain and targets on the Continent. If everything functioned properly there was no defense against the missile. It dropped down on its target at 3,500 miles per hour just five minutes after taking off.

But a myriad of things could go wrong with the complex missile, even if the launch went as planned —and it often didn't. The guidance system could fail, causing the V-2 to miss its target. The missile could explode on its journey out of the atmosphere or break up as it returned to Earth. Even if the target was reached, the warhead could turn out to be a dud. But the V-2's took their toll. More than 1,500 V-2's were reported to have landed in southern England or just off its shores, and they were responsible for more than 2,500 deaths and great property damage.

The V-2 offensive ended on 27 March 1945, nearly seven months after it began. The Germans could no longer provide support for a weapon that clearly was going to neither influence the war's outcome nor delay its end.

Although the V-1 and V-2 were the most spectacular missiles developed by Germany during the war, they were by no means the only ones. As early as 1937, the Germans were flying a rocket aircraft powered by a 1,300-pound-thrust Walter engine. This engine was intended for a fighter, the He-176, designed by Heinrich Hertel. Easily the boldest aviation project of its time, the He-176 would probably have been able to exceed the speed of sound had it been completed. The original plan, outlined in 1936, was for Von Braun's group to develop a more powerful alcohol–liquid oxygen engine to replace Hellmuth Walter's hydrogen peroxide engine. Von Braun's engine was successfully flight tested in a He-112 fighter plane. In 1937 the flight tests were conducted with a pressure-fed system, and in early 1939 with pump feeding. However, with the invasion of

Poland in the fall of 1939, the Air Ministry lost interest in the project and it was canceled. Instead, both Walter and Von Braun's group at Peenemünde worked on JATO units, and the Walter units were placed into production and operational use. The Peenemünde unit produced 2,200 pounds of thrust for 30 seconds on liquid oxygen and water-diluted alcohol. Flight tests showed that two of these units could help an He-111 or Ju-88 to take off from a short grass strip with a heavy payload.

The He-176 project was canceled after a few highly successful flight tests with a preliminary Walter engine. But the idea of a rocket-powered interceptor was continued with a design creation of Alexander Lippisch. This was a squat, tailless monoplane with wings swept back at a 30-degree angle. The undercarriage was jettisoned on takeoff, and the aircraft landed on skids.

Lippisch had been working on rocket planes since 1932, when he designed the Delta 4 airplane, which became, in 1935, the Delta 4a. By 1940, his DFS 194, powered by a Walter 660-pound-thrust hydrogen peroxide engine, reached 340 miles per hour. The Messerschmitt Me-163A followed in the spring of 1941, when engineless tow tests were made at Augsburg. Its rocket motor was installed in the early fall, and flights were made at speeds up to 640 miles per hour from the Peenemünde airfield.

The larger Me-163B was built around a more powerful Walter hydrogen peroxide–hydrazine hydrate/methyl alcohol engine. Tests of the new aircraft were held in 1943 at Bremen, Augsburg, and Brandes, near Leipzig. Two 1,000-pound-thrust JATO units helped get the airplane off the ground. About sixty of the aircraft were built by Messerschmitt.

Junkers built three hundred C models of this aircraft, which was called first the Ju-263, then the 8-263, and finally the Me-263, when Messerschmitt continued its development. The C model was glide-tested, but never flew under rocket power. The B model was 19.5 feet long, weighed 9,040 pounds, and could fly for less than 8 minutes at 550 miles per hour; it could climb to 32,800 feet in 3 minutes. The thrust of its throttlable engine varied from 660 to 3,500 pounds. The C model was 23.1 feet long, weighed 11,280 pounds, and was planned for an engine whose thrust varied from 440 to 3,740 pounds.

The Germans had one more go at a rocket-powered airplane in the closing months of the war. In August 1944, the Luftwaffe asked the Bachem-Werke firm to undertake the development of the aircraft officially known as the BA-349 and commonly called the Natter. The concept for such a plane had been proposed by Lippisch and P. Karlson, and the German military hoped that it could destroy enemy bombers before they dropped their bomb loads on German cities. There was a large element of desperation in the proposal, since the Natter was designed for use just once.

The Natter, made of wood, was supposed to go into action immediately after an air-raid alert. It would take off with the help of two solid-propellant JATO units and its Walter sustainer engine. Ground radar control would bring it within about a mile of the enemy aircraft, and the pilot would attack from there, using either 28 electrically fired rockets or two 30-mm guns. After the attack, the plane would glide down to two miles altitude, where the pilot would bail out; the plan was to recover the sustainer rocket for use in another mission.

The Natter was less than 19 feet long, weighed 4,925 pounds, and during its few minutes of flight hit speeds of from 500 to 600 miles per hour. After a number of unmanned tests, the first and only piloted flight was undertaken in February 1945. It was a complete failure. At 330 feet, the cockpit came off, killing the pilot. The Natter continued to climb. At 1,600 feet it turned and nose-dived into the ground. That ended the history of rocket-powered German aircraft. They had been much more successful than American attempts, but their military effectiveness fell far short of expectations.

The Germans got off to a late start on surface-to-air missiles, beginning development work only when the Allies began to dominate the skies over

The German rocket-powered airplane, Messerschmitt Me-163, is shown in rear view on ground. (U.S. AIR FORCE)

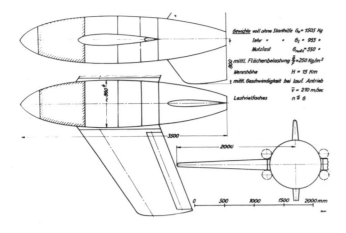

The Germans tested a variety of surface-to-air missiles, but the war was over before they were ready for use. Some of the missiles they developed were the Enzian FR6 (top), the Feuerlilie F-55 (center), and the Schmetterling (bottom).

Germany. A variety of models were test-fired with some success, but the war was over before they could be used against enemy bombers. The principal missiles developed were the Enzian (named for an Alpine plant), two models of the Feuerlilie (Firelily), the Hecht (a Fish), two Rheintochters (Rhinemaiden), the Schmetterling (Butterfly), the Taifun (Typhoon), and the Wasserfall (Waterfall).

Three basic series of guided air-to-surface missiles were developed by the Germans. Two were designed by the firm of Blohm and Voss, four by Henschel, and one, the SD 1400, by the Deutsche Versuchsanstalt für Luftfahrtzeug- und Fahrtzeugmotoren (German Research Center for Aeronautic and Automotive Propulsion). Though some air-to-surface missiles were used during the war, they could hardly be said to have left the testing phase.

The Germans did not have a guided air-to-air missile, but air-to-air rockets were fired on a number of occasions against Allied airplanes. Among these were an adapted ground rocket (Rz 73 or 7.3-cm Föhn) and the R4M. Air-to-air rockets were used against unescorted United States bomber formations in the summer of 1943; the first recorded use of air-to-air rockets in the war came when American bombers attacked Schweinfurt and were met by rocket-carrying German airplanes.

The Germans also had several successes with their ground-to-ground missiles in addition to the V-1 and V-2. They introduced their Nebelwerfer (Fog thrower) rocket firing device in rather large quantities on the Russian front in 1941 with considerable effect. Originally designed to produce smoke screens for infantry assaults, the Nebelwerfer's surprising accuracy led to its use as an artillery barrage rocket. A special launcher was created to fire five or six rockets. Later, an advanced Wurfgerät (Propelling Device) was developed. Both launchers fired solid-propellant rockets with diameters of 15, 21, 28, and 32 centimeters with fair accuracy. The 21-centimeter (8.3-inch) rocket, typical of the others, was 4.1 feet long, weighed 241 pounds, carried a 22.5-pound payload, and had a range of 4 miles. It was propelled by a compound of nitrocellulose and diethylene dinitrate.

The Germans also used imitations of the bazooka, developed when the effectiveness of the American weapon became apparent. The Panzerfaust (Tank Fist) fired a 2.36-inch rocket, the Panzerschreck (Tank Panic) a 3.46-inch projectile. Both could be launched by an individual against a tank, and both projectiles weighed between 7 and 9 pounds.

A more sophisticated antitank weapon, the X-7, was designed, and some components were devel-

Principal German Surface-to-Air Missiles[a]

Missile	Length (feet)	Weight (pounds)	Range (miles)	Velocity (mph)	Altitude (miles)	Characteristics
Enzian	12	4,350	18	600	9	Several plastic-wood, swept-wing Enzians built by Messerschmitt in Augsburg in late 1943; heavy bombing forced move to Oberammergau. From early 1944 to early 1945, when the program was canceled, twenty-five missiles were fired, of which a third was successful. Designed by Georg Madelung and powered by a Hellmuth Walter liquid-propellant rocket engine, Enzian consisted of three compartments: (1) steel and plastic-wood warhead, (2) monocoque fuselage (including propellant tanks), and (3) tail section. Launched from high-angle, 20-foot ramp, with aid of four fuselage-mounted solid-propellant JATO's. Radio controlled.
Feuerlilie F-25	6.7	265	3	600	1.8	The F-25 and F-55 were quite different missiles, the former subsonic and the latter supersonic. F-25 development was directed by the Luftfahrtforschunganstalt Hermann Göring E.V. at Braunschweig, fuselages being manufactured by Ardeltwerke and solid rocket engines by Rheinmetall-Borsig in Berlin. Behind warhead was main body section supporting wings and controls, and tail section containing engine and providing support for fins and stabilizer. Roll control by ailerons, stabilization by gyros and servomechanisms. First F-25 flight occurred in April 1943 at Leba, Pomerania. In 1944, after twenty missiles had been built, program was canceled, and F-55 development begun. Newer, more advanced missile was launched by a solid rocket and sustained by rocket engine operating on liquid oxygen and alcohol. Tapered, swept-back wings were positioned well to the rear. Sustainer developed by Deutsche Versuchanstalt für Kraftfahrtzeug und Fahrtzeugmotoren; booster by Rheinmetall-Borsig. First flight at Leba, May 1944; second at Peenemünde six months later.
Feuerlilie F-55	15.75	—	6	900	3	
Hecht	8.3	308	6	650	3–4	Looking much like small airplane, only one was flown before project was canceled in favor of Feuerlilie series. The missile featured two swept-back wings and a high central tail fin; it was powered by a Walter hydrogen peroxide rocket engine and was ramp-launched.
Rheintochter 1	20.7	3,850	7.5	680	3.7	Both versions of Rheintochter were test fired at Leba. Of eighty Rheintochter 1's fired, twenty-two were equipped with radio control, and of these eighteen were successful. Missile had six wooden stabilizing fins to rear, four control fins forward. Ramp-launched by solid JATO unit which separated from missile after burnout. Once aloft was controlled by radio and stabilized by gyro system. Both visual and radar tracking devices were employed. An unknown number of Rheintochter 3's were tested, some with solid-propellant sustainers, others with liquid-propellant sustainers of the Was-
Rheintochter 3	16.5	3,450	22	750	9	

Principal German Surface-to-Air Missiles (continued)

Missile	Length (feet)	Weight (pounds)	Range (miles)	Velocity (mph)	Altitude (miles)	Characteristics
						serfall type. Takeoff by solid JATO units mounted to fuselage. Airframe consisted of five sections: fuze, control, electric, propellant tank, and propulsion. It had four rather than six stabilizers.
Schmetterling	12.5	981	10	540	6–7	Occasionally called the V-3, and officially known as the Hs-117, about sixty missiles constructed by Henschel in Breslau. Midwing monoplane with cruciform tail. Liquid sustainer, manufactured by BMW, was mounted internally; solid boosters externally mounted, one above and one below fuselage. Fired rather successfully from rotatable platforms, it went into prototype production in 1943. Two operators were required to guide missile: one for positioning the aiming devices and the other to maneuver vehicle by control stick.
Taifun	6.3	66	7.5	2,800	4–5	Elektro-Mechanische Werke-Berlin and Peenemünde joint development, appearing as by-product of Wasserfall design study. Not guided, very small, it was a barrage weapon that was to have been manufactured and fired in vast quantities against Allied bomber fleets. Both liquid- and solid-propellant motors were in production when the war ended.
Wasserfall	26	7,800	17	1,900	8	Basically a one-third model of V-2, though of simpler construction and fitted with four small wings 11 feet from nose. Propulsion system of pressure-feed type, operating on nitric acid and vinyl isobutyl ether/aniline propellants. Designed to knock out planes at high altitudes, missile was to have incorporated radio guidance system under development by Telefunken when program terminated in February 1945. For terminal guidance, an infrared homing device was considered; the 674 pounds of explosives were to have been detonated by radio command. First firing last day of February 1944 at Peenemünde, about two years after the program began; this was followed by twenty-four others in 1944 (60 percent considered successful) and ten early in 1945.

[a] Data derived from the Ordway-Wakeford *International Missile and Spacecraft Guide.* (McGraw-Hill, 1960)

oped, but it was never used in combat. The X-7 projectile, designed to be fired from either a spring or rail ground launcher or a Panzerfaust-type shoulder launcher, was about 2.5 feet long, 5.5 inches in diameter, and had a wingspread of 1.3 feet. It had a two-stage solid-propellant Wasag motor (fast-burning powder for quick takeoff, slow-burning powder for steady acceleration) and was guided by wire that unrolled from wingtip spools. The missile would maneuver in response to signals sent along the wires.

Almost a sidelight to the major German rocket and missile effort were the experiments conducted in the Baltic Sea with missiles launched under water. Short-range 32-centimeter Army rockets with solid propellants were used. Their nozzles were sealed and special ignition systems were installed. A simple welded steel rack, mounted on the deck of a submarine, was the launcher. Six rockets were fired with complete success in the late fall of 1943. The project was the idea of Fritz Steinhoff, a U-boat commander whose brother, Ernst, was a key

Principal German Air-to-Surface Missiles[a]

Missile	Length (feet)	Weight (pounds)	Range (miles)	Velocity (mph)	Characteristics
BV-143	19.5	4,000	10	600	Antiship weapon. Pair V-shaped wings with elevators; two small rectangular tail fins. BV-143's flight profile called for an initial cruise at same altitude from which it was launched, then descent and level off at about 10 feet above surface. Latter maneuver was rarely successful, regardless of whether under pilot (who was guiding the missile from He-111 or He-177 control plane) or automatic altimeter control. About one hundred missiles built for Luftwaffe. An unsuccessful weapon, it was canceled and development shifted to the BV-246, a nonpowered guided ASM also used against ships. About four hundred were built, but never entered into combat service. Radar, infrared, and acoustic homing devices were tried out, as well as more standard radio guidance systems. Both missiles solid-rocket propelled.
BV-246	11	1,600	12	260	
Hs-293	12.5	2,300	10	470	The most widely built and used of the series was Hs-293, a glide-bomb to which was attached a Walter hydrogen peroxide rocket motor. Control from tracking aircraft was assured by elevator and aileron action, the pilot following bomb's flight by flare or electric lamp. Launched at 1,000 to 20,000 feet altitude from several types of Henschel and Dornier planes (optimum launch speed, 210 miles per hour). First tests undertaken at the Luftwaffen-Erprobungsstelle Peenemünde-West in December 1940. In November 1941 placed in production, and about a year later entered Luftwaffe inventory. Sunk several British ships in Bay of Biscay 1943. Hs-294 was an air-to-underwater torpedo missile launched by Ju-90 and He-177 airplanes and powered by twin Walter liquid rocket engines. Upon entering water the wings and engines sheared off and missile continued toward the target as torpedo. Also powered by twin Walter engines was Hs-295, designed for neutralizing lightly armored sea targets. Radio guided and armed with high-explosive, armor-piercing warhead. Missile first tested in 1943, went into production, but was canceled next year. Hs-296 was experimental, combining control system of Hs-293, rear fuselage and wings of Hs-294, and warhead of Hs-295. Liquid-rocket propelled.
Hs-294	20	4,800	8.5	580	
Hs-295	16.2	4,590	5	500	
Hs-296	17.1	6,000	4	500	
SD-1400	15.4	5,500	9	625	Earlier known as FX-1400X, Fritz X, and X-1, was an armor-piercing Esau bomb with four wings and a tail unit incorporating radio-controlled and solenoid-operated spoilers. Achieved world fame when it sunk the Italian battleship *Roma* following launch from a Do-217. The X-2, -3, -4, -5, and -6 models were developed with varying guidance systems.

[a] Data derived from the Ordway-Wakeford *International Missile and Spacecraft Guide.* (McGraw-Hill, 1960)

Principal German Air-to-Air Missiles[a]

Missile	Length (feet)	Weight (pounds)	Range (miles)	Velocity (mph)	Characteristics
Hs-298	6.7	265	4–5	535	Aluminum-and-magnesium alloy missile designed by F. Nikolaus, developed by Henschel, and carried by FW-190, Ju-88, and Do-217 aircraft. Although first flight tests in December 1944 were moderately successful, and it went into pre-production, program was soon canceled. After launch by its two-stage Schmidding 109-543 rocket motor, it would accelerate rapidly past the host aircraft which, by a Fevi line-of-sight guidance system, would direct the missile to its target. Two crew members were necessary, one to follow missile and one to guide it in with joy-stick.
X-4	6.6	132	2–3	550	Was guided by impulses sent along wires unspooled from missile as it flew toward prey. Program began at the Ruhrstahl firm in June 1943, with concurrent engine development at BMW, and first flight occurred in September 1944. About one hundred missiles were built and, as war ended, was considered to be in advanced development stage. Consisted of a fuze housing, warhead, main fuselage, two swept-back wings, four swept-back stabilizing fins, and control wire bobbins in housings at wing tips. Designed by Max Kramer of DVL.

[a] Data derived from the Ordway-Wakeford *International Missile and Spacecraft Guide*. (McGraw-Hill, 1960)

department head at the Peenemünde. Von Braun participated in the project with the two Steinhoffs. Despite the successful firings, the German Navy did not become interested in the project. One reason, apparently, was the Navy's fear that the launching rack would reduce drastically the speed, maneuverability, and rough-weather capability of its submarines.

In late January 1945, when it had become apparent that the Third Reich was in the throes of its final collapse, Von Braun met secretly with his top staff members to decide whether they should remain at Peenemünde and surrender to the advancing Russian Army or to move south and make contact with American forces. The virtually unanimous decision was to head south.

The confusion rampant in Germany in those critical days made the move easier. Von Braun had received nearly a dozen uncoordinated directives from ministries in Berlin, local army and navy commanders, the SS, and a flock of Nazi party bosses. Some of the orders directed him and the entire Peenemünde staff to evacuate the site so that the "top priority research and development work could

be continued at a safer location until ultimate victory was assured." Others directed the Peenemünde staff to stand firm and "defend the holy ground of Pomerania."

Von Braun and his intimates sorted out the "move" orders from the rest and disregarded the "stay put" orders. To bluff their way through the maze of military roadblocks and Gestapo check-points along the route, they equipped all the railroad cars, automobiles, and trucks to be used in the evacuation with blazing red-and-white signs reading *Vorhaben zur besonderen Verwendung*—a purely mythical Project for Special Disposition. The scheme worked. Von Braun, his close associates, and about five thousand employees and their families, along with large quantities of documents, drawings, and papers, left Peenemünde in February in ships, railroad cars, trucks, and automobiles. Heading south, dodging Allied planes and bluffing units of the Gestapo and the SS, they finally reached the town of Bleicherode in the Harz Mountains, where the Armament Ministry in Berlin had directed the rocket research work to continue.

By sheer chance, the area military commander

was the same SS General Kammler who had earlier tried to take over Peenemünde. As boss of several concentration camps, Kammler was growing increasingly jittery as the advance of Allied troops brought retribution closer and closer. He decided that he could bargain better with the approaching United States Army if he had hostages—Von Braun and several hundred of the Peenemünde scientists and engineers.

Kammler's first move in this game came on 2 April when he ordered the transfer of Von Braun and about five hundred other Peenemünde rocket experts that had just moved into the Bleicherode area to an empty army camp near Oberammergau in Bavaria, in the Alpine area that the Nazi hierarchy

The A-4b ground-to-ground missile, shown here on test stand and in cutaway, had twice the range of the V-2. It was experimentally fired at Peenemünde in the summer of 1944.

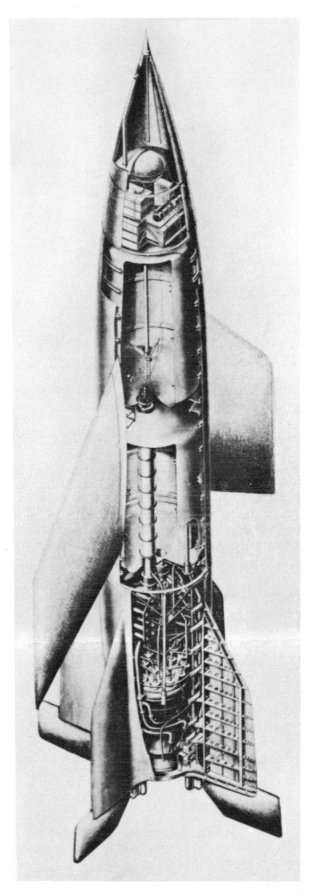

After the war, U.S. Seventh Army troops found this Natter rocket-powered interceptor, still in the experimental stage, on an airfield near St. Leonhard, Austria. (U.S. ARMY)

had designated its last retreat. Von Braun's counter-move on arrival at the scene was to express fear about the danger of air attack on the completely un-protected, blatantly visible barracks; together with Ernst Steinhoff he managed to persuade local SS officials to get his people out from behind the camp's barbed wire and scatter them among twenty small towns in the area. Later, General Dornberger, with a small military staff, joined one element of the now widely dispersed group in the Bavarian ski resort of Oberjoch.

A few days afterward, radio news of Hitler's death on 30 April spurred final plans for surrendering to the Americans. From their mountain retreat, Dornberger and Von Braun sent off Magnus von Braun, Wernher's English-speaking brother, to attempt to make contact. Magnus von Braun surrendered to PFC Fred P. Schneiker of the 44th Infantry Division at the town of Reutte, Tyrol, informing him that he represented a group of rocket scientists anxious to turn themselves over to the Americans.

Describing the circumstances of the initial contact, Charles L. Stewart, a special agent of Army Intelligence, told the authors:

I do recall that the war was still in progress, although it was near the end and the front in our sector was relatively quiet. I was in Reutte in the Austrian Tyrol at the time, and as many of the higher German civil and political offi-cials had sought refuge in that area, we were very busy.

Magnus von Braun came through the lines first. He was brought to our headquarters and explained that his brother and some 150 of the top German rocket personnel were lodged in an inn behind the German lines. They wished to join the Americans to continue their work in rocket development. They had selected the Americans, as they were favorably disposed to this country generally and also because this country was the one most able to provide the resources required for interplanetary travel. Furthermore, they were anxious to depart from the German side, as there was the possibility that an SS colonel in Innsbruck might eliminate them all, pursuant to last-minute Nazi orders to liquidate certain key German scientific talent to prevent them from falling into the hands of the Allies.

We made the necessary arrangements, and I went part of the way with them. When Dr. von Braun came out with General Dornberger and Colonel Axter, they lodged with us while we communicated with higher headquarters. None of us had scientific backgrounds, but the magnitude of their discoveries and their potential for the future was immediately apparent. We were dismayed when we could not arouse any interest in them at higher headquarters. Our first instructions were to the effect that they were to be thoroughly screened (a favorite solution of the military in dealing with high-ranking personnel if in doubt as to how to proceed). Our reply was to the effect that it made no difference if all were brothers of Hitler, because their unique knowledge made them extremely valuable militarily and from a national standpoint. After a few days we were able to arrange their transfer to higher headquarters.

All captured scientists were moved to German army barracks in Garmisch-Partenkirchen for continued interrogation. Several months later, Dornberger was turned over to the British. He spent two years in a prisoner-of-war camp before going to the United States.

Although the Americans were slow to react to Magnus von Braun's surrender, top United States intelligence officers—along with their British and Russian counterparts—were well aware of the importance of locating both the German rocket scientists and their rockets. Colonel Gervais W. Trichel, head of the Ordnance Corps Rocket Branch in Washington, knowing of the existence of an underground V-2 factory near Nordhausen, requested Colonel (later Major General) Holger N. Toftoy, chief of the Ordnance Technical Intelligence team in Paris, to ship V-2 assemblies out of the Mittelwerke plant as soon as it was captured. Trichel also had sent a member of his staff, Major Robert Staver, to London to work up a list of key German rocket personnel to be found and interrogated. This was the genesis of the American Intelligence project which, on 19 July

1945, was christened Overcast and which, nine months later, was given the name by which it became famous: Operation Paperclip.

V-2 production at the underground Mittelwerke plant had not been affected by the migration of the scientific team from Peenemünde into the Oberammergau area. But with the approach of Brigadier General Truman Boudinot's Combat Command B troops on 10–11 April, the remaining 4,500 workers dispersed into the neighboring villages and countryside. When Colonel John C. Welborn, Lieutenant Colonel William B. Lovelady, and Major William Castille entered the huge underground plant they found, to their surprise, that it was completely intact and that its lines of V-1 and V-2 assemblies had been left undisturbed. The Americans had come upon one of the greatest technical prizes in history. Toftoy and Staver were informed immediately of the capture.

Staver, aided by a General Electric engineering team under Richard Porter and by British Intelligence, had finished compiling the list of key personnel to be interrogated. After the capture of Nordhausen and Bleicherode, he went to Paris to see Toftoy, and the two mapped out plans to remove the invaluable materiel. Their sense of haste was heightened by the news that the section of Germany that so interested them was about to be turned over to the Soviets as a result of the Yalta agreement.

Toftoy set up "Special Mission V-2" under the command of Major James P. Hamill, who was instructed to ship from Nordhausen to Antwerp all the rocket equipment he could lay his hands on. Moving into the area, his group set up perimeter controls and, with the aid of the 144th Motor Vehicle Assembly Company, local laborers, and German railway hands, put the V-2 equipment onto flatcars and gondolas. The first trainload of materiel left Nordhausen on 22 May 1945; the last on 31 May, the day before the Russians were expected to arrive.

Von Braun (with arm in cast) surrenders to the Americans at Reutte, in May 1945. Left to right are Charles L. Stewart, U.S. counter-intelligence agent; Lt. Col. Herbert Axter, attached to Gen. Dornberger's staff; Dieter K. Huzel; Wernher von Braun; Magnus von Braun; and Hans Lindenberg.

In all, 341 cars were loaded, representing about a hundred V-2 ballistic missiles. Once in Antwerp, the equipment was crated and loaded into sixteen Liberty ships and transported to New Orleans—and thence to the New Mexico desert.

While Hamill removed the hardware from Mittelwerke, Toftoy ordered Staver to conduct a search for any engineering reports and other technical documents that might be in the area. Toftoy's hunch that such data were nearby was entirely correct.

Von Braun realized in early April when he was ordered to go with five hundred key rocket scientists from Bleicherode to Oberammergau that it would be impossible for the group to take with them the vast archive of documents that they had brought south from Peenemünde. This priceless collection of drawings, scientific papers, test and flight reports, supersonic wind tunnel studies, and so on, contained the essence of all the important rocket research conducted in Germany between 1932 and 1945. The materiel had been moved from Peenemünde to Bleicherode under the greatest difficulties. To leave it behind now would be to expose it to the dangers of Hitler's "scorched earth" policy. Von Braun therefore instructed two of his associates, Dieter Huzel and Bernard Tessman, to hide the archives in an abandoned mine or some similar place. Racing breathlessly against time, Huzel and Tessman secreted the documents in a tunnel near the town of Dörten at the northern edge of the Harz Mountains, just as the United States Ninth Army began occupying the area.

Staver left Paris in search of these papers on 30 April, accompanied by Edward Hull, a member of Porter's General Electric team. During the next few weeks Staver rounded up several rocket experts who had remained in the Bleicherode area after its capture, including Eberhard Rees, Karl Otto Fleisher, and Walther Riedel. With their assistance, the fourteen tons of documents were found on 21 May where they had been hidden near Dörten.

With both the missiles and the technical papers now in hand, Toftoy, who during May was made chief of the Rocket Branch in the Research and Development Division of Army Ordnance, recommended to his superiors that the German rocket scientists themselves be brought to the United States. On 23 July 1945 he was ordered to arrange such a move. Toftoy met Von Braun and his associates at Witzenhausen in early August of 1945, and offered them one-year contracts under the Paperclip program. The German scientists would be sent to the United States under Ordnance Corps custody. Their dependents would be left behind to be quar-

tered and fed by the Army, with the costs deducted from fees paid to the scientists. All 127 scientists to whom this offer was made accepted it.

As soon as the Nordhausen and Bleicherode areas were vacated by United States troops, the Red Army moved in and rounded up some 3,500 lower echelon personnel. (Only about 1,000 of the original 5,000 Peenemünde families had managed to leave for Bavaria after the Russians moved in, not counting the original 500 sent south under General Kammler's orders.) The principal German scientist to contract voluntarily with the Russians was Helmut Gröttrup, who was soon placed in charge of the technical personnel of the Nordhausen factory and the temporary laboratory facilities set up in and around Bleicherode. A new organization was established by the Red Army, which was called Institut für Raketenbetrieb Bleicherode (RABE). Gröttrup remained there until October 1946 when, with about 200 other German rocket specialists, he was shipped without advance notice to Russia.

The British and French also obtained the services of a few German rocket experts, but were unable immediately to undertake major post-war missile development programs. In Project Backfire, the British secured German aid in firing two V-2's from Cuxhaven out over the North Sea, but this did not lead to any sustained ballistic missile effort on their part.

It was the United States which reaped by far the biggest gains from the dismemberment of the German missile establishment.

Von Braun, Dornberger, and their fellow scientists and engineers brought more than just their knowledge and talents with them when they went south to be captured by the American army; they also brought to the West a vision of the future. A vision, moreover, that had been partially worked out in their plans for the continuation of the "A" series beyond the A-5, which had served as a test model for the A-4 (the V-2). Of the later designs in the "A" series, only the A-7 had actually been built during the war.

The A-6, complete on paper, was never converted to hardware. It was to be an improved V-2, powered by an engine using a nitric-sulfuric acid mixture as oxidizer and a fuel consisting of vinyl isobutyl ether mixed with aniline. The underlying idea was to have a liquid-propellant rocket with fuels that could be stored for faster tactical response and greater ease of handling—an idea that came into its own in the postwar years.

There also was an A-7, a winged missile that was about the same size as the A-5. The first A-7's did not have propulsion systems but were used merely for air-drop tests to gather ballistic data. Later models had 3,300-pound-thrust A-5 engines for ground-launch tests. The A-7 had a 30-mile glide range when launched from an airplane flying at an altitude of 5 miles, and a 15-mile range when launched under its own power from the ground.

The A-8, like the A-6, was never built. It would have been essentially an improved A-6 adapted to the same winged configuration used for the A-7 and A-9.

The objective of the A-9 program was increased range. Instead of hurtling to earth, the winged missile would have made an extended glide of up to 400 miles toward the target. Its approach velocity would be relatively low. During the later phases of the war, this fact led many people to doubt its military usefulness, especially in view of the heavy toll taken of the V-1's by defensive forces. Nevertheless, the potential of the boost-glide technique was energetically explored.

Something resembling the A-9 was actually flown in the closing days of the war. It was the A-4b (sometimes called the "bastard A-4"), a designation that was adopted in order to get the winged vehicle the same high priorities enjoyed by the true A-4. The A-4b was a standard V-2 whose external surfaces had been modified—rather crudely—to permit the attachment of supersonic wings and enlarged aerodynamic control surfaces. The A-9 would have looked about the same, but it would have been much more polished.

The A4-b concept was the result of the loss of V-2 launch sites in northern France, Belgium, and Holland that followed the Normandy invasion. Von Braun was faced with continuing demands to keep the V-2's—by now in full mass production—flying, even though the ranges were much longer than heretofore. On 19 October 1944, it was decided to modify some V-2's to extend their range. Although five A-4b's were put under construction, only two were actually launched, on 8 January and 24 January 1945. The first was a failure, but the second proved that the designers' calculations were sound. It was launched straight up, reached a maximum altitude of 50 miles, and attained a maximum speed of 2,700 miles per hour, which made it the first winged guided missile to exceed the speed of sound. The automatic control system worked satisfactorily.

One of the more intriguing aspects of the A-9 project was the plan for a piloted version of the missile. It was proposed to fit a tricycle landing gear to the A-9, so that it could land on a conventional airstrip after its 400-mile boost-glide. Flight time from takeoff to landing was to be 17 minutes —an incredibly short time in terms of 1945 aeronautical thinking.

The final "A" program on which some design work was accomplished before the end of the war was also the most ambitious. It was the A-10, which was not a complete vehicle but the first stage of a two-stage vehicle; the A-9 was to be the second stage. The A-10 was to have produced 400,000 pounds of thrust on a combination of nitric acid and Diesel oil. The stage was to be 65 feet long, with a diameter of 162 inches. The loaded weight of the entire vehicle was 174,000 pounds, only 30,000 pounds of it contributed by the A-9 second stage. Calculations showed that the missile could carry a one-ton payload roughly 2,500 miles.

Above and beyond the A-10 were ideas aimed at exploring space. One project, which could have become the A-11, visualized a third stage *under* the A-10/9 combination. The three-stage vehicle was to place the pilot of a modified A-9 into orbit. And there was even thought of an A-12 stage, producing a minimum of 2.5 million pounds of thrust; with the A-11 second stage and a winged A-10 third stage, it could possibly have orbited a payload of up to 60,000 pounds.

One final German dream should be mentioned: the Antipodal Bomber, designed by Eugen Sänger and fellow worker (later his wife) Irene Bredt. It was described in a long-secret report translated by the United States Navy under the title of "A Rocket Drive for Long-Range Bombers."

The report envisioned a 92-foot-long, 220,000-pound craft, to be launched from a sled driven by rockets developing 1,345,000 pounds of thrust. The sled would send the bomber into the air at 1,000 miles per hour; its own 220,000-pound-thrust liquid oxygen–gasoline oil rocket engine would boost it to a speed of 13,700 miles per hour and an altitude of over 160 miles. The bomber would skip along the top of the atmosphere like a stone on a pond, reaching New York with a bomb load of 6 tons. Sänger and Bredt calculated that the whole trip, takeoff to landing, would take 80 minutes. Dubbed "skip bomber" by Allied technical experts, the concept gave impetus to projects that later evolved in the United States and Soviet Union.

The ideas of the German scientists sounded fantastic—but the reality was hardly less fantastic. As American experts sifted through the tons of information from Peenemünde, it was plain that the past was just prologue to an almost unimaginable future. Rocketry had made great strides in World War II. Man had reached the edge of space.

6 POSTWAR MILITA

Since the end of World War II, the combination of nuclear weapons and advanced rocketry has changed the concept of warfare beyond recognition. Thermonuclear bombs, delivered by intercontinental missiles, hold the threat of immediate destruction of the vital centers of nations. The United States and Russia now confront each other from behind deterrent forces that have established a delicate balance of power without parallel in world history.

The history of rocketry since the end of World War II is almost entirely the story of events in the United States and Russia. The vast resources, great land areas, and technological know-how needed to develop, produce, and deploy intercontinental ballistic missiles have so far ruled out of the field all but these two goliaths. Many other nations have developed smaller rockets for other military purposes, but those do not represent a great advance over the technology available in World War II. The modern military missile in its most terrifying form is a product either of the United States or of the Soviet Union.

Most details of the Soviet experience are still unknown. Even the names of leading Soviet rocket scientists are mentioned only rarely and in guarded terms. Some of the major themes of Soviet rocket development are known in outline, but for the rest, it can only be assumed that the Russian program has run generally parallel to that in the United States.

There probably is one major difference, however. Within the United States, there are really three concurrent histories of military rocket development. Because of continuing interservice rivalry, the Army, Navy, and Air Force for many years carried on what were essentially separate missile-development programs that made contact with each other only occasionally. Not until the mid-1950's did the Defense Department come to grips with the problems caused by the three services' differing outlooks and stubborn independence. The Navy had strategic ambitions in extending its striking forces to intercontinental ranges by submarine-fired mis-

siles. The Air Force basically was more at home with the concept of long-range bombardment—although the missiles had a difficult time competing with the Air Force's own enduring love for airplanes. The Army, meanwhile, preferred to think of missiles as extensions of artillery, and argued on that basis that it should be given control of long-range missile development. Much time, money, and effort were wasted until the duplication and backbiting caused by the interservice feuds could be stopped—or at least controlled.

The Air Force was first in the field, by virtue of its concentration on long-range operations. In the early postwar days, it enjoyed a virtual monopoly on planning intercontinental strikes. The first Air Force attempt to develop long-distance missiles began in July 1944, before the end of the war. The model chosen by the then Army Air Corps did not follow the general concept of the V-2 but rather that of the V-1—an unmanned, winged, and slow-flying bomb. The result was the JB jet-propelled guided bomb series.

The first in the series, the JB-1, was basically a Northrop flying wing—which then enjoyed some transient popularity—built around two 2,000-pound general-purpose bombs and propelled by twin General Electric B1 turbojet engines. Five sled-mounted, 10,500-pound-thrust solid-propellant JATO units pushed the JB-1 into the air. The hoped-for range was 200 miles. After several unsuccessful launching attempts from the ground and the air, the program foundered.

The second try was simply a copy of the V-1. The JB-2, nicknamed the Loon, was manufactured by several auto and aviation companies, who turned out about three hundred of them before the war ended. The original intent was to use the Loon against Japan; the principal benefit of the program was to give some practical missile experience to American manufacturers.

Other members of the JB series included the 4 model and the final version, the JB-10. This, too, was based on the flying wing; it was powered by a modified V-1 pulsejet. About a dozen were built, but only a few performed at all well. The program was canceled in March 1946.

By then, the Air Corps was working on more ambitious, and ultimately more successful, programs along the same line. In retrospect, the Air Force now seems to have wasted much effort in developing relatively slow, winged missiles that cruised through the atmosphere and offered comparatively easy targets to defense forces. But the decision must be seen in the context of the times. The United States had almost no experience in building large-scale rockets and the sophisticated guidance systems they needed. There was keen awareness of the inadequacies of the V-2—despite enormous expenditures of talent and money, the missile still had a miss distance of 3 to 5 miles over its typical flight of 200 miles. And the great success of the Air Corps during World War II had conditioned it to think in terms of winged vehicles, whether manned or unmanned.

As a result, the Air Force's main efforts went into two subsonic missile programs, Snark and Matador, while development of the supersonic, longer-ranged Atlas proceeded slowly at first.

Snark was conceived in January 1946 as a cruise missile capable of traveling the full 5,000- to 7,000-mile intercontinental range. It went through a slow and often unenthusiastic development program. Built by Northrop, Snark weighed 50,000 pounds, was powered by a Pratt and Whitney turbojet engine, and was boosted to operational speed by two Aerojet 33,000-pound-thrust solid JATO's. Easily transported by land and air, Snark could carry a 5,000-pound nuclear payload. It finally entered operational service with the Strategic Air Command's 556th Strategic Missile Squadron in 1958, and was phased out as Atlas became operational.

The Matador was a smaller, shorter-range missile, designed to weigh 12,000 pounds and travel 650 miles. Preliminary specifications were established in August 1945, and the contract was let to the Glenn L. Martin Company two years later. Funding cutbacks made for slow progress, but final production design was approved in February 1951. Despite problems of production build-up and flight testing in 1954, Matador entered operational inventory during 1955. It went through several versions, one of which became the faster, heavier, more accurate, and longer-ranged Mace. Matador was phased out of inventory in the early 1960's, and Mace Models A and B were deployed in its place in Europe and the Far East.

The final Air Force cruise missile was at once the most advanced, the most useful, and, inevitably, the shortest lived. By the time the Navaho was being developed, the fate of cruise missiles was plain: they simply were not effective enough compared to intercontinental ballistic missiles. The ICBM's can travel thousands of miles along arcs that take them hundreds of miles out into space; their trajectories, once determined during the interval that the motors are in operation, are thence affected only by gravitational forces and by air resistance during their exit from and re-entry into the atmosphere. Critics of the Navaho project say it was a combination of short-sightedness, conservatism, and economics that led the Air Force to spend $690 million on this cruise missile, while Atlas and other truly effective ballistic missiles limped along on minimal budgets.

Planners were unwilling to approve the development of very large and expensive ICBM's that could carry the heavy and unwieldy nuclear bombs of the period for 5,000 to 7,000 miles; the costs, compared to those of cruise missiles, appeared far too high. (The Russians, however, believed otherwise and went ahead to develop and build the huge rockets they needed; that decision gave them a long-lasting lead in space exploration.) The Air Force continued up into the mid-1950's to concentrate on cruise missiles as an interim program while waiting for the Atomic Energy Commission to develop lighter bombs. The funds for both ICBM's and aerodynamic

The American version of the V-1 was the JB-2, shown here after being launched from its ramp by a multiple-powder-charge launcher. Known as the "Loon," this unmanned, slow-flying bomb was intended for use against the Japanese. (C. N. HICKMAN)

missiles were just not available. They were not available because of decisions made by key officials in the Department of Defense, in Congress, and in the executive branch.

The document that gave voice to these opinions was dated June 1947 and titled "Operational Requirements for Guided Missiles." This Pentagon study was probably the single document most responsible for stifling the nascent American ICBM program in the early postwar years. It canceled government support of a promising Consolidated Vultee MX-774 rocket program—fortunately, the company continued work, on a much reduced level, by using its own funds—and cut spending on ICBM's to a low level. There were few voices raised in protest. America felt safe with a monopoly of atomic weapons, and few people suspected that Russia was engaged in an all-out drive to develop large rockets. The eventual result was that Russia had the vehicles to launch heavy payloads into space when the time came, while the United States was caught almost completely off guard.

All this is hindsight, and the Navaho program was far from a complete waste. The vehicle itself was impressive. It weighed 300,000 pounds, was boosted into the air by three liquid-propellant rocket engines, each producing 135,000 pounds of thrust, and would have traveled to its target under ramjet power at a speed of Mach 3 (three times the speed of sound). Navaho was strangely shaped, with a huge finned booster assembly slung under a delta-wing

fuselage with tip-mounted ramjets. Built by North American Aviation, Navaho was 95 feet long and guided by an all-inertial guidance system. Many of its components were checked out in the X-10, a test vehicle powered by twin turbojets. Navaho itself was flown eleven times, beginning on 6 November 1956, and ending on 18 November 1958, even though the program was officially canceled on 11 July 1957.

Navaho might have survived if its timing had been different, but it was caught in a budgetary squeeze that developed as Snark neared operational status and its ICBM successor, the Atlas, went into its test program. The technological fallout from Navaho, however, almost justified the entire program. Uprated versions of the Navaho's 135,000-pound-thrust rocket engines, built by Rocketdyne, were applied to such missiles as the Jupiter, the Thor, and the Atlas, and Navaho technology also led to the Redstone engine. Navaho left other legacies. Problems of high-speed flight and design of large supersonic vehicles were at least partially solved in the Navaho program. The experience helped in the XB-70 and X-15 high-speed airplane programs, and in developing such missiles as the air-launched Hound Dog and the Minuteman ICBM. Possibly the most important development of all was Navaho's all-inertial guidance system, whose concept was used with modifications in the Hound Dog, the Minuteman, the XB-70, and the Vigilante bomber. Nautical versions of the system were used in the nuclear submarines *Nautilus* and *Skate*, which traveled under the polar ice pack, and in the Polaris fleet ballistic missile submarine series.

While the Air Force concentrated on cruise missiles, Army Ordnance got off to a quick start in ballistic missile development after the war, picking up right where the Germans had left off at Peenemünde with the V-2.

The first Paperclip group of seven scientists, headed by Von Braun, arrived in Boston's Fort Strong on 29 September 1945. Before this group departed from Germany, Von Braun spent two weeks in Britain, where he was questioned by Sir Alwyn Crow and other Ministry of Supply officials. After processing, six of the seven scientists went to the Aberdeen Proving Ground, where they began sorting out the tons of documents that had been shipped from the Dörten mine in Germany. Von Braun, who was met by Major James P. Hamill in Boston, stopped in Washington to meet with several high Army Ordnance officers, while the other members of the vanguard group—Erich W. Neubert, Theodor A. Poppel, August Schultze, Eberhard Rees, Wilhelm Jungert, and Walter Schwidetzky—went directly to Aberdeen.

Hamill began arranging to transfer the scientists to El Paso, Texas, where they were to start establishing a United States guided-missile program at Fort Bliss. The main body of Germans began arriving at Fort Bliss in December 1945, and by February 1946 over a hundred were on hand. They were quartered in converted hospital buildings that gradually became more homelike.

The test facilities became more elaborate as the program picked up speed. The first static firing test of a V-2 power plant in the United States took place on 14 March 1946, and soon afterward a series of test flights began. The first American-adapted V-2 was flown from the White Sands Proving Ground, New Mexico, on 16 April 1946, after its static test on 14 March. Other flights of missiles equipped with instruments to test the upper atmosphere and ionosphere followed quickly. Typical firings between 1946 and the end of the program in 1952 are summarized in the table below.

To coordinate these experiments, a V-2 Upper Atmosphere Research Panel was established on 16 January 1947. As newer rockets were developed, the group became the Upper Atmosphere Rocket Research Panel in March 1948 and the Rocket and Satellite Research Panel in April 1957. The group effectively coordinated the activities of government, industry, and universities in developing payload instrumentation and gathering and distributing data from the flights.

The last of the Air Force's cruise missiles, Navaho, flew at three times the speed of sound, but was still too slow to be an effective weapon. Boosted by high-thrust rocket engines, it provided the technological basis for later ICBM's. (NORTH AMERICAN AVIATION)

Selected V-2 Firings from White Sands, New Mexico

Date	Altitude (miles)	Range (miles)	Velocity (mph)	Engine firing time (seconds)	High-altitude studies
13 June 1946	73	40	2,877	59	Ionosphere, Solar radiation.
10 October 1946	102	12	3,647	68	Cosmic and Solar radiation, atmospheric pressure and temperature, ionosphere.
17 December 1946	116	21	3,683	70	Cosmic radiation, micrometeorites, biological research.
9 October 1947	97	28	3,400	63	Solar radiation, atmospheric pressure and composition.
5 August 1948	104	53	3,545	66	Ionosphere; atmospheric pressure and temperature, Solar and cosmic radiation.
14 June 1949	83	37	3,005	67	Atmospheric pressure, temperature and composition; cosmic and Solar radiation, ionosphere; Earth photography.
31 August 1950	85	36	3,136	85	Ionosphere, micrometeorites, atmospheric density, sky brightness, biological research.
22 August 1952	133	52.2	4,060	62.6	Training flight, maximum altitude desired.

Col. Holger N. Toftoy (left), chief of the Rocket Branch of Army Ordnance, with Wernher von Braun (right) at the guided missile center at Fort Bliss, Texas, 1946. A year earlier Toftoy had offered Von Braun a one-year contract to work on the United States missile program. (MAJ. GEN. H. N. TOFTOY)

The first American-adapted V-2 was flown from the White Sands Proving Ground, N.M., on 16 April 1946. Here it is shown (above right) during engine check-out on static test stand, (below) being raised to launch position, and (right) at takeoff. (U.S. ARMY)

To support the V-2 flights, Army Ordnance contracted for the services of the General Electric Company in what became known as the Hermes program. While the components of the missiles flown in 1946 were completely of German origin, increasing modifications were made from 1947 onward, primarily to accommodate larger and more complex payloads. By 1950 the V-2 rocket had been lengthened by 5 feet, increasing its payload capacity from 16 to 80 cubic feet.

The V-2 program, in addition to giving Americans experience in launching large vehicles, gave valuable information on every aspect of rocket flights and added considerably to information about the upper atmosphere. Most of the rockets were flown from White Sands, carrying instruments that measured atmospheric characteristics and the ionosphere. A V-2 carrying atmospheric sounding gear and a biological payload reached an altitude of 116 miles on 17 December 1946. The highest altitude attained was achieved on 22 August 1952, when vehicle TF-1, with no scientific instrumentation, flew to 133 miles above the New Mexico desert. The longest V-2 flight in the United States, 111.1 miles, took place on 5 December 1946.

For some time the Navy had been interested in the possibility of firing large missiles from ships at sea. As the V-2 was available in some quantity, it was decided to employ one of these missiles in what became known as Operation Sandy. Accordingly, on 6 September 1957 a fully fueled V-2 was launched from the deck of the aircraft carrier *Midway*. The launch was successful, but the missile exploded about 5,000 feet in the air. The program, conceived and realized by Rear Admiral Daniel V. Gallery,

had obvious implications for the future—but meanwhile, the inherent hazards of shipboard launch had to be thoroughly investigated.

This led to Operation Pushover, directed by Lieutenant Commander W. P. Murphey, wherein two completely fueled V-2 rockets were exploded to determine how much damage would occur to the launch area if an operational missile accidentally blew up. The tests, begun in 1948, caused such damage that submariners were scared away from the later Army-Navy Jupiter program. "Instinctively," said Murphey, "we knew that any missile ever launched from a sub would have to be solid-fueled."

The Army began to build on V-2 technology with the program code-named Bumper, in which a small American Wac Corporal rocket was used as the second stage of a V-2 in hopes of reaching extreme altitudes. Bumper was also intended to prove out techniques needed for firing two-stage missiles—ignition and separation of the stages at high altitudes, stability of the second stage at high velocities, and the aerodynamic characteristics of the vehicle.

The Army conducted a series of the eight Bumper research firings between May 1948 and July 1950. Flight 5, on 24 February 1949, was the only complete success, reaching an altitude of 244 miles and a velocity of 5,150 miles per hour. Flights 7 and 8 were significant for being launched from what was then called the Long-Range Proving Ground at Cape Canaveral, Florida. The purpose of both flights was to determine the aerodynamic characteristics of high-speed missiles flying shallow trajectories. No. 8 hit 200 miles from the coast after breaking all speed records within the atmosphere (No. 5 had hit its top speed in space).

Project Bumper Firing Summary

Flight No.	Date	Altitude (miles)	Velocity (mph)	Engine firing time (secs) V-2 Stage	Engine firing time (secs) Wac Corporal Stage	Launch Site	Remarks
1	13 May 1948	79.1	2,740	66	6	White Sands	Premature cutoff of second stage.
2	19 August 1948	8.3	850	33.8	0	White Sands	Premature cutoff of first stage.
3	30 September 1948	93.4	3,160	64.2	0	White Sands	Second stage did not ignite.
4	1 November 1948	3	875	28.5	0	White Sands	Explosion following cut off.
5	24 February 1949	244	5,150	68	28	White Sands	Successful.
6	21 April 1949	31	1,820	48	0	White Sands	Premature cutoff of first stage.
7	24 July 1950	—	—	—	—	Cape Canaveral	Low-angle firing.
8	29 July 1950	10	—	—	—	Cape Canaveral	Low-angle firing; vehicle impacted 200 miles away.

The Hermes A-2 rocket, at White Sands, March 1953. Under the Hermes program, the Army undertook experiments in both liquid and solid rocket technology. This solid-fuel model, with triangular tail fins, was never flown. (U. S. ARMY)

The V-2 firings were only a part of the Hermes program. It had been evident that the supply of V-2's would soon be exhausted, and that rocket technology was advancing. Both these considerations led to plans under GE's Hermes program for new missiles based on combined German-American experience. The experimental vehicles that resulted never entered operational inventory. The program itself became somewhat controversial with many experts charging that Hermes merely repeated German technology, instead of advancing the art of rocketry. Whatever its shortcomings, the program most certainly did provide the United States with valuable experience, while it initiated American industry in the technology of large rockets.

Component development for Hermes began in 1946, and many items were flight tested in V-2's. The telemetry system for Hermes A-1, for instance, was flown in a V-2 in January 1947, and the A-1's guidance and control systems were tested in V-2's and airplanes. The new rocket motor was static tested at General Electric's Malta Test Station in Schenectady, New York, during 1948 and 1949, and five missiles were flown from White Sands between 19 May

1950 and 26 April 1951. The Hermes A-1 was very similar in configuration to the German Wasserfall surface-to-air missile. It reached a maximum altitude of 15 miles, a range of 38 miles, and a speed of 1,850 miles per hour. It was powered by a liquid-propellant oxygen-alcohol engine.

A-2, which never flew, had triangular tail fins (compared to A-1's four small midwings). It was powered by a solid motor developed by the Jet Propulsion Laboratory and the Thiokol Chemical Corporation. The motor was tested successfully in December 1951, but changing requirements caused A-2's cancellation in October 1952. However, the motor was flown in RV-A-10 test vehicles in February and March 1953.

The third member of the Hermes family appeared in two models, A-3A and A-3B, neither of which was an overwhelming success. A-3 was supposed to fly a 1,000-pound payload over a 150-mile range. The outbreak of the Korean War caused an acceleration in the A-3 program in 1951. By the time the program ended in 1954, seven A models and six B models of the A-3 had been flown. Not many experts were impressed with the results. But the A-3 did lead to development of a stable platform and radio inertial guidance system and the successful testing of rocket engines with thrusts ranging from 18,000 to 22,600 pounds, at the then high specific impulse of 242 seconds (that is, 242 pounds of thrust produced by each pound of propellant consumed per second).

Another Hermes vehicle developed by the Hamill–Von Braun group at Fort Bliss, with General Electric merely providing support, never left the study stage. Hermes II was a supersonic ramjet that was to be accelerated to three times the speed of sound by a V-2 initial booster. A full-scale model of the ramjet second stage was designed, and in November 1948 it was tested successfully in the nosecone of V-2 flight 44. Hundreds of static tests with a new "split-wing" ramjet propulsion system proved the practicality of the scheme. With the advent of the Army's Redstone missile project, however, the Hermes II program was reduced to engine development only and, in December 1952, it was canceled.

Another study program conducted by General Electric in Schenectady, was the Hermes C. This was an ambitious three-stage missile weighing 250,000 pounds and powered by six 100,000-pound-thrust rocket engines in the first stage, with one such engine in the second stage. The third stage was a glider with a proposed range of 2,000 miles. Hermes C-1 was much more modest, yet much more important in the history of American rocketry. A single-stage rocket capable of carrying a 500-pound payload for 500 miles, Hermes C-1 never got out of the study stage. But it was to lead directly to the Redstone missile, the first major American effort in the field.

In the late 1940's, it became evident that the Army's growing missile programs needed more room than was available at Fort Bliss. After a long search, the decision settled on the Redstone Arsenal in Huntsville, Alabama. The arsenal was on a large tract of government property, and its location on the Tennessee River gave it access to the power resources of the Tennessee Valley Authority. The climate was good, and the arsenal was not too far from Cape Canaveral, whose Long Range Proving Ground was growing in importance. The transfer was formally approved by the Secretary of the Army on 28 October 1949; between April and November 1950 the move was made. More than 500 military personnel, 130 members of the original Von Braun team, several hundred General Electric employees and 120 government civilian workers moved to Huntsville, where they would write a new chapter in rocket history.

The Redstone organization was designated the Ordnance Guided Missile Center. It was headed by Hamill, who had been transferred from Toftoy's Rocket Branch of the Ordnance Research and Development Division in the Pentagon. The arsenal itself was commanded by Brigadier General Thomas Vincent, who was in charge of supplying support to the missile group.

Hamill and the vanguard of the group had hardly settled in when the Korean War broke out in June 1950. Their first assignment was to conduct a feasibility study for a 500-mile ballistic surface-to-surface missile. As the Korean War grew more intense, the missile's priority increased. After being called Ursa and later Major unofficially, the project was baptized Redstone, after the arsenal where it was being developed, on 8 April 1952.

Rather than develop a new engine, the group decided to use a modification of the liquid-propellant engine developed by North American Aviation for the Navaho. As the program proceeded, the Army's requirements changed. The desired range was reduced from 500 to 200 miles, which provided a bonus: The Redstone would be able to carry a nuclear warhead and, in addition, it would be a mobile weapon capable of being launched under battlefield conditions by combat troops.

The first Redstone was fired with moderate success from Cape Canaveral on 20 August 1953. It traveled an 8,000-yard trajectory. Thirty-six more research and development models were launched through 1958, 16 of them built by Redstone Arsenal, the rest by Chrysler Corporation. On 16 May 1958, a Redstone was fired for the first time by combat-ready soldiers, members of Battery A, 40th Field Artillery Missile Group. Redstone was put into service of United States Army units stationed in Germany the next month.

The years between 1952 and 1954, during which the Redstone was designed and developed, were critical ones in the history of the entire United States missile program. The basis for every missile now in the United States armory was established during this period, in which events came with dizzying swiftness. A historian can deal with these interwoven patterns only by pointing out key developments that affected the entire program and then disentangling the threads of the ensuing growth patterns.

Perhaps the most crucial development of all was the growing realization that the Soviet Union was threatening a breakthrough in weaponry that endangered the very existence of the United States. The Soviet Union, which had its first atomic bomb in 1949, ended the United States monopoly on the

In the Bumper series, the Army made a two-stage rocket out of the V-2 by adding a small Wac Corporal rocket as its second stage. In this flight from White Sands in April 1949, the V-2 propulsion was prematurely cut off, resulting in a maximum altitude of only 31 miles. (U.S. ARMY)

hydrogen bomb with an explosion on 12 August 1953. Before very long, intelligence produced evidence that the Soviets were pushing hard on a ballistic missile program and might well be ahead of the American effort. All three armed services began vigorous programs to develop long-range ballistic missiles, each concentrating on its own specialty: the Army on short- and intermediate-range missiles; the Navy on missiles to be fired from seagoing vessels; and the Air Force, while continuing its long-range cruise missile programs, began work on the Atlas ICBM. The lines of action were not very clear at the start of the period, but the over-all program was well established by the end of the decade.

The Army and the Navy first began a joint program to develop a medium-range missile that both could use. On 13 September 1955, a committee under James R. Killian, Jr., President Eisenhower's special advisor on science and technology, recommended to the National Security Council that the Navy should support the development of an Army intermediate-range missile that could be launched at sea. Secretary of Defense Charles E. Wilson, on 8 November 1955, gave approval to the Joint Army-Navy Bal-

America's first successful IRBM, the single-stage Jupiter, stood 58 feet tall on its launch pad at Cape Canaveral. Here it is shown at takeoff on its 18 May 1958 flight to test nose cone materials for re-entering the Earth's atmosphere. (U.S. ARMY)

listic Missile Committee to develop the missile. On 17 November, the Navy established the Special Projects Office, under the direction of Rear Admiral William F. Raborn, to oversee its part of the program. Raborn took over his new position on 5 December 1955.

The Army organization in the program was the Army Ballistic Missile Agency (ABMA), which came into existence on 1 February 1956, taking over what was then the Guided Missile Development Division at Redstone Arsenal. It was placed under the command of an aggressive, accomplished officer from the Ordnance Corps' Industrial Division, Major General John B. Medaris.

The missile that was to emerge from this combination was the Jupiter. At the beginning, it was able to use with good effect the technology developed by Redstone. Two rockets based on Redstone came into existence to support the Jupiter program.

The first modified Redstone was called the Jupiter A. Between September 1955 and June 1958 a total of 25 Jupiter A's were fired, all within the 37-missile Redstone test flight program, to check out certain components for the Jupiter.

Jupiter C, officially known as the Jupiter Composite Re-entry Test Vehicle, was designed primarily to test nosecone materials for the forthcoming IRBM. In addition, it provided the capability of a rudimentary carrier for placing a satellite in orbit, and later was known in this capacity as the Juno 1. Since a Redstone did not have the power to generate the high speeds needed to simulate conditions of re-entry for the Jupiter nosecone, two special upper stages were added to an uprated Redstone. The Redstone first stage was lengthened to hold more propellant, and the engine was modified to operate on a new fuel called hydyne, a mixture of unsymmetrical dimethylhydrazine and diethylene triamine. The second stage consisted of a cluster of eleven solid-propellant rockets, and the third stage was three solid-fuel rockets that fit within the inner ring of the second stage. To stabilize the upper stage assembly against disturbances caused by inequalities of its many rocket engines, the whole assembly was spun rapidly during flight. The three stages fired in sequence to produce the great speeds needed for the re-entry tests.

On its first flight, on 20 September 1956, Jupiter C reached the unprecedented altitude of 682 miles, landing 3,400 miles from Cape Canaveral—a record that was not equaled by the United States for another two years. The second shot lofted a scaled-down Jupiter nosecone into space, but guidance difficulties caused the nosecone to land outside the target area. The third and last test, on 8 August 1957, resulted in recovery by parachute of the revolutionary "ablative" nosecone after a 300-mile-high, 1,200-mile-long trajectory.

As development of Jupiter IRBM continued, the Navy became increasingly reluctant to continue with the program. A huge, liquid-propellant missile—the Jupiter emerged as a 58-foot-high, 110,000-pound vehicle—could not be launched easily from any submarine. In addition, the Navy had its own particular problem: the development of a navigation system that would allow a ship at sea to determine its own position under all weather conditions with an accuracy sufficient to place a nuclear warhead on a target 1,500 miles away.

In September 1956 came another event that helped shape the future. The Atomic Energy Commission announced a breakthrough in thermonuclear technology. By 1965 at the latest, and possibly by 1963, the AEC said, small high-yield warheads would be available. This meant that a relatively small missile would be able to carry a nuclear device that could neutralize major targets. With the feasibility of small missiles in the offing, the Navy broke away from the Jupiter program and developed what came to be the Polaris missile–submarine system.

Work on the Jupiter continued, but the Army lost out in the interservice rivalry for control of the nation's IRBM ICBM program. On 26 November 1956, Secretary of Defense Wilson issued his "roles and missions" memorandum that effectively stripped the Army of control over long-range missiles. The memorandum assigned operational control of the Jupiter to the Air Force. The Army was limited to developing surface-to-surface missiles with ranges of 200 miles or less. It could make "limited feasibility studies" of missiles with greater ranges, but that was all. Jupiter program funding was switched from the

Army to the Department of Defense, and later to the Air Force. The ABMA continued to serve as the development agency, but Jupiter was destined for another service.

The first Jupiter launching occurred on 1 March 1957, with the missile flying 60 miles. The third flight, on 31 May 1957, achieved a 1,600-mile flight from Cape Canaveral, making Jupiter the first successful American IRBM. ABMA delivered its first Jupiter to the Air Force in August 1958, and more than sixty eventually were based in Italy and Turkey.

A non-military Jupiter flight, meanwhile, sounded a note for the future. On 28 May 1959, two monkeys named Able and Baker rode a Jupiter 300 miles high and 1,600 miles down range and were recovered alive. They were the forerunners of other living space payloads.

All the other Army missiles developed by the Army had shorter ranges than the Redstone, with one exception—the ABMA-developed Pershing, the Redstone's replacement, which has a range of 450 miles. For example, the Corporal, the first operational surface-to-surface missile, had a range of 75 miles. Powered by monoethylaniline and red fuming nitric acid, the Corporal was developed by the Jet Propulsion Laboratory.

The Corporal was still a rather cumbersome weapon, which took about seven hours to fire after its 250-man missile battalion had selected the launch site. It was replaced in 1957 by the solid-propellant Sergeant, another JPL product, which was considerably smaller, could be fired in far less time, and had about the same range. Like the Pershing, the Sergeant has a solid-propellant engine, but unlike the Pershing, has only one stage.

While the Army's missile role contracted, the Navy's expanded. The Navy had never pictured the Jupiter as the final answer to its highly individual needs. When it first entered the joint Jupiter develop-

Comparison of American Short- and Medium-Range Ballistic Missiles

Name	Length (feet)	Diameter (inches)	Weight (pounds)	Propulsion	Range (miles)
Corporal	46	30	12,000	RFNA-monoethylaniline	75
Honest John	27.25	24.5	4,700	solid	12
Lance	20	22	32,000	solid	40
Little John	14.4	12.5	780	solid	10
Pershing	34.5	40	10,000	solid	450
Redstone	69	70	62,000	LOX-ethyl alcohol	200
Sergeant	34.5	31	10,100	solid	>75

ment program with the Army, the Navy had stated:

On a long-term basis, the Navy proposes a solid-propellant development program pointed toward surface ships and eventual submarine use. This development should be initiated immediately to alleviate the serious hazards and difficult logistic, handling, storage, and design problems associated with liquid fuels. Development of a solid-propellant missile and submarine system appears feasible, but not on the time scale of the original approach. The solid propellant is an integral part of the submarine program.

In March 1956, the Navy won permission from the Joint Army-Navy Ballistic Missile Committee to undertake both surface and subsurface missile development programs. That month, the Office of the Secretary of Defense (OSD) Ballistic Missile Committee approved a program to develop solid-propellant components to determine the feasibility of a solid-propellant missile. In mid-July, the OSD Scientific Advisory Committee went all the way, recommending that the Navy concentrate on the solid-propellant approach, cutting down on its use of Jupiter-derived hardware since "the suitability of the components was very questionable."

After the AEC announcement in September of the breakthrough in design of nuclear warheads, the next step was inevitable. On 23 October 1956 the Scientific Advisory Committee recommended that a solid-propellant missile "receive top priority, equal to that of the other [Jupiter] IRBM program . . . ." with an aim toward having an operational weapon by 1962 or 1963. The Navy officially pulled out of the Jupiter program on 8 December, with the full support of Chief of Naval Operations Arleigh A. Burke and Navy Secretary Charles S. Thomas. The joint Army-Navy committee was dissolved on 18 December, and the Navy Ballistic Missile Committee was established the next day to give broad direction to the development of the Polaris.

Although the joint Army-Navy committee had existed for only a year, cooperation between the two services during the period was responsible for great strides in the solution of the extremely difficult problem of accurately guiding a missile that had been launched from a rocking, moving platform to a target 1,300 to 1,500 miles distant. This breakthrough was accomplished by tying together the Navy's SINS —Ship Inertial Navigation System—and the ABMA-developed inertial guidance platform of the Jupiter in such a fashion that the motion and position of the ship would be reflected automatically in a bias in the setting of the missile's guidance system. As a result, the ship could move freely in any direction, either beneath or on top of the waves, while the unlaunched missile remained firmly "bracketed" on its faraway target. The guidance concepts worked out by the Army and Navy during 1956 were transferred directly to Polaris and still form the backbone of that missile's guidance system.

Raborn's Special Projects Office remained in charge of systems development after the Navy was authorized to build an IRBM of its own. In April 1956, a small study contract had been let with Lockheed Aircraft Corporation to determine the feasibility of an underwater-launched missile combined with a nuclear submarine. Lockheed recommended exactly what the Navy wanted all along—a two-stage solid-propellant vehicle that could be stored in and fired from a submarine.

The Polaris program came into existence officially on 12 January 1957. By March, the size, shape, and weight of the missile had been decided upon. Simultaneously, development of all the launch devices for the missile was undertaken. It became plain that special vessels would have to be designed, built, and tested as the Polaris was evolved. By mid-June, progress had been so great that the Chief of Naval Operations was able to approve the characteristics of the revolutionary submarine that was to fire Polaris.

As the program was accelerated, the estimates of the time needed for operational readiness were pushed forward. In October 1957, the AEC said a small-size, high-yield nuclear warhead would be ready by 1960, three to five years sooner than previously estimated. The Secretary of the Navy promptly proposed that the first-generation Polaris, with a range of 1,400 miles, could be in service by December 1959 aboard surface training ships and that the first missile-carrying submarines would be in operation by late 1960. The Secretary of Defense authorized faster progress on Polaris on 9 December 1957, and construction of the first three Polaris submarines was begun the next month. The submarines, the *George Washington*, *Ethan Allen*, and *Patrick Henry*, were designated SSBN—*B* for ballistic missiles, *N* for nuclear powered.

The Navy's arguments for a strong Polaris fleet were summarized in a classified memorandum dated 27 February 1958. The memorandum was prepared under the direction of J. E. Clark, director of the Guided Missiles Division of the Office of the Chief of Naval Operations. The memorandum, now declassified, listed these advantages of a fleet ballistic missile (FBM) over the conventional IRBM concept:

1. No negotiations were needed for Polaris launch sites, in the United States or abroad.

2. While liquid-propellant missiles cannot be launched immediately, a solid-propellant Polaris is

always ready for launch. "Also, each Polaris missile has its own launcher."

3. "Every unidentified submarine at sea is a potential FBM," which creates "serious antisubmarine warfare and intelligence problems for Soviets. . . ."

4. "Because FBM can be launched at Eurasia from all directions, Soviet missile defenses will have to be complex, versatile, and expensive."

5. A Polaris is less vulnerable than a land-based missile because its location cannot be pinpointed in advance, it is not easily sabotaged, and it cannot be affected by weapons aimed at other targets.

6. "Use of FBM affords greater physical safety for the U.S. and friendly nations (whereas land-based missiles) would be like magnets in drawing enemy fire on the U.S. and Allied centers of population."

As part of the Polaris program, a number of fleet test vehicles were developed to check out components. On 24 September 1958 the first AX vehicle, with Polaris's basic size and shape, was launched—unsuccessfully. Other partial or total failures followed. The first success was AX-6, which flew a 300-mile trajectory on 20 April 1959. The AX firings were followed by an A1X series. On 7 January 1960, the first inertially guided Polaris test-firing was conducted at Cape Canaveral.

The *George Washington* had been launched on 9 June 1959, and commissioned in December. Within six months of the Cape Canaveral test, on 20 July 1960, the *George Washington* made the first submerged firing of a Polaris test vehicle. In mid-November, the *George Washington* shipped out on its first

The Navy, needing a smaller missile that could be fired from underwater, began work on a solid-propellant missile. The result was the Polaris, which they fired successfully in 1960. Right, a filmstrip series showing an underwater launch from the submarine Theodore Roosevelt *off the coast of Florida, 19 March 1963.* (U.S. NAVY)

131

The A-3 Polaris missile rises from the water after its first submerged launching on 26 October 1963. In this flight a practice warhead flew more than 2,000 miles before landing on target. (U.S. NAVY)

operational cruise with sixteen Polaris missiles aboard. The Special Projects Office–Lockheed–AEC team had beat its original deadline of 1963 by an impressive margin.

Both missiles and submarines have been upgraded since. The first Polaris has been followed by the A-2, with a range of 1,700 miles, and the 2,900-mile A-3. The last A-1 was delivered in December 1961; two months earlier, the first A-2 test vehicle had been fired from a submerged submarine. The first test flight of the A-3 took place less than a year later, on 7 August 1962, and the first submerged launch was made on 26 October 1963. By September 1964, the first A-3's were operational on the SSBN *Daniel Webster*. By 1966, the missile submarine force was fully operational, with thirteen submarines armed with A-2's and twenty-eight carrying A-3's.

The Navy has since developed the Poseidon. It has twice the warhead weight of the A-3 and has been tested with multiple independently targetable re-entry vehicles (MIRV). As of 1969, four Polaris submarines had been converted to Poseidons.

The Navy has also had its subsonic missiles. Its 1946 Rigel program resulted in a series of test ve-

hicles built by the Grumman Aircraft Engineering Corporation and tested at Point Mugu, California. The aim was a 26,000-pound ramjet-powered missile that could be launched from a surfaced submarine up to 550 miles from its target. The program was canceled in the early 1950's. The Regulus, another cruise missile, was more successful. Manufactured by Chance-Vought Aircraft, Inc., the jet-powered, sub-launched missile made its first successful flight in 1951, and later entered the fleet inventory. It was followed by the larger, faster, and longer-ranged Regulus 2, which can be fired from subs, cruisers, and aircraft carriers for shore bombardment. Both Regulus missiles are vulnerable to countermeasures. The pride of the Navy remains the Polaris, which comes as close to being the invulnerable weapon as anything ever developed.

The Navy Polaris program is a textbook example of weapons development. The Air Force program, during its early days, came close to being the opposite. The Air Force's adventures with cruise missiles have already been detailed. Its ballistic missile program, after a false start in 1947, did not really get under way until the mid-1950's.

In April 1947, the Consolidated Vultee Aircraft Corporation—now the Convair division of General Dynamics—received a one-year study contract from the Air Technical Training Command of the then Army Air Corps to develop feasibility designs for both subsonic and supersonic surface-to-surface missiles with ranges from 1,600 to 5,800 miles. The company designed a preliminary test vehicle, but Army Air Corps—and Pentagon—support vanished within months. Adding company funds to some leftover contract money, Consolidated-Vultee built three MX-774 rockets, which were static-tested in mid-1947 at Point Loma in San Diego. The rockets were launched with partial success in July, September, and December 1948 from the White Sands Proving Ground. Nativ test rockets, built by North American Aviation, Inc., were fired from Holloman Air Force Base in New Mexico to get more data on ballistic missiles.

The outbreak of the Korean War, the development of smaller nuclear weapons by the AEC, and a growing realization that the Soviet Union was active in the field changed the situation. The AEC's nuclear experiment, code-named Mike, held on 1 November 1952, made it clear that an operational hydrogen bomb missile warhead would be available within a few years. The Air Force Scientific Advisory Board established an ad hoc committee, under Professor Clark B. Millikan, the next month to review Air Force policy. Soon afterward, Air Force Secretary Harold E. Talbott named as his special assistant for research and development Trevor Gardner, a civilian who would become a leading champion of the ICBM concept.

Pressure for a policy change began to build. In April 1953 Gardner asked for a reassessment of earlier Air Force estimates that an operational ICBM might take a decade to develop. In June, General Donald M. Yates, director of research and development at Air Force Headquarters, recommended that Secretary of Defense Wilson undertake a major review of the missile program of the Air Force and the other two services. That fall Gardner set up the Strategic Missiles Evaluation Committee, which became known as the Teapot Committee, to study the Air Force program.

John von Neumann, of the Institute for Advanced Study, was chairman of the committee, which included as members Hendrik W. Bode, Louis G. Dunn, Lawrence A. Hyland, George B. Kistiakowsky, Charles C. Lauritsen, Clark B. Millikan, Allen E. Puckett, Simon Ramo, Jerome B. Wiesner and Dean E. Wooldridge. In February 1954, the committee submitted its report to Gardner, who, supported by an independent Rand Corporation study, urged General Nathan F. Twining, the Air Force Chief of Staff, to undertake a greatly increased ICBM effort. The Teapot Committee said an effective ICBM could be ready in six years or less. It urged a new organizational setup to both dramatize the urgency of the program and give the officer in charge of the program all the power he needed.

All these events led to a spurt in the Air Force missile program. The Air Force had to seek outside help, not only for development of the hardware for what became the Atlas ICBM, but for technical management as well.

First, it had to set up an office of its own with authority to call on Air Force resources and facilities whenever and wherever they were needed. Gardner recommended that the Air Research and Development Command be given that authority, with a major general at the top and a brigadier general under him to handle project direction and liaison with industry. The choice fell on Major General James McCormack, ARDC vice-commander, and Brigadier General Bernard A. Schriever, who was then with the Air Staff. On 1 June 1954, Schriever took over direction of the ICBM program, under General McCormack's command.

Since most of the industrial facilities needed for the program were on the West Coast, Schriever set up the ARDC's Western Development Division (WDD) on 15 July, and moved West himself. Procurement support was provided by a Special Projects Office within the Air Materiel Command at Wright Field, Ohio.

The Air Force still needed technical management know-how. It had several alternatives. The ARDC-WDD could try to recruit its own talent. An existing organization—the Rand Corporation or a large university—could be used. The contractors themselves could provide the management skill. Or a new organization of consultants could be established to deal solely with what promised to be the biggest development program in history.

The final alternative was chosen. The Ramo-Wooldridge Corporation was created to give technical advice first to the Strategic Missiles Evaluation Committee and later to its successor, the Atlas Scientific Evaluation Committee. By September 1954, Ramo-Wooldridge had been given responsibility for technical direction of the entire Atlas program.

The corporation, which was forbidden to obtain production contracts, was led by Simon Ramo and Dean Wooldridge, both men of proven ability in the fields of missiles and program management. The corporation grew rapidly, later assuming responsibility for the Titan and Minuteman ICBM's, the Thor IRBM, and other projects. Its 170 employees in 1954 became nearly 5,200 in 1960. In late 1957, the company became Thompson-Ramo-Wooldridge and established a subsidiary, Space Technology Laboratories, which continued advisory and technical management services for the Air Force until mid-1960. At that time the Aerospace Corporation was established to take over some of these responsibilities. WDD itself went through a name change in June 1957, becoming the Air Force Ballistic Missile Division.

The Atlas program gathered momentum starting in 1954. By mid-1955, it had the highest of national priorities (the Thor was given the same high priority that November). Decisions came rapidly, and test vehicles were fired frequently to test the new components that were being developed. The first two launches of Series A Atlases were made on 11 June and 25 September. Both were failures, but the third firing, on 17 December, was a decided success. On the early flights, only the twin booster engines that were clustered around the main, or sustainer engine, were fired, so range was measured in only hundreds of miles. The first firing of a successful Series-B Atlas, with all three engines ignited, was held on 2 August 1958 at Cape Canaveral. The range achieved was 2,500 miles.

Because the Atlas program had started late and faced early and critical deadlines, the Air Force had to scrap accepted management principles and de-

America's first ICBM, Atlas, had to be fueled at the last minute with liquid oxygen and kerosene. Then it was raised to an upright position, where all three stages were ignited. This series of eight photos was taken during the 15 minutes before an Atlas launching at Vandenberg Air Force Base, Calif. (U.S. AIR FORCE)

velop its own. In most previous development programs, one element of a complex system was proved out before testing of the next element began. Only when every part of the system had been tried, were all put together and the total system tested. Then decisions were made about building support equipment for the system.

There was no time for these niceties. The philosophy that emerged was expensive but effective. It was called concurrency. Major decisions were frozen early in the program, with the risks that were involved, and the higher costs resulting from setbacks being taken for granted. Concurrency meant many more tests of components and subsystems had to be made, but it also meant a faster development cycle. Work on many different components went ahead simultaneously, and all were tested at once. Concurrency might cost more, but money was secondary to the vital matter of national defense. What was most important, concurrency worked—for Titan and Thor, as well as Atlas.

One of the major problems in developing a bal-

listic missile is the creation of a nosecone that can take the heat and friction of re-entry into the atmosphere after a 500- to 800-mile arc into space. Many different approaches were tried at first—blunt heat-sink shapes, an Air Force concept that would slow down the nosecone and absorb heat, and ablating types, a concept taken over from the Army, that would sear down being the two major ideas. Nosecone tests began with the Atlas C series, which first used a copper heat-sink and later an ablating nosecone. A range of more than 4,000 miles was attained in flight tests that began on 23 December 1958.

Flight testing of the operational Atlas D began in April 1959, and by August the missile had been proved out. Its initial operational test was made at the Pacific Missile Range (now the Western Test Range) on 9 September by a mixed crew drawn from the Ballistic Missile Division and the Strategic Air Command. Firings that continued into 1960 saw the Atlas D stretch its range to 9,000 miles. Meanwhile, a more powerful Atlas E was launched in October 1960 and the first Atlas F was fired in August 1961.

134

Both these models were designed to be fired from underground "silos."

While Atlas was being developed, the Thor IRBM was also taking shape. The Air Research and Development Command, acting on a Defense Department decision to allow the Air Force to produce a missile with the same performance characteristics as the Army's Jupiter, awarded a development contract to the Douglas Aircraft Company in December 1955. It was agreed that as many Atlas components and systems as possible would be used in Thor. Thus, Thor was fitted with the Atlas D nosecone and was powered by basically the same engine as used in the Atlas booster stage. Many components of both missiles were tested on the Thor-Able two-stage rocket, a pure test vehicle.

The first four test shots, between January and August 1957, were failures. On 20 September, a Thor achieved a range of close to 1,000 miles. It was about four months behind the Jupiter, which had flown some 1,600 miles on 31 May.

With very substantial budgetary support behind it, Thor moved into the operational stage quickly. It passed its first capability tests in the summer of 1958 and was turned over to the British for training and deployment in June 1959. The first Thor squadron went into active service in Great Britain on 22 April 1960. Jupiter, meanwhile, was poised in Italy and Turkey. Both missiles were phased out of service as more advanced systems came into volume production.

One of these more advanced missiles was the Titan, whose genesis was in reports by the Von Neumann Committee and the Rand Corporation in 1954 and 1955 on weaknesses in the Atlas philosophy. One serious weakness was the fact that all three of the Atlas engines were ignited on the ground before lift-off, with the two boosters dropping off later. A more efficient procedure is to fire only the first-stage engines at lift-off, drop the entire stage when its propellants are used up, and then continue the flight with the second-stage engine. This approach had been felt to be too risky to attempt in the earlier Atlas project because little experience had been built up at the time on igniting liquid-propellant rocket engines at high altitudes. In order to keep its weight down, Atlas also had been constructed with a thin pressurized airframe, which was not ideal for advanced, higher-acceleration takeoffs.

These and other considerations led to the development of the Titan 1, which was approved early in 1957 despite arguments that the missile resembled Atlas too closely to be worth the effort of development. In fact, a major source of components for the Titan 1 was the alternate systems and subsystems developed for Atlas to prevent the failure of a primary system to hold up development of the missile. Titan 1, a two-stage missile whose upper stage was ignited at high altitude after first-stage burnout, survived its detractors. Its first flight test was held on 6 January 1959, with only the first stage being powered, and Titan 1 went into service with the Strategic Air Command at Lowry Air Force Base, Colorado, on 18 April 1962.

Titan 1 was far from the last word in missiles. Advancing rocket engine technology and changing military strategy led to the decision to develop a more advanced two-stage missile, the Titan 2. The most pressing concern was the fact that both Atlas and Titan 1 had to be fueled with tons of liquid oxygen oxidizer and RP-1 kerosene fuel minutes before they were fired. The dangers and delays this produced

Comparison of American Intermediate-Range Ballistic Missiles

Name	Length (feet)	Diameter (inches)	Weight (pounds)	Propulsion	Range (miles)
Jupiter	58	105	110,000	LOX-kerosene	1,600
Thor	64.8	96	110,000	LOX-kerosene	1,600
Polaris A-1	28.5	54	28,000	solid[a]	1,400
Polaris A-2	31	54	30,000	solid[b]	1,700
Polaris A-3	31	54	35,000	solid[c]	2,900
Poseidon	34	72	60,000	solid	2,900

[a] Both first and second stages powered by polyurethane, ammonium perchlorate, and light metal mixture.
[b] First stage uses above propellant combination; newer second stage is powered by a double-base powder.
[c] First-stage propellant classified; second stage uses double-base powder.

made the development of storable fuels necessary. Titan 2 was built to use a mixture of unsymmetrical dimethylhydrazine and regular hydrazine fuel and nitrogen tetroxide oxidizer that could be loaded in the missile and left there for long periods of time without boiling off or evaporating. The development of storable fuels brought another bonus: Missiles could be emplaced in underground silos that could be hardened enough to resist all but an almost direct hit.

About the only characteristic Titan 2 shared with Titan 1 was its diameter—10 feet. Titan 2's first stage developed 430,000 pounds of thrust, compared to 300,000 pounds for the Titan 1. Its second stage was uprated from 60,000 to 100,000 pounds of thrust. Titan 2, at 103 feet, was 13 feet longer than Titan 1, and its weight of 330,000 pounds was exactly 50 percent greater than Titan 1's 220,000 pounds.

Helped by the management and technical lessons learned in earlier programs, Titan 2 made quick progress. By 16 March 1962 it had met all research and development objectives. Titan 2 went into operational service in nine missile squadrons at McConnell Air Force Base, Kansas; Davis-Monthan Air Force Base, Arizona; and Little Rock Air Force Base, Arkansas.

While it developed its liquid-propellant missiles,

The gigantic Titan 2 weighs 330,-000 pounds and stands 103 feet tall in its underground silo. Its fuels can be stored for months without boiling off or evaporating, an advantage which enables Titan 2 to be "hardened" in its site, ready for launching. (U.S. AIR FORCE)

The first ground test model of the Minuteman 3 ICBM is loaded onto a modified transporter-erector. The solid-fuel missile has a 1-ton payload, double that of Minuteman 1. Its initial test firing took place on 16 August 1968. (U.S. AIR FORCE)

the Air Force kept an eye on the Navy's Polaris program. The simplicity, safety, economy, and rapid launch readiness of solid-propellant missiles impressed the Air Force planners, but their major concern was to get the liquid-propellant rockets into service. Nevertheless, early in 1956, the Western Development Division gave the Scientific Advisory Committee plans for a solid-propellant missile. Contracts were let in April, with the ARDC's Power Plant Laboratory at the Wright Air Development Center, Ohio, in charge. By March 1957, the Western Development Division was ready to start working on an intermediate-range missile, and by July the Air Force had decided that the Minuteman—the name given to the

solid-propellant missile—could be upgraded to a range of 6,000 miles.

That September, a work group headed by Colonel Edward N. Hall partially defined the Weapon System Q that became the Minuteman. It would be a three-stage missile, lighter and smaller than the Titan and Atlas, and carrying a smaller warhead. But what Minuteman lacked in punch it would make up in numbers. It cost so much less than the bigger liquid ICBM's that it could be built in great quantities.

Drawing heavily on the Polaris technology, Minuteman advanced rapidly. Concurrency was used to the hilt; shortly after the missile's basic configuration had been established, plans for operational launch

137

Minuteman's smaller size makes it easier to transport and install than the bulkier Atlas or Titan. Above, a Minuteman arrives at the Malmstrom Air Force Base, Montana, inside its shipping and storage container. Right, a transporter-erector places a Minuteman into its silo at Vandenberg Air Force Base, Calif. (U.S. AIR FORCE; BOEING CO.)

138

sites—hardened, underground silos—were drawn up.

Minuteman's first flight, on 1 February 1961, was a first in United States ICBM history. With all stages operating, the missile met all its test objectives. (Tethered Minuteman missiles with live first stages had been fired from silos at Edwards Air Force Base, California, as early as 15 September 1959.) A Minuteman was successfully flown from an operational silo in November 1961. Thirteen months later, Minuteman 1 was in service. It was followed by Minuteman 2 and Minuteman 3, the latter having a one-ton payload, double that of Minuteman 1 and 400 pounds more than that of Minuteman 2. The first test firing of Minuteman 3 took place on 16 August 1968. The new missile is capable of handling MIRV (Multiple Independently-targetable Re-entry Vehicle) warheads which, if placed in service on a large scale, could set off a new round of arms spending by Russia and the United States. Undoubtedly Minuteman 3, in its turn, will be phased out and replaced by a fourth-generation missile, some $20 million being earmarked for development of a more advanced ICBM in 1970.

The Minuteman was a good solution to most of the shortcomings of ICBM's. The early Atlas D's had to be launched from open-air sites that were highly vulnerable to attack. The "coffin" sites constructed at Vandenberg Air Force Base, California, and Warren Air Force Base, Wyoming, which allowed the missiles to remain horizontal until just a few minutes before launch, were only a partial answer to the problem.

Atlas F and the two Titans came a step closer. They were installed in underground silos with built-in drainage and loading lines for propellants. Minuteman's solid-propellant system eliminated the complex procedures of loading and unloading liquid propellants. By the middle of the 1960's, Minuteman missiles were emplaced across the nation in sites so well protected that even a near surface burst of a nuclear weapon would not disturb them. They can be fired almost instantaneously to targets that are programmed into their all-inertial guidance systems. This is as close to push-button warfare as man has ever come.

By 1966, the Atlas D's and Titan 1's had been phased out, and the Jupiters and Thors deactivated. The United States relied on Atlas F's, Titan 2's, and Minuteman missiles on land, and Polaris A-3's at sea.

In 1967, Secretary of Defense Robert S. McNamara revealed that United States had a total of 934 ICBM's. He estimated the Russian total at 340. But the Soviets maintained the balance of terror during the next three years by putting in new Scarp and Savage missiles to bring their total up to more than 900. American ICBM emplacements, meanwhile, increased to only 1,054. NcNamara's successor, Melvin R. Laird, told the Senate Foreign Relations Committee in early 1969 that the Russians "have more ICBM's in being or under construction . . . than this country has." To the Soviet ICBM arsenal must be added some 750 IRBM's, including the mobile Scrooge and Scamp types. The United States, however, retained a large edge in submarine-launched fleet ballistic missiles, increasing its total from 512 in mid-1966 to 656 at the end of 1968; Russia, it is estimated, had only 45, plus at least 100 cruise-type vehicles.

The details of how the Soviets developed their missile force are largely unknown. It parallels the American effort only in its earliest stages; in fact,

Comparison of American Intercontinental-Range Ballistic Missiles

Name	Length (feet)	Diameter (inches)	Weight (pounds)	Propulsion	Range (miles)
Atlas (E Model)	82.5	120[a]	270,000	LOX-kerosene[b]	9,000
Titan 1	90	120	220,000	LOX-kerosene[c]	6,000
Titan 2	103	120	330,000	nitrogen tetroxide aerozine 50[d]	7,000
Minuteman 1	55.9	72	65,000	solid	6,500
Minuteman 2	59.8	72	72,000	solid	7,000
Minuteman 3	59.8	72	78,000	solid	7,000

[a] 192 inches across booster engine skirts at base.

[b] First-stage thrust 330,000 pounds for droppable booster engines, 57,000 pounds for sustainer engine.

[c] First-stage thrust 300,000 pounds, second stage 80,000 pounds.

[d] Aerozine is a blend of 50 percent hydrazine and 50 percent unsymmetrical dimethylhydrazine. First-stage thrust is 430,000 pounds, second 100,000 pounds.

The Soviet Union is reported to have flown an IRBM in 1956 and an ICBM a year later. Otherwise, little is known about their missile program. Shown here are three of their missiles, displayed during military parades in Moscow. They are (top to bottom) the Shyster intermediate-range ballistic missile, Frog 1, and the Skean IRBM. (U.S.S.R. EMBASSY, WASHINGTON; U.S.S.R. EMBASSY, LONDON)

the American effort is best viewed as a counter to the Soviet missile development program.

When the Red Army arrived at Peenemünde and Nordhausen-Bleicherode, the major part of the German rocket documents and scientists were already in American hands. Subsequently, the Soviets obtained only a handful of leading rocket engineers and scientists—among them were Helmut Gröttrup, an authority on guidance and control, Erich Putze, a production expert, and Werner Baum, whose chief interest was propulsion—together with hundreds of lower echelon personnel and tons of equipment. To this group they added their own corps of specialists, including A. G.

Kostikov, inventor of the Katyusha, and Sergei P. Korolev, whose impressive achievements earned him the high honor of a state funeral when he died in January 1966.

Gröttrup's rocket organization remained in Germany for about a year, during which time V-2 production was reintroduced at the Mittelwerke. On 22 October 1946, he and hundreds of other Germans were awakened without warning early in the morning and sent by truck and train to Russia. Near Moscow, a German Rocket Collective was established, and soon the Germans were at work, this time improving the V-2 rather than merely placing it back in production. A year later, on 30 October 1947, in Kazakhstan, the product of their labors underwent its first test flight, impacting nearly 200 miles down range. From then on, the authority of Gröttrup and the importance of the German team as a whole declined, and in the early 1950's they began to be repatriated. Gröttrup himself stayed until November 1953 when he returned to West Germany.

Western interrogation of the German scientists who worked on Soviet development into the early 1950's showed that they knew virtually nothing at all about the principal Soviet ballistic missile programs. The Germans were limited to working on specific elements of a given V-2 improvement program and were encouraged to submit their own ideas on more advanced rockets. But they were not given any detailed knowledge of current Soviet projects or future officially adopted plans.

Like the United States, the Soviets started by using the V-2 as a foundation. On 15 March 1947 a State Commission was formed to report to the highest Soviet authorities on the feasibility of developing long-range ballistic missiles. Its recommendations led to Gröttrup's upgraded V-2, which soon gave way to the Pobeda missile. With a range of well over 500 miles, the mobile Pobeda was a familiar sight at May Day parades in the early 1950's.

The Russians moved quickly from this limited start. One crucial stroke was to turn what appeared to be a handicap into a lasting advantage. The Soviets were far behind the United States in nuclear technology, and the Russian nuclear weapons were clumsy and bulky. United States planners decided to wait until smaller warheads were available to build ICBM's. The Soviets went ahead with the massive rockets needed to hoist their primitive bombs. The decision not only gave them a significant edge in ballistic missile technology for years, but was also a great factor in their leadership in space exploration.

Soviet sources have reported that their first

Comparison of Russian Short-, Medium-, Intermediate-, and Intercontinental-Range Rocket-Propelled Military Missiles[a]

Name[b]	Length (feet)	Diameter (inches)	Propulsion	Range (miles)	Remarks
Sagger	2	6	solid	2	Wire-guided antitank, armored-vehicle-mounted.
Snapper	4	5.5	solid	2	Wire-guided antitank, armored-vehicle-mounted.
Swatter	3	6	solid	—	Probably infrared-guided.
Frog 1	31	24	solid	15	Carried by tracked vehicle; weighs 6,000 lbs.
Frog 2	33.5	14.5	solid	30	Carried by tracked vehicle; two-stage, weighs 4,400 lbs.
Frog 3	33.5	14.5	solid	50	Carried by amphibious vehicle.
Frog 4	32	14.5	solid	70	Carried by tracked vehicle; two-stage.
Frog 5	—	—	—	—	—
Frog 6	—	—	—	—	—
Frog 7	31	18	—	—	Single-stage.
Scunner	46	65	liquid	150	Essentially a V-2.
Scuds A, B, C	31–38	30–36	liquid	200–400	Medium-range series; A and B on tracked carrier, C on wheeled carrier.
Sibling	—	—	liquid	200–300	Derived from V-2.
Shyster	75	60	liquid	700–800	First of IRBM arsenal.
Sandal	85	65	liquid	1,000	Somewhat advanced version of Shyster.
Skean	90	96	liquid	1,500–2,000	Stretch-range IRBM derived from Shyster.
Scamp	34	—	solid	1,500–2,000	Mobile; carried by tracked vehicle.
Scrooge	—	—	—	2,000	Mobile; carried by tracked vehicle.
Sapwood	—	—	liquid	3,000	First-generation ICBM (SS-6).
Sasin	85	108	liquid	3,500	Two-stage ICBM (SS-8).
Scarp	120	—	liquid	4,000	SS-9, most advanced ICBM, which may place payload into fractional orbit trajectory.
Savage	65	84	solid	5,000	Three-stage ICBM.
Scrag	120	108	liquid	5,000	Three-stage ICBM.
Sark	45	72	solid	—	Submarine-launched.
Serb	31	54	solid	—	Submarine-launched.
Sawfly	34	72	solid	1,500	Submarine-launched.

Note: All figures estimated.

[a] A half dozen or more air-breathing, cruise-type missiles such as Shaddock, Styx, and Samlet are known, many boosted by solid rocket engines. They are effective at ranges of from 20 to several hundred miles.

[b] Names given by NATO for convenience of identification.

Soviet missiles in action. Left, Frog 4, a short-range, solid-propellant missile, on its tactical launcher. Right, Snapper, wire-guided antitank rockets. (U.S.S.R. EMBASSY, LONDON)

De Gaulle's decision to make France a nuclear power resulted in the scheduling of an IRBM and the launching of test vehicles such as the Topaze (above). Now in the process of development, the IRBM is a two-stage, solid-fueled vehicle. (SEREB)

IRBM flew in April 1956, about a year before the United States flew Jupiter and Thor. The Soviet lead in ICBM's was even greater. Their first flight was in August 1957, fifteen months before Atlas made its maiden full-range flight.

Little is known about the Soviet program except that considerable resources have been devoted to it. An estimated 200,000 to 220,000 men are attached to the Russian rocket force, and its missile inventory is in the tens of thousands. At the end of the 1960's, deployment in Siberia of the Scarp ICBM, also known as the SS-9, gave impetus to the American Safeguard (formerly Sentinel) antiballistic missile system. The Soviet Union also is strengthening its offensive capability by installing the new Sawfly aboard nuclear-powered submarines.

The only other nations to think about getting into

Two 660-pound Saab 305A air-to-surface missiles mounted on a Swedish Saab 35. (SVENSKA AEROPLAN AKTIEBOLAGET)

the high-stakes game of long-range rocketry by the 1960's were Britain and France. Britain's contribution, the Blue Streak IRBM, drew heavily on American technology from its inception in 1955. Powered by twin Rolls-Royce liquid-propellant engines built under a Rocketdyne license, the Blue Streak was developed by the De Havilland organization (which became Hawker-Siddeley Dynamics, Ltd.). Blue Streak made good progress, but it was canceled in April 1960. It has survived in modified form to become the first stage of a joint British-French-German space carrier vehicle.

The French effort is a child of Charles de Gaulle's decision to make France a world power. De Gaulle established the Société pour l'Étude et la Réalisation d'Engins Balistiques (SEREB) to create both a ballistic missile and a vehicle for space exploration. Test vehicles such as the Topaze, Agate, and Bérénice have been flown as part of the program. A two-stage silo-launched strategic ballistic missile resulting from the IRBM program was shown at the 1967 Paris Air Show. Its range is believed to be 2,200 miles, and its first and second stages to have thrusts of 110,000 and 92,000 pounds, respectively. A submarine-launched ballistic missile, about 35 feet long and weighing 40,000 pounds, also is being developed.

While the ICBM's and IRBM's have dominated the technological and military planners of the past two decades—the United States Air Force alone has spent $17 billion on ballistic missiles—other military rockets have not been neglected. Short-range surface-to-surface missiles can be as small as the 3.5-inch bazooka, which is fired by one man, or the more complicated wire-guided antitank rocket, launched from an armored vehicle. Or they can be as complex as a Pershing, capable of hitting a target 450 miles away. Coast-to-ship and ship-to-ship missiles also have become popular, and were used in late 1967 by the Egyptians to sink the Israeli destroyer *Eilat*. These missiles often share targets with air-to-surface missiles, such as the Bullpup, which has a speed of over 1,400 miles per hour and a range of 5 to 6 miles. The Bullpup AGM-12C, with a 1,000-pound warhead, has been used effectively in North Vietnam in clear weather, but not under cloudy skies. Into the early 1960's, the United States and Britain were working on air-to-surface ballistic missiles with ranges of 1,000 miles or more. The experimental GAM-87A Skybolt exemplified this concept, which has been dropped for a variety of technical and strategic reasons. Instead, efforts have gone into improving the short-range (up to 25 miles) rockets, such as the one-pound, 7-inch-long Wasp that was introduced in 1964 to augment the firepower of helicopters.

The few long-range air-to-surface missiles that survived the shakeout are jet-powered. The Air Force maintained in its 1965–1970 inventory two such missiles, the 600-mile-plus Hound Dog, a "defense suppression" weapon, and the Quail ADM-20C decoy. Launched from B-52 bombers, the Quail is designed to confuse enemy radar defenses with its electronic countermeasure equipment. The latest ASM's include the 120-mile-range, inertially guided SRAM (short-range attack missile); the ARM (anti-radiation missile); and the ADR (air-to-surface decoy rocket). During 1969, the Navy's Condor for the A-6 aircraft remained in development, as did the Air Force's Hornet anti-tank missile.

Air-to-air missiles have also undergone intensive development during the postwar years. The first postwar American program resulted in the Firebird XAAM-A-1 two-stage missile, boosted by a solid rocket and sustained over its 5- to 8-mile trajectory by a liquid-fuel motor. The Firebird was replaced by the more advanced Falcon, whose descendants are still in service with the Air Force. All have ranges of slightly more than 5 miles and operational ceilings of over 50,000 feet. Other air-to-air missiles include the Sidewinder and Sparrow, which evolved from programs begun in the late 1940's and early 1950's. These are designed for use by fighters against enemy fighters or bombers at a maximum range of 10 miles.

There have been attempts to extend the range of air-to-air missiles out to 100 miles. The United States Navy began its 100-mile-range Eagle missile program in the late 1050's, replacing it later by the Phoenix program. The Phoenix, first tested in 1965, is still undergoing development for the F-14A. At about the same time, the AIM-47A version of the Falcon was mated to the 2,000-miles-per-hour YF-12A interceptor. This missile, 12 feet long, weighing 800 pounds, and capable of carrying a nuclear warhead, could also destroy aerial targets up to 100 miles away.

These are only sidelights to the main show. In the mid-1960's, however, another type of missile began to be as important in military thinking as the ICBM. It was a surface-to-air missile of a special kind, a missile designed to knock down an attacking ICBM.

The anti-ballistic missile (ABM) challenged the basic tenet of all military thinking about rockets. It had been assumed that there was no defense against an incoming ICBM. But technology had developed to the point where an effective anti-ICBM began to seem practical. Behind that development were years of work on other surface-to-air missiles designed for defense against attack by airplanes.

The United States Navy's SAM (surface-to-air missile) program began during World War II, in plans for missiles to knock down Kamikaze planes. The first concrete result of this Bumblebee program was the Terrier 1, whose development was begun in 1949 by the Applied Physics Laboratory of Johns Hopkins University under a Bureau of Ordnance contract. Within three years, service models of Terrier 1 were available. Sea firings first took place from the USS *Mississippi* in 1954, and Terrier 1 was operational in 1956 aboard such ships as the guided-missile cruisers *Canberra* and *Boston* and the destroyer *Gyatt*. Terrier 1 gave way to the more advanced Terrier 2, which has an effective range of over 10 miles. It is operational aboard six cruisers and a dozen missile frigates.

Another result of the Bumblebee program is the

A Hound Dog air-to-surface missile flies over New Mexico. (U.S. AIR FORCE)

British Blue Steel air-to-surface weapon mounted on the Vulcan Mk-2 bomber. (HAWKER SIDDELEY DYNAMICS)

Red Top, a British air-to-air missile, is 11½ feet long and runs on a solid fuel. It is shown here mounted under a Sea Vixen Mk-2 airplane (top) and just after release from the airplane (bottom). (HAWKER SIDDELEY DYNAMICS)

Tartar, which is smaller, lighter, and considerably less expensive than the Terrier. First test-fired in December 1956, it went into use at sea in August 1959, and is now standard armament on more than twenty guided-missile destroyers and several cruisers. Its range is also more than 10 miles.

A third "T" missile, designed for longer fleet defensive operations, is the Talos. Unlike Terrier and Tartar, which are powered by two-stage solid-propellant systems, Talos has a solid-fuel booster and a ramjet sustainer engine powered by kerosene and naphtha. A test configuration, designated RTV-N-6, was fired in early 1950; the basic Talos configuration was fired in May 1954. Talos first went into service on the guided-missile cruiser *Galveston*, and later on the *Little Rock, Oklahoma City,* and the nuclear cruiser *Long Beach,* as well as three Albany-class destroyers. Talos has an effective range of 75 miles and carries a nuclear warhead.

The Air Force began its SAM program in 1945, with the Gapa—ground-to-air pilotless aircraft—test vehicle series. More than one hundred Gapas were built before the program was canceled in 1949. All were two-stage missiles with solid-propellant boosters. The 600 series had solid second stages; the 601, liquid second stages; the 602, ramjet second stages. The 603, had it been built, would have been a ramjet-sustained, 6,000-pound vehicle with a top speed of Mach 2. But the Air Force, instead, used the Gapa data, together with the Wizard studies of the University of Michigan Aeronautical Research Center and the General Electric Project Thumper research, to develop a new missile called the Bomarc.

The Bomarc took shape in 1951, and a partially successful booster propulsion test flight was made on 10 September 1952. But the basic Bomarc was not flown with all propulsion systems operating until February 1955. On 23 October 1957, a Bomarc knocked down a target drone at an altitude of 12 miles and a range of more than 100 miles. The current Bomarc B model replaced the A model, with its range of 200 to 250 miles, in 1965. Bomarc B, officially designated AIM-10B, weighs about 16,000 pounds, carries a nuclear warhead, and has a range of about 400 miles. It is built by the Boeing Company.

It is the Army that has had the most ambitious SAM program, with missiles ranging from shoulder-fired weapons weighing only 20 pounds and used against helicopters to giant multistage vehicles for defense against ICBM's.

The principal Army programs come under the blanket designation of Nike, which has been developed by a Bell Telephone Laboratories–Western Electric Company team under a mandate that dates back to the closing months of World War II. The first member of the family, Nike 1 (later redesignated Nike A and then Nike-Ajax), was flown at the White Sands Proving Ground in 1951, knocking down a target drone in November of that year. Nike-Ajax, with a range of 25 miles, an effective altitude of 10 to 12 miles, and a velocity of 1,500 miles per hour, started protecting American cities in 1953.

That same year, Army Ordnance authorized development of the second of the series, Nike-Hercules. The development-test cycle was completed by 1957, and Nike-Hercules was operational in 1958. It was emplaced first around New York, Chicago, Baltimore, and Washington. Nike-Hercules, with a range of 75 miles and a speed of 2,200 miles per hour, is a considerable advance over Nike-Ajax. Both its stages use solid propellants, while Nike-Ajax had a solid first stage and liquid second stage. The major development problem involved guidance; Nike-Hercules has an elaborate ground array of three radars for acquiring and tracking enemy aircraft, and equally elaborate on-board devices. More than eighty batteries of Nike-Hercules missiles are deployed in the United States, with ten more in Europe and Taiwan.

Nike-Hercules is the most advanced member of the Army's stable of antiaircraft guided missiles. Others include: the Hawk, a defensive missile against low-flying airplanes, which is in inventory in many parts of the world; the Redeye, a bazooka-type weapon launched from the shoulder against helicopters and strafing jets, which now is in operational service, the Chaparral, a defensive missile for use in forward areas, now in the procurement stage; and the Mauler, another field army defensive missile, which was canceled in 1965 while in an advanced experimental stage. The Army is improving upon the Hercules and Hawk systems by developing the SAM-D terminal defense missile for use against advanced fighter planes and short-range ballistic missiles like the Pershing. For close-in defense of ships, the Navy is developing its PDSMS (point defense surface missile system), based on Sparrow technology. SAM-D and PDSMS were expected to be operational by 1970.

The ABM program, which evolved within the Nike framework, faces problems of such vast dimensions that for many years they appeared insoluble. Many experts argued that an ICBM could not be knocked down, either as it rose from its launch site or as it hurtled along its re-entry trajectory. The only defense, it was asserted, was a good offense—a massive ICBM force that would wreak vengeance on any attacker, and so deter the attack.

The deterrent argument was dominant for many years, because it seemed unanswerable. The only way to prove that there was a defense against ICBM's was to inaugurate a major program, costing billions of dollars, to develop an anti-ICBM missile. One look at the basic problems involved in developing such a system would give anyone pause.

The potential enemy, the Soviet Union, was clearly capable of launching hundreds of ballistic missiles against the United States in a very short period of time. The nosecone-warhead of each missile would fly 500 to 800 miles into space, re-enter the Earth's atmosphere at more than 15,000 miles per hour, and detonate its nuclear device, each of many megatons, over a preselected target. On the way in, the warheads might release decoys whose trajectory and shape would confuse radar defense systems, which would find it difficult to distinguish them from the true warheads.

The task of picking out the real warheads and destroying them seems so difficult that the antimissile missile program, the Nike-Zeus concept, has been restudied, reviewed, and re-evaluated for years. Somehow, despite all its critics and all the problems it

Comparison of Selected American Surface-to-Air Missiles

Name	Length (feet)	Diameter (inches)	Weight (pounds)	Propulsion	Range (miles)
Bomarc B	45.1	35	16,000	(1) solid (2) ramjet	450
Chaparral	9.5	5	185	solid	—
Hawk	16.8	14	1,295	solid	22
Nike-Hercules	41	31.5	10,000	solid	85
Redeye	4	3	20	solid	—
Talos	31.25	30	7,000	(1) solid (2) ramjet	75
Tartar[a]	15	13.4	1,200	solid	12
Terrier[b]	26.5	13	3,000	solid	25

[a]Being replaced by SMMR (standard missile, medium range).
[b]Being replaced by SMER (standard missile, extended range).

An early test model of the Nike-Zeus surface-to-air missile fired at White Sands on 16 December 1959. Designed to intercept enemy missiles, this three-stage, solid-propellant missile is 48 feet long and carries a radar and computer command guidance system. (U.S. ARMY)

The Sprint component of Safeguard (formerly Sentinel) flashes away from its launcher in May 1965. While its companion Spartan is planned for longer-range defense, Sprint would attack incoming missiles once they have re-entered the atmosphere. (U.S. ARMY)

faces, it has survived, and it is stronger than ever. But it is far from being operational.

Nike-Zeus did not start out in the conventional way, with a predetermined configuration into which were built propulsion, guidance, and other systems. The technology just was not available. Instead, the engineers worked on developing individual components—structure, propulsion, guidance systems, ground radar, and so on. A preliminary test firing of a Nike-Zeus research vehicle took place at White Sands on 26 August 1959; a second test occurred on 14 October. Out of these and later tests, the Nike-Zeus emerged: a three-stage solid-propellant missile more than 48 feet long, weighing nearly 23,000 pounds, and carrying a fully automatic radar and computer-command guidance system.

During 1963 and 1964 Nike-Zeus showed that it could destroy incoming Atlas and Titan nosecones fired from Vandenberg Air Force Base over the Pacific. The Nike-Zeus anti-ICBM's were launched from Kwajalein Island and reached velocities of 8,000 miles per hour.

Despite these tests, doubts still existed about the success of the missile under actual attack conditions. One unanswered question was whether the enemy warhead should be attacked at long range or when it had re-entered the atmosphere, where radar could more easily distinguish it from decoys. To assess the two approaches, a new master program, named Nike X, was introduced. Zeus became the long-range intercept phase and Sprint, the short-range intercept concept. The Army recommended an operational system of both Zeus and Sprint missiles mixed in the same batteries. Control of both would be exercised by radar systems that could track and control several missiles at once.

The argument against Sprint is that the enemy warhead should be destroyed as far from the target as possible, preferably while it is still in space. The argument for it is that the decoys released by the approaching missile will not be distinguishable from the warhead itself until they re-enter the atmosphere. Being much lighter than the warhead, the decoys will have different atmospheric trajectory characteristics.

But to take advantage of this weakness, the Sprint missile must get started with unbelievable swiftness. Sprint's contractor, the Martin Company, has looked into many different methods of getting quick acceleration since it began work in March 1963. Some possibilities include a launcher, partially above ground, that can be aimed in any direction; an ICBM-type silo; and a special silo from which the missile would be driven by a gas piston. Several studies point to the

The Soviet Union displayed this anti-ballistic missile in the 7 November 1965 parade in Moscow. (U.S.S.R. EMBASSY, LONDON)

The Thunderbird 2 mobile surface-to-air missile is in service with the British in Germany. Guided by a continuous-wave radar system, it has a range of 25 miles. (BRITISH AIRCRAFT CORP.)

The smaller Tigercat is used for airfield defense. The control equipment is at right. (SHORT BROTHERS & HARLAND)

latter "pop-out" approach as the best. It uses less land, reduces the size of the missile, and decreases the over-all cost.

The high cost of Nike X—the price tag for a fully operational system for the protection of just a few primary target-objects in the United States was estimated at $20 billion—was a major reason why the Department of Defense could not decide whether to produce Nike X by 1966. Defense experts also had lingering doubts about Nike X's ability to overcome salvo attacks and sophisticated enemy countermeasures, and there was some belief that better anti-ICBM systems were down the road. Some officials pointed out that even if Sprint were a complete success, the radioactive debris produced by the low-altitude destruction of enemy warheads would contaminate a large part of the United States.

While debate swirled over the ABM, China began to emerge as a ballistic-missile power, firing a missile over a 400-mile range in October 1966 and exploding a prototype thermonuclear missile warhead in June 1967. These events, coupled with the fear that China might act irrationally and attack the United States despite the threat of massive retaliation, persuaded American planners that the United States would require at least a "thin line" ABM defense system by the early or mid-1970's. Such a program was announced on 18 September 1967 by Defense Secretary McNamara, who estimated its cost at $5 billion (by 1969 the estimate had doubled). The system, soon named Sentinel, would consist of fifteen to twenty Spartan and/or Sprint batteries, the Spartans providing long-range coverage and the short-range Sprints defending local areas.

The issue was complicated two months after McNamara's announcement by reports that Russia was developing two new weapons: an extremely long-range ICBM that might approach America's unprotected "underbelly" via the South Pole, and a satellite method, dubbed the fractional orbital bombardment system (FOBS), of delivering thermonuclear warheads. Soviet spacecraft that exploded in orbit on 17 September 1966 and 2 November 1967 are believed to have been FOBS development flights. An FOBS craft would fly at an altitude of about 100 miles, and the target nation would receive no warning until three or four minutes (compared with thirty for an ICBM) before impact, when the craft's retrorockets would be fired to place it in its final trajectory. Accuracy of the FOBS, however, is still an open question.

Debate over the ABM system was further complicated in 1968 and 1969 by the change from the

Johnson to the Nixon Administration. McNamara, in his 1967 announcement, had attempted to halt the weapons spiral by declaring that the United States would not try to build a missile defense against Russia. Nonetheless many critics of the ABM concept believed that Sentinel, although designed to defend against the Chinese, would force the Soviets to build more ICBM's, and that the United States in turn would have to react by building a full-scale, $50-billion ABM system. Supporting the Sentinel, Melvin R. Laird, McNamara's eventual successor, revealed in early 1969 that Russia already had deployed 175 new Scarp ICBM's. This he interpreted as a move toward "first strike" capability, that is, the ability to mount such a huge attack as to negate the United States threat of massive retaliation.

On 14 March 1969, President Richard M. Nixon announced a decision to modify Sentinel, principally by moving batteries away from major cities, but also in terms of scheduling. The purpose of the system, which he re-named Safeguard, now would be to preserve America's threat of massive retaliation by defending ICBM sites. Batteries would be deployed at Malmstrom Air Force Base in Montana and Grand Forks Air Force Base in North Dakota. During the year, critics continued to assert that the decision to go ahead with the system was unwise and that the system itself was unworkable (its radar and computer elements still required much development). Proponents argued that Safeguard was, in the President's words, the "best preventive for war." As the controversy raged in Congress, development of Safeguard proceeded. The three-stage Spartan test vehicle is 55.2 feet long, weighs 33,400 pounds, and has a range of over 100 miles; the two-stage Sprint is 27 feet long, weighs 7,500 pounds, and has a range of 25 miles.

Little is known about Russia's ABM program. An anti-ICBM that NATO calls the Galosh has been deployed around Moscow since 1968, and unauthenticated reports indicate that it has successfully intercepted unarmed target ICBM's. Western observers doubt that the radar for the system is fully operational; it appears, also, that an ABM far more advanced than Galosh is under development.

It is known definitely that the Russians have a variety of conventional SAM's, several of which have been shown in military parades in Moscow. Since little is known about their development, only general information about them is tabulated. The SA-2, or Guideline, has been in the headlines fairly often. It was set up in Cuba in the fall of 1962 and was deployed in Viet Nam in 1965. The SA-2 was apparently the missile that knocked down Francis Gary Powers'

U-2 over Sverdlovsk in May 1960, and it is believed to have destroyed a U-2 over Cuba. The SA-2's record is not especially impressive elsewhere, perhaps because it is being used far from Soviet maintenance and control centers. In Viet Nam, the missile's hit rate was only 5 per cent in 1965–1966, with United States pilots usually nullifying the defense by evasive action and radar jamming. In Egypt, the SA-2 faired even worse in June 1967; Israeli air strikes were so effective that Egyptian crews never had a chance to open fire.

Many other nations have developed SAM's, as indicated in the table below. A number of the newer missiles are joint projects, including the French–West German Roland low-altitude defense missile and the Italian-Swiss Indigo, which has a range of 5 to 6 miles.

In Great Britain, postwar missile development was first coordinated by the Guided Projectile Establishment at Wescott, then by the Rocket Propulsion Department of the Royal Aircraft Establishment, and finally by the independent Rocket Propulsion Establishment. The first SAM program of several that got underway in 1949 and 1950 was the Bloodhound, a solid-rocket-boosted, twin-ramjet-sustained missile that became operational in 1958. Bloodhound, whose range is 50 miles, is now used by the Royal Air Force Fighter Command in the United Kingdom and in Sweden and the Far East. The Army's SAM,

Thunderbird, began development in 1950 and also went operational in 1958. Early models of the missile used a pulsed radar guidance system, while the more advanced MK-2 model has a more accurate continuous wave radar system. Thunderbird, whose range is 25 miles, is deployed with the British Army in Germany. For low-level targets, the ET-316 anti-aircraft missile was developed. The mobile firing unit carries four missiles and is designed primarily for use in the field and around airfields. The Royal Navy also has a variety of SAM's, including the short-range Seacat; Seaslug, a two-stage, all-solid-fuel missile; and the smaller Sea Dart, intended as a replacement for Seaslug.

Fortunately for mankind, only the smaller missiles developed in the Cold War years have been fired in anger. The warheads of the hundreds of long-range missiles that stand poised in the United States and the Soviet Union could kill hundreds of millions of people and destroy a large percentage of the world's industry if they are ever used. The tenuousness of the balance of power that has prevented their use was shown in 1962, when the Soviets began setting up offensive ballistic missiles in Cuba. The world came close to nuclear holocaust in the confrontation between President John F. Kennedy and Premier Nikita S. Khrushchev in October 1962. There are still no guarantees that the holocaust will not be triggered by some confrontation in the future.

Comparison of Selected European Surface-to-Air Missiles

Name	Country	Length (feet)	Diameter (inches)	Weight (pounds)	Propulsion	Range (miles)	Guidance
Crotale	France	9.5	6	—	solid	6	Radio command
Masurca	France	28.2	16	3,300	solid	20	Radio command
Roland	France-Germany	7.8	6.3	139	solid	4	Radio command
Vega	France	19.67	4	1,430	ramjet	100+	—
Bloodhound 2	Great Britain	25.4	21.5	—	ramjet with 4 solid boosters	15	Semi-active homing
Blowpipe	Great Britain	4.5	3	28	solid	—	Radio command; TV tracking
Rapier	Great Britain	7.4	6	—	solid	—	Optical; command link
Sea Dart	Great Britain	14.3	16	—	ramjet with solid booster	—	Semi-active homing
Seacat	Great Britain	4.9	7	130	solid	—	Radio command
Seaslug 1	Great Britain	19.7	16	—	solid	15	Beam rider
Seaslug 2	Great Britain	20.1	16	—	solid	25	Beam rider
Seawolf	Great Britain	—	—	—	—	—	—
Thunderbird 2	Great Britain	20.9	21	—	solid	25	Semi-active homing
Tigercat	Great Britain	4.9	7	130	solid	—	Radio command
Indigo	Italy-Switzerland	10.2	7	243	solid	5-6	Radio command
Gainful	Soviet Union	10	—	—	solid	—	—
Ganef	Soviet Union	26	32.5	—	solid	—	—
Goa	Soviet Union	22	20	—	solid	—	—
Griffon	Soviet Union	49	35	—	—	—	—
Guideline (SA-2)	Soviet Union	35.5	26	3,000	solid	30	Radio command
Guild	Soviet Union	40	28	—	solid	10-15	Radio command
Micon	Switzerland	18	17	1,760	solid	20	Radio command

7 PROBING THE FR

The rocket enthusiasts of the 1920's and 1930's who confidently looked forward to the exploration of space did not realize the magnitude of the task ahead of them. The accelerated development of World War II and the advanced technology of the postwar years were needed to make the dream come true. But it did come true, and rockets now soar into the upper atmosphere and outer space routinely. The rocket has become a valuable scientific tool.

Rockets that are used solely for measurements within the atmosphere are called sounding rockets; those that carry scientific payloads into orbit around the Earth or to other planets are called launch or carrier vehicles. The distinction is somewhat arbitrary, since sounding rockets that soar 200 or 300 miles above the Earth effectively are in outer space. A convenient dividing line is 250 miles; the rockets primarily designed for use up to that altitude are sounding rockets, while those primarily concerned with exploring space above the 250-mile point are carrier vehicles. However, all rockets that launch satellites into Earth orbit are carrier vehicles, even though their orbits are often below 250 miles altitude all or part of the time.

Postwar sounding rockets preceded space carrier vehicles by more than a decade, showing the way into space. While the carrier vehicles are more spectacular, sounding rockets are extremely useful tools for the exploration of the upper atmosphere. Their relative simplicity and low cost make it possible for most nations to use them for scientific research programs. Today, after twenty-five years' experience, sounding rockets are flown in every part of the world —the polar regions, the equator, ships at sea, airplanes aloft, even from balloons. The nations that cannot make their own can pick the type and model they want from a long list of rockets available from many different countries.

Sounding-rocket payloads require sophisticated design. They must be as small and lightweight as possible, able to resist the friction and vibration of a rocket flight, and they often must be able to take the shock of re-entry and landing. Their readings are converted to electronic signals that are telemetered to Earth.

Sounding rockets measure, directly or indirectly, the temperature, pressure, density, composition, structure, and movement of the atmosphere from a point several miles up to the border of outer space. They can also investigate radiation from the Sun and from deep space and their effects on and interactions with the atmosphere. Some measure communications at high altitudes, others the type and amount of cloud cover at given localities over a period of time. Many sounding rockets have photographed the Earth from great heights.

Sounding rockets come in a variety of sizes and shapes and capabilities. The larger ones can accommodate many instrument packages in multipurpose flights; smaller rockets house one or two experiments. The availability of small rockets makes it possible for even technologically undeveloped nations to contribute to atmospheric research. A rocket can be tailored for a specific flight; by lessening payload, altitude can be increased, and vice versa. Instruments, too, can be tailored for a given purpose. The trend has been for sounding rockets to become smaller and simpler, and to carry fewer experiments. There are sound reasons for this seeming reverse in evolution. Quite often, different experiments cannot be carried in the same payload; one instrument may interfere with its neighbor's operation. For example, an instrument that scoops in air for sampling can disturb the environment of another instrument in the same payload. Both can be launched separately if small, cheap rockets are available. Perhaps of greater importance, smaller rockets can be fired from almost any location, on land or at sea, from simple launch pads with minimal control stations, so that the nature of the atmosphere can be sampled all over the world, not at just a few well-established launch sites.

The first rocket to be used on a sustained basis for upper-atmosphere sounding was the V-2. It did its job rather well, considering that it had not been built for the purpose. Inevitably, the supply of V-2's ran out, and new atmospheric sounding rockets were developed.

In the United States, the Navy took the first steps toward inaugurating an upper-atmosphere research program. As early as December 1945, a Rocket-Sonde Research Branch was established within the Naval Research Laboratory (NRL). The plans that were drawn up for a Navy research rocket were shelved when the Army's supply of V-2's became available, but the NRL soon began thinking of a rocket that could lift scientific instruments to altitudes of 50 or 100 miles or higher. A prime goal was low cost, so that as much money as possible could go into instrumentation and data processing.

One flaw in the V-2 was the aerodynamic instability that caused the rocket to tumble after its propulsion system cut off. The Navy wanted a stable platform that would enable a scientist to keep an instrument pointing in the same direction; at the Sun, for instance, or at the Earth below. It wanted a balanced rocket that would need no ballast, so that for a limited-instrument payload, the attainable altitude would be as large as possible. And the Navy wanted a reliable rocket.

The Navy tried two different approaches. It produced the Viking, which was derived in great part from the V-2, and it upgraded the Wac Corporal, which had flown payloads to altitudes of 40 miles toward the end of the war, into the Aerobee. Both approaches were successful. The Aerobee is still flown today, in a modified and advanced version.

The Navy's Bureau of Ordnance awarded a contract for twenty Aerobees to the Aerojet Engineering Company in 1946, with the Applied Physics Laboratory at Johns Hopkins University supplying technical supervision. Later, the Office of Naval Research contracted for more Aerobees to be used by the NRL. As Aerobee's reliability was demonstrated, both the Army and the Air Force ordered some. Weighing slightly more than 1,000 pounds, Aerobee could carry a 100-pound payload to an altitude of 75 miles. Later

models improved on that; Aerobee-Hi, for instance, carries 150 pounds between 150 and 200 miles.

The first Aerobees were boosted by a 21,000-pound-thrust solid-propellant motor and had a liquid engine sustainer that used RFNA and aniline as the propellant combination. Later versions used JP-4 gasoline fuel or solid propellants. The most widely used has been Aerobee-Hi, which was first flown in 1954; Aerobee 300 (Spaerobee) also became popular.

The Viking program has not survived, although it gave birth to far greater programs. Plans for the rocket (which was first called Neptune) were drawn up early in 1946 by a group in the NRL under Ernst H. Krause and Milton W. Rosen. The Glenn L. Martin Company of Baltimore won the competitive bidding and was given a contract in August for building ten rockets, a number later increased to fourteen.

The sub-contract for Viking's 20,000 pound-thrust liquid oxygen–alcohol controllable engine was given to Reaction Motors, Inc. At the time, the Viking was the most advanced liquid-propellant rocket under development in America. Its engine compared favorably to the 8,000-pound-thrust MX-774 and the 13,500 pounds of thrust produced by the Hermes A-1, military rockets which were being developed at the same time.

Reaction Motors had been founded in 1941 by members of the American Rocket Society, and the Viking propulsion system was designed by a veteran ARS experimenter, John Shesta, who was supported by Edward Neu and others on the company's engineering staff. In October 1947, about a year after work had begun, the first engine was ready for testing. The test program was divided into three phases. First the motor was hung on a massive A-frame structure, which measured its thrust. Later, the turbopump, designed to feed the fuel and oxidizer to the motor, was connected. Finally, an almost complete rocket was mounted on a rotating platform for testing. After that last test, the propulsion system was shipped to White Sands to be static-tested in the completed rocket prior to launching.

The first American high-altitude sounding rocket, Viking, reached a height of 50 miles on its maiden flight on 3 May 1949. Above, Viking 4 is seen through a hatch manhole on the USS Norton Sound, *prior to its launch on 11 May 1950.* (U.S. NAVY)

The Navy's Aerobee sounding rocket, an upgraded Wac Corporal, proved so successful that it was adopted by the Army and Air Force as well. Here an Aerobee 150A launches a 208-pound Australian payload of scientific instruments on 9 May 1963 from Wallops Island, Va. (NASA)

Motor A burned itself out after a partially successful test program that yielded useful information for following engines. On 21 September 1948 a prototype engine produced 21,000 pounds of thrust for 66 seconds, a performance that satisfied the NRL. The first production engine was shipped to the Viking group at Martin soon afterward, and Viking No. 1 took shape at the Martin plant near Baltimore in December. It was sent to White Sands in January. The Navy's Lieutenant Commander W. P. Murphy had overseen construction of launch and support facilities, and January and February were taken up with preparations for static testing.

After a dry run on 28 February, the first static test took place on 11 March, after several postponements. Steam from the turbine exhaust started a fire in the tail section's pipe insulation, but the rocket was not damaged. The second static test, on 28 April, was cut short prematurely when someone saw smoke, but no evidence of a fire was found. Plans went ahead for the first launching.

It took place on 3 May 1949; at 9 A.M. Viking 1 reached an altitude of slightly over 50 miles—a highly creditable performance for the maiden flight of any rocket. American high-altitude sounding had come of age.

Since the experience of early flights was applied to the design of later models, no two Vikings were exactly alike. Flights 2 and 3, which took place in September 1949 and February 1950, reached approximately the same altitude as the first Viking. Viking 4 was fired at sea on 11 May 1950. The same Admiral Daniel V. Gallery who had promoted the V-2 Operation Sandy flight was involved in the firing of the Viking 4 from the USS *Norton Sound* in the Pacific. The test gave new information about the problems of launching missiles at sea and allowed scientists to gather data on the behavior of cosmic rays in the upper atmosphere at the geomagnetic equator. Despite the difficulties of a shipboard launch, Project Reach, as the operation was called, was successful. The Viking soared to a height of 105 miles, very nearly the theoretical maximum of that particular vehicle.

The next three flights were made from White Sands. Viking 5 reached an altitude of 108 miles in November 1950. The following month, Viking 6 reached only 40 miles, because of a rapid deterioration of aerodynamic stability after fin control was lost. Viking 7, flown in August 1951, established a record height of 136 miles. All three carried instruments that included Geiger counters, ionization chambers, photomultiplier tubes, and cameras.

More than a year went by before the next firing.

The time was used to carry on design work, in process since 1950, for a larger, heavier Viking that would fire for more than 100 seconds, compared to the 50 to 80 seconds of the earlier rockets. Almost all the extra 3,500 pounds that went into the new Vikings was propellant, not structure. The new rocket could go higher than the old Vikings or carry heavier payloads to the same altitude.

Seven of the new Vikings were built and flown. The only failure was the first one, Viking 8, which experienced one of the most unusual accidents in rocket history. On the morning of 6 June 1952, as Viking 8 was being static-tested, it broke loose from the test stand, flew four miles up, and crashed on the desert five miles away. The scientists and engineers on the scene could hardly believe their eyes as the rocket rose into the air. On future models, they used four tie-down points rather than two and strengthened the tail sections of the rockets.

The remaining six Vikings were fired between 15 December 1952 and 1 May 1957. Viking 11 distinguished itself in May 1954, by soaring to a record height of 158 miles with 852 pounds of instruments aboard. Its rocket engine fired for 103 seconds and brought the vehicle up to a speed of 4,300 miles per hour, also a record for the series. Viking 12 was, in many ways, the last true member of the family. It reached a height of 144 miles on 4 February 1955.

The last two Vikings were fired, not for high-altitude research, but to check out components for the forthcoming Vanguard space carrier vehicle. They were flown from Cape Canaveral, rather than White Sands.

Viking was the largest and most ambitious of the many sounding rockets created in America. A partial roster of American sounding rockets includes —in addition to the Aerobee family—the Arcas, Arcon, Asp, Aspan, Astrobee, Dan, Deacon, Exos, Hawk, Iris, Metroc, Nike-Apache, Nike-Cajun, Terrapin, Trailblazer, Viper, and Wasp, each with different configurations and capabilities. Two unusual vehicles were the Rockaire and the Rockoon, names derived from the fact that they were flown from airplanes and balloons respectively. The Rockaire was launched from jets—usually an F-86D—at a height of nearly 7 miles, and soared up to 30 miles. The Rockoon was developed by scientists at the State University of Iowa under Navy sponsorship. It could lift a 20-pound payload to between 60 or 70 miles. First used in 1952, it was fired in great numbers during the International Geophysical Year of 1957–1958, from points as widely separated as Greenland and the South Pacific.

The ICY, an eighteen-month period of sustained scientific cooperation on an international scale, was responsible for the firing of large numbers of sound-

Summary of Viking Sounding Rockets

Viking No.	Date	Length (feet)	Diameter (inches)	Weight (pounds) Loaded	Propellant	Payload	Altitude (miles)	Velocity (mph)	Thrust (pounds)	Firing time (seconds)
1	3 May 1949	45.25	32	9,650	6,855	464	50	2,350	20,450	54.5
2	6 September 1949	46.5	32	9,885	7,265	412	32	1,820	20,465	49.5
3	9 February 1950	47.4	32	11,050	8,310	520	50	2,340	20,450	50.6
4	11 May 1950	48.6	32	11,440	8,280	959	105	3,520	20,450	74
5	21 November 1950	48.6	32	11,390	8,430	675	108	3,510	18,800	79
6	11 December 1950	48.6	32	10,890	8,360	373	40	2,740	20,800	70
7	7 August 1951	48.6	32	10,728	8,257	394	136	3,998	21,080	71.8
8	6 June 1952	41.6	45	12,810	9,370	a	4	—	21,400	61
9	15 December 1952	42	45	14,615	11,745	765	135	3,940	21,170	99
10	7 May 1954	42	45	14,750	11,815	830	136	3,900	20,990	100
11	24 May 1954	42	45	15,005	11,985	825	158	4,300	21,400	103
12	4 February 1955	45	45	14,815	11,805	887	144	4,025	20,500	102
13	8 December 1956	48.5	45	15,035	12,010	d	126[b]	4,297	20,268	105.9
14	1 May 1957	47.3	45	15,030	11,976	d	120[c]	3,780	21,429	99.9

[a] Destroyed during static test (broke away from launching stand); did not carry payload.
[b] Range, 183 miles.
[c] Range, 450 miles.
[d] Carried Vanguard carrier vehicle elements.

A United States sounding rocket, Nike-Cajun, carries a Japanese payload to an altitude of 75 miles and a range of 73 miles on 26 April 1962. (NASA)

The Australian Aeolus sounding rocket. (WOOMERA RESEARCH EST.)

The Soviet Union began upper-atmosphere research in 1949. Shown left, a Russian geophysical rocket at takeoff. (U.S.S.R. ACADEMY OF SCIENCES)

Two French sounding rockets. The Tactite (left), capable of reaching 120-mile heights with a 400-pound payload, is used to study infrared radiation. The Bérénice four-stage rocket (right) is designed to test the heating characteristics of the atmosphere on re-entering payloads at 12 times the speed of sound. (OFFICE NATIONAL D'ÉTUDES ET DE RECHERCHES AÉROSPATIALES)

ing rockets by many of the major nations. The United States alone launched 210 vehicles, from Fort Churchill in Canada, the Antarctic, San Nicolas Island off California, the Arctic, White Sands, Guam, and Danger Island in the Pacific. The Soviet Union flew 125 of its Meteo and Geophysical rockets from locations in the Arctic, the Antarctic, and central Russia.

The Meteo is a relatively small, 1,500-pound rocket similar in many ways to Aerobee. With a solid-propellant booster engine and a liquid-propellant sustainer rocket, it can carry 160 pounds of instruments to a height of 60 miles. At 40 miles, the rocket separates into two parts, the body and the payload. Both float down by parachute, and the rocket can be used again.

What the Soviets call simply Geophysical Rocket is actually a series of different rockets that began upper atmosphere research in 1949. One of the largest models which the Soviets have reported carried a payload of 4,850 pounds to a height of 132 miles in May 1957, a feat far beyond the capability of either the V-2 or the Viking. Its payload included a capsule containing two dogs, who were parachuted safely to Earth.

The 34-foot-long launching tube of the British Skua sounding rocket. The rocket is accelerated by a boost carriage (shown here at rear of tube) and recovered by a parachute. (BRISTOL AEROJET)

Another Geophysical Rocket soared 294 miles into space on 21 February 1958 with a 3,350-pound payload. These rockets carried instruments to study the Earth's magnetic field, the physical and chemical nature of the atmosphere, the ionosphere, cosmic and Solar radiation, X rays and ultraviolet radiation, and micrometeoroids.

Many other nations are conducting research programs with their own sounding rockets: Britain (Skylark, Skua), France (Monica, Véronique, Dauphin, Eridan), Australia (Aero-High, HAD, HAT, Long Tom), and Japan (Kappa series, Lambda series, LS-A, S-B). Japan, for example, started in the early 1960's with modest Sigma and Pi rockets, which carried 6- to 9-pound payloads. By 1965 the Japanese were launching Lambda 2's to altitudes of 375 miles. On the other side of the world, an eight-year European sounding-rocket program began in July 1965 when a British Skylark was fired from the Italian Salto di Quirra Range on Sardinia with a mixed German and Belgian payload. Other nations, such as France and Argentina, also are cooperating in sounding research. The United States National Aeronautics and Space Administration participated in experiments that involved some twenty nations and about 350 sounding rockets during 1961–1968.

The wide range of rocket-sounding activities is indicated by the record of a single month: March 1967. On 7 March, a French Vesta lofted a monkey above Hammaguir, Algeria, to provide data on behavior of animals under acceleration and weightlessness. Two days later, an Aerobee 150 made Solar observations from 133 miles above New Mexico. A week later, a Solar radiation detector was launched from Wallops Station, Virginia, by an Aerobee 150A to provide a check on the readings obtained from the orbiting Solar observatory, then passing overhead. On 16 March a Nike Apache was launched from Wallops Station, in a joint Indian–United States study of ionospheric particles. The next day, a Javelin, launched from the Churchill Research Range, Canada, measured characteristics of auroral particles. And on 30 March, its mission timed with the passage of the Canadian Alouette 2 satellite overhead, a Nike Tomahawk was launched from Wallops Station in order to make ionospheric measurements.

No matter how much they add to human knowledge, the sounding rockets will remain the unromantic drudges of rocketry. Much more glamorous are the carrier rockets. These are the apotheosis of rocketry—the culmination of centuries of aspirations.

They have carried instruments and men from just beyond the atmosphere out to the Moon and have hurled automated probes to the nearby planets. Probes and manned spaceships in the distant future may even be able to make incredibly long journeys to the stars.

Carrier rockets are direct outgrowths of the technology of sounding rocket and military missile programs. In both the United States and the Soviet Union, missile technology in the mid-1950's had reached the point where practical planning for space missions could realistically begin. The Russians approached space travel with a much more aggressive attitude than the United States. It is still too early to analyze thoroughly the reasons for the reluctance, at the highest military and political levels in the United States, to move energetically into space. It apparently resulted from lack of imagination, concern that a space program would hold back ballistic missile development, fear that it would be too costly, and a complacent feeling that space travel would be possible sooner or later and needed no special emphasis at the moment. The result of the differing national attitudes was a propaganda bonanza and an implied military advantage for Russia, as well as a lasting blow to American prestige.

Carriers can be divided roughly into four major groups. First are the so-called small carriers derived from missiles and sounding rockets, such as Redstone and Viking, and producing less than 100,000 pounds of first-stage thrust. Second, there are the carriers that have been developed by adding upper staging to intermediate-range ballistic missiles, such as Jupiter and Thor. Next in scale are the ICBM-based carriers with first-stage thrusts ranking upwards from 300,000 to 1 million pounds, exclusive of booster rockets that might be strapped on. Finally, the most modern carriers in use or under development have first-stage thrusts of well over 1 million pounds. They are conceived and designed from the start as carrier vehicles, and while they may use military rocket technology, they are not mere modifications of missiles.

Of historical interest is a fifth group of the small carriers that have been flown from balloons and airplanes. Six Far Side rockets were fired from balloons by the United States in 1957. One of them, launched on 20 October, may have carried its small payload to an altitude of 4,000 miles; transmitter failure prevented confirmation of its flight. In 1958 six Caleb rockets were launched from F4D airplanes, but they failed to achieve the planned orbits around the

Atmospheric Research Rockets

Country	Designation	Typical Payload (pounds)	Typical Altitude (miles)	Country	Designation	Typical Payload (pounds)	Typical Altitude (miles)
Australia	Aero High	45	130	Japan (cont.)	MT-135	—	40
	HAD	20	80		S-135	20	40
	HAT	20	40		S-300	120	100
	Long Tom	30	100		SB-11A	150	50
Canada	Black Brant 1	100	100	Poland	Rasko 1	20	2
	Black Brant 2	150	125		RM-3W	6	5
	Black Brant 3	50	110				
	Black Brant 4	50	600	Soviet Union	Meteo geophysical rockets[a]	160	60
	Black Brant 5A	500	85				
	Black Brant 5B	225	250				
France	Agate	800	50	Switzerland	Zenit 1	100	110
	Aurore	10	40		Zenit 2	100	200
	Bélier	65	55				
	Centaure	65	100	United States	Aerobee 150A	150	150
	Crapel	20	500		Aerobee 170	35	300
	Dauphin	—	85		Aerobee 350	600	200
	Dragon	440	200		Arcas	12	40
	Émeraude	425	350		Archer	40	90
	Emma	10	45		Arcon	40	250
	Éridan	220	250		Argo A-1	400	110
	Lex	10	60		Argo D-4	100	600
	Rubis	85	1,500		Asp	30	25
	Saphir	—	75		Aspan	60	160
	Titus	900	150		Astrobee 200	125	200
	Topaze	—	80		Astrobee 250	500	220
	Vesta	1,100	230		Dan	60	60
Germany (West)	621	50	50		Exos	40	300
Great Britain	Petrel	40	85		Hawk	8.5	75
	Petrel 200 (Petrel Thrush)	30	200		Honest John Nike	250	50
	Skua 1	8	45		Hydra Iris	100	200
	Skua 2	13	50		Javelin	—	500
	Skylark	500	125		Judi Dart	2	40
India	Meneka	10	40		Loki Dart	2	40
Italy	355-160	65	135		Metroc	3	20
Japan	Kappa 6	45	130		Nike Apache	50	150
	Kappa 8	170	130		Nike Tomahawk	100	250
	Kappa 9	160	200		Nike Cajun	50	100
	Kappa 10	375	150		Niro	50	150
	Lambda 1	1,100	50		Phoenix	20	170
	Lambda 2	100	400		Raven	10	50
	Lambda 3	500	700		Sandhawk	200	100
	Lambda 4	20	930		Terrier Sandhawk	200	250
					Tomahawk	80	80
					Viper Dart	10	75
					Wasp	6	22

[a]Various configurations, capabilities; see text.

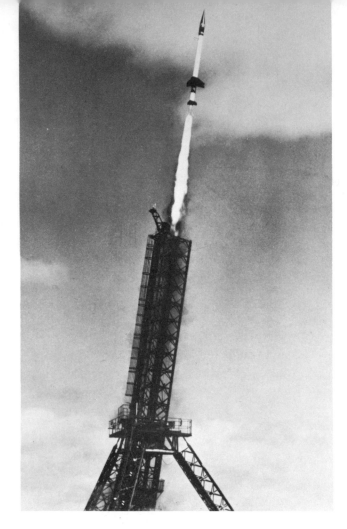

The Skylark upper-atmosphere sounding rocket leaves its launch tower. (BRITISH AIRCRAFT CORP.)

Japanese Kappa 150 sounding rocket, an early experimental version of the modern Kappa series. By 1965, Japan was launching rockets to altitudes of 375 miles.

Earth. Both of these programs were discontinued as the maximum effort went into ground launching of much larger vehicles.

To the Soviet Union goes the honor of building and firing the world's first carrier rocket to place an artificial satellite in orbit. The U.S.S.R. launched Sputnik 1 on 4 October 1957, one of history's most significant dates. Typically, the Russians did not disclose very much information about this carrier vehicle. It was thought to be based on one of their military missiles, probably an IRBM that has been generally designated T-2. The satellite itself weighed 184 pounds, but there was evidence that the total weight placed in orbit was much greater. Subsequent Sputniks, probably launched by more powerful carriers, weighed from 1,000 to 3,000 pounds.

It is necessary to distinguish between the over-all weight injected into orbit and the useful payload, which is often difficult to do with limited Soviet data. Frequently, entire upper stages of carriers are placed into orbit. Their weights sound impressive but do not add to the usefulness of the operation. Added to this is confusion about the exact nature of a payload. Does it include structural material, or just instruments? Should power supplies be included? And so on.

Discussion of Soviet carriers is still largely a matter of guesswork. The Soviets have apparently added to the power of their carrier vehicles, since increasingly heavier payloads have been orbited or sent to the Moon or the planets. In January 1959, the Russians propelled their first probe past the Moon and into permanent orbit around the Sun; it weighed just under 800 pounds. By 1965, Soviet Lunar spacecraft—specifically, the Luna 9 that made a soft landing on the Moon and sent back close-up pictures of the surface—had an "injected" weight of about 3,000 pounds. Mars and Venus probes launched at about the same time weighed in the neighborhood of 1,500 pounds.

The orbital ability of Soviet carriers also increased strikingly, exceeding 12,000 pounds in 1964 and 25,000 pounds in 1965. It seemed likely the Soviets used the same basic carrier for both orbital and Lunar-planetary shots, although they probably modified the vehicle's upper stages. The Russians were believed to be conservative about introducing new vehicles, preferring to rely on tried and proven components.

At the thirteenth International Astronautical Congress in Varna, Bulgaria, Soviet cosmonaut Gherman Titov mentioned that the carrier vehicle for his

Vostok 2 satellite was powered by five engines. Theorizing—correctly, as it turned out—about the carrier's configuration, Heinz Mielke, vice-president of the East German Astronautical Society, wrote in 1963:

Let us consider, for instance, a five-engine system. The conventional engine arrangement would include four engines, one mounted at each corner of a square, with the fifth engine in the center. The following propulsion system can then be realized: Initially, all five engines are ignited [first propulsion stage]. After having burned for a certain length of time, two engines are switched off and jettisoned, and the remaining three engines continue burning [second propulsion stage]. When the fuel in the two side engines has burned out, these engines are also discarded. The central engine goes on burning [third propulsion stage] and puts the spacecraft into its orbit.

Known as parallel staging—as opposed to the more common tandem, or series, staging in which the stages are mounted on top of each other and fired in sequence—this multistage rocket configuration also was used in the Atlas missile. A carrier with parallel staging should be relatively fat and squat; at first glance, it would not appear to be a multistage vehicle—which may explain why some communist sources imply that single-stage rockets are used for many Russian space missions.

The orbiting of the giant 26,840-pound Proton 1 satellite in July 1965 signaled the introduction of an entirely new generation of Soviet carrier vehicles. Proton's only announced mission was the measurement of high-energy cosmic radiation, which did not require such massive weight.

Extrapolations from earlier launchings set the takeoff thrust of the Proton's carrier at above 2 million pounds, making it the most powerful rocket in the world at the time. It was difficult to speculate on the vehicle's configuration, but if Proton 1 was indeed its maiden effort, improvements in the carrier are inevitable. It might even have been the prototype of the vehicle Russia intended to use for manned Lunar exploration.

While it was known in 1966 that the Soviets had launching sites at Kapustin Yar and Tyura Tam, it remained for a group of English schoolboys from Kettering Grammar School, Northamptonshire, to find a third, previously unannounced, site. Using war surplus equipment, the boys and their faculty advisers tracked several Kosmos satellites in late 1966 and established their launch site at a point south of Archangel near Plesetsk. Subsequent analysis of orbits showed that the range must have opened with the launching of Kosmos 12 on 17 March 1966.

The Russians ended much speculation in the West about the size and configuration of their carriers in May 1967 when they unveiled at the Paris Air Show the launch vehicle that had orbited the Vostok series of spacecraft. It was, indeed, a five-unit, clustered propulsion system, each unit itself having a cluster of four engines. The core vehicle, probably a modified Sapwood SS-6 ICBM, was powered by four clustered RD 107 engines operating on liquid oxygen and kerosene. The central unit, together with four strap-on units, each with four clustered engines of the same type, provided a lift-off thrust of between 950,000 and 1,150,000 pounds. The vehicle, including the Vostok spacecraft stage, was 124 feet long. Diameter of the main stage was 9.7 feet. Many of the structural features of the vehicle resembled those of the Scrag, an early three-stage ICBM in the Soviet arsenal. At the Paris show, the new launch vehicle was displayed on a railroad flat car erector similar to that used for the World War II German V-2 rocket.

In sharp contrast with the guesswork needed to discuss Russian carriers, many details of the American program have been made public. The record goes back to 29 July 1955, when President Eisenhower announced that plans had been approved for "the launching of small unmanned Earth-circling satellites" as part of America's contribution to the International Geophysical Year.

Almost immediately, the program went wrong.

There were two options for the selection of a carrier vehicle for the first satellites. The United States could rely on sounding rocket technology and build on the Viking and Aerobee, or it could modify existing military rockets or their test vehicles. For reasons that are still not thoroughly understood, the United States took the first choice. The Russians made the other choice. They got there first.

The American decision was not made without debate—in the Department of Defense and elsewhere. Under Homer J. Stewart, an ad hoc Advisory Group on Special Capabilities was assembled to examine several proposals for carrier rockets. The committee, whose creation had been requested by Donald Quarles, Assistant Secretary of Defense for Research and Development, studied proposals for an Atlas-based carrier, a Redstone-based vehicle, and a Viking-based carrier with an improved Aerobee second stage and a new solid-propellant third stage.

A carrier based on technology and experience gained in the Viking program was chosen. The reason for the selection of the new configuration—later

Like others in the Vanguard series, vehicle SLV-5 malfunctioned and was unable to place into orbit either a 13-inch-diameter magnetometer satellite or a 30-inch-diameter aluminum sphere to measure air density. (NASA)

Juno 1 orbited the first United States satellite, Explorer 1, on 31 January 1958. This four-stage vehicle permitted America to commence the task of "catching up" with the Russians in the space race.

called Vanguard—was that its efficiency would be better since it was being designed from the start as a carrier, and that it would make only minimum demands on the military ballistic-missile program, which was then in a desperate effort to catch up with the Russians. In hindsight, it appears logical to have bypassed the unproven Atlas. But the refusal to add a single small stage to the Redstone-based Jupiter C—which on 20 September 1956 demonstrated its capabilities by hurling a payload 3,400 miles across the Atlantic—is difficult to explain. The analogous situation would have been to refuse to use the V-2 for atmospheric sounding because it had been designed for a different role. Stewart himself favored the Jupiter C option, but was overridden by his committee—and once the decision was made, the United States had to live with it.

Scientific responsibility for the Vanguard program was given to the National Academy of Sciences, with the funds coming from the National Science Foundation. The Defense Department, which was assigned the job of carrier-vehicle development, passed the management function along to the Navy.

The team put together to create the Vanguard carrier was built around the NRL's Viking group, and was supported by many of the same contractor personnel. John P. Hagen, in charge of NRL's Radio Physics Research Group since 1950, was named program director. Milton W. Rosen, who had experience in the Viking program, became technical director. The prime contractor was the Martin Company,

which was supported by General Electric (first-stage propulsion), Aerojet-General (second-stage propulsion), Grand Central Rocket Company and Alleghany Ballistics Laboratory (third-stage propulsion), and Minneapolis-Honeywell (guidance).

Project Vanguard began officially on 9 September 1955, when the Department of Defense authorized the Navy to start development. Later, when defending Vanguard against criticism, Hagen noted that he received clear instructions from the start that he was not to interfere with the ballistic missile programs by requesting technical assistance from them—which inevitably deprived him of many flight-proven components and much readily available assistance. This kind of thinking, not weaknesses in the Vanguard team, led to a second-place finish for the United States. Hagen, Rosen, and their NRL team actually did a very professional job that ended with the orbiting of several outstanding satellites.

The final design of the Vanguard carrier emerged between September 1955 and March 1956. Its first stage, using liquid oxygen and kerosene, would develop 27,000 pounds of thrust. The second stage had a 7,500-pound-thrust engine burning white fuming nitric acid and unsymmetrical dimethyl hydrazine. The third stage, with solid propellant, would develop between 2,800 and 3,100 pounds of thrust. The carrier itself would be 72 feet long, 45 inches in diameter, and weigh 22,600 pounds—twice as long as the later Vikings, just as thick, and 8,000 pounds heavier. The first Vanguard components were flown on Vikings

13 and 14, which were designated TV-0 and TV-1. The first real Vanguard carrier was TV-2, with a powered first stage and dummy upper stages. Launched from Cape Canaveral on 23 October 1957, it sent a 4,000-pound payload on a 109-mile-high, 335-mile-long trajectory.

The next two flights failed. TV-3, with all stages powered, settled back on the launch pad, toppled over, and exploded. Two months later, on 5 February 1958, TV-3BU veered off course and broke up at an altitude of less than 4 miles.

By then, of course, it was too late for a "first"; Sputnik was already up. Vanguard TV-4 successfully orbited a small, 3¼-pound experimental satellite with two radio transmitters aboard, just "two years, six months and eight days after the initiation of the program from scratch," as John Hagen pointed out.

TV-5 failed to orbit a satellite when the third stage malfunctioned, and second-stage troubles caused the failure of the first nontest, operational Vanguard vehicles, SLV-1, -2, and -3. On 17 February 1959, the NRL placed its first full-scale Vanguard into orbit, following it with Vanguard 3 in September,

after two more carrier vehicles failed. The Vanguard program, a "goat" through no fault of its own, was over.

But it did provide American engineers with valuable lessons. It bequeathed its second and third stages to later Thor- and Atlas-based carriers, and its third stage to Scout. Later vehicles would use the swiveling techniques developed first for Viking and later improved for Vanguard's first-stage motor. But Vanguard in history was upstaged not only by the Soviets but by another American program.

This was the creation of the Medaris–Von Braun group at the Army Ballistic Missile Agency in Huntsville. They evolved a carrier vehicle named Juno 1— a four-stage rocket virtually indistinguishable from the three-stage Jupiter C. There was little doubt at Huntsville that Jupiter C could be quickly adapted for a satellite launching—if authority, and a rather modest amount of money, could be obtained.

After the Stewart committee made the choice for Vanguard, the Army's Office of the Chief of Ordnance turned over to Quarles's Research and Devel-

The Thor-Delta carrier rocket, shown here leaving the launch pad at Cape Canaveral, placed the British Ariel 1 satellite into orbit on 26 April 1962. Its first stage was based on the Thor IRBM. (NASA)

The first stage of the powerful TAT-Agena D, or Thrust Augmented Thor, consists of a central Thor engine with auxiliary engines mounted on each of the four corners of the base. The side engines drop off as their fuel burns out. (DOUGLAS AIRCRAFT CORP.)

Juno 2 lofted a number of American satellites and probes, including Pioneer 4, which flew along a Lunar by-pass trajectory into orbit around the Sun in March 1959. (NASA)

Neatly spaced ICBM row stretches out along Florida's east coast at Cape Kennedy. The two complexes in the foreground are Atlas Centaur LC36A (left) and B (right). (NASA—KENNEDY SPACE CENTER)

opment Council a critique of the committee's decision. The council, whose members included Trevor Gardner, General Donald L. Putt, and other high service officials, turned down the ABMA again. The Redstone missilemen went ahead with their Jupiter C program, filling the fourth stage with, as Medaris put it, "sand instead of powder." During 1956 and into 1957, the Army was turned down again and again. ABMA was not arguing *against* Vanguard but *for* Jupiter C (with the fourth stage that made it Juno 1) as a back-up.

In a plan submitted in April 1957, ABMA recommended the launching of six 17-pound satellites. The first, according to the enclosed schedule, would orbit in September 1957, and the second, two or three months later. "In various languages our fingers were slapped and we were told to mind our own business, that Vanguard was going to take care of the satellite problem," Medaris recalls. "We followed in the spring and summer of 1957 with two shots with the scale-model nosecone [referring to Jupiter C firings 2 and 3], the first of which we were unable to recover —it fell too far away from the target area—but the second of which went directly into the target area, was recovered, and was the one that was shown . . . by the President [in a television presentation]."

After Sputnik 1, Secretary of the Army Wilber M. Brucker renewed his service's offer to orbit a satellite, saying that the ABMA would need "four months from a decision date to place a satellite in orbit . . . we would require a total of $12,752,000 of non-Army funds for this purpose [a six-vehicle program.]"

Suddenly, the atmosphere in Washington had changed. On 25 October 1957—just three weeks after the Russians orbited Sputnik 1—the Stewart committee endorsed the ABMA plan, and on 8 November the Secretary of Defense authorized the preparation of two satellites for launching in March 1958. The next week, ABMA was given $3.5 million for the mission; a few days later, the target date for the first satellite was pushed up to 30 January.

Later, Medaris described why the ABMA was so effective in the program:

. . . being obviously a Government instrumentality we do not need to make contractual changes in order to make a change in our program, and therefore all that is required to meet the day-to-day exigencies of a fast-moving development program is that I make up my mind . . . by having . . . access to the complete ramification of resources as well as decision elements that are required to do these things, we just cut out all the falderal, if you want to put it in simple terms . . . I can flip six keys and I can talk to six laboratory chiefs and I can get an answer.

With almost everything it needed at one installation, ABMA, assisted by the Army-controlled Jet Propulsion Laboratory, could move quickly without having to renegotiate industrial contracts and deal with subsidiary elements scattered all across the country.

Of the six Juno 1's built under an incredibly accelerated schedule, three orbited satellites. The first was Explorer 1, the first United States satellite, which went up on 31 January 1958—one day behind schedule. The United States had taken a hard look at the realities of space and vowed never to be caught lagging again.

As Juno 1 and Vanguard partially redeemed America's image, a new generation of carriers was coming along—those based on IRBM first stages. Both the Jupiter and the Thor were brought into service, the first with Juno 1 upper staging and the second with either Vanguard staging or a specially designed Agena upper stage. These vehicles were variously called Juno 2, Thor Able, Thor Delta, Thor Epsilon, and Thor Agena. Thor-based carriers are still in operation. All these vehicles have a place in American space history. Juno 2 launched America's first successful Lunar fly-by, Pioneer 4, on 3 March 1959; Thor Able sent a much more elaborately instrumented deep-space probe, Pioneer 5, into orbit around the Sun on 11 March 1960 (Pioneer 4 also went into Solar orbit, but it was tracked only to a distance of 400,000 miles). Thor Agena A orbited a 1,450-pound Air Force satellite (Discoverer 1) on its first launch on 28 February 1959; Thor Delta, on its second flight, placed the Echo 1 passive communications satellite into orbit on 12 August 1960. Meanwhile, small carriers were developed for light payloads: the Scout, with four solid stages; a series of Argos carriers; and the Blue Scout, with either three or four stages.

Reliability of the smaller carriers and those based on IRBM first stages improved during the 1960's, and the few that did fail were subjected to painstaking investigation to ensure that malfunctions would not recur. Thus, the failure of a Thor Delta to orbit the Intelsat 3-A communications satellite in mid-September 1968 resulted in changes in manufacturing, testing, and inspection techniques. Prior to the aborted launch, fifty-four out of fifty-eight Thor Deltas had flown successfully; since then, there were eight straight successes, making Thor Delta NASA's most successful carrier vehicle.

The third major carrier category includes those based on Atlas and Titan 2 ICBM's. The Atlas Score flight of 18 December 1958 orbited a 122-pound communications payload. Atlas Able failed three times to launch Moon probes between November 1959 and December 1960; but, with an Agena upper stage, it orbited a 5,000-pound Midas reconnaissance satellite on its second try on 24 May 1960. Atlas has been a workhorse since, as Atlas Agena B and D, Atlas Mercury (orbiting America's first manned satellite on 20 February 1962), and Atlas Centaur. Atlas Agenas completed their Lunar Orbiter launches by the end of 1967 and were withdrawn from NASA service after putting up the fifth orbiting geophysical observatory in March 1968. Atlas Centaur wound up its eight-vehicle research and development program in October 1966 with the AC-9 flight, whose second stage was re-started in space. The carrier later lofted Surveyors 1 through 4 Moonward, and an improved version went into service with Surveyor 5. After lofting the seventh and last Surveyor in January 1968, Atlas Centaur was shifted to the Mariner program and the application technology satellite series. Titan 2, meanwhile, was completely successful during 1965–1966 in orbiting the Gemini series of two-man spacecraft.

The Titan-Gemini carrier, used in the Gemini program to orbit a series of two-man spacecraft, was based on the Titan 2 ICBM. It is shown in its 90-foot test cell in Baltimore. (MARTIN CO.)

One of history's most significant dates is 4 October 1957. On that day the Soviet Union put into orbit Sputnik 1, the world's first artificial satellite. It weighed 184 pounds and traveled in an elliptical orbit that took it around the Earth every one and one half hours.

The Soviets quickly followed this dramatic success with another. Sputnik 2, launched less than a month later, carried a passenger—a dog named Laika—and weighed 1,120 pounds. Sputnik 3, orbited on 15 May 1958, was even larger and heavier. It contained instruments for measuring the pressure and composition of the upper atmosphere, the incidence of micrometeoroids, and Solar and cosmic radiation.

Although the Russians had dropped a number of hints prior to 1957 that they were planning to launch a satellite, the event nevertheless took the world by surprise. Ironically, the failure of the United States to be first in space was due partly to its superiority during the early 1950's in weapons technology and strategic military position. The initial hydrogen bombs of both countries were bulky affairs, but the United States was ahead in reducing the weapon's size. United States planners, therefore, decided to defer building ICBM's until smaller warheads became available. In the meantime, their nation would be well defended by manned bombers operating from a network of bases that encircled Russia.

The Soviet Union took the opposite course. It went ahead and developed the massive rockets needed to carry its primitive bombs—the same vehicles that later gave it a significant edge in space exploration.

The first United States satellite, Explorer 1, went into orbit on 31 January 1958, four months after the first Sputnik. It was launched by Juno 1, a four-stage carrier vehicle hastily adapted from the Jupiter C by the Army's team at Redstone Arsenal. The subsequent successes of the Explorer series and of the Vanguard satellite project helped salve America's pride.

Following up their initial achievements, the United States and Russia inaugurated diversified satellite programs. Probably the most successful of the American satellites have been the Tiros meteorological series, begun in 1960. Tiros 1 eventually broadcast more than 19,000 pictures of cloud formations, literally adding a new dimension to weather forecasting. Later models in this series transmitted more than 100,000 pictures each. The United States also has been very successful with communications satellites: Echo, Telstar, Relay, Syncom, Early Bird, and Intelsat. Comparatively little is known about similar Russian projects. Nearly 300 Kosmos satellites were orbited by mid-1969, accounting for approximately three quarters of all Soviet satellite launchings.

Both nations also launched many probes toward the Moon in preparation for sending men there. In September 1959, a Russian probe crash-landed on the Moon; two months later another probe took the first pictures on the far side of the Moon; and in February 1966, after at least four unsuccessful tries, a Soviet probe achieved a soft landing on the Moon. The United States, following a series of discouraging failures in 1962, scored outstanding successes in 1964 and 1965 with Rangers 7, 8, and 9, which transmitted back to Earth thousands of pictures of craters as small as a few feet across on the Lunar surface. Ranger was followed by Surveyor and Lunar Orbiter series, which provided vital information for the Apollo program.

The Russians have sent a number of probes toward both Mars and Venus since 1960, but apparently have been successful only with probes of the latter planet that were launched in 1965, 1967, and 1969. Four of these sent back information from within the atmosphere of Venus while another made a close fly-by. The United States, meanwhile, sent Mariner 2 to within 21,000 miles of Venus in 1962 and in 1965 took the first pictures of the surface of another planet when Mariner 4 passed by Mars at a distance of 6,118 miles. In 1967, Mariner 5 missed Venus by only 2,500 miles, while in mid-1969, Mariners 6 and 7 took excellent photographs of Mars from less than 2,200 miles away.

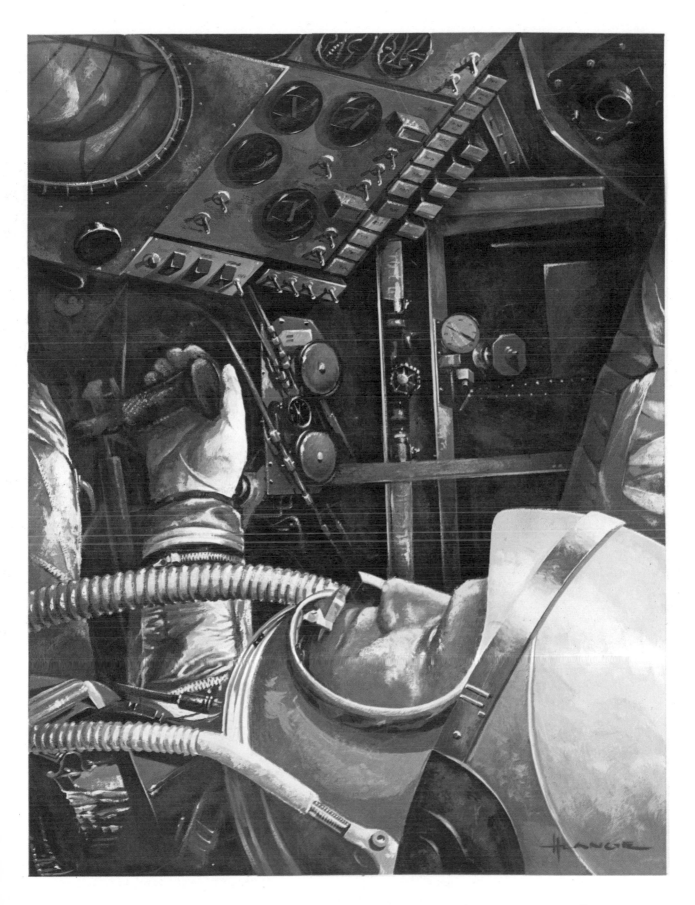

Astronaut in pressurized crew compartment of Mercury spaceship, America's first manned satellite. Four Mercury capsules were orbited between February 1962 and May 1963. The last, with Major Gordon L. Cooper, made 22 orbits before coming down within 4.5 miles of the recovery ship.

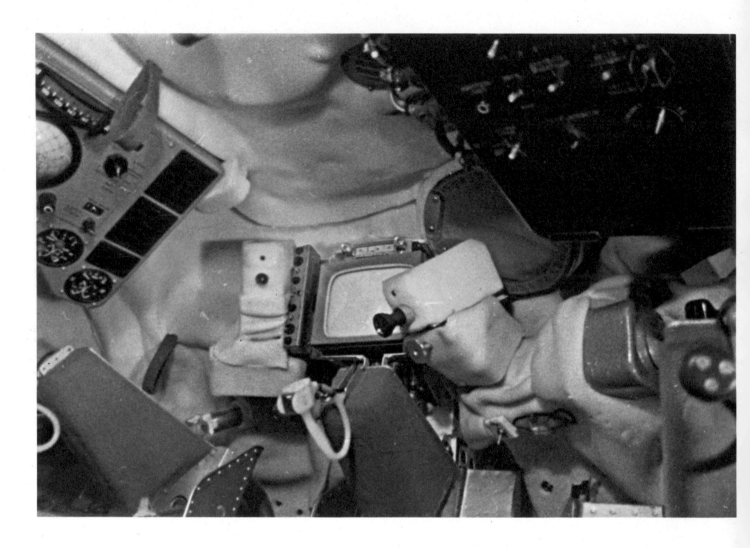

ABOVE: *On 18 March 1965, Soviet cosmonaut Aleksei A. Leonov became the first man to leave his spacecraft for a ten-minute "walk" in space. This is the cabin of Voskhod 2, which he left through an airlock.*

RIGHT: *Floating outside Gemini 4, astronaut Edward H. White propelled himself with a compressed-air gun. After a 21-minute "walk," he rejoined pilot James A. McDivitt to complete 62 orbits between 3 and 7 June.*

In addition to exploring outer space, the Gemini astronauts have gathered scientific data on the Earth's land and water and recorded it with such striking photographs as this view of the Nile Valley in southern Egypt. It was taken with a hand-held 70-mm Hasselblad camera on the 3–7 June 1965 flight of Gemini 4.

The feasibility of space-rendezvous techniques was demonstrated on 15 December 1965, when Gemini 6 and Gemini 7 came within one foot of each other. This photograph, taken by astronaut Thomas P. Stafford from Gemini 6, shows clearly the conical shape of the spaceship. Larger and heavier than the Mercury, it weighs 7,000 pounds and is 18 feet 5 inches long.

The Saturn 1B launches Apollo 7, the first manned spacecraft mission in the Apollo series, on 11 October 1968 from Complex 34 at tower-studded Cape Kennedy, Florida. During their eleven days in orbit around the Earth, astronauts Walter M. Schirra, Jr., Donn F. Eisele, and Walter Cunningham performed many demanding tasks, including rendezvous and simulated docking maneuvers with the Saturn S-4B stage.

The Lunar module for landing men on the Moon's surface was first tested under manned flight conditions during the ten-day mission of Apollo 9 in March 1969. While the Lunar module was docked to the command and service modules, astronaut Russell L. Schweickart went for a 38-minute space walk, during which he took this photograph of the CSM from the LM's "porch."

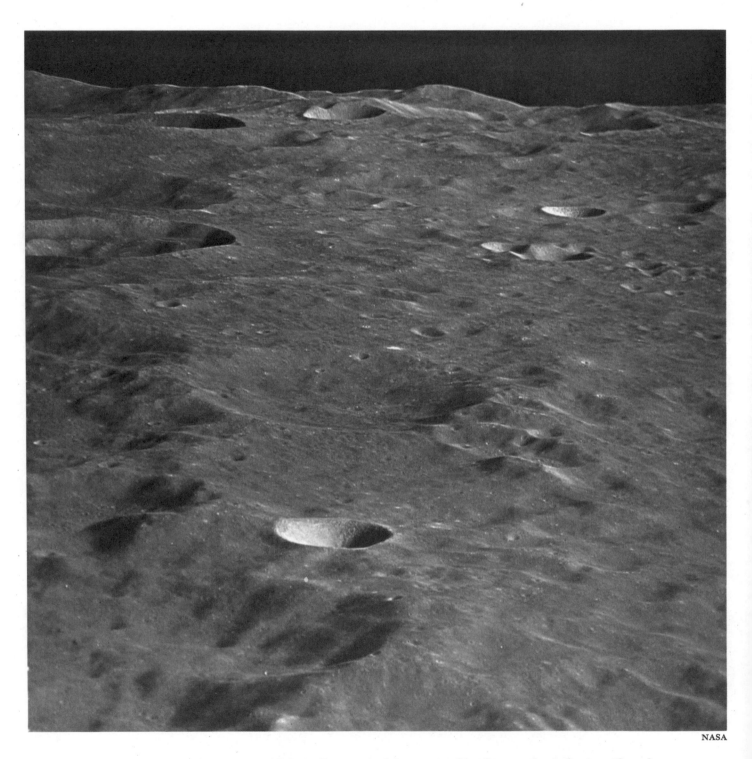

The Lunar landscape is revealed in all its rugged beauty in this photograph of the far side, taken in May 1969 during the voyage of Apollo 10. During this eight-day mission, astronauts Thomas P. Stafford and Eugene A. Cernan piloted the Lunar module to within 10 miles of the Moon's surface, in what amounted to a full dress rehearsal for the Apollo 11 manned landing two months later.

The seeds of the organization that was to manage these programs were planted in early 1958 when the President's Science Advisory Committee recommended that a central agency be created to take charge of the scientific exploration of space, both manned and unmanned. The agency was to be kept separate from the Department of Defense but was to benefit from its resources and help it to apply "space science and technology to military purposes for national defense and security." President Eisenhower sent the message to Congress with his endorsement on 2 April 1958, and the National Aeronautics and Space Act became law on 29 July. T. Keith Glennan, president of the Case Institute of Technology, became the first administrator of the National Aeronautics and Space Administration.

NASA started as a name only, but it grew by absorption. First it took over the 8,000-man National Advisory Committee for Aeronautics, an organization created before World War I for aviation research. Hugh L. Dryden, NACA's director, became NASA's deputy administrator. John Hagen's 170-man Vanguard team and the NRL's 46-man Upper Atmosphere Sounding Rocket group, under John W. Townsend, Jr., also were transferred to NASA. In December, the Army-owned Jet Propulsion Laboratory at the California Institute of Technology, with 2,800 employees under William H. Pickering, became part of NASA's resources.

NASA still had a great need for a group of scientists and engineers with long experience in the fields of missiles and carrier rockets. The only group in the nation that met the description was the Medaris–Von Braun team at the Redstone Arsenal. A number of the Army's space projects had automatically passed into NASA hands when the new agency was created, although technical responsibility was not fully transferred until March 1960. But with responsibility for operational deployment of Jupiter gone to the Air Force and the other projects to NASA, the Army Ballistic Missile Agency found itself without a really major mission. This kind of resource could not be left untapped. No one was surprised when the President, on 14 January 1960, called for revisions in the National Aeronautics and Space Act that would include the transfer of 4,600 ABMA employees, under Von Braun, into NASA. The transfer was made on 1 July 1960, and the facility became the George C. Marshall Space Flight Center, with Von Braun as director. President Eisenhower personally dedicated the center, his visit coinciding with Congressional approval of the full $915 million budget requested by NASA for the coming fiscal year.

A large part of that budget was slated for a carrier that had been conceived at Huntsville before NASA came into being. In 1956, the Development Operations Division at Redstone had begun studies on carriers that would go far beyond anything else that was being planned.

As he worked, Von Braun knew that the ICBM-based carriers would not be adequate for manned missions in Earth orbit, let alone manned Lunar and interplanetary flights. The largest ICBM-based carrier vehicle then in the proposal stage was what later became known as the Titan 2. Since the trend was toward lighter nuclear warheads, it was apparent that subsequent ICBM's would have smaller and less-powerful rockets—an appraisal later confirmed in full by the development of the Minuteman ICBM. Von Braun and his team of advance planners also recognized, however, that even the most ambitious carrier proposal would have to be built on existing technology.

Thus, the vehicle and propulsion engineers at ABMA set out to see how far they could go with the basic elements of Jupiter and Redstone.

Cutaway of the Titan-Gemini two-stage carrier vehicle. (NASA)

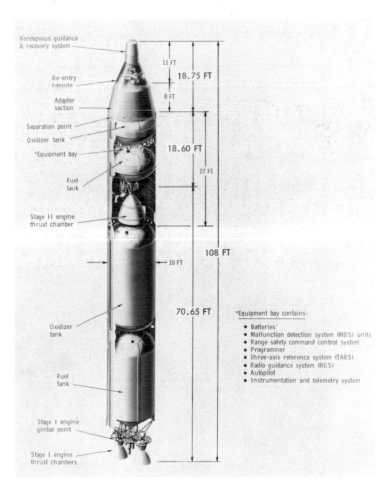

*Equipment bay contains:
- Batteries
- Malfunction detection system (MDS) units
- Range safety command control system
- Programmer
- Three-axis reference system (TARS)
- Radio guidance system (RGS)
- Autopilot
- Instrumentation and telemetry system

In a speech to Congress in 1961, President John F. Kennedy outlined a program for landing an American on the Moon within ten years. He is shown here touring the Marshall Space Flight Center, Huntsville, Ala., in 1962. Flanking him are Wernher von Braun, Director, MSFC, and Maj. Gen. Francis J. McMorrow, commander of the Army Missile Command at Redstone Arsenal. Lyndon B. Johnson is on the far right. (NASA—MSFC)

Dr. von Braun (center) heads a Saturn planning meeting at Huntsville. With him are (left to right) Werner Kuers, Walter Häussermann, Willy A. Mrazek, Dieter Grau, Oswald Lange, and Erich W. Neubert (NASA-MSFC)

The idea was to cluster a number of Jupiter engines around Redstone and Jupiter propellant tanks to build a large carrier vehicle that would use to the fullest the experience, hardware, and facilities of ABMA and its associated Army and industrial supporters. From this basic idea came the family of Saturns.

On 15 August 1958, the Department of Defense's Advanced Research Project Agency (ARPA) gave its approval for a research and development program whose aim was a carrier powered by eight uprated Jupiter S-3D engines. These engines, whose thrust would total 1.5 million pounds, would be mounted on a structure consisting of eight Redstone-type 70-inch-diameter tanks clustered around a single 105-inch Jupiter tank.

By October 1959, four Saturn configurations had been evolved. Each had essentially the same first stage, with distinct variations in the upper stages. The NASA–Defense Saturn Vehicle Evaluation Committee picked one of the four configurations, the Saturn C-1, and development began in December. This highly significant development in America's growing space program led immediately to a number of important administrative changes in Washington, both in the Department of Defense, which was funding Saturn through ARPA and thence through Army channels, and the new National Aeronautics and Space Administration, which was soon to take over development responsibility. ARPA was placed under Army Brigadier General Austin W. Betts and made subject to the authority of the newly created office of Defense Research and Engineering under Herbert F. York. Simultaneously, Air Force Major General Don R. Ostrander left as acting head of ARPA to take over a just-created launch vehicle office at NASA. There was close cooperation between NASA and ARPA as the Saturn project unfolded, paving the way for the transfer, first of Saturn, then of Von Braun and his team, to the civilian space agency.

The upper stages of Saturn C-1 (later simply Saturn 1) configuration were approved on 31 December 1959, and a ten-vehicle research, development, and test-flight program began. The second stage, designated S-4, would have four 20,000-pound-thrust engines; the third, S-5 stage, two such engines. After it won approval, Saturn was given the coveted DX rating, meaning it enjoyed high national priority for materials, personnel, and other resources.

Some changes were made in the upper stages during 1960. Six 15,000-pound-thrust engines, all using the high-energy combination of liquid oxygen and liquid hydrogen, replaced the four 20,000-pound-thrust second-stage engines. The 15,000-pound-thrust engines were identical to the 20,000-pound-thrust en-

gines except for the reduction in their thrust rating. The third stage was eliminated. Testing of the first-stage engine cluster began in March, when two engines were fired. On 29 April, all eight engines were ignited for eight seconds, producing 1.3 million pounds of thrust, an American record.

New facilities were built at Huntsville and at Cape Canaveral, and plans were made for shipping complete first stages by barge to New Orleans and then on to Florida. Assembly of the first flight vehicle began in May 1960, while the Rocketdyne Division of North American Aviation, Inc., and Pratt and Whitney Aircraft Division of the United Aircraft Corporation continued to work on engine improvements.

By 1961, Saturn 1's role as a test vehicle for the Apollo program, which was to take three Americans to the Moon, had been defined. Two editions of the carrier would be built, Block 1 and Block 2. The Block 1 Saturns would have dummy upper stages and would be fired to prove out the basic concept of the vehicle. The first stage of Block 2 vehicles, designated S-1, would carry more propellants and would be powered by upgraded engines, H-1's, which would develop 188,000 pounds of thrust each. The Block 2 Saturns would have stabilizing tail and stub fins, which the Block 1's did not; the later carriers would also have live S-4 upper stages, an improved instrument unit, and a dummy, or boilerplate, model of the Apollo capsule.

After the first Saturn, designated SA-1, was static tested in Huntsville in May 1961, plans were made for shipping it to Cape Canaveral. By the end of August, SA-1 was being assembled on its launch site. The 162-foot-long carrier, weighing nearly 1 million pounds, lifted majestically off the ground on 27 October in a virtually flawless maiden flight. As it flew its short, 200-mile trajectory, more than five hundred different measurements were recorded.

The rest of the Block 1 vehicles were fired smoothly during 1962 and 1963. The first Block 2 vehicle was launched on 29 January 1964; its second stage propelled a total weight of 37,700 pounds payload into orbit. Dummy Apollo capsules were orbited in May and September by Saturns SA-6 and SA-7, in flights that showed that the spacecraft and its carrier were compatible. The final three Block 2 Saturns orbited Pegasus micrometeoroid-detection satellites, as the Saturn 1 program ended with an unprecedented 100 percent successful flight-test record.

In 1962 the Air Force announced a plan to increase the payload-carrying capability of its Titan 2 ICBM by giving it an initial solid-propellant rocket boost. The new configuration became known as Titan 3C.

Developed for the Air Force to orbit payloads

Saturn 1's first stage, S-1, is 21 feet in diameter and 80 feet tall. Together with its second stage, the Saturn 1B version launched experimental Apollo capsules into Earth orbit in preparation for later manned Lunar flights. (NASA-MSFC)

Watching the first Saturn 1 launch from Blockhouse 34 at Cape Canaveral, October 1961. Left to right: George E. Mueller, NASA Associate Administrator for Manned Space Flight; Wernher von Braun; and Eberhard F. M. Rees, Deputy Director, MSFC. (MITCHELL R. SHARPE)

of from 5,000 to 25,000 pounds, depending on the altitude, the Titan 3C has a "core" consisting of a Titan 2 carrier. Strapped to it are twin solid-propellant booster rockets of great capability. On a typical flight, the two "zero-stage" solid boosters provide 2.4 million pounds of thrust to lift the vehicle off the ground. The first-stage engine ignites at high altitudes to give 470,000 pounds of thrust. Then the second-stage engine produces its 100,000 pounds of thrust. The twin third-stage, or "transstage," engines produce 16,000 pounds of thrust.

More than 125 feet tall, Titan 3C is impressive in many ways. It is the first United States carrier to use both parallel and tandem staging. Its 120-inch-diameter solid-fuel boosters can be replaced by 156-inch boosters for even more lifting capacity. Since its third stage is restartable in space, the Titan 3C can change the orbit or inclination of its spacecraft up to 25,000 miles from the Earth, even sending them on interplanetary trajectories. On its first flight from Cape Kennedy (formerly Cape Canaveral), Titan 3C placed a 21,000-pound payload in a nearly circular orbit over 100 miles high.

Titan 3C grew out of studies by the joint Department of Defense–NASA Large Launch Vehicle Planning Group, which concluded, in November 1961, that a large carrier would be needed for military space missions in the late 1960's and the early 1970's. An Air Force–funded study began the next month, and the Space Systems Division of the Air Force Systems Command, under Major General Ben I. Funk, took charge of the development program in December 1962. Program director was Brigadier General Joseph S. Bleymaier. Among the missions assigned to Titan 3C were orbiting of military communications satellites, sending nuclear detection satellites aloft, and (with the 3M version) launching the manned orbital laboratory (MOL), a small space station in which two astronauts could live and work for a month. The MOL program, however, was canceled in June 1969, partly to reduce military spending and partly because inadequate funding and other support had so lengthened its development period that the MOL promised to be obsolete before it was ready to fly.

The Titan 3C research and development (R and D) program moved forward rapidly, often yielding benefits in addition to carrier vehicle checkout. Thus, on 16 June 1966, an R and D vehicle was launched from Cape Kennedy and placed in a nearly circular orbit about 100 miles high. After about an hour, the transstage was re-ignited, lifting the apogee to nearly 21,000 miles. Just more than six hours later, the transstage again fired, bringing itself into a nearly

On its first flight on 18 June 1965, Titan 3C placed a 21,000-pound payload in orbit 100 miles above the Earth. Here it is shown at Cape Kennedy prior to the flight (above) and in cutaway (below). (U.S. AIR FORCE)

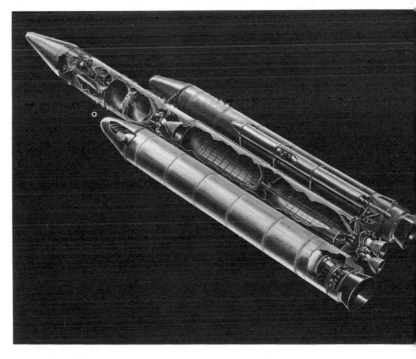

circular orbit just greater than 21,000 miles high and at the same time changing the original inclined orbit to a near-equatorial orbit—the greatest plane change effected to the time by the United States. Once in the final orbit, seven communications satellites and a single gravity gradient satellite were ejected as part of a program to deploy a global system of communications satellites for the Defense Communication Agency. Later, on 2 November 1966, five small satellites were injected into a low orbit from a single container; moreover, the carrier placed an unmanned Gemini B Capsule on a re-entry trajectory in a test of a new heat shield. By 1969, Titan 3C had completed its twelve-flight R and D program, and in each launch the 120-inch, five-segment booster motors had worked perfectly. In late April 1969, the first static test of the new seven-segment, 120-inch solid boosters to be used on the 3M configuration took place in Coyote, California.

While Titan 3C was being developed, work proceeded on the larger Saturn 1B. Resembling the first Saturn, 1B had a Chrysler-built improved S-1 first stage with eight 205,000-pound-thrust engines. In the second stage, designated S-4B, there was substituted for Saturn 1's six 15,000-pound-thrust liquid engines a Rocketdyne J-2 engine which initially (it was later upgraded) developed 200,000 pounds of thrust on liquid oxygen—liquid hydrogen propellants. Saturn 1B is 224 feet high, 21.7 feet in diameter, and weighs 650 tons fully loaded. The first stage was test fired for the first time at Huntsville on 1 April 1965. Two months later, in Sacramento, California, the second stage went through acceptance testing. The first vehicle was assembled on 25 October at Launch Complex 34 at Cape Kennedy; less than forty months had gone by since the development program had been authorized. Its maiden suborbital flight from Cape Kennedy on 26 February 1966 with an unmanned Apollo spacecraft as payload was highly successful.

The carrier's second and third flights were made in July and August 1966. In the July AS-203 flight, the S-4B stage was filled with some 20,000 pounds of unneeded liquid hydrogen in a test proving that it was possible, despite the near-zero gravity environment, to seat the fuel in its tank for a second engine burn. Since the S-4B is not only Saturn 1B's second stage but Saturn 5's third, this test was highly significant for the Apollo Lunar landing program. AS-202, flown after AS-203, was designed primarily to check out an unmanned Apollo 3 command module (which was put into a suborbital trajectory that caused it to re-enter the atmosphere at the maximum heating angle), the service module propulsion system

(which was started in space for the first time), and guidance and control systems.

Saturn 1B flight testing of Apollo hardware was halted for a year after the AS-204 fire that killed three astronauts in January 1967. The carrier went back into service on 22 January 1968 when AS-204 lofted the Lunar module element from Cape Kennedy. By October, both the re-designed Apollo spacecraft and the Saturn 1B were judged to be fully safe for manned flights. On the 22nd the "101 percent" successful, long-duration Apollo 7 mission began, with the Saturn 1B performing flawlessly. Following this launch, which ended the initial fifteen-vehicle Saturn 1 series program (ten Saturn 1's and five 1B's), launch complexes 34 and 37 at Cape Kennedy were closed, awaiting Saturn 1B's in the Apollo applications program.

Large as they were, Saturns 1 and 1B were only preludes to an even more powerful carrier that was needed to fulfill the goal that had been outlined by President John F. Kennedy in a speech to Congress on 25 May 1961—landing an American on the Moon within a decade. "With the advice of the Vice-President [Lyndon B. Johnson, who was to succeed Kennedy in less than three years] . . . we have examined where we are strong and where we are not, where we may succeed and where we may not," Kennedy said. ". . . Now is the time to take longer strides—time for a great new American enterprise—time for this nation to take a clearly leading role in space achievement, which in many ways may hold the key to our future on Earth."

To carry out the President's declaration, a NASA–Defense Department Executive Committee for Joint Lunar Study and a Joint Lunar Study Office were established. And work on the Saturn 5, the carrier that would take Americans to the Moon, was accelerated at the Marshall Space Flight Center.

On 25 January 1962, NASA approved a development program for the carrier, which was given the highest priority. Saturn 5 was to have three stages: the S-1C stage, the S-2, and the already familiar S-4B from the Saturn 1B.

The S-1C stage, developed by the staff at the Marshall Center with the support of the Boeing Company, was turned over to Boeing for production assembly at the huge NASA-owned Michaud plant in New Orleans. The S-1C stage is about 138 feet tall and 33 feet in diameter. The 1969 model weighs nearly 300,000 pounds empty and holds some 4.7 million pounds of liquid oxygen and RP-1 kerosene fuel. Saturn 5's first-stage thrust is about 7.7 million pounds, with each of its five F-1 engines capable of developing more than the 1.5 million pounds of

Above, the eight flaming engines of its first stage launch Saturn 1B on its first flight from Cape Kennedy on 26 February 1966. It lofted a test Apollo payload to an altitude of 310 miles. (NASA—MSFC)

thrust produced by the entire first stage of Saturn 1.

The S-2 stage, developed by North American Aviation, Inc., in Downey, California, is 81.5 feet long and 33 feet in diameter. It is powered by five liquid oxygen–liquid hydrogen J-2 engines producing 1,164,000 pounds of thrust. The third stage is the S-4B, 58.1 feet long and 21.7 feet in diameter, and powered by a J-2 engine whose thrust is variable in flight from 184,000 to 230,000 pounds. When put together, the Saturn 5 stands 363 feet tall; fully fueled it weighs nearly 6.4 million pounds. It is able to send a spacecraft weighing about 50 tons to the Moon, or to place a 150-ton payload into orbit around the Earth.

In order to accommodate the mammoth carrier, equally mammoth facilities had to be erected at Cape Kennedy. The 54-story, 526-foot-high vertical assembly building has 130 million cubic feet of space, making it the world's largest building. It contains four huge bays, where four carriers and their spacecraft payloads can be erected and assembled.

Erection of the AS-501 vehicle for the first Apollo flight began in the autumn of 1966. By the end of August of the following year, the carrier, with the Apollo 4 capsule, had been loaded on a mobile launch tower, and the whole assembly transported by a giant crawler vehicle to the launch pad. It took about ten hours to move the rocket the three miles from the assembly building to the pad.

All three stages were prepared for firing on the maiden flight, the first using propellant at a rate of 15 tons per second and generating 7.5 million pounds of thrust, the second producing 1 million pounds, and the third 200,000 pounds. Apollo command and service modules and a simulated Lunar module also were prepared.

The countdown went off without a hitch and the launch took place right on schedule at 7:00 A.M. on 9 November. Each of the stages performed flawlessly, including the re-ignition of the third (S-4B) stage which boosted the command module to 25,000 miles per hour, simulating the velocity it would reach on a return trip from the Moon. The command module splashed into the Pacific some 600 miles off Hawaii, 8 hours and 37 minutes after liftoff. The orbital weight of 278,699 pounds broke all records.

Saturn 5's were also used on Apollo 6, 8, 9, 10, and 11 flights. Carrier performance was virtually perfect on all but the April 1968 Apollo 6 mission, during which two second-stage engines shut off early and the S-4B, which fired the first time as programmed, failed to re-ignite. Later analysis showed that the carrier had suffered rather severe longitudinal oscillations and that the system for controlling the rates of fuel and oxidizer consumption did not perform as planned.

Thousands of man-hours were required to determine the causes of the malfunctions and to correct them, but so successful were the engineers that Saturn 5 behaved beautifully on subsequent Apollo flights. On the recommendation of Lee B. James at Flight Readiness Review, the center engine of the second stage was cut off about 80 seconds early in the Apollo 10 mission, in mid-May 1969, in order to suppress longitudinal oscillations that had occurred late in the S-2 firing period in both the Apollo 8 and 9 flights. To compensate for the thrust loss, the four outer engines burned some 15 seconds longer. The S-4B stage placed itself and the Apollo 10 into orbit so accurately that an early mid-course correction was not required. After separation from the Apollo 10, the S-4B moved along a path that brought it close enough to the Moon so that the Moon's gravitational field could be used to help propel it into orbit around the Sun—the so-called "slingshot effect."

Comparison of Modern United States Carrier Vehicles (Non-Saturn Series)

Designation	Stages	Propulsion	Thrust (pounds)	Length (feet)	Maximum Diameter (feet)	Lifting Capabilities	Typical Uses
Scout	4	1. Algol 2 solid 2. Castor 2 solid 3. Antares 2 solid 4. Altair 2 solid	100,950 60,765 20,925 6,480	72	3.5	300 lb. into 300-mile orbit	Explorer, Ariel, San Marco, ESRO, Secor, etc., satellites
Thrust-Augmented Improved Thor Delta	3 + booster	Booster. Castor 1 solid 1. MB3-3 liquid 2. AJ10-118E liquid 3. FW-40 solid	162,000 170,000 7,800 6,200	92	8	1,190 lb. into 300-mile orbit; 250 lb. to escape	Explorer, ESSA, OSO, Isis, Geos, Heos, etc., satellites; Pioneer probes
Thrust-Augmented Thor Delta (elongated)	3 + booster	Booster. Castor 2 solid 1. MB3-3 liquid 2. AJ10-118E liquid 3. TE 364-3 solid	156,450 170,000 7,800 9,980	105.5	8	2,000 lb. into 300-mile orbit; 575 lb. to escape	Developed as standard launch vehicle for NASA satellites, probes
Thor Agena D	2	1. MB3-3 liquid 2. Agena D 8092 liquid	170,000 16,000	76	8	3,500 lb. into 120-mile orbit	Air Force military satellites, and such NASA satellites as OGO, Nimbus, and Pageos
Atlas Agena D	2	1a. LR-89-3 liquid 1b. LR-105-3 liquid 2. Agena D 8092 liquid	300,000 88,000 16,000	104	16	6,000 lb. into 300-mile orbit; 1,450 lb. to escape	Air Force military satellites; NASA OGO, ATS, OAO satellites; Lunar Orbiter and Mariner probes
Atlas Centaur	2	1a. LR-89-3 liquid 1b. LR-105-3 liquid 2. RL10-A3 liquid	300,000 88,000 30,000	66	10	9,900 lb. into 300-mile orbit; 2,700 lb. to escape	Surveyor and Mariner probes
Titan 3B Agena D	3	1. LR-87-AJ-9 liquid 2. LR-91-AJ-9 liquid 3. Agena D 8092 liquid	430,000 100,000 16,000	124	10	8,000 lb. into 300-mile orbit	Air Force military satellites
Titan 3C	3 + booster	Booster. UA 1205 solid 1. LR-87-AJ-9 liquid 2. LR-91-AJ-9 liquid 3. AJ10-138 liquid	2,400,000 470,000 100,000 16,000	124	30	25,000 lb. into 100-mile orbit; 5,000 lb. to escape	Air Force military satellites; tactical communications satellites; Vela, Dodge, and other research satellites

Comparison of Saturn 1, Saturn 1B, and Saturn 5 Carrier Vehicles

	Saturn 1, Block 1	Saturn 1, Block 2	Saturn 1B (vehicle AS-205)	Saturn 5 (vehicle AS-505)
Total length, stages + payload body (feet-inches)	162-6	187-11	224	363
Total weight, loaded (pounds)	925,000	1,165,000	1,290,000	6,391,120
First stage				
Length (feet-inches)	81-7	80-3	80-4	138
Diameter (feet-inches)	21-5	21-5	21-5	33
Engine thrust (pounds)	1,300,000	1,504,000	1,640,000	7,680,000[b]
Propellants	LOX-kerosene	LOX-kerosene	LOX-kerosene	LOX-kerosene
Second stage	(Dummy)			
Length (feet-inches)	43-11	41-5	58-5	81-7
Diameter (feet-inches)	18-4	18-4	21-8	33
Engine thrust (pounds)	—	90,000	225,000[a]	1,150,000[c]
Propellants	—	LOX—liquid hydrogen	LOX—liquid hydrogen	LOX—liquid hydrogen
Third stage	(Dummy)	(No third stage)	(No third stage)	
Length (feet-inches)	23-4			58-7
Diameter (feet-inches)	10-0			21-8
Engine thrust (pounds)	—			230,000
Propellants	—			LOX—liquid hydrogen
Payload body				
Length (feet-inches)	23-10	63-5	52-6	82

[a] Maximum; can be operated at lower thrust, averaging 200,000 pounds.
[b] To maximum of 9,115,000 pounds at stage burnout.
[c] Maximum; each 230,000-pound-thrust engine can be operated as low as 184,000 pounds thrust.

Western European Carrier Vehicles

Designation	Nation; Agency; Contractor(s)	Stages	Propellants, by Stage	Thrust, by Stage	Launch Weight (pounds)	Length (feet)	Diameter (inches)
Black Arrow	Great Britain;	3	1. Hydrogen peroxide–kerosene	1. 50,000	40,000	43.1	78
	Ministry of Technology;		2. Hydrogen peroxide–kerosene	2. 15,350			
	Westland Aircraft		3. Solid	3. —			
Diamant B	France;	3	1. Nitrogen tetroxide–UDMH[a]	1. 78,500	53,800	78.4	48.6
	Centre National d'Études Spatiales;		2. Solid	2. 33,800			
	Nord, Sud		3. Solid	3. 11,500			
Europa 1	European consortium; ELDO;	3	1. LOX-kerosene	1. 300,000	230,500	92	120
			2. Nitrogen tetroxide–UDMH	2. 60,000			
	Hawker Siddeley Dynamics, SEREB, Nord, ASAT		3. Nitrogen tetroxide–hydrazine and UDMH mixture	3. 5,000			

[a] Unsymmetrical dimethylhydrazine.

Saturn 5 performed equally well in the Apollo 11 Lunar landing mission of July 1969. The craft was injected onto trans-Lunar trajectory just 1.1 seconds later than predicted, and the trajectory again was so accurate that there was no need to make an early mid-course correction.

Saturn 5 is a tribute to the industrial wealth of the United States. Only the very richest of nations can afford carriers on the scale of Saturn; even highly advanced nations have found it advisable to pool their resources for more modest space programs.

To get into space, the European nations have created the European Launcher Development Organization (ELDO), whose headquarters are in Paris. ELDO came into existence on 31 March 1962, and its first offspring is Europa 1, a three-stage carrier with a truly continental makeup.

The first stage is based on Britain's Blue Streak, which was canceled as an intermediate-range ballistic missile in 1960 but survived for peaceful purposes. After a series of static tests at Spadeadam in Britain, the stage was flight-tested at Woomera, Australia, on 5 June 1964. Blue Streak reached an altitude of 620 miles on its maiden flight. In its second test, held on 20 October 1964, the carrier soared nearly 1,000 miles.

Europa 1's second stage is the responsibility of SEREB, the French agency. The stage, whose structure is built by Nord Aviation, has four engines that produce a total of 61,600 pounds of thrust on unsymmetrical dimethylhydrazine (UDMH) and nitrogen tetroxide. The engines are built by the Délégation Ministérielle pour l'Armement. The third stage is built by Germany's Arbeitsgemeinschaft Satellitentrager. It is powered by a 5,000-pound-thrust engine using hydrazine-UDHM and nitrogen tetroxide. The initial satellites assigned to the carrier weigh between 1,100 and 1,300 pounds, and will be placed in 300-mile-high orbits. Eventually, Europa 1 should be able to orbit nearly 3,000 pounds. Its first test flight, with dummy second and third stages and payload, was made on 24 May 1966 from Woomera, Australia. Because of faulty radar data from the Mirrikata radar station indicating (incorrectly) that the carrier was off course, the safety officer destroyed Europa 1 after 2 minutes and 15 seconds of flight. On 15 November 1966, Europa 1 vehicle Number 5 was successfully fired at Woomera with a live first stage and inert second and third stages. The next vehicle (F 6/1) incorporated new RZ12Mk engines, developing 136,000 pounds of thrust each in the first stage; a live second stage; and a non-powered third stage. Launched on 4 August 1967, the second-stage separation was successful, but the French-built engine in that stage did not fire.

The French have developed and flown their own carrier, the Diamant, a three-stage vehicle that can orbit satellites of 80 to 90 pounds. The first stage of the newest model, Diamant B, uses nitric acid and turpentine to produce 78,500 pounds of thrust. The solid-propellant second stage produces 33,800 pounds of thrust and the third stage, also solid, 11,500 pounds of thrust. Diamant was conceived in 1960; plans took definite shape by the end of 1961, and its first satellite was launched on 26 November 1965, forty-

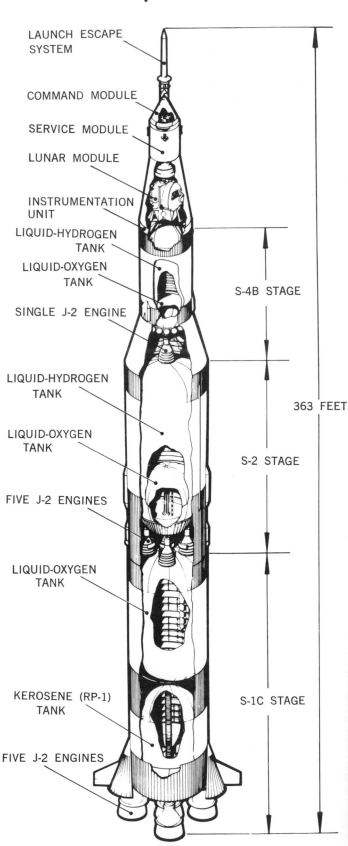

APOLLO/SATURN V

LAUNCH ESCAPE SYSTEM

COMMAND MODULE

SERVICE MODULE

LUNAR MODULE

INSTRUMENTATION UNIT

LIQUID-HYDROGEN TANK

LIQUID-OXYGEN TANK

SINGLE J-2 ENGINE

LIQUID-HYDROGEN TANK

LIQUID-OXYGEN TANK

FIVE J-2 ENGINES

LIQUID-OXYGEN TANK

KEROSENE (RP-1) TANK

FIVE J-2 ENGINES

S-4B STAGE

363 FEET

S-2 STAGE

S-1C STAGE

Cutaway of the huge Saturn 5 Moon rocket, showing its three stages and modules of the Apollo payload. Fully fueled and loaded, the Saturn weighs more than 6 million pounds. (NASA-MSFC)

Combining the rockets of three European nations, Europa 1 has a British first stage, a French second stage, and a German third stage. It is shown at left in position for first-stage static testing at the Spadeadam Rocket Establishment, England. (HAWKER SIDDELEY DYNAMICS)

The twin RZ.2 rocket engines installed in the first stage of Europa 1. Based on Britain's Blue Streak, the first stage flew to a height of nearly 1,000 miles in a test on 20 October 1964. (ROLLS-ROYCE)

three months after the final design was frozen. The French A-1 satellite was orbited from Hammaguir in North Africa by the Centre National d'Etudes Spatiales, the French equivalent of NASA. With the launching, France became the third nation in space.

France, while cooperating with ELDO, has continued to improve its own launch vehicles, including the Diamant B and Hyper Diamant, the Diogène 2, and the Vulcain, which is capable of placing satellites weighing nearly 2,500 pounds in low orbits. The original Diamant carrier orbited two Diadème satellites in 1967.

Britain also has decided to conduct a national program in addition to participating in multi-national enterprises. By the end of 1966, the Ministry of Aviation had approved the development of the Black Arrow rocket system, the goal being to launch a number of small 200-pound satellites into low polar orbits from Australia. Black Arrow is based on Black Knight, which had been fired successfully for many years. The British are endeavoring to pare development costs by using equipment and design concepts that already have been proved with the older vehicle.

ce became the third nation in space with its three-stage
nant carrier, shown here (above) in its service tower at St.
ard en Jalles, and (right) on its maiden flight on 26 No-
ber 1965 from Hammaguir in the Sahara. (SEREB; ETABLISSE-
T CINEMATOGRAPHIQUE DES ARMEES)

8 THE REMOTE EXP

It is odd, in retrospect, to consider how little thought most of the pioneers of rocketry gave to the unmanned spacecraft that were to dominate the opening years of space exploration. True, Goddard did write about sending a spacecraft to the Moon, but he was more concerned with proving the capability of the rocket than getting information back from the probe. And both Tsiolkovsky and Oberth spent more time describing manned spaceships than they did on possible unmanned spacecraft.

This might seem puzzling now, when the full complexities of sending men into space and the relative ease of getting information back from unmanned spacecraft is known. But it is understandable in terms of the technology of the time when the pioneers wrote.

Unmanned spacecraft rely completely on automatic instrumentation to gather scientific data and transmit them back to Earth. But, while the technology of rocketry and its theoretical implications had been worked out more than half a century ago, the development of techniques for sending information over long distances by remote means is a fairly recent development. The method, called radio telemetry, was not applied seriously to missile research until the initiation of the development of the V-2 (although it had been considered for sounding rockets in the early 1930's), and it did not become an indispensable part of the research that was conducted with the aid of rockets until the V-2 was used for atmospheric sounding in the United States after World War II.

The theory and practice of radio telemetry now appear simple. Instruments in a sounding rocket, an artificial satellite orbiting the Earth, or a probe to another world first gather the desired information and convert it into distinct electric signals. These signals are then transmitted to Earth. At the receiving station on Earth, the information is converted into some kind of visual display, such as a graph. A great deal of ingenuity has gone into working up efficient methods for displaying these data. In special cases messages are temporarily stored on tape prior to transmission to Earth.

Telemetry was an undeveloped art when Goddard, Oberth, and Tsiolkovsky wrote; since no way of getting information to Earth from an unmanned spacecraft was open to them, they thought in terms of manned spaceships. (Goddard's attempt to deal with the problem of transmitting information from the Moon was to use a crude flare.) But the art was well enough advanced by the early postwar years to spark speculation about small unmanned artificial Earth satellites. Three Englishmen, K. W. Gatland, A. M. Kunesch, and A. E. Dixon, published a paper on artificial satellites in a 1951 issue of the *Journal of the British Interplanetary Society*. And a University of Maryland physicist, S. Fred Singer, came up with the MOUSE (Minimum Orbital Unmanned Satellite of the Earth) at the Fourth International Astronautical Congress in 1953. MOUSE, details of which were published in British and American journals, was a 100-pound satellite that would operate its radio telemetry transmitter by batteries that were energized by the Sun.

While these proposals were being made, the military services in the United States were quietly studying the possibility of orbiting artificial satellites. The Navy, in 1945, apparently was the first to begin considering the idea.

The Navy's effort started with the organization of the Committee for Evaluating the Feasibility of Rocketry (CEFSR) within the Bureau of Aeronautics in October 1945. After preliminary studies CEFSR recommended that the development of an instrumented Earth satellite be started. The Guggenheim Aeronautical Laboratory at the California Institute of Technology was given a contract in December to investigate the relationship between carrier vehicle performance, the weight of the satellite, and the height of its orbit. The results showed that a satellite could be orbited, but only at a price that looked sky-high to the Navy in those postwar years of tight military budgets. The Navy went to the

Army Air Corps to ask for help, and a meeting was held between the Navy's Captain W. P. Cogswell and Commander Harvey Hall, the originator of the Navy study, and three Air Force generals, on 7 March 1946.

The Army Air Corps officers noncommittally said they would take up the project with General Curtis LeMay and other high officials. When LeMay met with Hall later that month, it became clear that the Air Corps had no intention of cooperating with the Navy. What LeMay did not tell Hall was that the Army Air Corps also had begun a study of artificial satellites. The Navy learned about the Army Air Corps study, which was being made by Project Rand (then a part of the Douglas Aircraft Company and later the Rand Corporation) at a June conference called by the War Department's Aeronautical Board. While the Board did not discourage the continuation of either of the feasibility studies, no attempt was made to get cooperation between the services, and each went on alone.

The Navy came up with a plan for a single-stage, liquid oxygen–liquid hydrogen carrier vehicle with a takeoff weight of 101,000 pounds and a thrust of 233,000 pounds. The vehicle, named HATV for High Altitude Test Vehicle, evolved from studies by North American Aviation, the Bureau of Aeronautics, the Glenn L. Martin Company, and Aerojet Engineering Corporation. The carrier rocket was to boost itself into orbit, with its empty structure becoming the satellite—an idea later fulfilled in the orbiting of the Atlas Score in 1958. HATV's instrumentation was to be in its nose, with the data it gathered being telemetered to Earth. But the idea never got off the ground. Faced with continuing reductions in appropriations, the Navy cut back its satellite studies until they petered out in 1948.

The Army Air Corps study had taken a different tack. Recognizing the difficulties of developing a single-stage orbital carrier-satellite combination, the Project Rand staff, aided by personnel from North American and Northrop, concentrated on a multi-stage vehicle. The results of the study were contained in a historic report—"Preliminary Design on an Experimental World-Circling Spaceship"—that was presented to the Air Materiel Command on 12 May 1946.

Rand said that a 500-pound satellite could be launched by a carrier that would utilize the technology acquired in the V-2 and other vehicle programs, and that a launch date as early as 1951 was feasible. The report recommended a three-stage carrier that would weigh 233,669 pounds and be powered by liquid oxygen and alcohol. The launching would take place at an island in the Pacific, to take advantage of the fact that the Earth's speed of rotation is greatest at the equator; this would provide a boost in putting the satellite into an eastward-heading orbit. Several uses were suggested for the satellite. Among them were meteorological research, communications, and reconnaissance—for example, observing the effects of American bombing attacks on a hypothetical enemy. The cost envisioned for the satellite carrier was $150 million.

The report included the prophetic statement that the "achievement of a satellite craft by the United States would inflame the imagination of mankind, and would probably produce repercussions in the world comparable to the explosion of the atomic bomb," a prediction whose truth was proved bitterly to the United States some eleven years later. The report also urged:

It is our earnest hope that under the terms of this new study and research contract with the Army Air Force we may be able to enlist the active cooperation of an important fraction of the scientific resources of the country to solve problems in the wholly new fields which man's imagination has opened. Of these, space travel is one of the most important and challenging.

As more analyses were made on the basis of better data, Rand refined its thinking. A revised study, published in April 1947, recommended among other things a much smaller and lighter (82,000 pounds) carrier vehicle that would use higher energy liquid

On 29 December 1948, James V. Forrestal, America's first Secretary of Defense, revealed that the United States was studying the feasibility of artificial Earth satellites.

hydrogen instead of conventional alcohol for its fuel. The cost of the program was estimated at $82 million. But the basic recommendations for a satellite launching did not change. Nor did the chilly attitude of policy-makers.

In October 1947, the Committee on Guided Missiles of the Joint Research and Development Board (the successor of the War Department's Aeronautical Board) assumed responsibility for coordinating the work being done on artificial satellites by the various services. A technical evaluation group, under Clark B. Millikan, made a thorough review of studies conducted by the Navy and the Air Force, which had become a separate service in July of that year. Millikan's group concluded that an Earth-satellite program could not be authorized until some definite military uses for satellites were established. Although this meant the Rand report had to be shelved temporarily, advocates of the satellite concept continued to press for support within the now-independent Air Force. The best they could get, however, was a statement on 15 January 1948, from Vice-Chief of Staff Hoyt S. Vandenberg, that satellites should be developed "at the proper time."

The Army entered the picture on 15 September

1948, when the Committee on Guided Missiles recommended that the Hermes project provide a continuing analysis of the problems of developing an Earth satellite—the first official recognition of the capability of the Army Ordnance–Von Braun team for contributing to satellite carrier-rocket development. And on 29 December 1948, James V. Forrestal revealed publicly for the first time that the United States was looking into the feasibility of artificial satellites. In his *First Report of the Secretary of Defense*, Forrestal wrote:

The Earth Satellite Vehicle Program, which was being carried out independently by each military service, was assigned to the Committee on Guided Missiles for coordination. To provide an integrated program with resultant elimination of duplication, the committee recommended that current efforts in this field be limited to studies and component designs; well-defined areas of such research have been allocated to each of the three military departments.

Although receiving only meager encouragement, the military continued their studies of artificial satellites. In 1949 the Rand Corporation, which had become independent of Douglas in November 1948, concentrated on proving the military utility of satellites. There was hope that the Department of Defense would approve a true development program if it was convinced that a satellite would do some useful work for the armed forces. Among the purposes listed by Rand for artificial satellites were surveillance and reconnaissance, communications, a display of American technical and scientific leadership, and psychological "cold warfare"—Rand calculated that the mere presence in the sky of an artificial satellite would have a strong psychological effect on a potential enemy.

The early postwar studies made by the services and their civilian contractors later proved to be remarkably accurate, in specific details as well as in their broad outlines. At the time, though, they were dismissed. There was no hope of orbiting a satellite when the United States did not even have an adequate program to develop ballistic missiles. One glimmer of hope came when the Air Force reactivated the Convair MX-774 program in January 1951, and named it the Atlas. Unless adequate rockets were developed, no satellite would ever be placed into orbit. The Atlas was intended for military uses, but it was a step in the right direction.

What little debate about artificial satellites that went on in the United States took place in a vacuum. Americans had the complacent idea that no one else was interested in placing a satellite into orbit. Little or no mention was made of the possibility that the

Soviet Union was working on a satellite program. Russia was regarded as too backward technologically and too devastated by war to compete with the United States in any field. And, of course, the Russians were saying very little about their space program.

What they did say was extremely interesting.

For example, on 4 October 1951, Soviet rocket expert M. K. Tikhonravov said that Russian technology was at least on a par with that of the United States, and that the Soviet Union would be able to launch artificial satellites. And at the World Peace Council in Vienna on 27 November 1953, A. N. Nesmeyanov of the U.S.S.R. Academy of Sciences announced that "science has reached such a stage that . . . the creation of an artificial satellite of the earth is a real possibility." These were important voices that were talking, but the United States was deaf to them. It was also deaf to voices that were closer to home.

The work done by Rand, the Navy, and the missile development team under Von Braun had begun to mesh. Building on the technology of the Hermes and Redstone programs, Von Braun's team soon was in possession of the ability to launch small satellites. It was inevitable that the supporters of space programs should get together.

A small group of experts met in Washington on 25 June 1954 in the first step toward the joint Army Ordnance–Office of Naval Research program that was to be named Orbiter. Called together by Commander George W. Hoover, the group consisted of Frederick C. Durant III, Alexander Satin, S. Fred Singer, Wernher von Braun, Fred L. Whipple, and David Young—all leading proponents of artificial satellites, representing government, academic, and industrial backgrounds.

At the meeting, Von Braun presented an ABMA proposal to use a modified Redstone missile with three upper stages of spinning clustered Loki rockets to orbit the satellite. It was calculated that the first satellite would weigh 5 pounds; by substituting scaled-down Sergeant rockets for the upper stages satellites weighing 15 or 20 pounds could be orbited. Rear Admiral Frederick R. Furth, Chief of Naval Research, approved the basic idea and Project Orbiter was born.

A second Army-Navy meeting was held in Huntsville on 3 August 1954. The next month Von Braun published a paper for the group, "The Minimum Satellite Vehicle Based Upon Components Available from Missile Development of the Army Ordnance Corps," in which he demonstrated that a satellite could be orbited with existing hardware. The following January the Air Force was asked to join Orbiter; the invitation went to Assistant Secretary of Defense Donald A. Quarles. Quarles later set up the ad hoc Advisory Group on Special Capabilities that killed Orbiter by voting, on 9 September 1955, to try Vanguard, the alternate Naval Research Laboratory proposal. Quarles upheld the committee's 7 to 2 vote and the Defense Policy Committee added its approval.

While the unpublicized debate that led up to this decision was going on, artificial satellites were getting wider public discussion. On 4 October 1954, a special committee of the International Geophysical Year, meeting in Rome, recommended "that thought be given to the launching of small satellite vehicles, to their scientific instrumentation, and to the new problems associated with satellite experiments, such as power supply, telemetering, and orientation . . . ." The United States National Committee for the IGY approved the idea on 14 March 1955, and on 29 July the National Academy of Sciences and the National Science Foundation announced that the United States would launch a satellite during the IGY. In October

Meeting of the Project Orbiter Committee on 17 March 1955 in Washington, D.C. Shown here are (left to right): Seated—Cdr. George W. Hoover, Office of Naval Research; Frederick C. Durant III, Arthur D. Little, Inc.; James B. Kendrick, Aerophysics Development Corporation; William A. Giardini, Alabama Tool and Die; Philippe W. Newton, Dept. of Defense; Rudolf H. Schlidt, Army Ballistic Missile Agency; Gerhard Heller, ABMA; Wernher von Braun, ABMA; Standing—Lt. Cdr. William E. Dowdell, USN; Alexander Satin, ONR; Cdr. Robert C. Truax, USN; Liston Tatum, IBM; Austin W. Stanton, Varo, Inc.; Fred L. Whipple, Harvard Observatory; George W. Petri, IBM; Lowell O. Anderson, ONR; Milton W. Rosen, NRL. (FREDERICK C. DURANT III)

Richard W. Porter was named chairman of a technical panel to plan experiments, set up tracking facilities, and see to similar details.

Few Americans noticed that the Soviet Union was making statements of equal importance. On 15 April 1955, the Soviets announced that the Council of the U.S.S.R. Academy of Sciences had set up a Permanent Interdepartmental Commission for Interplanetary Communications, whose work included coordinating the development of meteorological satellites. On 30 July, just one day after the American announcement, the Soviets disclosed that they had their own program. At the Sixth International Astronautical Congress in Copenhagen that August, Leonid I. Sedov, chairman of the new Soviet commission, said, "In my opinion, it will be possible to launch an artificial satellite of the Earth within the next two years, and there is the technological possibility of creating artificial satellites of various sizes

The Space Age officially began with Sputnik 1, launched 4 October 1957 by the Soviet Union.

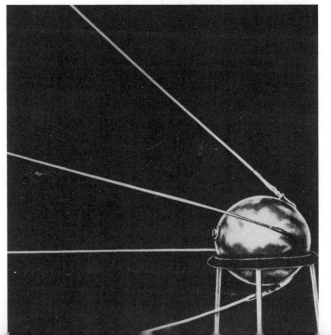

and weights." Sedov also mentioned that the satellites that could be launched within the following two years might be much larger than those conceived by the United States.

After the flurry of interest aroused by the 1955 announcements, interest subsided. By 1956 it was widely known that both the United States and the Soviet Union had satellite programs under way, but no one regarded the efforts as a race to space—at least, the United States government chose not to view its project in those terms. Vanguard's payload was conservative and the project was poorly funded, with minimal goals—almost an afterthought to the main efforts that went into the International Geophysical Year. Details of the Soviet program were not known. Vanguard's progress and setbacks were widely publicized, and the lack of similar Soviet publicity led the world to assume that the first artificial satellite would be American. But for those who were listening carefully, there were other indications.

In June 1957, the same A. N. Nesmeyanov who in 1953 had predicted the early development of satellites said that both the carrier vehicle and the instrumentation for the first Soviet satellite were ready, and that the first launching would occur within a few months. On 10 June, Lloyd V. Berkner of the American IGY Committee received a document from the Soviet Union stating bluntly that a satellite would be launched within months. Nesmeyanov repeated the prediction the next day. In August, E. Federov said that no definite launch date had been established, but on 18 September Radio Moscow said it would be soon. The Russians announced the transmission frequencies of the first satellite on 1 October.

On 4 October, to the amazement of the world, the Soviets orbited Sputnik 1, thereby reaping the glory of opening the age of space. The world's first artificial satellite weighed 184 pounds and carried instruments to study the density and temperature of the upper atmosphere and the concentration of electrons in the ionosphere. It circled the Earth about every 1½ hours in an elliptical orbit that ranged in altitude from about 140 to 560 miles. Sputnik 1 remained in orbit, gradually losing altitude, until 4 January 1958, when it disintegrated upon re-entering the denser portion of the atmosphere. Despite the plain-spoken Soviet forewarnings, Sputnik stunned the world. Americans, who had become accustomed to laughing at Russia's technological efforts, suddenly found themselves in the uncomfortable position of second place in a two-horse race. Sputnik started a national re-evaluation whose ef-

Vanguard 1, the second United States satellite, was orbited on 17 March 1958. (U.S. NAVY)

fects in fields from politics to education are still being felt.

One immediate result was an extensive series of Congressional hearings that began in November 1957 and ran well into 1958. Another was the formation by the National Advisory Committee for Aeronautics of an advisory committee for space technology. It was headed by H. Guyford Stever of the Massachusetts Institute of Technology. The NACA soon was expanded into the National Aeronautics and Space Administration, created to handle the civilian space program, while the Advanced Research Projects Agency was set up to direct military space efforts.

But the initiative remained with the Russians. On 3 November came Sputnik 2, huge for the time at 1,120 pounds and carrying a dog, life-support equipment, instruments to measure the effects of space flight on the animal, and some unrelated instruments to measure cosmic and Solar radiation. Sputnik 3, still larger and heavier, carried instruments to determine the pressure and composition of the upper atmosphere, the incidence of micrometeoroids, and Solar and cosmic radiation. It was orbited on 15 May 1958.

The first three Soviet satellites, and many of those that followed, were clearly scientific satellites, designed to investigate the upper atmosphere, outer space, or astronomical bodies. Satellites offer scientists advantages that sounding rockets cannot begin to match. Instruments that orbit the Earth every 90 minutes can deliver a quick, worldwide picture, rather than the few scattered readings possible with sounding rockets. And satellites stay up for prolonged periods, so they can record changes in atmospheric and space phenomena in both time and space. Satellites can catch the fleeting phenomena that sounding rockets are likely to miss. The costs of satellites are high, but so are the scientific returns.

The Soviet habit of secrecy has made it impossible to determine just how much of its unmanned satellite effort has been devoted to pure science and how much has military motives. The Soviets have faithfully reported the orbiting of their satellites, but they have been far from generous with descriptions of their purposes. And the Russians are most reluctant to talk about their failures. Nevertheless, the broad outlines of the Soviet space program are clear.

Students of that program believe that the period from October 1957 to October 1964 was one distinct development phase for the Soviets, and that another phase, possibly scheduled to last another seven years, opened in November 1964. The first phase was dominated by the Kosmos series of unmanned satel-

Designed as test vehicles for later manned flights, the Russian series of five Korabl Sputniks carried live dogs into orbit. Three were successfully recovered, proving that animals could not only survive space travel, but could also return safely to Earth. Above, the recovery capsule for Korabl 2, launched 19 August 1960. (U.S.S.R. ACADEMY OF SCIENCES)

lites, which accounted for nearly three-quarters of all Soviet launches, manned or unmanned, through the end of 1965.

After orbiting the three successful Sputniks in 1957 and 1958, the Soviets shifted during 1959 to carry out a three shot Lunar exploration program. Returning to satellites in 1960, they orbited five Korabl Sputniks during that and the succeeding year. Each was larger and heavier than the earlier Sputniks, weighing more than 10,000 pounds, and each contained a recoverable re-entry capsule. They served as test vehicles for the manned Vostok spacecraft that followed. Capsules from three of these satellites were recovered with live dogs aboard, proving that animals could not only survive the trip into space, but could also return to Earth safely. Another Sputnik, number 4, was orbited during this period. It was quite heavy—14,292 pounds—and the Soviets would say only that its purpose was the study of "the parameters which characterize the operation of its design."

On 16 March 1962 the Kosmos series was inaugurated. The Soviets have said much less about these satellites than about the earlier Sputniks and Korabl Sputniks, leading Westerners to think that at least some of the Kosmos satellites have a military use. The Russians have disclosed neither weight nor configuration of most Kosmos satellites. About all

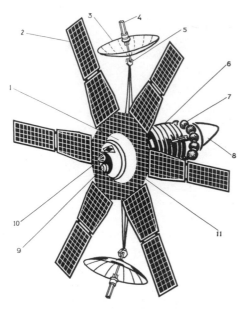

Molniya communications satellite, the first of which was orbited by the U.S.S.R. on 23 April 1965. Components shown in this drawing are: (1) hermetically sealed body; (2) solar battery; (3) pencil-beam antenna; (4) antenna orientation to Earth detector; (5) antenna drive; (6) radiation-refrigerator; (7) reserve of operating heat for effecting microcorrection; (8) correction engine installation; (9) orientation transducer for effecting correction; (10) Solar orientation transducer; (11) heater panel. (NOVOSTI PRESS AGENCY, LONDON)

they would say of Kosmos 1 was that it was designed to verify and improve "elements of space vehicle construction" and to measure "the effect of meteoric matter on the construction elements of space vehicles." Later they announced that Kosmos 1 was instrumented to study the Earth's magnetic field, the radiation belts, the ionosphere, and Solar and cosmic radiation.

By mid-1969, nearly 300 Kosmos satellites had been orbited. Although information about them was still scanty, it appeared that about two-thirds were military and one-third scientific. They were launched from Tyura Tam at Aral'skoye More in Kazakhstan; Kapustin Yar, east of Volgograd; and a newer range near Plesetsk. It is thought that the Kapustin Yar satellites have electromagnetic surveillance and meteorological equipment aboard; they may also serve as navigational aids for submarines. The Tyura Tam satellites are normally recovered after a week, indicating that they are reconnaissance satellites whose photographs are being returned for processing. The pace of reconnaissance satellite launching has been increasing; thus 1967's total of twenty-two was equaled during the first nine months of 1968 (whose total was twenty-nine).

Within the Kosmos program, the Soviets con-

ducted the world's first unmanned rendezvous and docking maneuvers. On 29 October 1967, Kosmos 186, which had been orbited two days earlier, linked up with Kosmos 188 shortly after the latter was launched. The craft remained attached for two and one-half hours, then separated on command from the ground. Both were later returned to the Earth.

Some weapon testing appears also to have been conducted under the Kosmos cover. On 2 October 1967, Kosmos 244 was launched and then recovered after a single orbit. Its altitude never exceeded 100 miles. Some Western observers believe the satellite was a prototype of a fractional orbital bombardment system (FOBS), which, when operational, could deliver nuclear warheads to almost any point on the globe.

While study of the environment in space is an important element in the Soviet unmanned satellite program, it is believed that they place even greater emphasis on development of new systems. For example, Polyot 2, launched on 1 November 1963, a few weeks after the orbiting of Kosmos 20, was designed to prove that a satellite could be maneuvered to change the size and shape of its orbit. In describing the experiment, Mstislav V. Keldysh, president of the U.S.S.R. Academy of Sciences, disclosed that the Polyot 1 system had been tested earlier in the Kosmos series. Other Kosmos satellites are believed to have tested many components needed for manned orbital

Proton 1, which weighed more than 26,000 pounds, was orbited on 16 July 1965. Numbers indicate: (1) Solar power plant panels; (2) hermetically sealed body; (3) transducers of the indicating system of the position of the station's axes in space; (4) external casing; (5) antennas for telemetering and radio command; (6) chemical current sources. (NOVOSTI PRESS AGENCY, LONDON)

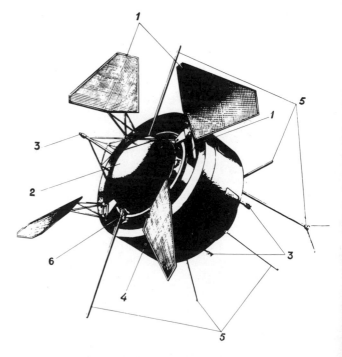

satellites. Some Kosmos spacecraft are believed to be designed solely to perfect components and techniques needed for more advanced space vehicles.

The Soviets have developed several other satellite series. Two Elektron satellites were launched on 30 January 1964. One was placed in an elliptical orbit whose high point was more than 4,000 miles above the Earth and whose low point was within 250 miles of the Earth. The other had an orbit whose high point was more than 40,000 miles from the Earth. Two more Elektrons were orbited on 11 July 1964. The Soviets said their prime purpose was to measure the radiation belts around the Earth.

The first Molniya communications satellite was launched in April 1965; through spring of 1969, a total of eleven were orbited. Color television programs have been exchanged between Moscow and Paris with this system, which also provides multi-channel telephone and telegraph communications links.

Russia also initiated its Proton series in 1965, launching huge 27,000-pound satellites on 16 July and 2 November. Proton 3 followed on 9 July 1966. Their announced purpose was to study high-intensity radiation particles, but their large size led to speculation that they were prototypes of manned space stations. This theory was supported by Proton 4, orbited in mid-November 1968. Weighing 37,500 pounds, it was put into an orbit different from those of earlier Protons and similar to that employed for manned satellites.

As for the number of failures that accompanied these Soviet successes, the best guide is America's experience. The United States has demonstrated increasing reliability in its launch efforts. For example, only five of the seventeen launching attempts in 1958 were successful. The next year, the United States succeeded in nine of nineteen satellite-launching attempts. The record since then is more complicated, since some carrier vehicles launch two or more satellites at once, but the general pattern of improvement is clear.

Thus, thirty-eight of forty-six carriers fired in 1963 performed successfully, and sixty of a total of seventy-one satellites were placed into orbit. According to figures compiled by the National Aeronautics and Space Council, from 1958 to 1965 the United States moved from a 71-percent failure rate to a 91-percent success rate. In 1965, NASA had twenty-three mission successes in twenty-eight attempts, for an 82-percent success rate, and twenty-six successful carrier rocket firings in thirty attempts, for a grade of 87 percent. Since 1966, the number of NASA launches has decreased, but reliability has continued to increase.

Defense Department records are understandably less easy to determine. However, published figures show that there were only six failures compared to fifty successes in orbiting Defense Department satellites in 1964, an 89 percent success rate. The Soviets are believed to be in the same neighborhood.

America's first three satellites, Explorer 1, Vanguard 1, and Explorer 2, were not in the same league with the Soviet Sputniks in size, but their miniaturized instruments gathered data of extreme value to scientists. Launched between January and March 1958, the two Explorers measured cosmic rays, micrometeorites, and temperatures, while the Vanguard beeped out signals from its transmitters, which were powered by both batteries and Solar cells. Explorer 1, 80 inches long and 6 inches in diameter, was an integral part of the carrier's fourth-stage motor case. Its payload was developed by the State University of Iowa under the direction of James A. Van Allen. The satellite, which weighed 18 pounds, was responsible for the discovery of the radiation belts that bear Van Allen's name; the discovery was confirmed by Explorer 4. Vanguard 1 was a 6.4-inch sphere to which were attached six Solar-energy converters and antennas. Both were still in orbit as of January 1966. On 31 January 1966 Explorer 1 marked its eighth anniversary in space, circling the Earth every 103.9 minutes—only 11 minutes less than its original period—in an orbit that ranged from 950.9 to 211.9 miles in altitude.

More Explorers and Vanguards were orbited in 1958 and 1959. The first Discoverer went into orbit on 28 February 1959. The Discoverers, sponsored by the Air Force, were designed for space research, communications, and photographic missions. Many carried capsules that brought back to Earth film, biological specimens, and other valuable material.

One of the most successful satellite series started on 1 April 1960, when NASA orbited Tiros 1, a meteorological satellite that gave weathermen their first look at the Earth from above. Tiros 1 sent down a dazzling series of cloud pictures that literally added a new dimension to weather forecasting. Before it was through, Tiros 1 had broadcast more than 19,000 pictures to Earth. It was followed into orbit by Numbers 2 through 5, which sent from 23,000 to 60,000 pictures each. Subsequent Tiros orbitings were just as successful, Numbers 9 and 10 obtaining increased coverage by going into polar orbits. Altogether, the Tiros series provided meteorologists more than a half million cloud cover photographs and set the stage for improved meteorological satellites operating within a weather forecast system.

Vanguard 3, launched September 1959, carried many complex instruments and provided a comprehensive study of the Earth's magnetic field. (NASA-GSFC)

As Tiros was progressing toward operational status, experimental equipment was being tested in a new satellite series, Nimbus. Carrying an automatic picture transmission (APT) system, an advanced vidicon camera system, and a radiometer, Nimbus 1 was launched on 28 August 1964. It provided day and night cloud pictures for about a month before

the Solar paddle drive system failed and the satellite ceased operation for lack of power. Nimbus 2, containing the same sensors as its predecessor plus additional equipment to measure the Solar radiation reflected by the Earth, was launched on 15 May 1966. It remained in operation until January 1969, far beyond its six-month design lifetime.

A Nimbus was lost in May 1968 when its carrier had to be destroyed during the launch; so another satellite was built and orbited as Nimbus 3 on 14 April 1969. This 1,269-pound satellite carried seven experimental packages, including a new interrogation recording and location system, designed to pinpoint the positions of small transmitters placed in balloons, on buoys at sea, on an ice island, and even on an elk—the last being an experiment in the ability to determine migratory patterns of wildlife by means of a satellite.

Through the APT system that feeds into more than 400 ground stations, meteorologists all over the world are able to obtain Nimbus weather pictures. Nimbus satellites have advanced man's knowledge of the life history of storms and have aided in the construction of maps of the jet stream. The pictures also have been valuable to oceanographers, geologists, and geographers. The 10,000-foot-high Mount Siple, for example, was moved westward nearly fifty miles on maps of Antarctica as a result of Nimbus photographs. The boundaries of the Gulf Stream and other ocean currents have been detected in Nimbus pictures, and the photographing of icebergs has led to the belief that the iceberg patrol may be handled exclusively by satellites in the future.

While Nimbus continues as an experimental research and development program for testing new sensors and techniques, the Environmental Science Services Administration employs the Tiros operational satellite system to provide "everyday" weather information. The system relies principally on NASA-launched environmental survey satellites (ESSA), the first of which was orbited on 3 February 1966. ESSA satellites have been launched regularly since then, Number 9 going into orbit in late February 1969. Two types of ESSA satellites are involved: those with odd numbers carry APT equipment, which transmits pictures instantly to the ground; those with even numbers store pictures on magnetic tape for later transmission.

The United States and Soviet Russia have been exchanging meteorological data from satellites since August 1966. America first sent Russia six to ten photos a day from the ESSA 1 satellite and received five to fifteen Kosmos photos per day in return. Because of the complicated data link from Moscow

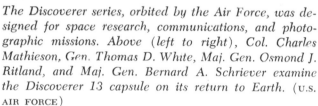

The Discoverer series, orbited by the Air Force, was designed for space research, communications, and photographic missions. Above (left to right), Col. Charles Mathieson, Gen. Thomas D. White, Maj. Gen. Osmond J. Ritland, and Maj. Gen. Bernard A. Schriever examine the Discoverer 13 capsule on its return to Earth. (U.S. AIR FORCE)

A satellite for detecting micrometeoroids is prepared for an environmental test at Langley Research Center, Hampton, Va. During this test, the satellite is subjected to the widely varying temperatures it will encounter on an actual orbital flight. (NASA—LANGLEY RESEARCH CENTER)

to Washington, however, picture quality was not good.

There is no question that weather satellites have paid back all the money that went into their development. They have saved many lives by giving advance warnings of the approach of hurricanes that developed at sea, far from the nearest weather station.

Almost as successful has been the series of communications satellites orbited by the United States. The first was Echo 1, orbited on 12 August 1960. Echo was a passive satellite—that is, it was just a balloon that reflected back to Earth the signals sent from the ground. The first active repeater communications satellite, with the ability to amplify the signals before returning them, was the Army Courier, which went up on 4 October 1960.

The first direct television connection between continents was made possible by Telstar 1, a Bell Telephone active repeater satellite which was orbited by a NASA vehicle on 10 July 1962. RCA's Relay 1 went into orbit on 13 December. Relay did not work at first, but engineers on the ground were able to find the trouble and correct it. On 5 January 1963 the remarkable "remote repair job" was complete, and two test transmissions were made between receiving stations at Andover, Maine, and Goonhilly

Downs, England; on 7 January, signals went from England to the United States. It began transmitting regular civilian television broadcasts between the United States and Europe on 9 January.

Telstar 2 was orbited on 7 May, and the first transatlantic color-television pictures were sent the next day. On 22 November, Relay 1 transmitted the first live television pictures across the Pacific. Japanese audiences saw NASA Administrator James E. Webb and the Japanese ambassador to Washington, Ryuji Takeuchi. They were to have seen a taped greeting from President Kennedy; instead, they were told of his assassination in Dallas a few hours earlier.

Telstar and Relay, which orbited only a few hundred miles above the Earth, had to be tracked as they appeared over the horizon, and they could transmit signals only when they were in sight of ground stations. As early as 1945, Arthur C. Clarke had suggested that if a communications satellite were placed at 22,300 miles, it would orbit the Earth at just the proper speed to appear to be hanging in space above one point on the planet's surface. The advantages of having such a synchronous orbit were plain. A synchronous satellite would always be in position to relay radio, television, and telephone signals, and no elaborate tracking devices would be needed.

185

The second Intelsat 3 satellite was placed in a synchronous orbit over the Atlantic in May 1969. It is part of the satellite network owned by the International Telecommunications Consortium, of which the American firm Communications Satellite Corporation is manager. (COMMUNICATIONS SATELLITE CORP.)

The first synchronous satellite, Syncom 1, was launched on 14 February 1963. It went into orbit, but its radio equipment failed to work. Syncom 2 was launched on 26 July into an orbit 22,230 miles high. It was maneuvered into position over Brazil in three weeks by firing jets from small onboard hydrogen peroxide rockets. On 13 September, Syncom 2 and Relay 1 were used to link Rio de Janeiro, New Jersey, and Lagos, Nigeria, in a three-continent conversation. The signals went from the USNS *Kingsport* in Lagos harbor to Syncom 2 to Lakehurst, New Jersey, then by land to Nutley, New Jersey, then to Relay 1, and finally to Rio.

Because Syncom 2 was not orbiting quite in the plane of the equator, it appeared to describe a figure 8 as the Earth turned beneath it. Syncom 3 was placed into a true equatorial orbit, with no north-south swing, on 19 August 1964. Drifting over the Pacific Ocean near the International Dateline on 10 October, it telecast the opening-day ceremonies of the Olympic games in Tokyo.

Big Horn antenna at Andover, Me., links Europe and North America by transmitting and receiving signals from Intelsat satellites. Built by the American Telephone and Telegraph Co., it weighs 380 tons and has a 14-foot dish antenna on the cone of a giant horn. (COMMUNICATIONS SATELLITE CORP.)

By this time is was apparent that communications satellites were rapidly moving out of the experimental area into the realm of paying propositions. The Communications Satellite Corporation, Comsat for short, was set up to develop communications satellite systems, with half the stock going to the public and the other half to large communications companies. Comsat's first venture was Early Bird, a synchronous satellite providing a 240-circuit two-way voice channel link between Europe and North America; it was orbited on 6 April 1965.

Comsat is the United States member, as well as general manager, of the International Telecommunications Satellite Consortium (Intelsat for short). By 1969, nearly seventy nations had joined the consortium, whose satellites are launched at cost by NASA.

Early Bird, also known as Intelsat 1, now has a number of companions. In 1967 (after one 1966 failure), Intelsats 2 F-2 and 2 F-4 were orbited over the Pacific, and a second link was established over the Atlantic with Intelsat 2 F-3. Four improved series 3 satellites, each with 1,200 circuits and capable of handling television and telephone communications simultaneously, were orbited during 1968 and 1969. Still larger Intelsat 4's, with 5,000 circuits apiece, are now ready to go into service.

Since it is not always feasible to use operational satellites to check out newer and better systems and components—Intelsat, for example, is naturally reluctant to commit its satellites to untried equipment or techniques—NASA began orbiting a series of applications technology satellites (ATS) in 1966. Cylindrical craft some 4 feet and 8 inches in diameter, they vary in length and weight (650 to 790 pounds) and have thousands of Solar cells that enable them to operate for years. ATS-2 and ATS-4 never entered the desired orbits, but ATS-1, launched in December 1966, and ATS-3, launched in November 1967, have been highly successful.

Since 1960, the military services have orbited a variety of satellites for many different purposes. On 13 April 1960, the Navy put its first Transit navigation satellite into orbit. The Air Force inaugurated its Midas program to detect ICBM launchings (by the infrared radiation they gave off) on 24 May 1960, after a previous launch effort failed. And on 31 January 1961, exactly three years after Explorer 1 was launched, the Air Force orbited its first Samos reconnaissance satellite. For security reasons, little is made public about these and other military satellite programs, but it is known that launchings of military satellites occur fairly frequently. In 1965, for example, the Department of Defense orbited a total of seventy artificial satellites, using forty-one carrier vehicles, nearly three times the amount orbited by NASA during the same year. Among the missions of those under control of the Air Force were radiation measurement, nuclear explosion detection, communications, radar calibration, nuclear power supply test, and radio amateur experimentation. The Navy was responsible for seven Surcal satellites used to calibrate their satellite surveillance tracking network, two Solrad vehicles, and a Greb radiation monitor. The Army, for its part, handled four Secor geodetic satellites.

Much of the military effort has gone into establishing communications networks. During 1966 and 1967, the Defense Communications Agency orbited eighteen satellites in its initial defense communication satellite program (IDCSP). The 100-pound satellites were orbited in three groups of seven, eight, and three, and were spaced so that communication could occur between most parts of the world most of the time; at least one satellite, for example, is in position to handle London–Washington communications 85 percent of the time. In mid-June 1968, eight more IDCSP satellites went into service, supplementing the original eighteen (seventeen of which were still in operation).

The military also has been developing a tactical satellite communications (Tacsatcom) system whose ground elements can be transported by Army trucks under battlefield conditions. Prototypes for this system have often been orbited with other payloads; for example, the July 1967 launch of three IDCSP satellites included a 225-pound experimental Tacsatcom, LES-5, as well as a Navy Dodge gravity gradient craft.

The Defense Department also has sought to ensure that the United States will detect the explosion of any nuclear weapons in space, in violation of the 1963 test ban treaty, by launching a series of Vela satellites. The first six Velas, launched in pairs in 1963, 1964, and 1965, weigh nearly 500 pounds. They were stationed in orbits about 70,000 miles high. In April 1967, they were joined by two larger, 730-pound Velas which carried, in addition to their sensing equipment, 7,600-pound-thrust rocket engines, permitting adjustments of their orbits. Two more Velas, Numbers 9 and 10, were orbited in May 1969.

In addition to the Solrad, Surcal, Secor, and Greb craft, the Defense Department has continued to launch other scientific and engineering research satellites at frequent intervals. These include the Air Force's orbiting vehicle satellites—which typically carry cosmic ray and radiation belt detectors, satellite-to-satellite communications gear, and ionospheric research devices—as well as the environmental research satellites. The payloads of many of these, and other, satellites are often classified.

Although most satellites had specific applications, the United States by no means neglected pure

NASA's Orbiting Astronomical Observatory is designed to study the stars while it circles the Earth. Shown here *are an exploded view of the satellite and the star acquisition sequence of the OAO in orbit.* (NASA)

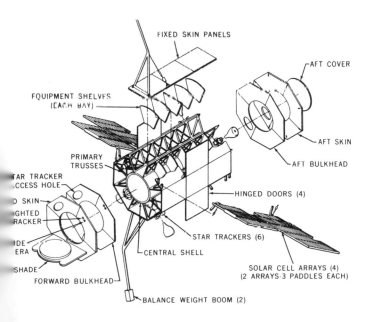

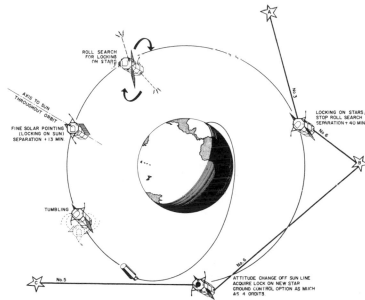

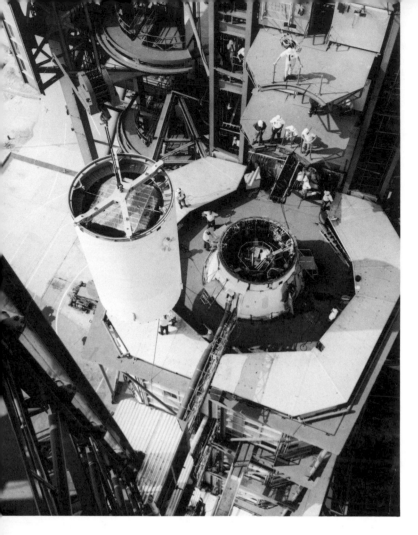

The Pegasus 2 satellite being mated to the SA-8 carrier vehicle in the Saturn 1 series at Cape Kennedy. It was orbited on 25 May 1965 to gather information on the meteoroid hazard for future manned and unmanned spacecraft. (NASA)

science. Explorer continued to be the mainstay of the scientific satellite field, and by August 1968 Number 40—in a dual launch with Number 39—had been placed in orbit. Explorers have proved invaluable when single or small numbers of experiments are desired on an individual spacecraft. With them, scientists have learned much about the composition of the ionosphere (Explorer 11), the micrometeoroid environment (Explorers 16 and 23), and the nature of the magnetosphere and interplanetary space (Explorer 18—which, incidentally, confirmed the existence of a "shock wave" around the Earth).

Larger and more complex experiments are mounted on orbiting geophysical observatory (OGO) satellites, which weigh upward of 1,000 pounds. OGO-1, launched on 4 September 1964, entered an elongated orbit that carried it as far as 90,000 miles away from the Earth and as close as 175 miles. It was only a partial success because two of the booms, on which instrument packages were mounted, failed

to swing into place. The next year, OGO-2 was launched, as well as Pegasus 3—the last of three huge micrometeoroid measurement satellites. (It and its two predecessors were turned off by ground command on 29 August 1968.)

OGO's were orbited annually in the 1966–1969 period. OGO-6, the last in the series, was a 1,393-pound craft with twenty-five experiments aboard. It was launched on 5 June 1969 into an orbit of from 248 to 683 miles by a Thorad Agena D carrier. At the time, four other OGO's were still in operation; they had provided more than 1,200,000 hours of scientific data involving a total of 130 experiments.

Another scientific satellite series, the orbiting Solar observatories (OSO), is especially important because these satellites supply data on Solar flares, which are a potential danger to astronauts on extended orbital and Lunar flights. The first two OSO's were launched in 1965, but only one went into orbit. Since then, OSO's 3, 4, and 5 have been orbited, the last on 22 January 1969.

The largest and most complex unmanned satellite that has been launched by the United States was OAO-2, part of the orbiting astronomical observatory program. (OAO-1 was a victim of battery failure on its second day in orbit in April 1966.) OAO-2 was launched on 7 December 1968 into a nearly circular orbit about 480 miles high. Weighing 4,446 pounds, it contained eleven telescopes and represented a major breakthrough for astronomers, who for the first time were able to make long-term observations unhampered by the disturbing effects of the Earth's atmosphere. OAO-2 was designed to study young, hot stars that emit most of their energy in the ultraviolet regions of the spectrum; to photograph some 700 stars each day as part of a stellar survey of the universe; and to observe gases in interplanetary space. During its first month of operation, it gathered a total of 65 hours of astronomical data, including twenty times more information about ultraviolet characteristics of stars than had been obtained during fifteen years with sounding rockets.

Within the 1957–1969 period, 1966 was the peak year for United States satellite launches, with seventy successes out of seventy-two attempts. And many of these launches orbited several satellites at a time. Among the new satellites orbited that year was the first biosatellite, or Bios, which was designed to study the effects of zero gravity and radiation on fruit flies, wheat seedlings, frog eggs, and other specimens. The mission failed since the re-entry capsule was lost, but Bios 2, launched in early 1967, was successful. Bios 3, launched in June 1969, carried a 14-pound pig-tailed monkey in what was planned as a 30-day study of the effects of weightlessness on the animal's emotional, physiological, and mental processes. The flight was terminated after just nine days, however, because the monkey was reacting sluggishly and failing to respond to signals from the ground. The animal died shortly after its capsule splashed into the Pacific on 7 July. Another new satellite in 1966 was Pageos 1, which served as a source of reflected light, enabling geodesists to determine the relative positions of islands and continents to within 50 to 100 feet.

These and dozens of other satellites daily added to man's knowledge of the Earth, its atmosphere, and the universe beyond, and helped ensure the success of his ventures toward the Moon. Dozens of unmanned spacecraft were launched, for example, during the forty days that preceded the Apollo 8 Lunar-orbiting mission in December 1968. Heos 1 and Pioneer 9—supported by Pioneers 6, 7, and 8, which had been launched earlier—provided data on cosmic and Solar radiation levels. ESSA-8, and its companion weather satellites, compiled vital information for the launch and splashdown phases of the mission, while Intelsat 3 F-2 took on a major portion of the traffic in reporting the flight to other nations —although it, too, was aided by previously launched Intelsats, ATS-1 and ATS-3, and Defense Department communications satellites.

The United States and Russia are not the only nations to have put satellites in orbit. The first international satellite launching occurred on 26 April 1962, when an American Thor Delta orbited Ariel 1, a 132-pound British-built satellite carrying instruments to measure the ionosphere and its interactions with Solar radiation. On 28 September a Thor Agena B orbited the Canadian Alouette 1 satellite, which measured electron-density distribution and variation in the ionosphere, and cosmic radiation.

Ariel 2 went up in March 1964 and Alouette 2 in November 1965. The Italian San Marco 1 satellite was orbited in December 1964 and the French FR-1 in December 1965. All used American carrier vehicles. The French achieved their own satellite program with successful orbitings of their 92.4-pound Asterix A-1 on 26 November 1965 and of the A-2 on 17 February 1966, both launched from Hammaguir in the Sahara. In 1967, France orbited two 50-pound Diadème satellites from Hammaguir and then transferred launchings to a new site between Kourou and Sinnamaly in Guinea. Because it is located closer to the equator, where the Earth's rotational speed is greatest, the new site is more suitable for placing satellites in equatorial orbits.

Britain and the United States, meanwhile, coop-erated in launching Ariel 3 aboard a Scout carrier in May 1967 from Vandenberg Air Force Base in California. A Scout also was used the preceding month to launch Italy's San Marco 2 from a "Texas tower" site in the Indian Ocean off the coast of Kenya. The 285-pound satellite was instrumented to measure air density and characteristics of the ionosphere at a height of 465 miles. Australia became a space nation in November 1967 by orbiting its 100-pound Wresat 1 satellite. The satellite was launched by adding two solid-propellant stages to a Redstone supplied by the United States.

During 1968, the ten-member European Space Research Organization (ESRO) began its space program by launching satellites with NASA-provided carriers. Two types bearing the ESRO name were planned, the first to study ionospheric and auroral phenomena in the polar regions, and the second to investigate Solar and cosmic radiations. As it turned out, the second series was the first to be orbited, ESRO 2B going into orbit on 16 May (2A had failed a year earlier), and ESRO 1 on 3 October. Another ESRO satellite, Heos 1, was launched on 5 December 1968 to study Solar and cosmic radiations and the Earth's magnetic field during a period of high Solar activity.

By the end of 1968, according to the *TRW Space Log*, the United States had orbited 544 satellites, not including non-functional upper stages and "debris." Russia, meanwhile, had orbited 314 identified satellites; France, 5; Great Britain, 3; Canada and Italy, 2 each; Australia, 1; and ESRO, 3. The grand total was 874, of which 357 were still in orbit at year-end. During NASA's first ten years of operation, through August 1968, it made 234 launches of satellites, probes, and manned spacecraft, of which 189 resulted in carrier vehicle success and (since some payloads placed in orbit did not function properly) 174 in mission success.

While the pace of unmanned satellite launching has declined somewhat since 1966, it is expected that meteorological, communications, and navigational satellites will continue to play important roles in the years to come. And on the horizon is a new type of craft, the earth resources technology satellite (ERTS). Early ERTS satellites are expected to weigh about 1,000 pounds and to enter near-polar orbits about 500 miles high. They will be used to make photographic, radar, radiometric, and other surveys that will be useful in such areas as agriculture, forestry, geography, geology, hydrology, and oceanography. Photographs from ERTS satellites, for example, would assist mining and petroleum companies by identifying terrain features and fault lines which

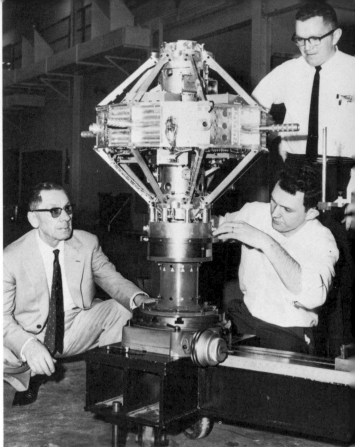

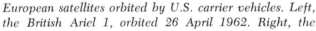

*European satellites orbited by U.S. carrier vehicles. Left,
the British Ariel 1, orbited 26 April 1962. Right, the*

Italian San Marco 1, orbited 15 December 1964. (NASA)

may be associated with buried oil and minerals.
Pictures taken from space also could be used to
determine the depth and extent of snow cover, which
could in turn be used to predict the runoff for irri-
gation, power production, and flooding. Similarly, by
monitoring plant growth, it might be possible to
detect areas of incipient dust-bowl conditions,
drought, and even blight. The list of possible uses
of ERTS satellites is practically endless.

While satellites were exploring space around the
Earth, man began reaching out to the Moon and the
planets of the Solar System, in his effort to fulfill
the oldest dream of astronautics—interplanetary
travel. The probes he has used resemble artificial
satellites in all but purpose. They are sent out from
the Earth to send back information about the Moon,
the planets, and the vast expanses of space between
the planets.

Because the Moon is closest to Earth, it was the
first target, and probes have been sent out to fly
close by the Moon, orbit it, or even land on it. The
Soviets started Lunar exploration, firing their first
three Luna spacecraft (inevitably called Luniks in
western nations) in 1959. Luna 1, also called Mechta,
was launched on 2 January 1959. It flew within 4,660
miles of the Moon's surface and on into space, broad-

casting data about the space environment from
373,125 miles from the Earth. The United States did
essentially the same thing two months and a day
later. Pioneer 4 (Numbers 1 through 3 had been
failures in 1958) flew within 37,300 miles of the
Moon and was tracked to a distance of more than
400,000 miles.

On 12 September 1959, the Russians launched
Luna 2, a 3,000-pound probe that carried 858 pounds
of instruments and transmitting equipment. Luna 2
became the first man-made object to hit the Moon,
crashing between the craters Archimedes and Autoly-
cus in the Mare Imbrium on 14 September. Luna 2
sent back signals before impacting the Moon's
surface, which showed no significant magnetic
field.

Luna 3, also called an Automatic Interplanetary
Station, was an equally significant landmark.
Launched on 4 October, it circled behind the Moon,
approaching within 4,372 miles of the Lunar surface,
and sent back the pictures that gave man his first
view of the far side. The spacecraft weighed 3,300
pounds, of which 614 pounds was the instrumented
Automatic Interplanetary Station that gave Luna 3
its name.

After this promising beginning, the Russian program for exploring the Moon came to a halt for four years for reasons as yet unexplained. Meanwhile, the United States tried to match the Soviet feat of getting significant scientific data from a Lunar probe. After orbiting Rangers 1 and 2 to check out instrumentation, the United States sent Ranger 3 toward the Moon on 26 January 1962. The probe missed its target completely and sailed on into a useless Solar orbit. Ranger 4 did hit the Moon on 23 April, but a failure within the spacecraft prevented it from sending back any useful information. Ranger 5, fired on 18 October, not only missed the Moon by 450 miles but also lost power when its Solar cells malfunctioned. Ranger 5 was tracked for 8 hours and 44 minutes before its reserve battery went dead. After these three disappointments, the Ranger program was reorganized, and further launches were put off until 1964.

On 2 April 1963 came the next Soviet attempt at Lunar exploration, an attempt that apparently was not a success. The Russian Luna 4, a 3,135-pound spacecraft, flew within 5,300 miles of the Moon. The Soviets never revealed what its purpose was; their terse announcement said that the "experiments and measurements which were conducted . . . are completed. Radio communication with the spacecraft will continue for a few more days."

There was speculation in the West that the Soviets had attempted a soft landing on the Moon— that is, a landing at less than 20 miles per hour. If nothing is done to slow a probe as it approaches the Moon, it will impact at no less than 5,400 miles per hour, but the difficulties of flying a spacecraft to the Moon, orienting it so that its rockets slow it to soft-landing speed, and then putting it down gently are considerable. While the first Rangers had carried seismometers in spherical containers designed to withstand the impact of semihard landings, NASA's growing realization of the landing difficulties resulted in a basic change in the program. All the Rangers after Number 5 were designed only to take pictures of the Lunar surface and they were inevitably destroyed when they hit the Moon. While the United States worked toward this goal in 1964 and 1965, the Soviets continued to try for a soft landing. The United States, after a slow start, appeared to have better results.

Ranger 6, fitted with six television cameras, was launched on 30 January 1964 by the Atlas Agena B that was to carry the entire family into space. Ranger 6's cameras were switched on during the last 10 minutes of the 66-hour flight, but they did not send any pictures. Later investigation indicated that the spacecraft's electrical system had been burned out when the cameras were accidentally turned on earlier in the flight.

After being redesigned to eliminate this danger, Ranger 7 was launched on 28 July 1964. It was a complete success. The 4,316 pictures it sent back included some that showed craters only a few feet across; the best Earth-based telescopes had been able to see were Lunar features a half mile across. Ranger 8, flown on 17 February 1965, sent back 7,137 pictures. Ranger 9, launched on 21 March 1965, gave millions of Americans the thrill of seeing television live from the Moon, as some of its 6,007 pictures were broadcast direct onto commercial television.

Soviet launchings came with equal frequency but, having picked a more ambitious goal, with less success than the Rangers. Luna 5, launched on 9 May 1965 for a soft landing, crashed at full speed onto the Moon's surface. Luna 6, launched on 8 June, missed the Moon entirely. Luna 7, sent up on the eighth anniversary of Sputnik 1, crashed, apparently because the rockets that were to ease it to a soft landing fired too soon. The mission was not a total failure, since signals were transmitted for about three seconds after impact, but it fell far short of its goals. Luna 8, sent up on 3 December, was the heaviest of the series, weighing 3,421 pounds. It, too, destroyed itself in a hard landing.

The Soviets finally were successful with Luna 9, which eased onto the Moon's surface on 3 February 1966. In the next few days Luna 9 sent back a series of truly close-up pictures—some showed objects only a few inches in size—that demonstrated that the

The first Moon probe, Luna 1, was launched by the Soviet Union on 2 January 1959. It flew within 4,660 miles of the Moon's surface, broadcasting data back to Earth. (U.S.S.R. ACAD. OF SCIENCES)

On 3 February 1966 Soviet spaceship Luna 9, pictured in the above drawing, made the first soft landing on the Moon. A selection of remarkable close-up photos, taken by Luna 9 and transmitted back to Earth, are shown below. Notice parts of the spacecraft in the bottom frame. (NOVOSTI PRESS AGENCY, LONDON)

Moon's pitted, barren surface was hard enough to support the weight of a manned spacecraft.

When the Russians achieved this triumph, the American program for a soft Lunar landing was bogged down in difficulties. The Surveyor program, formally approved by NASA in the spring of 1960 and placed under the management of the Jet Propulsion Laboratory, started with the aim of landing a complex craft, weighing 2,500 pounds. Hughes Aircraft Company received the Surveyor contract.

By 1962, the second stage of the proposed Atlas Centaur carrier was in enough trouble to indicate that Surveyor's weight would have to be trimmed by more than 300 pounds. As a result, many original experiments were abandoned. The craft that finally emerged was basically a tubular aluminum structure fitted with a solid-propellant retro (landing) rocket, three landing legs, a vertical mast carrying the Solar-cell panel and antenna, and two compartments of electrical equipment. Aside from television cameras, the seven Surveyors were equipped with strain gauges for making soil mechanics measurements, samplers to scoop out surface materials, and instruments for analyzing subsurface materials by measuring the back-scatter from radioactive sources. Some of the craft also were equipped to detect the presence of magnetic elements in the Lunar soil.

The United States also was working on a probe to orbit the Moon. As far back as 1959, attempts were made with Atlas Able carriers to put probes into Lunar orbits, but after three failures it was decided

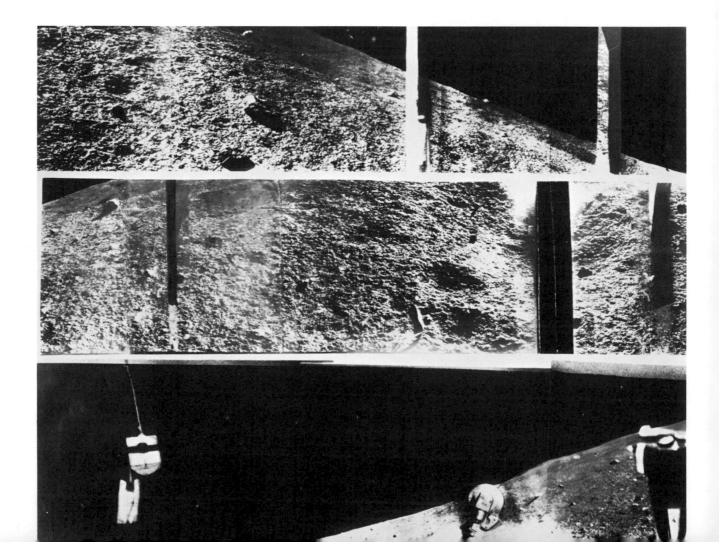

to build a larger spacecraft and use the more advanced Atlas Agena D as the carrier. In March 1964 the Boeing Company began work on Lunar Orbiter, an 850-pound craft fitted with two antenna booms and four Solar-cell panels. Each of the five Orbiters had a dual lens camera that could detect objects 1 and 9 yards across, respectively, from an altitude of 30 miles.

Before the United States could launch either of its two Lunar craft, Russia achieved another first by placing Luna 10 into orbit around the Moon on 3 April 1966. Weighing 3,500 pounds, the spacecraft was instrumented to study micrometeoritic particles, the Moon's magnetic field, Solar plasma streams, and surface gamma radiations.

The pioneering voyages of Lunas 9 and 10 led off what proved to be a remarkable series of unmanned Lunar missions by the United States and Russia. During the period from May 1966 to November 1968, America launched seven Surveyors, five Orbiters, and one far-ranging Explorer. Russia, meanwhile, launched four more Lunas (three orbiters and a soft-lander) and three Zonds.

The Surveyor, launched 30 May 1966, was a resounding success, landing gently on the Moon's surface on 2 June. It took more than 10,000 pictures before the onset of Lunar night on 14 June and then returned to life on the following Lunar day, which began on 29 June. By the time the craft power failed in mid-July, it had sent 1,150 photographs back to Earth.

The first Lunar Orbiter was equally successful, entering into an orbit on 14 August that ranged from about 1,150 miles to 120 miles above the Moon's surface. Picture transmission began on 18 August. Later, the craft approached to within 36 miles of the surface for close-ups. The last photo was made on 29 August; two months later the craft was deliberately crashed onto the far side of the Moon in order to prevent the possibility of its radio disturbing communications with Lunar Orbiter 2.

The United States gained information from the Surveyor and Orbiter programs that was vital for the impending Apollo manned landing on the Moon. Of the first six Surveyors, two (Numbers 2 and 4) crashed, but the others proved that the surface of the Lunar maria was strong enough to support the Apollo landing craft. The seventh and final Surveyor, therefore, was given a purely scientific mission, successfully probing the rugged highlands near the crater Tycho. Each of the five Orbiters, meanwhile, provided photographs of potential landing sites. An unexpected by-product of the Orbiter program was the discovery that the Moon's gravitational field was

not uniform, owing to the existence of "mascons"—mass concentrations of dense material beneath the surface. The mascons, which cause orbiting spacecraft to speed up slightly when they pass over them, are associated with maria, and they may be composed of sediments deposited in actual seas long ago when the Moon had an atmosphere.

Russia, after conducting three Luna missions during the latter half of 1966, did not aim for the Moon again until 1968 when the Zond program, apparently dormant since 1965, suddenly came back to life with the launching of Numbers 4, 5, and 6. Luna 14, an orbiter, also was conducted in this period, its mission falling between those of Zonds 4 and 5. The new Zonds, unlike the first three in the series, were sent along trajectories that took them around the Moon and back to the Earth. The flights are believed to have been unmanned tests of modules to be used for manned Lunar flights. Zond 4 was not recovered, but the next two were. Zond 5 was picked up in the Indian Ocean, while Zond 6, after skipping off the atmosphere above the Indian Ocean, re-entered at a lower speed and descended by parachute onto Russian territory. Zond 6's method of re-entry, which reduces deceleration stress and heat loads considerably, was an important step forward in the Soviet manned Lunar landing program.

Just three days before the liftoff of America's Apollo 11 manned Lunar spacecraft, the Soviets fired their unmanned Luna 15. Its announced purpose was "to check the systems on board . . . and to conduct further scientific exploration of the Moon and the space near the Moon." Almost immediately, Western observers speculated that the craft would attempt to land on the Lunar surface, scoop up soil samples, and then return to Earth ahead of Apollo 11. However, Luna 15 first entered into a long elliptical orbit around the Moon, then a lower orbit; and finally, on 21 July 1969, it landed in Mare Crisium and ceased signaling.

As the Russians were first into space and the first to try for the Moon, they were also the first to approach the planets. Their success in interplanetary exploration has been relatively limited, however. Their first two efforts to fire probes to Mars, made in October 1960, were failures that were not announced to the world but were detected by American tracking stations. Four months later the Soviets launched a Venus explorer. However, the Soviets lost contact with the 1,419-pound probe, and it returned no useful information, although it subsequently passed within 62,000 miles of its target.

A number of attempts to send probes toward Venus and Mars were made by the Soviets during

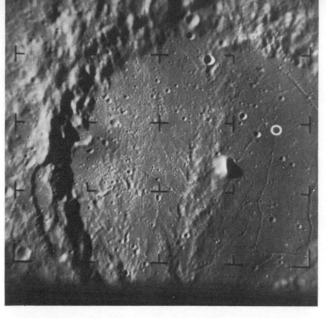

Series of photographs of the Moon taken by Ranger 9 prior to impact in the crater Alphonsus at 6:08:20 A.M. (PST) on 24 March 1965. The circle indicates the point of impact. Top left: 140 miles high, 1 minute 35 seconds before impact; area covered is 67.5 miles across and 62 miles from top to bottom. Top right: 50.3 miles high, 33.7 seconds before impact; area is 24 miles by 22 miles. Bottom left: 12.2 miles high, 8.09 seconds before impact; area is 5.8 miles by 5.3 miles. Bottom right: 8.3 miles high, 5.5 seconds before impact; area is 1.6 miles by 1.4 miles. (JET PROPULSION LAB., CALIF. INST. OF TECH.)

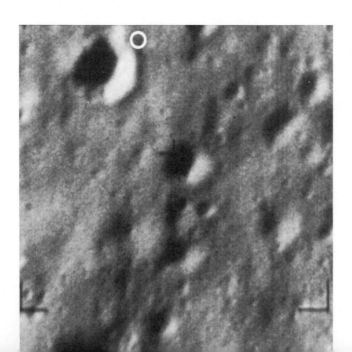

Left, last picture taken by Ranger 9 camera at an altitude of .68 mile, .453 second before impact. Area covered in picture is 154 feet across by 125 feet high. The impact point (indicated by the circle) is on the edge of a 25-foot crater. (JET PROPULSION LAB., CALIF. INST. OF TECH.)

Summary of Unmanned Attempts to Explore the Moon[a]

Launch Date	Spacecraft	Country	Results
17 August 1958	Pioneer	U.S.A.	Launch failure.
11 October 1958	Pioneer 1	U.S.A.	Reached 70,700 miles from Earth; failure.
8 November 1958	Pioneer 2	U.S.A.	Reached 963 miles from Earth; failure.
6 December 1958	Pioneer 3	U.S.A.	Reached 63,580 miles from Earth; failure
2 January 1959	Luna 1[b]	U.S.S.R.	Bypassed Moon by 4,660 miles; exact objective unknown.
3 March 1959	Pioneer 4	U.S.A.	Bypassed Moon by 37,300 miles instead of programmed 15,000 miles.
12 September 1959	Luna 2[c]	U.S.S.R.	Impacted on Moon.
4 October 1959	Luna 3[d]	U.S.S.R.	Circum-Lunar flight; photographed rear side.
26 November 1959	Pioneer	U.S.A.	Lunar orbit attempt; launch failure.
25 September 1960	Pioneer	U.S.A.	Lunar orbit attempt; launch failure.
15 December 1960	Pioneer	U.S.A.	Lunar orbit attempt; launch failure.
26 January 1962	Ranger 3[e]	U.S.A.	Bypassed Moon by 22,862 miles; failed in mission to take close-up TV pictures, hard-land instrument on surface.
23 April 1962	Ranger 4	U.S.A.	Impacted on rear of Moon; failed to achieve photography and hard landing.
18 October 1962	Ranger 5	U.S.A.	Bypassed Moon by 450 miles; same target mission as Rangers 3 and 4.
2 April 1963	Luna 4	U.S.S.R.	Bypassed Moon by 5,300 miles; possibly intended to soft land.
30 January 1964	Ranger 6	U.S.A.	Impacted on Moon; failed in TV photographic mission.
28 July 1964	Ranger 7	U.S.A.	Successfully photographed Moon, returning 4,308 pictures of surface.
17 February 1965	Ranger 8	U.S.A.	Returned 7,137 pictures of Lunar surface.
21 March 1965	Ranger 9	U.S.A.	Returned 5,814 pictures of Lunar surface.
9 May 1965	Luna 5	U.S.S.R.	Impacted on Moon; failed to soft land.
8 June 1965	Luna 6	U.S.S.R.	Bypassed Moon; failed to achieve soft landing on surface.
4 October 1965	Luna 7	U.S.S.R.	Impacted on Moon; failed to soft land.
3 December 1965	Luna 8	U.S.S.R.	Impacted on Moon; failed to soft land.
31 January 1966	Luna 9	U.S.S.R.	Successful soft landing on Lunar surface; televised photographs to Earth.
31 March 1966	Luna 10	U.S.S.R.	Entered into Lunar orbit on 3 April; perilune, 217 miles; apolune, 632 miles; measured magnetic field, gamma rays.
30 May 1966	Surveyor 1	U.S.A.	Successful soft landing on Lunar surface; televised photographs to Earth.
10 August 1966	Lunar Orbiter 1	U.S.A.	Successfully entered into orbit around Moon; returned photos of front and rear; on 23 August took world's first photo of Earth seen from Moon.
24 August 1966	Luna 11	U.S.S.R.	Entered into Lunar orbit; made Luna 10 type of measurements.
20 September 1966	Surveyor 2	U.S.A.	Failure of vernier engine during mid-course maneuver led to failure of soft landing; impacted on Moon 23 September.
22 October 1966	Luna 12	U.S.S.R.	Orbited Moon, sent back surface photographs.
6 November 1966	Lunar Orbiter 2	U.S.A.	Entered into Lunar orbit, returned photographs to Earth; deliberately crashed on Moon at conclusion of mission on 11 October 1967.
21 December 1966	Luna 13	U.S.S.R.	Successful soft landing; first return of close-up surface photos on Christmas Day.
4 February 1967	Lunar Orbiter 3	U.S.A.	Successfully entered into Moon orbit; returned photographs, one of which showed Surveyor 1.
17 April 1967	Surveyor 3	U.S.A.	Successful; returned photographs and soil-bearing-strength data.
4 May 1967	Lunar Orbiter 4	U.S.A.	Successful; entered into near-polar orbit; problems of moisture on optical system solved by remote correction.
14 July 1967	Surveyor 4	U.S.A.	Unsuccessful; communications lost just prior to touchdown on Moon; may have exploded.
19 July 1967	Explorer 35	U.S.A.	Successful; instrumented to study Solar wind and magnetic field in Lunar space.
1 August 1967	Lunar Orbiter 5	U.S.A.	Successful completion of program; photographed previously unseen regions of far side.
8 September 1967	Surveyor 5	U.S.A.	Successful soft landing; photographs and chemical analyses taken on surface.
7 November 1967	Surveyor 6	U.S.A.	Successful soft landing; returned thousands of photos; carried soil analyzer.
7 January 1968	Surveyor 7	U.S.A.	Final, and most difficult, landing mission of series; came down near Tycho, returned over 21,000 photos of surface; photographed Earth and Jupiter.
2 March 1968	Zond 4	U.S.S.R.	Probably test vehicle for manned Lunar landing spacecraft; launched from Earth parking orbit along an undisclosed trajectory; elements of still-in-orbit satellite launch platform not maintained.
7 April 1968	Luna 14	U.S.S.R.	Entered into selenocentric orbit; instrumented to study relationship between masses of Earth and Moon, Lunar gravitational field, Solar wind's interaction with Moon, and so on.
14 September 1968	Zond 5	U.S.S.R.	Circum-Lunar, free Earth-return flight by Soyuz type of manned spacecraft module with biological specimens aboard; successful recovery in Indian Ocean.
10 November 1968	Zond 6	U.S.S.R.	Similar to Zond 5 mission; recovery in Soviet Union; made micrometeorite and radiation measurements, photographed far side of Moon, and conducted biological research.
13 July 1969	Luna 15	U.S.S.R.	Launched on "slow" 102-hour trajectory to Moon, around which it subsequently orbited; landed later in Mare Crisium.

[a] All American attempts listed, but only those officially announced by the Russians (who do not announce launch failures).
[b] Called Lunik 1 by West, originally Mechta by Soviets.
[c] Called Lunik 2 by West, sometimes Lunnaya Raketa by Soviets.
[d] Called Lunik 3 by West, Automatic Interplanetary Station (Automaticheskaya Mezhplanetnaya Stantisiya) by Soviets.
[e] Rangers 1 and 2 placed in Earth orbit in systems checkout testing.

The early writers of science fiction, limited only by their imaginations, blithely assumed that man would go from the Earth to the Moon in one grand leap. During the 1960's, this dream was tempered by reality. The closer man came to achieving space travel, the more difficult the accomplishment appeared, and progress toward fulfilling the dream, while rapid, was much slower than had been predicted by the early enthusiasts.

The Soviet Union, which in 1957 was the first nation to successfully launch an artificial satellite, also was the first to put a man into orbit. He was Major Yuri A. Gagarin, who made one trip around the Earth in a Vostok 1 spacecraft on 12 April 1961.

This was the first of six Vostok flights made during the opening phase of the Russian manned space flight program. The series culminated in June 1963, with the paired flight of Vostoks 5 and 6, which at one point traveled within three miles of each other.

The initial Soviet manned flights did not shock the United States as had Sputnik 1. On 25 May 1961, just a month after Gagarin's flight, President John F. Kennedy told Congress that the United States intended to land an astronaut on the Moon within the decade. Work on the $20 billion Apollo program, which had been announced by the National Aeronautics and Space Administration the previous year, now was accelerated.

The huge Saturn 5 carrier vehicle that was developed for this mission is a monument to the technological and industrial wealth of the nation. When its three stages are assembled and fully fueled, the vehicle stands 363 feet tall and weighs more than 6 million pounds. The Apollo spaceship launched by Saturn 5 carries three astronauts, two of whom actually land in a detachable Lunar module. To prepare for Lunar voyages, the United States, like the Soviet Union, conducted an extensive series of preliminary unmanned and manned space flights.

Project Mercury was the United States equivalent of the Vostok series. Marine Colonel John H. Glenn, Jr., who circled the Earth three times on 20 February 1962, was the first American in space. The last and longest—22 orbits—of the Mercury flights was made by Air Force Major L. Gordon Cooper on 15 May 1963.

The next step in manned space travel for both the Russians and the Americans was to orbit spacecraft with more than one occupant. Again, the Russians were first. On 12 October 1964, they launched three cosmonauts in the first Voskhod spacecraft. The second Voskhod flight, launched on 18 March 1965, proved to be an even more important event when one of its two crew members, Lieutenant Colonel Aleksei A. Leonov, left the craft through an airlock for a 10-minute "walk" in space.

The United States made the first of a series of two-man Gemini flights on 23 March 1965, just five days after Voskhod 2. A 3-orbit mission, it was succeeded during 1965 and 1966 by longer and more elaborate flights. During the flight of Gemini 4, Major Edward H. White II matched the Russian spacewalk. The third manned Gemini flight, Gemini 5, went 120 orbits, with one of its occupants, Major Cooper, becoming the first astronaut to make two trips in space. Geminis 6 and 7, in a paired flight, maneuvered to within one foot of each other, dramatically demonstrating the feasibility of space rendezvous techniques. The first actual docking operation in space was accomplished by Gemini 8, which linked up with an Agena target vehicle. After the Voskhods and Geminis came Soyuz and Apollo testing, the last of the preliminary steps in man's journey to the surface of the Moon.

The landing on the Moon presents the beginning of a new era with new objectives. While still reaching for the Moon, the United States conducted studies during the early and middle 1960's of the feasibility of manned flight to Mars. These suggested that it would be logical to start a planetary program with a fly-by rather than a landing. Such a trip around Mars or Venus may be possible by the early 1980's, followed by landings in 1985.

RIGHT: *On 3 November 1957, less than a month after launching the first Sputnik, the Soviet Union marked another first by placing a dog, Laika, in orbit around the Earth in Sputnik 2. Laika's carrier was 19 feet long and 4 feet in diameter at the base.*

BELOW: *The instruments and antennas on Sputnik 3 give a clue to its purpose—to measure and record gravity and irradiation. Launched on 15 May 1958, it too was conical in shape and measured 12 feet high by 5.5 feet in diameter.*

ABOVE: *While the Sputniks were being built and tested, the Soviet Union launched the first ICBM in the summer of 1957, more than a year before the United States. At present the Russians maintain a nuclear force of about 270 ICBM's, 750 IRBM's, and 120 fleet ballistic missiles. Some were displayed in the above parade in Red Square on 7 November 1965.*

RIGHT: *A Minuteman 2 ICBM leaves its underground silo momentarily preceded by a smoke ring. These three-stage missiles, which form a major part of the deterrent force of the United States, are placed throughout the nation, ready to be fired almost instantaneously to targets that are programmed into its guidance system.*

On its first flight in 1961, Saturn 1 recorded more than 500 measurements on a 200-mile trajectory. Designed as a test vehicle, it gathered basic information for the Apollo program that eventually took three Americans to the Moon. Here the first stage of a Saturn 1 carrier is being lifted onto the static test stand at the George C. Marshall Space Flight Center at Huntsville, Alabama.

The tiny Explorer satellites, which discovered the Van Allen radiation belts, made measurements of cosmic rays, temperatures, and the Earth's magnetic field. Launched in 1961, Explorer 12 was only 5.5 inches high and 26 inches wide, but its complex structure included an octagonal platform and four spring-loaded Solar paddles.

ABOVE: *The first successful probe of another planet occurred on 14 December 1962, when Mariner 2 passed within 22,000 miles of Venus. The 447-pound probe recorded Venus' surface temperature at 700°F. and sent back valuable data on previously unexplored space.*

LEFT: *By photographing the Earth from above, the Tiros meteorological satellites have added a new dimension to weather forecasting. Tiros 6, launched in December 1962, took pictures of hurricanes in the Atlantic and Pacific.*

After a trip of more than 7.5 months in space, Mariner 4 flew within 6,118 miles of Mars on 14 and 15 July 1965, taking 22 pictures which were transmitted back to Earth. Mariner's camera equipment included wide- and narrow-angle sensors (top two cylinders) and a television camera (bottom cylinder). The pictures revealed a pockmarked surface that resembled the Moon more than the Earth.

America's Surveyor soft-landing craft showed that the Moon's surface is strewn with rocks and pocked with tiny craters. At left, photograph of a rock 6 inches high by 12 inches long, transmitted from Surveyor 1 on 2 June 1966.

Right, photograph by Surveyor 6, launched 7 November 1967, shows small, irregular craters, ranging up to 18 inches in diameter, near the craft's landing pad. (NASA)

1962, but only the Mars 1 spacecraft got off to a good start. Sent off on 1 November, the 2,000-pound probe suffered the same fate as the Venus spacecraft. The U.S.S.R. Academy of Sciences was relatively detailed about the instruments on board Mars 1, disclosing that it carried television cameras, a spectrograph to measure the Martian atmosphere, instruments to measure radiation and the planet's magnetic field, and equipment to measure low-energy protons and electrons. The Academy also said Mars 1 would pass within 120,000 miles of the planet. But the Soviets had to admit failure again. At the sixth annual meeting of the International Council of Scientific Union's Committee on Space Research, Soviet delegate A. A. Blagonravov said that when Mars 1 was 106 million kilometers from the Earth "a defect in the probe's orientation system resulted in a violation of the directionality of the probe's antenna to Earth, making it impossible to maintain further radio contact . . . ."

The United States interplanetary program, like its Moon effort, was initially less ambitious than that of the Russians, but has had a higher percentage of successes. The interplanetary program started with Pioneer 5, which was launched toward the orbit of

Venus on 11 March 1960. Pioneer's 94.8-pound payload enabled it to make valuable measurements—man's first—in deep interplanetary space. Information was sent back 17.7 million miles to Earth. Pioneer 5 was tracked to a record distance of 22.5 million miles.

The first real United States effort to probe another planet came on 22 July 1962, when Mariner 1 was launched for Venus. The probe's Atlas Agena B carrier veered off course and was destroyed. Mariner 2, a back-up spacecraft, was quickly readied and was launched on 27 August to an outstanding destiny. Mariner 2 flew within 22,000 miles of Venus on 14 December, sending back across 35 million miles of space information not only about the planet but data on vast reaches of previously unexplored space. For once, the United States had scored a major space first.

The probe that did it weighed 447 pounds, of which slightly more than 40 pounds consisted of scientific instruments. It sent back data indicating that Venus' surface had a temperature of over 700 degrees Fahrenheit. Mariner found one "cold spot" in the planet's southern hemisphere, possibly caused by a

197

high mountain, and it showed that there were no significant breaks in the blanket of clouds that hides the surface of Venus from the sight of astronomers. Communications with Mariner 2 were maintained until the spacecraft was almost 54 million miles from Earth.

In March 1963, plans for a more ambitious Mariner voyage, this time to Mars, were defined. A launch date in November 1964 was set, because the Earth and Mars would then be in a favorable position. Once again, two spacecraft and two carrier vehicles were prepared as a hedge against failure.

The Russians resumed interplanetary flights first, however. On 2 April 1964 they sent the first of a series of probes, Zond 1, off toward Venus. Again, they lost contact with the spacecraft before it reached the target. Then, in the space of a few weeks, three spacecraft were launched by both nations toward Mars.

The first to be launched was Mariner 3, which was placed in a good trajectory toward Mars on 5 November 1964 by an Atlas Agena D (which, incidentally, was making its maiden flight). But the shroud that protected the spacecraft during its launch through the atmosphere unfortunately could not be jettisoned. Mariner 3's solar panels could not be spread to produce electricity. Deprived of the power it needed, Mariner 3 went dead within hours.

A new shroud was hastily built and tested, and Mariner 4 was launched on 28 November 1964. Two days later, the Soviets sent Zond 2 off toward Mars. It was initially successful, but an ultimate failure. However, the Soviets managed to track Zond 2 until May 1965—three months before its scheduled arrival near Mars—getting much useful information about interplanetary space.

Mariner 4, meanwhile, was in the process of completing a tremendously successful operation. The 575-pound spacecraft's original trajectory would have taken it 150,000 miles from Mars. On 5 December, in response to commands from Earth, Mariner fired its onboard rocket to change its course. The new trajectory would bring it close enough to Mars to take pictures of the planet. Mariner soared through space, maintaining its orientation by locking itself electronically on the Sun and Canopus, a bright star in the Southern Hemisphere. Mariner lost its hold on Canopus once, but commands from Earth corrected the mistake.

Mariner 4 flew by Mars at a distance of 6,118 miles on 14–15 July 1965 after traveling a looping path of 325 million miles in a little more than 7½ months. Twenty-two pictures of the planet were taken, stored on magnetic tape, and played back to Earth at a slow rate of speed. The nineteen useful photographs—the last three were taken on the dark night side of the planet—showed a pockmarked surface that resembled the Moon more than the Earth. A preliminary report by the Jet Propulsion Laboratory–Cal Tech team that had managed the flight revealed "more than 70 clearly distinguishable craters ranging in diameter from 4 to 120 km. It seems likely that smaller craters exist; there also may be still larger craters . . . since Mariner 4 photographed, in all, only about 1 percent of the Martian surface."

More than a year later, during October 1966, American tracking stations re-established contact with Mariner after its 1.5-billion-mile orbit around the Sun. The craft responded to selected commands, and monitoring continued during 1967 and 1968. In December 1968, the craft encountered a dense micrometeorite shower, hundreds of impingements on its hull being registered.

Americans were exhilarated by Mariner 4, but if the Russians were discouraged, they did not show it. On 18 July 1965 they launched Zond 3, which took detailed pictures of the far side of the Moon from a distance of 6,000 to 7,000 miles and then continued on into space. The mission of Zond 3 was something of a mystery. First the Soviets said only that it carried equipment to study "conditions of prolonged flight." Later its photographic mission was revealed. Although its pictures, covering some 2 million square miles of the Moon's surface, were taken on 20 July, they were not transmitted to Earth until 29 July, when the probe was 1.4 million miles away. Soviet reports that Zond would continue to send back photographic signals from tens of millions of miles led to speculation that it might take far-off photos of Mars in a test for later close approaches. Soviet spokesmen denied these reports. There were other speculations that Zond 3 was a test bed for the cameras and transmitting equipment that the Soviets would use to photograph the planets.

Two more Soviet interplanetary probes were fired on 12 and 16 November, both toward Venus. The 2,000-pound spacecraft were at least partially successful. One, called Venus 3, impacted on Venus—on 1 March 1966, the first man-made object to touch another planet—while the other, Venus 2, bypassed the planet on 27 February 1966 at a distance of nearly 15,000 miles. Unfortunately, communications with the probes were lost just when they were approaching Venus, so vital scientific information could not be obtained. Venus 2's mission was to fly close to the sunlit side of the planet while Venus 3 was to have landed in the center of the planet's visible disc. Both probes did make many measurements of interplanetary space, carrying instruments to measure interplanetary magnetic fields, cosmic rays, low-energy charged particles, magnitude and energy spectra of Solar plasma streams, micrometeoroids, and longwave cosmic radio emanations. In addition, Venus 2 contained photographic and television devices, while Venus 3 incorporated a three-foot diameter sphere made of heat-resistant material insuring the survival through the atmosphere of the instruments that were to have analyzed the atmosphere and surface.

The twin Venus shots were followed up on 16 December by the American Pioneer 6 probe, which entered an orbit similar to that of Pioneer 5; that is, it was not directed at a specific planet but rather into the inner Solar System. On 19 May 1966 it reached its closest approach to the Sun, about 75.7 million miles, or 18 million miles closer than the Earth's orbital path. Pioneer 6 made significant investigations of the average number of particles in interplanetary space, Solar flare activity, the Solar wind, and Solar and interplanetary magnetic fields. Between the time of its launch and its closest approach to the Sun it transmitted to Earth 340 million readings of 3,300 separate scientific measurements and 3 million readings of 100 individual engineering measurements.

Pioneer 7 was launched on 17 August 1966, just three months after its predecessor, but the next two heliocentric orbit probes were spaced further apart. Pioneer 8 was launched on 13 December 1967 and Pioneer 9 on 8 November 1968, their missions coinciding with the latter part of the eleven-year Sun cycle that peaked in 1969.

The Soviets have not admitted to trying to explore Mars when it was in a favorable position for such flights in January 1967, but Western experts have speculated that Kosmos 139, orbited on 19 January, was the launch platform for a probe which for some reason never left parking orbit. The Kosmos satellite re-entered the atmosphere that same day.

Both nations did take advantage of an opportunity to send probes to Venus six months later, with Russia launching Venus 4 from Tyura Tam on 12 June. It was followed in two days by Mariner 5 from Cape Kennedy. When the Soviet probe neared Venus, it separated into two modules, the 842-pound lander parachuting slowly through the atmosphere on 18 October 1967, while the other unit acted as a relay station, continuing into orbit around the Sun. The descending module ceased communications 1 hour and 38 minutes after entering the atmosphere. The Russians have maintained that Venus 4 landed on the surface, but subsequent analysis has suggested that it may either have touched down on a 15-mile-high peak or failed while still descending. Mariner 5, meanwhile, by-passed Venus the next day at a distance of 2,480 miles.

Two more Russian probes were sent toward Venus in January 1969. Arriving just a day apart in mid-May, they descended by parachute on the planet's dark side, reporting temperatures of up to 750 degrees F and atmospheric pressures 60 times that of the Earth. (The comparable American estimates were 900 degrees and 75 Earth atmospheres at surface.) Venus 5 and 6 instruments showed that the atmosphere contained from 93 to 97 percent carbon dioxide,

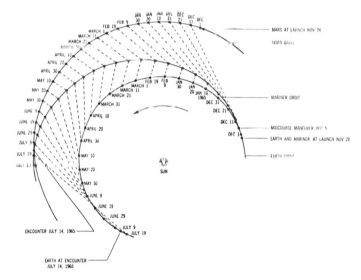

Before passing Mars, Mariner 4 traveled 325 million miles in a little more than 7½ months. The upper right picture shows Mariner's orbit compared to those of the Earth and Mars. The picture at right (reading right to left) shows its trajectory as it approaches, bypasses, and departs from Mars.

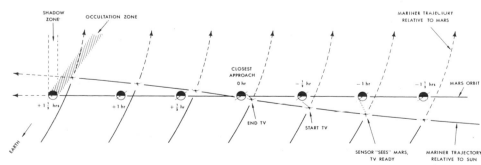

199

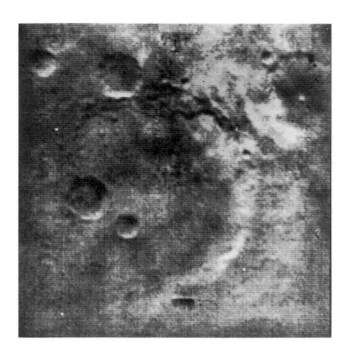

From a height of 7,300 miles, the surface of Mars looks more like the Moon than like the Earth. This photograph was taken on 14 July 1965 by Mariner 4. (JET PROPULSION LAB., CALIF. INST. OF TECH.)

Further resemblance to the Moon was seen in the remarkably clear pictures of Mariner 6. At least 100 craters are shown in this photograph, taken on 30 July 1969. (NASA)

and not more than 7 percent nitrogen nor 0.4 percent oxygen. Both capsules apparently were crushed by high atmospheric pressures before reaching the surface.

The United States matched this feat by sending twin 910-pound probes to within 2,200 miles of Mars in 1969. Mariner 6, launched on 24 February, bypassed Mars on 31 July; Mariner 7, launched on 27 March, traveled a shorter course and made its closest encounter on 5 August, less than a week after the first probe.

Both Mariners were launched from Cape Kennedy by Atlas Centaur carriers. They were equipped with TV cameras capable of distinguishing objects of less than 1,000 feet in diameter, radiometers for making thermal maps, and spectrometers for determining the composition of the Martian atmosphere.

Photographs from the two probes confirmed Mariner 4's finding that the Martian surface is more Moonlike than Earthlike. Huge craters—one three hundred miles across—were revealed. Many older, heavily eroded craters had smaller, newer craters inside. One striking geographical anomaly was discovered: a large circular region, known as Hellas, that was found to be almost completely smooth, presumably due to some process that has erased the scars of meteorite impacts in the area.

Although methane and ammonia, two gases closely associated with biological processes on Earth, were detected near the South polar region, the Martian environment appeared to be hostile to life, with the surface apparently bathed by lethal ultraviolet rays from the Sun. Carbon dioxide (the chief constituent of the Martian atmosphere) as well as small amounts of oxygen, hydrogen, and water vapor also were detected. Temperatures as high as 75 degrees F were measured near the equator in dark areas; bright areas were somewhat colder—usually below freezing even during the day. Temperatures across the polar cap and on the night side were far below zero.

By the end of the 1960's, American planners already were considering manned flights to Mars. A likely first step would be to place modified Mariners in orbit around Mars during the 1971 launch opportunity. Viking probes with two modules, one to enter orbit and the other, a 40-pound instrument package, to be sent to the surface, could be launched in 1973 by the new Titan 3D carrier with a Centaur upper stage. And as larger carriers become available, it will be possible to probe the composition of comets; to examine Mercury, Jupiter, Saturn; and to fly very close to the Sun. One day, probes will roam to every part of the Solar System. And in the distant future, they may be dispatched even to the stars.

Summary of Interplanetary/Planetary Probe Firings[a]

Launch Date	Spacecraft	Country	Results
11 March 1960	Pioneer 5[b]	U.S.A.	Interplanetary probe in toward the orbit of Venus; conducted magnetic field, micrometeorite, and radiation measurements of deep space.
12 February 1961	Venus 1	U.S.S.R.	Launched toward Venus, missing planet by 62,000 miles. Mission unsuccessful due to communications failure on 27 February.
22 July 1962	Mariner 1	U.S.A.	Carrier vehicle failed shortly after launch in attempt to launch probe to Venus.
27 August 1962	Mariner 2	U.S.A.	Bypassed Venus by 21,645 miles on 14 December 1962. Measured temperature of Venus surface and atmosphere, structure of cloud cover, planetary and interplanetary magnetic fields, cosmic radiation, micrometeorites, and Solar particle flux.
1 November 1962	Mars 1	U.S.S.R.	Launched toward Mars, missing planet by some 120,000 miles. Mission not successful due to communications failure on 21 March 1963.
2 April 1964	Zond 1	U.S.S.R.	Launched toward Venus; communications failed.
5 November 1964	Mariner 3	U.S.A.	Mission failed when spacecraft's Solar-cell panels did not deploy, causing power loss and communications failure.
28 November 1964	Mariner 4	U.S.A.	Bypassed Mars by 6,118 miles, taking pictures of planetary surface on 14–15 July. En route studied magnetic fields, Solar wind, radiation, cosmic rays, micrometeoroids.
30 November 1964	Zond 2	U.S.S.R.	Launched toward Mars; communications failed on 2 May 1965.
18 July 1965	Zond 3	U.S.S.R.	Deep-space probe that photographed rear of Moon en route; sent pictures back to Earth.
12 November 1965	Venus 2	U.S.S.R.	Bypassed Venus on 27 February 1966 by 15,000 miles. Communications lost as the planet was approached.
16 November 1965	Venus 3	U.S.S.R.	Impacted on planet Venus on 1 March 1966; failed to soft land.
17 December 1965	Pioneer 6	U.S.A.	Flown into similar orbit as Pioneer 5 to measure Solar wind, electron density of space, interplanetary magnetic fields, and cosmic rays.
17 August 1966	Pioneer 7	U.S.A.	Entered heliocentric orbit to measure Solar magnetic fields and wind, cosmic radiations.
12 June 1967	Venus 4	U.S.S.R.	Conducted interplanetary measurements en route to Venus. On arrival in mid-October 1967, ejected lander which made parachute descent to surface.
14 June 1967	Mariner 5	U.S.A.	Interplanetary measurements and Venus by-pass probe; approached to within 2,480 miles of planet on 19 October 1967, conducted variety of studies of planet—its atmosphere, magnetic field, and so on.
13 December 1967	Pioneer 8	U.S.A.	Placed in heliocentric orbit outside that of Earth to investigate Earth's magnetic "tail," interplanetary magnetic fields, Solar plasma, and cosmic rays.
8 November 1968	Pioneer 9	U.S.A.	Similar craft designed to study radiations from Sun and interplanetary magnetic fields inside the Earth's orbit around the Sun.
5 January 1969	Venus 5	U.S.S.R.	Reached planet Venus on 16 May 1969, descended into atmosphere, measuring temperature, pressure, and chemical composition.
10 January 1969	Venus 6	U.S.S.R.	Arrived day after Venus 5, entered Venus' atmosphere less than 200 miles from earlier craft. Descent by parachute took 51 minutes, during course of which measurements were made.
25 February 1969	Mariner 6	U.S.A.	By-passed Mars on 31 July 1969 at distance of 2,120 miles. Photographed planet, made thermal maps and spectrographic measurements of atmosphere; studied inter-planetary environment en route.
27 March 1969	Mariner 7	U.S.A.	Identical spacecraft to Mariner 6. Successfully carried out same scientific mission, by-passing Mars on 5 August 1969.

[a] Includes all American attempts, whether successful or not. Only officially announced Soviet flights are given, not probes that failed because of launch aborts. These are given at right.
[b] Pioneers 1–4 were Lunar probes (q.v.).

Objective Mars	Objective Venus
10 October 1960	4 February 1961
14 October 1960	25 August 1962
24 October 1962	1 September 1962
4 November 1962	12 September 1962
	23 November 1965

9 MANNED SPACE I

From the earliest days of science fiction, manned space travel has been the ultimate goal of astronautics. Ever since Lucian of Samosata made his fictional voyage to the Moon, there has never been any doubt that manned journeys into space would take place as soon as the technology made them possible.

The early writers, relying on nothing but imagination, gravely underestimated the complexities of manned space travel. Even so knowledgeable a writer as Jules Verne had his space travelers stepping blithely into their spaceship for a trip to the Moon with no previous test flights. But as scientific and engineering knowledge grew, it became apparent that man could not go to the Moon—as the nearest heavenly body, the natural goal for manned flights—without first trying out his skills closer to home. Man's vision of the future was scaled down. Instead of voyaging directly to the Moon, he would initially put space stations in orbit around the Earth, such as the Brick Moon proposed by Edward Everett Hale.

As far as can be determined, Hermann Oberth was the first man to offer a scientifically thought-out idea for a space station, in his *Die Rakete zu den Planetenraümen* (*The Rocket into Interplanetary Space*) of 1923. An Austrian Imperial Army captain named Potočnik, writing under the pseudonym of Hermann Noordung, expanded Oberth's ideas into a book, *Das Problem der Befahrung des Weltraums* (*The Problems of Space Flight*), that deals at length with orbiting space stations.

Noordung pictured a three-part station: A wheel spinning on its axis to provide artificial gravity, a Solar power plant, and an astronomical observatory. Among other innovations, he counted on harnessing the energy of the Sun by using a huge parabolic mirror to focus its rays. The book, published in 1929, considered in remarkable depth all the practical problems in manning a space station—cooking, eating, bathing, and even walking. Another Austrian, Guido von Pirquet, went Noordung one better by proposing a system of three space stations, in different orbits, to help in Lunar and interplanetary flights, as well as for research.

In the postwar years, H. E. Ross presented a paper on orbital bases to the British Interplanetary Society in November 1948. Ross's space station had a mirror to collect solar energy and was to spin on its axis to provide artificial gravity.

In 1951, Wernher von Braun proposed a 100-foot-radius, doughnut-shaped space station that would be assembled in orbit from twenty cylindrical segments, each 12 feet in diameter and made of a flexible plastic. The station would have a central hub, connected to the rim by two arms, where spacecraft from Earth would arrive and depart. Later, Von Braun expanded and refined the space station proposal. He pictured the station in a 1,075-mile-high orbit that would take it around the Earth once every two hours.

As rocketry made dramatic advances during the 1950's, interest in the space station concept increased. Many different designs, uses, and orbits for space stations were suggested. Perhaps the most grandiose scheme was that suggested in 1956 by Darrell Romick, who envisioned a station that could grow into an orbital city. It would be built up gradually from parts sent into orbit by carrier rockets. It would have a "tubular terminal," 900 feet long, that would be connected to a wheel 500 feet in diameter. Later another hull would be added, this one 3,000 feet long and 1,000 feet across. The wheel would grow to 1,500 feet in diameter and possibly more. The station would contain offices, supermarkets, gymnasiums, and other facilities to make life in space comfortable. Answering the inevitable criticisms of his ambitious plan in advance, Romick wrote, "Any prediction of future developments representing significant advances is always looked upon by many as unduly optimistic, yet eventually turns out, in the back light of history, to have been unduly conservative."

Romick's plan may eventually appear conservative, but the space stations being planned today are far smaller than the one he proposed. In fact the progress of manned space flight, while rapid, has been much slower than it was pictured by astronautical enthusiasts and science-fiction writers of the past. The fanciful theories of the prewar days have

LIGHT

been tempered as the difficult realities of space travel have emerged.

Manned vehicles designed for either orbital or Lunar missions are outgrowths of two roots: the airplane and the unmanned spacecraft. The Soviets appear to have relied heavily on unmanned spacecraft in their development program, while the United States has placed emphasis on airplanes and spacecraft alike.

As early as 1944, the National Advisory Committee for Aeronautics, the Army, and the Navy had begun both independent and cooperative programs to develop high-altitude and high-speed vehicles. Starting with the wartime MX-324, the services advanced to the more advanced MX-653, which led to the XS-1 (later X-1) rocket plane. The basic goal, laid down in preliminary form in March 1944, called for a one-man rocket-powered aircraft that could exceed the speed of sound in level flight.

The X-1 program was managed by the Air Force, which had the Bell Aircraft Company build the airframe and Reaction Motors design and build a 6,000-pound-thrust liquid-propellant rocket engine with a four-chamber configuration. Since throttles to control rocket-engine thrust had not yet been perfected, the four chambers gave the pilot a wider choice of power level. By cutting in chambers, he could boost the thrust by 1,500-pound increments from 1,500 pounds to 6,000 pounds.

Since the X-1's propellant supply was very limited, the rocket plane was designed for launching from another aircraft, a modified B-29. Motorless glide trials were held in 1946, with Jack Woolams at the controls, and propulsion tests took place in 1947, with Chalmers H. Goodlin and Alvin M. Johnson as pilots. On 14 October 1947 Charles E. Yeager flew the X-1 past the speed of sound, and by 1949 it had set a speed record of nearly 970 miles per hour at an altitude record of 14 miles.

Improved models, the X-1A, X-1B, and X-1D, had larger propellant tanks. The X-1A set a speed record of 1,635 miles per hour in December 1953, within a month after its flight testing had started. The X-1B made important contributions to both aircraft and spacecraft development by allowing tests of rocket controls in the rarefied upper atmosphere, where the air is too thin for conventional aerodynamic controls.

While the Air Force was developing the X-1's, the Navy was testing the D-558-2, which also was powered by a 6,000-pound-thrust rocket engine. The aircraft's maiden flight took place on 4 February 1948, with an interim jet engine supplying the power. Once the ship's rocket engine had been installed, it became the first manned vehicle to fly at nearly twice the speed of sound, 1,325 miles per hour, on 20 November 1953, piloted by A. Scott Crossfield. Earlier, on 31 August, the D-558-2 reached a record altitude of 15 miles, Lieutenant Colonel Marion E. Carl at the controls.

Plans for more ambitious flights were already under way. On 24 June 1952, NACA's Committee on Aerodynamics recommended an increase "in research efforts on the problems of manned and unmanned flight at altitudes between 12 and 50 miles and at speeds of Mach 4 through 10," that is, four to ten times the speed of sound. This NACA recommendation was the genesis of Project Mercury, the program of the United States for sending astronauts into orbit around Earth. But before manned satellites could be built, more airplane tests had to be made.

Following up on the NACA recommendation, Langley Aeronautical Laboratory (now NASA's Langley Research Center) identified several problem areas. Two were "aerodynamic heating and the achievement of stability and control at very high altitudes and speeds. Of the two . . . aerodynamic heating [was considered] to be the more serious, and, until this problem was resolved, the design of practical spacecraft impractical."

The Bell X-2, powered by a Curtiss-Wright rocket engine that delivered 15,000 pounds of thrust and was throttlable, came to grips with these problems. The X-2 made its first powered flight in November 1955. On 7 September 1956, Captain Ivan C. Kincheloe flew the X-2 to a record height of 24 miles. The X-2's last flight, on 27 September, ended in tragedy. The aircraft went out of control after a record run at more than three times the speed of sound. The pilot, Captain Milburn G. Apt, was killed in the crash.

Craft that flew even higher and faster were needed to fulfill the needs of research. Two approaches were taken to meet those needs. One was the manned ballistic missile approach that led directly to Project Mercury. The other was the development of the X-15 rocket airplane.

The X-15 is the closest thing to a winged spacecraft that has ever been built. The performance goals, laid down in the early 1950's, included an altitude of at least 50 miles and a speed of six to seven times the speed of sound, both double the records set by the X-2. The Air Force awarded a development contract to North American Aviation in December 1955, the first aircraft was delivered in October 1958, and the first flight took place on 8 June 1959. The X-15 was powered by a Reaction Motors engine that developed 57,000 pounds of thrust on liquid propellants.

Because engine development lagged, the X-15 could not meet its objectives for some time. Testing was started with two X-1 units supplying 12,000 pounds of thrust, which sped the X-15 to a speed of nearly 2,300 miles per hour and an altitude of over 25 miles.

The X-15 underwent demonstration tests during November and December 1960. Its first flight by an Air Force pilot, Captain Robert M. White, took place on 7 March 1961. NASA pilot Joseph A. Walker flew it at 4,105 miles per hour on 27 June 1962, and to a record altitude of 67 miles on 22 August 1963. Air Force, Navy, and NASA pilots employed the three X-15 aircraft in a sustained test-flight program to explore many aspects of flight at high altitudes and extreme speeds. In 1964 alone, twenty-seven flights were made, nineteen of them at more than five times the speed of sound. By 1966 the X-15 had accumulated more than 4 hours of flight above Mach 3, 2½ hours above Mach 4, 40 minutes above Mach 5, and 12 seconds above Mach 6.

On 26 April 1967 X-15 Number 3 developed low pressure in the fuel pump and had to make an emergency landing near Edwards Air Force Base, California. Neither the plane nor its pilot suffered ill effects. On 29 June, plane Number 1 had to make an emergency landing only 59 seconds after being released from its B-52 mother ship. It had an electrical power failure. Again, no damage was incurred. The all-time X-15 speed record was set on 3 October 1967, when Major William J. Knight flew plane Number 2 to an altitude of 99,000 feet at a velocity of 4,520 mph (Mach 6.7). The new speed topped the old record, set on 18 November 1966, by 270 miles per hour. After the flight, it was found that a hole six inches in diameter had been burned through the vertical tail and that a 40 pound dummy ramjet had torn loose before it was scheduled to be jettisoned. The primary purpose of the flight was to see how the new paint coating reacted. Indications were that temperatures of 3,000 degrees F had formed on the leading edges of the ramjet — more than twice what was expected. Later, in mid-November, Major Michael J. Adams was killed when his X-15 Number 3 went into a spin at an altitude of over 50 miles near Johannesburg, California. The pilot apparently had suffered disorientation, mistaking a roll indicator for a sideslip indicator.

Nineteen sixty-eight saw the completion of the basic research for which the X-15 series was conceived: the last (and 199th) flight occurred on 24 October, when pilot William H. Dana took the craft to an altitude of 225,000 feet.

Having set, during its lifetime, unofficial world records of 67 miles altitude (in 1963) and 6.7 times the speed of sound (in 1967), it was the most impressive research airplane in history. Planes Numbers 1 and 2 are displayed at, respectively, the Smithsonian Institution in Washington and the Air Force Museum near Dayton, Ohio.

In particular, the X-15 provided unique experience in controlling a high-speed vehicle under what amounted to space-flight conditions. At X-15 altitudes, aerodynamic controls do not work because the air is too thin. Small rockets in the nose and wings of the X-15 are fired to control the aircraft's attitude and path.

Proposals to put the X-15 into orbit by using a

The X-1B, first flown in 1954, tested rocket controls in the rarefied upper atmosphere, where the air is too thin for conventional aerodynamic controls. (BELL AEROSYSTEMS CO.)

carrier rocket were made frequently but got nowhere. The Air Force did begin an X-20 Dynasoar program to put a winged, reusable spacecraft into orbit, but it was killed for budgetary and military reasons. Beyond the X-20 were proposals for aerospaceplanes capable of taking off from the ground, flying into orbit, and then gliding back. By the mid-1960's, however, the X-15 approach to space flight had fallen into relative neglect in the United States.

While the rocket plane remained a valuable research tool, and contributed to the manned space flight program, the goal of placing a man in orbit was achieved through the rapid advances that led from ballistic missiles, to sounding rockets, to unmanned spacecraft launched by carrier vehicles.

Again, it is the Russians who were first. On 12 April 1961, Major Yuri A. Gagarin was orbited in a cylindrical 10,400-pound Vostok 1 spacecraft. While there was shock in the United States, it was not as great as Sputnik 1 had caused. The Russians had not only predicted a manned space flight, they had been openly practicing for it for a year.

Between 15 May 1960 and 25 March 1961 five Korabl Sputniks had been launched. Four contained recovery capsules; three were retrieved. The capsules carried both instruments and animals. Korabl Sputnik 2, for example, carried two dogs, forty mice, two rats, and several hundred insects, as well as plants and biological specimens, all of which returned to Earth unharmed after seventeen orbits. Guinea pigs and frogs were added in the third and fourth flights, along with mannequins. Both were brought back to Earth after one orbit—an exact rehearsal for the flight of Vostok 1. And it was certainly no coincidence that Vostok 2, with Major Gherman S. Titov aboard, stayed up for exactly seventeen orbits, or 25 hours, on 6 August 1961. When he was ready to return to Earth, he fired his retrorockets, causing the capsule to re-enter the Earth's atmosphere. Parachutes brought Vostok 2 slowly to the ground, but Titov preferred to complete the trip with his individual parachute.

The Russians flew four more Vostoks, in two paired missions. Major Adrian G. Nikolayev went aloft in Vostok 3 on 11 August 1962, and Lieutenant Colonel Pavel R. Popovich followed him into orbit in Vostok 4 on the same day, in a remarkable example of precision launching. The two spacecraft, often in sight of each other, circled the Earth for several days. Nikolayev came down after 94 hours and 1,645,000 miles of travel, and Popovich after 71 hours and 1,242,000 miles. Both cosmonauts left their slowly descending capsules and parachuted to

Earth near Karaganda in Kazakhstan. The flight was a forerunner of later missions when spacecraft would rendezvous in orbit.

The next Soviet double-mission resulted in two close orbital approaches. Vostok 5 was flown into orbit on 14 June 1963 by Lieutenant Colonel Valery F. Bykovsky. Vostok 6, launched two days later, had the distinction of carrying the first woman, Valentina V. Tereshkova, into orbit. The two spacecraft came within three miles of each other at one point, although they were usually much farther apart. Bykovsky set a record of 119 hours in orbit, and 2,063,377 miles of flight, before he came down by parachute more than 300 miles northwest of Karaganda.

One sidelight of the flight showed how far space research had come. Television pictures of the mission, seen over the East European Intervision network, were received in Helsinki, telecast to London, taped and flown to Goonhilly Downs, and then broadcast via Telstar 2 to the United States for nationwide viewing.

The United States counterpart to the six-flight Vostok series was Project Mercury. Its four manned orbital flights took place between the orbiting of Vostok 2 and Vostok 5. Like the Soviet program, it was preceded by unmanned flights and relied on modified ICBM's as carriers. Mercury was a highly successful project.

While some work on space flight had been done before Sputnik 1, the Russian success galvanized the United States into action. One important result of the research effort on rocket planes at Langley had been the publication in March 1958 of a paper by Maxime A. Faget and others entitled "Preliminary Studies of Manned Satellites, Wingless Configurations: Nonlifting." At about this time a working committee also decided that a "ballistic entry" vehicle, powered by a military missile, was the best way to get an American into orbit quickly.

Flying at six times the speed of sound and soaring to 67 miles above the Earth, the rocket-powered X-15 contributed to the manned space program by testing high altitudes and extreme speeds. Rear view shows the nozzle of its 57,000-pound-thrust rocket engine. (NASA)

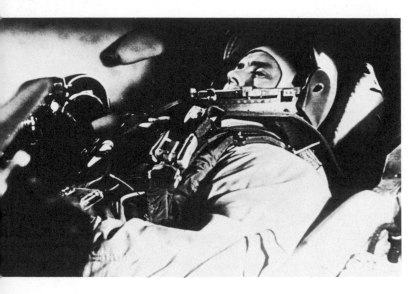

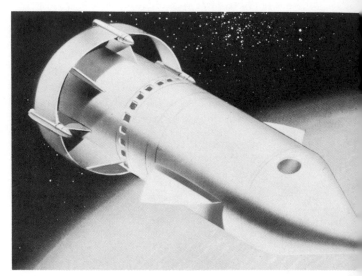

In a remarkable paired flight with Vostok 3, Soviet space-craft Vostok 4 circled the Earth for 71 hours with cosmonaut Pavel Popovich in the cabin (left). Right, a drawing of the exterior of Vostok 4, launched 11 August 1962. (NOVOSTI PRESS AGENCY *and* U.S.S.R. ACADEMY OF SCIENCES)

The basic design of the Mercury spacecraft was worked out between April and June 1958 by Faget, Charles W. Mathews, and their associates. This led to the creation of a committee, headed by Robert R. Gilruth, which presented a proposed manned satellite program on 3 October 1958 to the Advanced Research Projects Agency, and a few days later to NASA administrator T. Keith Glennan. NASA gave its approval, and a Space Task Group under Gilruth was set up at Langley to supervise the program. Late in 1959 the McDonnell Aircraft Corporation was chosen as prime contractor, and Mercury entered the development stage.

A three-phase flight-testing program was set up for Mercury. In the first phase, Redstone missiles would be used to send men on ballistic trajectories (as far back as August 1958 the Army Ballistic Missile Agency had proposed this under the code name Adam). In phase 2, Jupiters would be used for longer trajectories. Finally, Atlas ICBM's would orbit the

On 31 January 1961 the chimpanzee Ham soared 157 miles into space in a 16-minute, 39-second flight aboard a Mercury capsule. Right, back on Earth, Ham reaches for an apple, his first post-flight meal. (NASA—MSC)

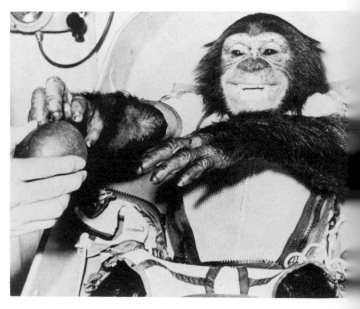

manned capsule in phase 3. For preliminary testing of the capsule and its parachute system, a cluster of Little Joe solid-fuel rockets would be used.

Mercury's basic mission was to put a man in orbit, test his ability to function in space, and bring him back safely. NASA set four guidelines for the program:

1. Existing technology and off-the-shelf equipment should be used wherever practical.

2. The simplest and most reliable approach to system design would be followed.

3. An existing launch vehicle would be used to orbit the spacecraft.

4. The test program would be progressive and logical.

Stringent requirements were laid down for the spacecraft. It would have a reliable escape system to rescue the crew in case of an accident just before, during, or after the launch. It would be controllable by the pilot. It would be capable of landing on water. It would carry retrorockets capable of taking it out of orbit and starting it back to Earth. And it would not glide in when it landed, but would fall along a ballistic path until its parachutes deployed to control the descent.

The spacecraft that emerged was basically a capsule that would keep one man alive in orbit for more than 24 hours. It was 11 feet long, counting the package of retrorockets that slowed the Mercury for re-entry, and slightly more than 6 feet in diameter. Mercury had an emergency solid-fuel rocket escape tower that could pull it free of its carrier vehicle if trouble developed during the launch; the escape tower was jettisoned after the launch.

Mercury's test flights started on 21 August 1959 with the first of eight Little Joe capsule launches, two with rhesus monkeys aboard. Redstones were used first to send the spacecraft on ballistic trajectories and thereafter Atlases to orbit them, once with a chimpanzee on board, and twice with dummy astronauts in the capsule.

The plan to use Jupiters was canceled in July 1959 when it was determined that the same aerodynamic information could be obtained by shortening the range of an Atlas missile; and, only six of the eight planned Redstone flights were made. The first four of these were test vehicles, the next two were manned. In May 1961 Commander Alan B. Shepard was launched by a Redstone on a suborbital flight, and an identical flight was made two months later by Major Virgil I. Grissom. Both flights enabled the astronauts to test the spacecraft's controls, evaluate their response to rocket-powered flights, and familiarize themselves with space flight.

The MA-9 Mercury capsule undergoing automatic stabilization control systems test. (NASA—MSC)

The first American in orbit was Marine Colonel John H. Glenn, Jr., who orbited the Earth three times on 20 February 1962. As Glenn prepared to re-enter the atmosphere, he found that the automatic control system had malfunctioned. He handled the retrorocket firing himself and made a successful landing 166 miles east of Grand Turk Island in the Bahamas. Glenn was picked up by the destroyer *Noa* after his 4-hour-and-46-minute, 81,000-mile flight.

The next Mercury flight, under the control of Lieutenant Commander M. Scott Carpenter, took place on 24 May 1962. It was basically a repeat of the Glenn flight, although a re-entry error not attributable to the pilot brought Carpenter down 250 miles off target. The third orbital Mercury flight, flown by Commander Walter M. Schirra on 3 October 1962, went for six orbits. The Mercury program was closed out by Air Force Major Gordon L. Cooper's twenty-two-orbit flight on 15 May 1963. Cooper made a pinpoint landing, coming down only 4½ miles from the recovery ship.

Aside from proving that man could go into space, the first one-man flights of both nations produced some scientific data. The American astronauts photographed the Earth in color, observed the Moon and the Sun, and made observations of the zodiacal light and the night glow. One space mystery was the discovery by Glenn of small luminous particles drifting alongside his spacecraft. In later flights they were found to be small ice crystals emerging from the life-support systems on the spacecraft.

The next step in manned space travel was the orbiting of spacecraft with more than one occupant. Once again the Russians led the way. On 12 October 1964, they orbited the first of their Voskhod series of spacecraft, with three men aboard. Voskhod was not only heavier than Vostok, weighing 11,525 pounds, but it also represented a considerable advance in

Summary of Test and Orbital Launchings for Mercury Spacecraft Program

Spacecraft No.	Use	Mission	Delivered to launch site	Date launched	Weeks of Preparation	Remarks
1	Beach abort	System qualification test, escape landing, postlanding, unmanned	1 April 1960	9 May 1960	5	No carrier vehicle used.
2	MR–1A	Ballistic unmanned	23 July 1960	19 December 1960	21	Spacecraft reworked after MR–1 launch attempt where carrier vehicle malfunctioned.
3	LJ–5	Maximum dynamic pressure abort, unmanned	27 September 1960	8 November 1960	6	All objectives not accomplished.
4	MA–1	Maximum acceleration, maximum heat on afterbody, unmanned	23 May 1960	29 July 1960	10	All systems not complete; all objectives not accomplished.
5	MR–2	Ballistic, primate	11 October 1960	31 January 1961	16	Successful mission, Ham chimpanzee occupant.
6	MA–2	Maximum acceleration, maximum heat on afterbody, unmanned	1 September 1960	21 February 1961	25	Successful mission.
7	MR–3	Ballistic, manned	9 December 1960	5 May 1961	21	First manned ballistic mission; mission successful; Shepard, astronaut.
8	MA–3	Orbital, unmanned	18 November 1960	25 April 1961	23	Launched and aborted; all mission objectives not accomplished.
8A	MA–4	Orbital, unmanned	11 May 1961	13 September 1961	18	Spacecraft refitted and flown same configuration; mission successful.
9	MA–5	Orbital, primate	24 February 1961	29 November 1961	40	Mission changed after delivery; 2 orbits flown successfully; Enos chimpanzee occupant.
10	Ground test	Orbital flight, environmental test	31 March 1961	1 June 1962		Used at St. Louis in project orbit; completed ground test.
11	MR–4	Ballistic, manned	7 March 1961	21 July 1961	19	Manned ballistic mission; flown successfully; spacecraft lost on recovery; Grissom, astronaut.
12B	Unassigned	Orbital, manned 1-day mission				Mission canceled, spacecraft not delivered.
13	MA–6	Orbital, manned	27 August 1961	20 February 1962	25	Unusually long pad period, 4 holds; first manned orbital mission; mission successful; Glenn, astronaut.
14	LJ–5A	Maximum dynamic pressure abort, unmanned	20 January 1961	18 March 1961	8	All mission objectives not accomplished.
14A	LJ–5B	Maximum dynamic pressure abort, unmanned	4 April 1961	28 April 1961	3.5	Spacecraft refitted and flown same configuration; mission successful.
15B	MA–10	Orbital, manned 1-day mission	16 November 1962			Mission canceled after success of MA–9, spacecraft 20.
16	MA–8	Orbital, manned	16 January 1962	3 October 1962	37	Mission changed from 3- to 6-orbital, manned; mission successful; Schirra, astronaut.

Summary of Test and Orbital Launchings for Mercury Spacecraft Program (continued)

Space-craft No.	Use	Mission	Delivered to launch site	Date Launched	Weeks of Preparation	Remarks
17	Unassigned	Orbital, manned 1-day mission	18 April 1963			Delivered to Cape Canaveral for parts support of manned 1-day missions.
18	MA–7	Orbital, manned	15 November 1961	24 May 1962	27	4 holds in pad period, 2nd 3-orbital mission; successful; Carpenter, astronaut.
19	Unassigned	Orbital, manned	20 March 1962			Mission canceled after MA–8.
20	MA–9	Orbital, manned 1-day mission	9 October 1962	15 May 1963	31	22 orbit manned flight; mission successful; Cooper, astronaut.

Notes: MR refers to capsules launched by Redstone carriers LJ refers to capsules launched by Little Joe test vehicles; early LJ flights tested boilerplate capsules. MA refers to capsules launched by Atlas carriers.

capability. Among other innovations, the craft used an ion-propulsion device for attitude control. During at least part of their flight, the three cosmonauts were dressed in lightweight clothing, rather than space-suits, indicating Soviet confidence in Voskhod's performance. And all three men chose to land with their craft after sixteen orbits, rather than parachuting during the descent as former cosmonauts had done. After the craft re-entered the atmosphere, braking parachutes and "other aerodynamic deceleration devices" were deployed. When the capsule reached a lower altitude, a special type of parachute was used to guide the craft to its landing site. Finally, just above the ground, a retrorocket was fired to assure a gentle landing. The crew on Voskhod 1 consisted of Colonel Vladimir M. Komarov of the Air Force Engineer Corps, Lieutenant Boris B. Yegorov, an Air Force doctor, and Konstantin P. Feoktistov, a civilian scientist.

Voskhod 2 provided an even more important first when it was orbited on 18 March 1965. One of its two crew members, Lieutenant Colonel Aleksei A. Leonov, left the spacecraft through an airlock and spent ten minutes in space while the other crew member, Colonel Pavel I. Belyayev, observed him.

Voskhod 2, at 11,730 pounds, was some 200 pounds heavier than the first Voskhod. The airlock and other devices needed for Leonov's "space walk" are believed to have added the weight. As described by Soviet sources, the airlock was mounted to permit access from the cabin through a hatch, which was

The first seven astronauts selected for Project Mercury. Shown here in space suits, they are (front row, left to right) Walter M. Schirra, Jr., Donald K. Slayton, John H. Glenn, Jr., M. Scott Carpenter, (back row) Alan B. Shepard, Jr., Virgil I. Grissom, and L. Gordon Cooper, Jr. (NASA)

Earth seen through porthole of Voskhod 2, orbited 18 March 1965. During this flight, cosmonaut Aleksei A. Leonov left the spacecraft for a 10-minute "spacewalk." (NOVOSTI PRESS AGENCY, LONDON)

activated by an electric drive mechanism. Once in the airlock, the cosmonaut could open the outer hatch either manually or electrically. Cameras recorded his activities automatically, and more cameras were on the exterior, as were air tanks for pressurizing the airlock after he returned from space. The airlock was jettisoned after he returned to the cabin.

The United States' two-man Gemini program represented a similar step forward in manned orbital capability. Gemini had been conceived before the first Mercury orbital shot, and was announced publicly on 7 December 1961. Again, McDonnell was the prime contractor.

The Gemini space craft had the same conical shape as the Mercury capsule, but it was heavier (7,000-8,000 pounds), bigger (18 feet, 5 inches long and 10 feet in diameter), roomier by 50 percent, and required a Titan 2 carrier, with 430,000 pounds of thrust, to put it into orbit. Gemini was also considerably more complicated.

The spacecraft consisted of four sections: the re-entry module, made of titanium and beryllium, in which the astronauts rode; the rendezvous and recovery section, which also contained the parachutes that eased the module to Earth and the radar system; the re-entry control section, with propellant tanks,

Left, astronauts James A. McDivitt and Edward H. White walk up the ramp on their way to the elevator that will take them to the Gemini 4 spacecraft. Right, the Gemini 4 atop the Titan 2 carrier vehicle three hours before *launch at Cape Kennedy on 3 June 1965. McDivitt and White are aboard. Gemini 4 traveled 62 orbits, during which White left the cabin for his famous "walk" in space.* (NASA)

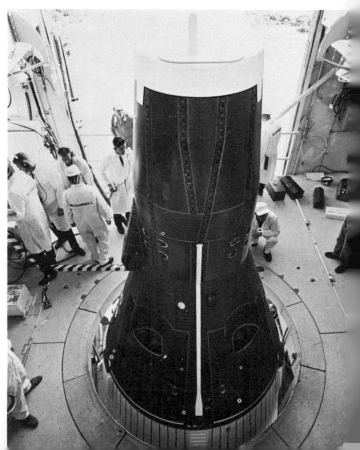

sixteen fixed liquid-propellant 25-pound-thrust rocket
engines for control during re-entry, and a parachute
adapter assembly; and the adapter section, which included the four solid-propellant 2,500-pound-thrust
retrorockets, part of the environmental control system, propellant storage systems, and power supply
for the spacecraft. Rocket engines ranging in thrust
from 25 to 100 pounds were mounted on various
parts of the satellite to help it maneuver in space;
an onboard computer got data from the rendezvous
radar to help bring two satellites together in space.

An unmanned Gemini was launched from Cape
Kennedy on 8 April 1964. The second Gemini flight,
also unmanned, was a suborbital ballistic flight on
19 January 1965, with two simulated astronauts
aboard. The first manned Gemini flight took place
on 23 March 1965, five days after Voskhod 2 was
launched.

The flight went off perfectly. Major Grissom and
Lieutenant Commander John W. Young made three
orbits in the Gemini spacecraft, using their onboard
rockets to change the size and shape of their orbit
twice and the orbital plane once. The spacecraft itself functioned almost without flaw.

The second manned Gemini flight, on 3 June
1965, was doubly significant. It was the first American flight whose length matched the longer Russian
missions, and it allowed the United States to match
the Russian space walk. Majors James A. McDivitt
and Edward H. White II rode Gemini for sixty-two
orbits; early in the flight, White left the cabin to
spend 21 minutes floating in space and maneuvering
with a hand-held gas gun.

The United States captured the space endurance
record with the next Gemini flight, which started on
21 August 1965. Gordon Cooper—who became the
first astronaut to make two space journeys—and
Charles Conrad, Jr., orbited for 7 days, 22 hours, and
59 minutes, a total of 120 orbits.

That record was nearly doubled in the next
Gemini mission, which was distinctive for several
reasons. The Gemini 6 spacecraft, which was to have
been next in orbit, was held back from launch in
October 1965 because the Agena with which it
would practice rendezvous was destroyed after
launch. Instead, Gemini 7 was sent up first, on 4
December, and the same launch pad was quickly
made ready for Gemini 6. As Lieutenant Colonel
Frank Borman and Commander James A. Lovell, Jr.,
orbited in Gemini 7, Schirra and Major Thomas P.
Stafford went into orbit on Gemini 6 on 15 December.

Gemini 6 caught up with its sister craft, and in a
series of impressively precise and complex maneuvers, came within one foot of Gemini 7, approxi-

*Edward H. White floating in space outside Gemini 4. The "walk"
lasted 21 minutes, during which he maneuvered with the gas gun
in his right hand.* (NASA)

mately 185 miles above the Earth. The two spacecraft flew in close formation for nearly 8 hours, in a
dramatic demonstration of Gemini's ability to rendezvous in space. Gemini 6 splashed down in the Atlantic
after 26 hours aloft, but Gemini 7 continued on for
a record-breaking 206 orbits that had taken it more
than 4 million miles in two weeks. The flight gave
the United States nearly 1,353 man-hours in space,
compared to 507 man-hours for Russia.

Gemini 8 got off to a fine start on 16 March 1966
when it went into orbit shortly after the launch of
an Agena target vehicle. Late in the fifth orbit, after
having accomplished the first docking operation in
space, the coupled Gemini 8 and Agena commenced
pitching and rolling motions, which persisted after
astronauts Neil A. Armstrong and Major David R.
Scott detached their craft. The mission was quickly
aborted, Gemini 8 splashing down in the western
Pacific Ocean instead of the Atlantic as planned.

NASA had planned to launch its Gemini 9 spacecraft on 1 June 1966, directly after an "augmented
target docking adapter" was orbited by an Atlas.

Summary of Manned Orbital Flights

Launch Date	Designation	Country	Astronaut(s)	Number of orbits	Flight time (hours, min)	Perigee-apogee (miles)		Weight (pounds)	Remarks
12 April 1961	Vostok 1	U.S.S.R.	Gagarin	1	1, 48	112	203	10,418	World's first manned orbital flight.
6 August 1961	Vostok 2	U.S.S.R.	Titov	17.5	25, 18	113	152	10,430	Total distance covered: 435,000 miles.
20 February 1962	Mercury MA-6	U.S.A.	Glenn	3	4, 55	100	163	4,265	Friendship 7 capsule made 81,000-mile flight; difficulty with auto pilot.
24 May 1962	Mercury MA-7	U.S.A.	Carpenter	3	4, 56	100	167	4,244	Aurora 7 capsule made 81,200-mile flight; 200-mile landing overshoot.
11 August 1962	Vostok 3	U.S.S.R.	Nikolayev	64	94, 22	112	146	10,430	With Vostok 4 launched next day, purpose to "obtain experimental data on the possibility of establishing close contact between the two ships, coordinating the actions of the pilot-cosmonauts, and to check the influence of identical conditions of space flight on human beings."
12 August 1962	Vostok 4	U.S.S.R.	Popovich	48	70, 57	112	147	10,430	
3 October 1962	Mercury MA-8	U.S.A.	Schirra	6	9, 13	100	176	4,325	Sigma 7 capsule made 160,000-mile flight, landed in Pacific.
15 May 1963	Mercury MA-9	U.S.A.	Cooper	22	34, 20	100	166	4,000	Faith 7 capsule landed 2 miles from USS *Kearsarge* in Pacific near Midway.
14 June 1963	Vostok 5	U.S.S.R.	Bykovsky	81	119, 6	99	146	10,430	Dual flight with Vostok 6, which carried a woman cosmonaut. On first orbit the two spacecraft came within 3 miles of one another.
16 June 1963	Vostok 6	U.S.S.R.	Tereshkova	48	70, 50	112	141	10,440	
12 October 1964	Voskhod 1	U.S.S.R.	Komarov Feoktistov Yegorov	16	24, 17	110	254	11,525	First multiman satellite flight. Other than a cosmonaut, a scientist and a physician were carried.
18 March 1965	Voskhod 2	U.S.S.R.	Belyavev Leonov	17	26, 2	108	307	11,730	For first time cosmonaut (Leonov) left orbiting satellite, emerged spacesuited into space.
23 March 1965	Gemini GT-3	U.S.A.	Grissom Young	3	4, 53	100	140	7,100	Attitude and orbital plane changes successfully undertaken.

Summary of Manned Orbital Flights (continued)

Launch Date	Designation	Country	Astronaut(s)	Number of orbits	Flight time (hours, min)	Perigee-apogee (miles)		Weight (pounds)	Remarks
3 June 1965	Gemini GT-4	U.S.A.	McDivitt White	62	97, 48	100	182	7,800	First extravehicular activity in which astronaut maneuvered with hand-held reaction device.
21 August 1965	Gemini GT-5	U.S.A.	Cooper Conrad	120	190, 59	100	219	7,000	Cooper became first astronaut to make a second orbital flight.
4 December 1965	Gemini GT-7	U.S.A.	Borman Lovell	206	320, 35	183	185	7,000	With Gemini 6, first in-space rendezvous successfully achieved, the
15 December 1965	Gemini GT-6	U.S.A.	Schirra Stafford	15	25, 51	100	167	7,000	two craft approaching within 1 foot, at about 6 hours into the mission. Both craft landed within 10 miles of predicted impact zone.
16 March 1966	Gemini GT-8	U.S.A.	Armstrong Scott	7	10, 42	100	169	7,000	First docking maneuver successfully performed (with unmanned Agena target satellite). Two vehicles went into roll, Gemini quickly separated, slowly regained attitude. Mission aborted; precise landing.
3 June 1966	Gemini GT-9	U.S.A.	Stafford Cernan	45	72, 22	185	185	7,700	Demonstrated new rendezvous techniques but failed to dock because of stuck nose cover on target vehicle. Cernan left spacecraft for 2 hour 7 minute walk in space. Most accurate landing yet, only 2 miles from target.
18 July 1966	Gemini GT-10	U.S.A.	Young Collins	43	70, 46	99	165	8,248	Rendezvous, docking with two targets; change of altitude using one target's propulsion system; long EVA.
12 September 1966	Gemini GT-11	U.S.A.	Conrad Gordon	44	71, 17	100	175	8,509	Successful rendezvous, docking, Agena-effected apogee lift. EVA successful though fatiguing for Gordon, ultraviolet star photography.

Summary of Manned Orbital Flights (continued)

Launch Date	Designa-tion	Country	Astro-naut(s)	Number of orbits	Flight time (hours, min)	Perigee-apogee (miles)		Weight (pounds)	Remarks
11 November 1966	Gemini GT-12	U.S.A.	Lovell Aldrin	59	94, 34½	100	168	8,297	Multiple rendezvous, docking; extensive EVA, including working with tools. Star and Sunrise photography.
23 April 1967	Soyuz 1	U.S.S.R.	Komarov	18	27	125	139	14,000	Communications and stabilization problems caused premature cutoff of mission. Parachute recovery system failed on re-entry, resulting in death of cosmonaut and destruction of craft.
25 October 1968	Soyuz 2	U.S.S.R.	Unmanned	48	70, 48	115	139	14,000	Unmanned target vehicle against which Soyuz 3 rendezvoused.
26 October 1968	Soyuz 3	U.S.S.R.	Beregovoy	64	94, 51	127	139	14,000	Cosmonaut maneu-vered in orbit, achieved radar lock-on but no docking with unmanned Soyuz 2. Retro-rocket-parachute landing.
14 January 1969	Soyuz 4	U.S.S.R.	Shatalov	48	71, 14	108	140	14,000	On third day in orbit, approached to within 20 miles of passive Soyuz 5, then moved in for automatic docking maneuver until separation distance was reduced to less than 350 feet. Manual completion.
15 January 1969	Soyuz 5	U.S.S.R.	Kolynov Khrunov Yeliseyev	49	72, 46	124	144	14,000	Joined to Soyuz 4 for about 4 hours at perigee-apogee altitude of 131–156 miles. Yeliseyev and Khrunov performed EVA and entered Soyuz 4.

Note: Perigee and apogee values given are initial conditions only; many vehicles maneuvered in orbit, changing orbital altitudes and planes.

However, due to problems in the command data link, the launching was postponed until the 3rd. Colonel Thomas P. Stafford was commander, and Lieutenant Commander Eugene A. Cernan was pilot.

In many ways, the Gemini 9 mission was the most significant to date, since it underscored the difficulties man must undergo in solving problems and working in an alien environment. Cernan's activities were so intense that he lost about ten pounds in weight during the flight; two pounds of water were found in his space suit after recovery. His respiration rate went as high as 30 breaths per minute, compared with a normal 12 to 15.

Both astronauts suffered considerable fatigue during the flight because their workload was about four times greater than had been anticipated. In a rendezvous phase, for instance, they had to resort to hand calculations when the onboard computer malfunctioned. When they finally approached the target (once as close as 3 feet), they saw that the clamshell-like shrouds of the cone were open but still fastened; Stafford likened it to "an angry alligator" as it slowly tumbled in space. Ground controllers made several attempts to dislodge the shrouds by radio commands, but these were futile.

During this flight, Cernan took a space walk that lasted more than three times as long as Edward White's extra-vehicular activity (EVA) on the Gemini 4 mission. Cernan, however, had difficulty with his maneuvering unit, and he exerted himself so greatly in his attempts to maintain position at the rear of the vehicle's adapter section that he exceeded the limits of his spacesuit's life support system. This resulted in fogging of his helmet visor, which in turn so disturbed him that he was unable to use the very maneuvering unit he was trying to put into service. He reported that his tether was of little aid in maneuvering. But he did accomplish many tasks, which included making his way to the bow of the spacecraft and attaching a mirror, and evaluation of the usefulness of Velcro patches to permit adhesion to surfaces during zero-gravity flight.

The mission ended successfully after forty-five orbits, and Gemini 9 landed in the Atlantic less than two miles from the predicted point of splashdown.

Six weeks later, on 18 July 1966, both the Gemini 10 and its Agena target vehicle were orbited after flawless launches by both carriers from Cape Kennedy. The 8,248-pound Gemini 10 and its two astronauts, Commander John W. Young and Major Michael Collins, first entered into a relatively low orbit with a perigee of 99 miles. Preparations were made to raise the perigee and attempt rendezvous with the Agena 10 target. This was achieved after

some six hours and the expenditure of an excessive quantity of propellant. Docking was successful. Using Agena 10's propulsion system, Gemini 10's perigee was raised to 184 miles and its apogee to over 476 miles. Later, rendezvous was also made with the dormant Agena target vehicle left over from the Gemini 8 mission.

During the successful 38-minute EVA, Collins used a hand-held maneuvering unit similar to the one employed in the Gemini 4 mission. He performed a number of tasks on his Gemini 10 spacecraft, and then went over to the Agena 8 target to remove some microfilm and to replace an instrument package for detecting micrometeoroids. This exchange was an important "first" that heralded a new technique in space research.

The mission of Gemini 10 came to an end on 21 July, after a flight of 70 hours and 46 minutes. Splashdown took place only five miles from the aircraft carrier *Guadalcanal* in the Atlantic Ocean.

Gemini 11 was launched with great precision on 12 September 1966, less than a second later than programmed and 97 minutes after the Atlas-Agena-launched Agena target vehicle. The 8,509-pound Gemini 11 capsule carried Commander Charles Conrad, Jr., and Lieutenant Commander Richard Gordon into an orbit that ranged from 100 miles to 175 miles in altitude. Gordon's EVA went smoothly, although, as in the case of astronaut Cernan in Gemini 9, over-exertion in working outside the spacecraft resulted in an overload of the life support system. After a completely successful rendezvous and docking maneuver, the Agena target's propulsion system was ignited to lift the two vehicles to an apogee of 851 miles, a new manned record. Later, the Agena was re-fired to adjust the perigee to 185 miles. During the course of the flight, the two astronauts observed Russia's Proton 3 satellite, which had been launched on 6 July. (Its orbit decayed and the satellite fell back into the atmosphere on 16 September.)

Gemini 11 returned to Earth in a completely automatic re-entry maneuver, established by the IBM onboard computer. Splashdown occurred less than two miles from the target point on 15 September. Recovery was made by the USS *Guam*.

The twelfth and final spacecraft in the Gemini series carried Captain James A. Lovell (it was his second Gemini flight) and Major Edwin E. Aldrin. Both Gemini 12 and its Agena target vehicle were launched from Cape Kennedy on 11 November 1966; the former splashed down in the Atlantic on the 15th — 94 hours and 34½ minutes after liftoff — and the orbit of the latter decayed into the atmosphere on 23 December. All the planned onboard experiments were conducted during the flight, although some equipment malfunctions and other difficulties occurred; for example, four of the thrusters used for maneuvering in space failed to operate. Rendezvous and docking with the Agena target were performed several times.

The flight was highlighted by a space walk by Aldrin, building up total EVA time by American astronauts to about 12 hours. Aldrin performed a number of tasks, operating specially designed space tools. He cut wire, made lock connections, hooked and unhooked spring-loaded snap hooks, and used a torque wrench. In order to maintain his body position, portable Velcro handholds and foot restraints plus tethers leading from his spacesuit were used during EVA.

While the space walks and the docking of two vehicles were perhaps the most dramatic features of the Gemini program, each flight accomplished many different missions, including the study of prolonged weightlessness in humans, the development of rendezvous and docking techniques, the demonstration of an astronaut's ability to leave his spacecraft, and landing techniques. Gemini also had some purely scientific purposes, and other experiments with a military potential. More than twenty experiments were performed on Gemini 7 alone.

The Gemini astronauts took vivid color photographs of the Earth's land and water, to help geologists, oceanographers, geophysicists, and meteorologists. They tested their ability to spot patterns on the ground. There was a series of medical experiments and measurements to determine whether the heart and bones are weakened by long space flights, and whether mental ability changes in the stress of space. Measurements of radiation and charged particles were made, and an attempt was made to communicate with the ground by laser. These and other experiments gave a generally optimistic picture of man's ability to survive and function usefully in space. As far as could be determined, flights up to two weeks long did not damage the human body, and man's ability to make observations and evaluations remained intact.

In the spring of 1967, five months after the end of the Gemini program and some two years after the Voskhod 2 mission, the Russians resumed manned space flights — disastrously, as it turned out. Their Soyuz 1 was launched from the space center at Tyura Tam on 23 April, in what probably was planned as a rendezvous flight with other cosmonauts to be orbited a day later. However, the spacecraft developed troubles in communications and stabilization. Cosmonaut Vladimir Komarov apparently resolved the stabilization problem, but the mission was terminated after 27 hours in space. Then, during the re-entry phase, the parachute recovery system of the Soyuz failed to deploy properly and the capsule crashed, killing Komarov. This was the first known death of a space flier during the course of an actual mission since manned space flight began in the spring of 1961. A monument was erected on the steppe near Orenburg where cosmonaut Komarov met his death.

The accident prompted a painstaking review of the spacecraft's guidance and recovery systems, and caused considerable delay in the Soviet manned space flight program. The Russians re-entered the

Experience in manned orbital flights is being gained in this rapid decompression chamber at the Brooks Air Force Base, Texas. Left, technicians observe astronaut undergoing simulated extreme-altitude, low-pressure tests. Right, the astronaut watches an opaque cloudlike liquid, which simulates the effect of space conditions on the blood. (U.S. AIR FORCE SCHOOL OF AEROSPACE MEDICINE)

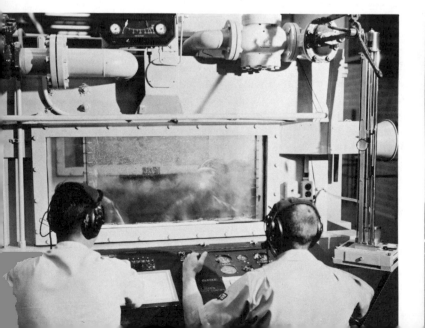

field a year and a half later with re-designed spacecraft in the same Soyuz series. Unmanned Soyuz 2 was the first to be placed into orbit, on 25 October 1968, followed a day later by Soyuz 3, with cosmonaut Georgi Beregovoy aboard. He was able to rendezvous with the target satellite, but did not dock for undetermined reasons. Beregovoy also did some maneuvering in orbit and undertook extensive ground and astronomical observations before returning to Earth on 30 October. Apparently the problems that had led to the loss of Soyuz 1 in April 1967 were fully corrected, putting the Soyuz — and presumably the related Lunar — program back into full stride.

In mid-January 1969, two more manned Soyuz spacecraft were orbited. Soyuz 4, carrying Lieutenant Colonel Vladimir Shatalov of the Russian Air Force, went into orbit on the 14th, followed the next day by Soyuz 5, with a three-man crew consisting of Lieutenant Colonels Boris Volynov and Yevgeni Khrunov, and civilian physicist-engineer Alexei Yeliseyev. Both launches were given a great deal of publicity and television coverage by the Russians. After several hours of maneuvering in orbit, the two spacecraft rendezvoused and then docked. Once the vehicles were coupled, Yeliseyev and Khrunov passed first into the work compartment and then out into space through the hatch of their craft. After about an hour they entered Soyuz 4's work compartment and thence the command area. The cosmonauts then returned to their own craft, and the two vehicles were separated about four hours after their initial docking. The Soyuz 4 capsule came down northwest of Karaganda, while Soyuz 5 descended southwest of Kustanai in Kazakhstan.

This twin flight demonstrated that the Soviets had made great progress toward their goal of perfecting space station technology, and marked an important step in their Lunar flight program. Whereas the United States chose the Lunar orbital rendezvous means of in-space staging for the Moon landing, the Soviets have traditionally leaned toward Earth orbital rendezvous, which, in the long run, may provide a more solid base for the astronautical exploration of the Solar System.

Russia's predilection for talking in generalities makes it futile to speculate on the future course its space program will take. Soviet literature contains many references to manned orbital laboratories, space stations, Lunar—and even interplanetary—spaceships, but descriptions of concrete programs have not yet emerged. The United States efforts, on the other hand, are laid out clearly, for all the world to see, with the NASA Apollo lunar landing and post-Apollo applications programs dominating the near future.

Until June of 1969, the Air Force had its own man-in-space program, the MOL (manned orbital laboratory), which was first announced by Defense Secretary McNamara on 10 December 1963 and was placed under full development on 25 August 1965. When ready, it was to have accommodated two to three men in orbit for up to 30 days — and possibly even longer. The purpose of MOL was to shed light on the military value of man in space, to demonstrate the possibility of assembling structures in orbit, and to test the effect on man of long exposure to weightlessness. In describing the 40-foot-long, 10-foot-diameter laboratory to the Senate Committee on Aeronautical and Space Sciences, then Deputy Secretary of Defense Cyrus R. Vance said that it

will likely consist of a pressurized section, an unpressurized equipment section, and an experiments module. The pressurized section should include an operating compartment with about 500 cubic feet [of] volume, and a separate living-working compartment large enough to accommodate needs for 30 days' flight, probably some 500 to 700 cubic feet . . . Payload capacity should be as large as possible. Estimates of a meaningful test program have included about 3,000 to 5,000 pounds of discretionary test equipment. . . . [The personnel module] will operate in a quiescent mode for the on-orbit duration, and then have the ability to loiter, manned, for about 12 hours, re-enter safely for water recovery . . .

Although originally estimated to cost some $1.5 billion and to be ready for flight testing by 1970, rising costs, competing requirements for other military projects, and program re-evaluations led to funding stretchouts that would have delayed initial manned orbital testing till at least 1972. Meanwhile, spectacular progress in the Apollo program and important advances in unmanned-satellite observation techniques helped make the MOL and its Gemini B ferry spacecraft obsolete before the system could be made operational. Like the earlier Dynasoar, MOL never made it.

While MOL first languished and then died, Apollo moved forward toward the Kennedy-announced goal of landing two astronauts on the Moon. One of the oldest themes in science fiction, it began to get serious attention from scientists several decades ago. As was the case with the space station idea, the proposals became less grandiose as a more refined technology for the implementation of the plan emerged from practical development.

The Apollo program is based on the development of Saturn carriers. NASA first disclosed the Apollo

217

program on 29 July 1960, at a conference it called to acquaint industry with its plans for the future. Since the Saturn designs were not firmly established at the time, the development of Saturn and Apollo were interrelated almost from the beginning.

Some very basic decisions had to be made before a spacecraft could be designed. For example, how many crew members were needed for the trip? And how much equipment would they need to survive and perform scientific experiments?

The planners could choose from three fundamentally different flight plans.

The first, the direct approach plan, was the simplest in concept. A carrier would launch Apollo from the Earth and it would fly directly to the surface of the Moon, take off, and return. The problem with this approach was that a spacecraft based on existing technology and capable of going directly to, and returning from, the Moon would have to be very heavy. To lift it initially, an extremely powerful carrier would be needed; one that would require a substantially longer and costlier developmental program. Therefore, the direct approach idea was abandoned.

An alternate flight plan was the Earth orbital rendezvous, or EOR. The spaceship would be placed in orbit around the Earth, where it would be refueled. Only then could it fly to the Moon and return. This would require two Saturn 5 carriers, one to orbit the spacecraft attached to a partially fueled Saturn third stage and a second to launch a liquid-oxygen tanker to replenish the Saturn 5's third stage. There were advantages to this method—no huge carriers would have to be developed, and the experience in orbital rendezvous and fueling could be applied to later interplanetary missions—but EOR lost out to the third flight plan.

This is Lunar orbital rendezvous, or LOR, an approach conceived by John C. Houbolt of the Langley Research Center early in 1962. LOR seems complicated, but it offers one great advantage: Only one Saturn 5 is needed for the trip. The carrier would send a three-module Apollo spaceship into orbit around the Moon. One of the modules, a two-stage rocket in itself, would be detached to make the landing. After spending a short time on the Moon's surface, the astronauts would return to the mother spacecraft, then discard the landing module, and return to Earth in the remaining two modules. NASA's decision to choose LOR was made in July 1962, and work on a final design for Apollo began.

The more than $20 billion that Apollo would cost aroused considerable opposition to the project. NASA had to turn to some bread-and-butter arguments to build up public acceptance for Apollo. Thus, NASA

Deputy Administrator Hugh L. Dryden pointed out in June 1961 that the money for Apollo "would not be spent on the Moon . . . [but rather] in the factories, workshops, and laboratories of our people for salaries, for new materials, and supplies, which in turn represent income for others." Vigorous support for the program came from President Kennedy, who said in his 1962 State of the Union message that America's aim was "not simply to be first on the Moon . . . our objective in making this effort, which we hope will place one of our citizens on the Moon, is to develop in a new frontier in science, commerce, and cooperation, the position of the United States and the free world. This Nation belongs among the first to explore it. And among the first, if not the first, we shall be."

North American Aviation (now North American Rockwell) was awarded a contract for the Apollo re-entry capsule and its attendant deep-space propulsion unit, consisting of the command and service module (CSM), before the LOR approach was selected. In November 1962, Grumman Aircraft Engineering Corporation was given a contract for the Lunar excursion module (LEM), in which two astronauts were to actually touch down on the Moon. This module later came to be known simply as the LM, or Lunar module. North American retained responsibility for the other two modules.

The three men in the Apollo crew spend most of the period (upwards from eight days) required for a Lunar mission in the command module (CM), the only part of the Apollo spacecraft that returns to Earth. Nearly 11 feet high and 13 feet in diameter at its base, the conical module weighs approximately 12,000 pounds with the crew aboard. The CM serves as the flight control center, living quarters, and re-entry vehicle at the end of the mission. It is divided into three compartments: forward, crew, and aft.

The forward compartment is built around the tunnel that connects the command and Lunar modules when they are docked. It contains parachutes, recovery antennas, the beacon light, the "sling" for retrieving the capsule after it lands in the sea, reaction control engines, and a mechanism for jettisoning the forward heat shield during re-entry so that the parachutes can be deployed. The crew compartment provides the three astronauts with some 210 cubic feet of living space, vehicular controls and display panels, and other operational equipment. It is fitted with two hatches, the first employed for normal entering and exiting and the second for moving into and later back out of the Lunar module once the Apollo has entered into orbit around the Moon. In addition, the crew compartment has two side windows, two front windows that are used in

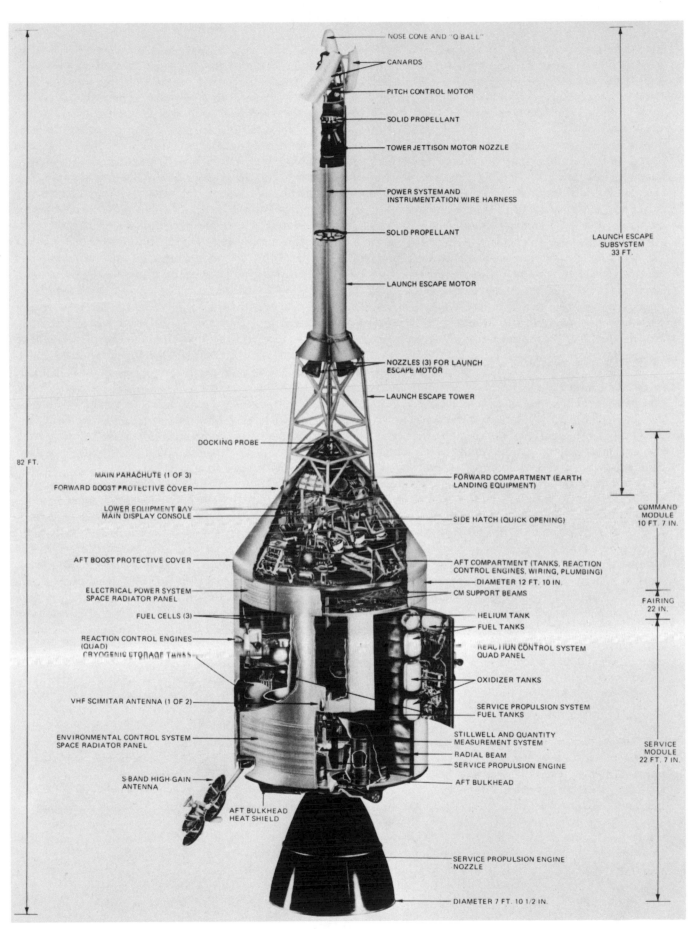

NOSE CONE AND "Q BALL"

CANARDS

PITCH CONTROL MOTOR

SOLID PROPELLANT

TOWER JETTISON MOTOR NOZZLE

POWER SYSTEM AND INSTRUMENTATION WIRE HARNESS

SOLID PROPELLANT

LAUNCH ESCAPE MOTOR

LAUNCH ESCAPE SUBSYSTEM 33 FT.

NOZZLES (3) FOR LAUNCH ESCAPE MOTOR

LAUNCH ESCAPE TOWER

DOCKING PROBE

MAIN PARACHUTE (1 OF 3)
FORWARD BOOST PROTECTIVE COVER

FORWARD COMPARTMENT (EARTH LANDING EQUIPMENT)

LOWER EQUIPMENT BAY
MAIN DISPLAY CONSOLE

SIDE HATCH (QUICK OPENING)

AFT BOOST PROTECTIVE COVER

AFT COMPARTMENT (TANKS, REACTION CONTROL ENGINES, WIRING, PLUMBING)

DIAMETER 12 FT. 10 IN.

ELECTRICAL POWER SYSTEM
SPACE RADIATOR PANEL

CM SUPPORT BEAMS

FUEL CELLS (3)

HELIUM TANK
FUEL TANKS

REACTION CONTROL ENGINES
(QUAD)
CRYOGENIC STORAGE TANKS

REACTION CONTROL SYSTEM
QUAD PANEL

OXIDIZER TANKS

VHF SCIMITAR ANTENNA (1 OF 2)

SERVICE PROPULSION SYSTEM
FUEL TANKS

ENVIRONMENTAL CONTROL SYSTEM
SPACE RADIATOR PANEL

STILLWELL AND QUANTITY
MEASUREMENT SYSTEM

RADIAL BEAM
SERVICE PROPULSION ENGINE

S-BAND HIGH-GAIN
ANTENNA

AFT BULKHEAD

AFT BULKHEAD
HEAT SHIELD

82 FT.

COMMAND
MODULE
10 FT. 7 IN.

FAIRING
22 IN.

SERVICE
MODULE
22 FT. 7 IN.

SERVICE PROPULSION ENGINE
NOZZLE

DIAMETER 7 FT. 10 1/2 IN.

Schematic diagram of the Apollo command and service module
combination and the launch escape system. (NASA)

rendezvous and docking operations, and a hatch window. Each window has both inner and outer panes, the former of tempered silica glass and the latter of amorphous-fused silicon. All ultraviolet and most infrared radiation is filtered out by these windows.

Inside the crew compartment, the astronauts spend most of their time on form-fitting, padded couches, but two can stand if the seat portion of the center couch is stowed. Two astronauts at a time can sleep in sleeping bags located underneath the left- and right-hand couches. Food, water, and waste elimination devices are kept in storage bays around the walls of the compartment. The environmental control system maintains a constant temperature of 75 degrees F and an atmospheric pressure of 5 pounds per square inch. Normally, the crew do not wear space suits, donning them only during the launch, docking, crew transfer, and re-entry phases of the mission.

Although the three astronauts are cross-trained, the flight commander (who occupies the left couch) generally operates the flight controls; occasionally the CM pilot (in the center couch) will take over. The latter's principal jobs are to guide and navigate the spacecraft along its trajectory and, when the Apollo has been placed in orbit around the Moon and the Lunar module detached, to monitor the other two astronauts as they make their descent onto the surface. In the right hand couch is the LM pilot; while in the CM, he manages all subsystems. In the event of an emergency, the CM could be handled by any of the three astronauts.

The final compartment of the command module, located aft above the rear heat shield, is divided into twenty-four bays containing propellant, helium, and water tanks; ten reaction control engines; wiring and umbilical connections with the service module; part of the impact attenuation system; and various instruments.

The inner shell of the CM is an aluminum sandwich structure with a welded inner skin, a bonded honeycomb core, and an outer sheet. The outer heat shield is a three-piece structure of brazed honeycomb stainless steel, to which is bonded a phenolic epoxy resin that absorbs heat by burning away, or ablating, as the module descends through the Earth's atmosphere after the long Lunar voyage. The shield weighs some 3,000 pounds and varies in thickness from ½ to 2 inches.

Mounted directly behind the command module is the service module (SM), a cylindrical unit more than 24 feet long and nearly 13 feet in diameter. It weighs about 55,000 pounds when loaded with propellant, and 11,500 pounds when empty. This module contains the principal propulsion system of the Apollo spacecraft, propellant, the electrical system, water, and other supplies. The CM and SM fly together as a unit until the end of the Lunar round trip, when the SM is jettisoned prior to atmospheric entry. It is of honeycomb aluminum alloy, with solid aluminum radial beams separating six pie-shaped sectors. On the exterior of the SM are heat-dissipating radiators tied to the environmental control and electrical subsystems, and small reaction engines for controlling the spacecraft's attitude.

The propulsion system of the service module operates on nitrogen tetroxide and a hypergolic (self-igniting) mixture of hydrazine and unsymmetrical dimethylhydrazine. The engine develops 20,500 pounds of thrust and is used to effect all major changes in velocity once the craft has left its temporary parking orbit around the Earth and begun the voyage to the Moon. Developed by the Aerojet-General Corporation, it can be re-started up to 50 times during a mission. The engine has no throttle, but it can provide small bursts of power by burning for as little as 0.4 second at a time. Normally, the engine receives commands for thrusting from the computer located in the CM, but it can be operated manually.

In addition to the main rocket engine, the service module is fitted with four clusters of small reaction control engines mounted 90 degrees apart around the upper outside structure. In each cluster, two of the Marquardt-made engines are pointed upward and downward, and two in opposite lateral directions. They supply thrust for attitude maneuvers, both emergency and normal, during the flight and are activated either automatically by control signals from the stabilization and control subsystem or manually by an astronaut. Each engine develops about 100 pounds of thrust on a propellant combination of monomethylhydrazine and nitrogen tetroxide. They can be fired both in short bursts and continuously.

The module in which two of the three astronauts descend onto the Moon's surface is the Lunar module, or LM. During flight out to the parking orbit, it is housed in the spacecraft–Lunar module adapter (SLA), a 28-foot-long tapered cylinder between the SM and the instrument unit located above the third stage of the Saturn 5 carrier. After leaving the parking orbit, the combined command and service modules separate from the combined LM, SLA, and S-4B and turn around to dock with the LM, so that the astronauts can later transfer to the landing vehicle. Once the docking is completed, the LM is pulled out of the SLA, whose panels are jettisoned,

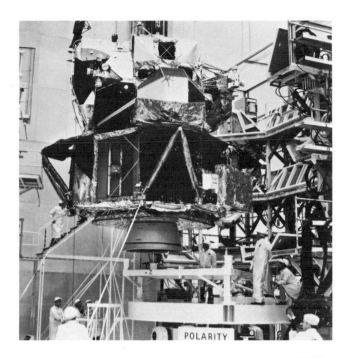

The Lunar module at Cape Kennedy undergoing check-out. (GRUMMAN AIRCRAFT ENGINEERING CORP.)

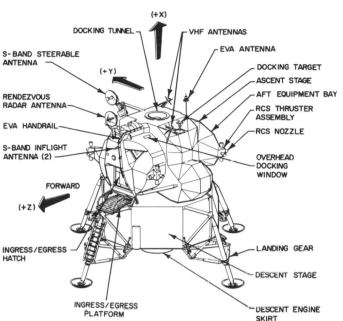

Diagram showing the major external elements of the Lunar module. (GRUMMAN AIRCRAFT ENGINEERING CORP.; NASA)

and the CSM and LM continue to the Moon. The S-4B, meanwhile, is sent into a trajectory that puts it into orbit around the Sun.

Built by Grumman Aircraft Engineering Corporation, the Lunar module has two distinct parts: the descent stage and the ascent stage. Using the rocket engine of the descent stage to brake its landing, the LM settles softly onto the Lunar surface, where it serves as the astronauts' temporary home and base of exploration, communications center, and supply compartment. The descent stage becomes a stationary launch platform from which the ascent stage, with the two astronauts aboard, takes off for Lunar orbit and subsequent rendezvous and docking with the waiting Apollo command and service module combination.

A number of Lunar module vehicles were constructed as part of the research, development, and test program. First came the M series, which were simply mockups; then the TM, or test, series; the LTA, or test article, series; and finally the LM manrated series. Early LM vehicles were tested in Earth orbit, where conditions to be met in flights to the Moon were simulated.

The engine that powers the octagonal descent stage can be throttled from 1,050 to 9,870 pounds thrust and swiveled to permit flight control. Around the engine are located the four main propellant tanks, a variety of scientific equipment, life support and electrical system batteries, and helium, oxygen, and water tanks. The descent stage's landing gear, which is not deployed until after the LM is disconnected from the CSM, consists of four leg-like assemblies fitted with crushable aluminum honeycomb material to help absorb the shock of the landing. Attached to the forward landing leg is a ladder down which the astronauts descend onto the Moon's surface.

The ascent, or return, stage is joined to the descent stage by four fittings, which are disconnected explosively when the upper unit takes off. The major element of this stage is the crew compartment used for both descent and ascent, an aluminum alloy structure with titanium fittings. Of cylindrical shape, it is 7 feet and 8 inches in diameter, 3 feet and 6 inches wide, and arranged with control and display panels, body restraints, forward hatch, overhead hatch, docking tunnel, three windows (two for viewing the Moon and one for docking), landing aids, and accessory equipment. It is protected on the outside by an insulating thermal blanket and a micrometeoroid shield of aluminum sheet. The outer surface also has thermal coatings for additional temperature control. The total pressurized volume of the LM is 235 cubic feet, of which 160 is "habitable" space.

221

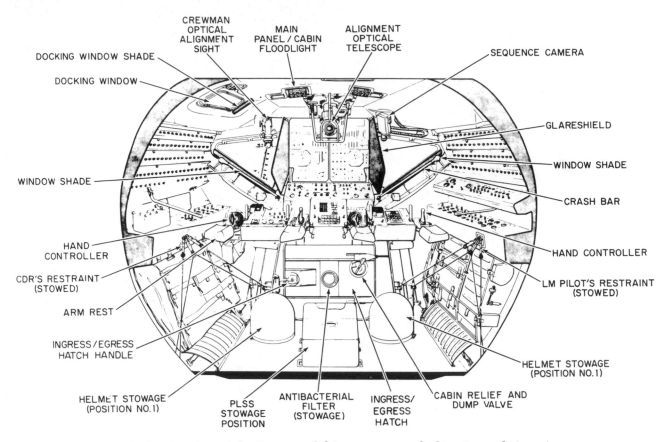

CREWMAN OPTICAL ALIGNMENT SIGHT

MAIN PANEL / CABIN FLOODLIGHT

ALIGNMENT OPTICAL TELESCOPE

DOCKING WINDOW SHADE

DOCKING WINDOW

SEQUENCE CAMERA

GLARESHIELD

WINDOW SHADE

WINDOW SHADE

CRASH BAR

HAND CONTROLLER

HAND CONTROLLER

CDR'S RESTRAINT (STOWED)

ARM REST

LM PILOT'S RESTRAINT (STOWED)

INGRESS/EGRESS HATCH HANDLE

HELMET STOWAGE (POSITION NO.1)

HELMET STOWAGE (POSITION NO.1)

PLSS STOWAGE POSITION

ANTIBACTERIAL FILTER (STOWAGE)

INGRESS/ EGRESS HATCH

CABIN RELIEF AND DUMP VALVE

An interior view of the Lunar module's ascent stage, looking forward. (NASA)

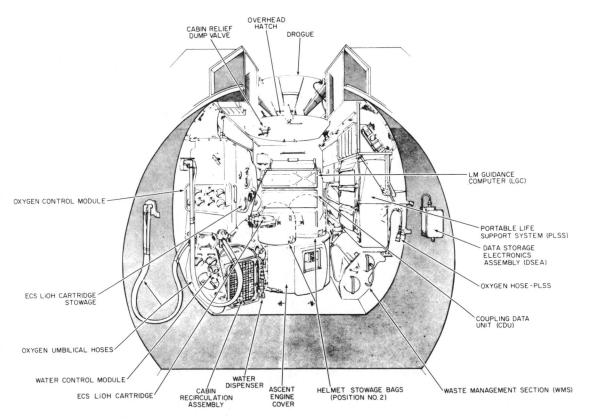

CABIN RELIEF DUMP VALVE

OVERHEAD HATCH

DROGUE

OXYGEN CONTROL MODULE

LM GUIDANCE COMPUTER (LGC)

PORTABLE LIFE SUPPORT SYSTEM (PLSS)

DATA STORAGE ELECTRONICS ASSEMBLY (DSEA)

OXYGEN HOSE-PLSS

ECS LiOH CARTRIDGE STOWAGE

COUPLING DATA UNIT (CDU)

OXYGEN UMBILICAL HOSES

WATER CONTROL MODULE

WATER DISPENSER

ECS LiOH CARTRIDGE

CABIN RECIRCULATION ASSEMBLY

ASCENT ENGINE COVER

HELMET STOWAGE BAGS (POSITION NO. 2)

WASTE MANAGEMENT SECTION (WMS)

An interior view of the Lunar module's ascent stage, looking aft. (NASA)

The LM commander, stationed on the left side of the compartment, handles engine controls, the mission timer, and lighting controls, while the LM pilot, on the right, is responsible for the abort guidance controls. Both are able to see out and below through two triangular windows canted downward and to the side. The windows are electrically heated to avoid any possibility of their becoming fogged. The astronauts exit through the forward hatch in the crew compartment to reach the Moon's surface. To prevent the flow of contaminants out of the hatch while it is open, an anti-bacterial filter is fitted to the cabin air relief and dump valve. A variety of equipment (including personal-hygiene devices, the camera, and tools) are stowed under the control and display panels. From the crew compartment, the astronauts maintain communications with the CSM in orbit around the Moon and with the manned space flight network back on Earth.

Behind the crew compartment is the mid-section, an elliptical area about 5 feet high and 4½ feet deep. It holds numerous items, including a container for Lunar samples, a fire extinguisher, Lunar overshoes, food, the waste management system, and the ascent engine assembly. Overhead is a 33-inch-diameter hatch through which the astronauts transfer themselves and their equipment between the CM and the LM; it can be opened from either side. Above this hatch is the docking tunnel — the structural link between the two modules. The final element of the ascent stage is the aft equipment bay, in which equipment racks and gaseous oxygen and helium tanks are located.

The descent stage is never manned and hence contains no environmental control systems. Since it supports the entire ascent stage and contains more propellant, it is stronger and heavier than its companion. The stage is entirely protected by a thermal and micrometeoroid shield.

Both the descent and the ascent propulsion systems operate in close conjunction with the reaction control system (RCS), which consists of sixteen small 100-pound-thrust rocket engines used to maneuver the LM and control its attitude. The engines are mounted in clusters of four, spaced around the outside of the ascent stage. All operate from the same propellant supply. Since eight of the sixteen engines can provide adequate control of the LM, the two groups of eight engines are independently controlled, providing extra safety through redundancy.

Flight testing for the Apollo manned mission to the Moon began in November 1963, when the launch escape system of a so-called "boilerplate" module,

Interior view of the Lunar module, looking toward the front left hand side and showing the commander's flight station. (GRUMMAN AIRCRAFT ENGINEERING CORP.)

Interior view of the Lunar module, showing the main flight control panels. (NASA)

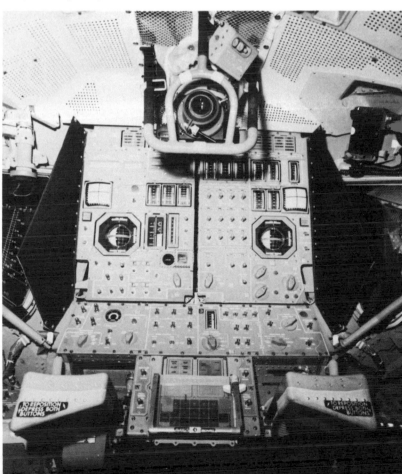

BP-6, was tested at White Sands, New Mexico. In 1964 and 1965, flights were made with Little Joe 2 solid-propellant rockets; and during the Saturn 1 program, engineering test models of the spacecraft were sent into orbit. By the end of February, 1966, Apollo had graduated to the more powerful Saturn 1B, which carried a production model of both the command and the service modules along a suborbital ballistic trajectory. Some 600 measurements radioed back to the ground satisfied engineers that performance was good. Other 1B tests in July and August were also satisfactory. The program seemed to be progressing smoothly.

Then came tragedy. Not in the air. Nor out in the reaches of space. But on the ground. The nation, perhaps grown overconfident from continuous success, was thunderstruck. On 27 January 1967, at Cape Kennedy, astronauts Virgil I. Grissom, Edward H. White, and Roger B. Chaffee died in a flash fire that destroyed an AS-204 spacecraft undergoing routine tests at Launch Complex 34. The three Americans were to have been the first astronauts in the Apollo manned flight program. They would have been boosted into Earth orbit by a Saturn 1B carrier vehicle on 21 February to check out the Apollo in the space environment, during what could have been a two-week trip.

The astronauts had entered the spacecraft, and the entrance hatch was sealed. All three astronauts were in their couches, participating in one of a long series of pre-launch checkouts; Grissom had just stated his intention to change over from external to internal power when, at 6:31 p.m. (EST), a fire of undetermined origin broke out in the cabin and raged for some fourteen seconds. The tragedy came as a shock to the United States' eminently successful space program, which had seen six manned flights in the Mercury program and ten manned missions in the Gemini program, ending with Gemini 12 on 15 November 1966. A total of fourteen United States manned flights carrying twenty-four astronauts (nineteen individuals; some made repeat flights) had accumulated 1,993 man-hours of experience in space since the first United States manned space flight by Alan Shepard on 5 May 1961; meanwhile, the Russians had accumulated only 507 man-hours with eleven cosmonauts, who made a total of eight flights.

After the fire, extensive investigations were made to learn its cause and to determine what could be done to prevent similar accidents. In April, NASA's Apollo Review Board, established under Dr. Floyd L. Thompson, Director of the Langley Research Center, issued its findings. The Board concluded that the "most probable initiator [of the fire] was an electrical arc," the exact location of which was unknown. Most probably, the Board said, the arc was "near the floor in the lower forward section of the left-hand equipment bay where environmental control system instrumentation power wiring leads into the area between the environmental control unit and the oxygen panel. No evidence was discovered that suggested sabotage." The Review Board gave a series of recommendations — technical as well as managerial — for preventing a recurrence of the accident in the future.

NASA moved as quickly as possible to reduce to an absolute minimum the dangers of fire aboard the command module in particular, and aboard the entire spacecraft in general. It was decided, first of all, to change the cabin atmosphere from 100 percent oxygen to a mixture of 60 percent oxygen and 40 percent nitrogen, and to employ non-combustible materials at every possible place. The matter of atmospheric composition had been considered at great length, and despite weight increases, this decision was universally approved. It was also decided to provide a new aluminum and fiber-glass access hatch that could be opened from the inside in a matter of ten seconds. The astronauts' space suits also were re-designed to incorporate non-flammable glass fabric. Flameproof coatings were placed on wire connections, plastic switches were replaced with metal ones, and an emergency oxygen system was installed to isolate the crew in case toxic fumes began to fill the module. The changes increased the weight of the CM by about 1,400 pounds.

During 1967, three other space fliers also died. Soviet cosmonaut Vladimir M. Komarov's death in April has been mentioned. The deaths of two Americans did not involve space activities: Edward G. Givens was killed in an automobile accident near Houston, Texas, on 6 June; and Clifton C. Williams died in the crash of his T-38 jet plane near Tallahassee, Florida, on 5 October.

Despite temporary setbacks — the fire being by far the worst — development of the Saturn-Apollo system progressed essentially on schedule, according to a series of discrete, well-planned steps. In the first phase of the program, the spacecraft was tested and crew operations procedures were developed. Saturn 1B's were flight tested in 1966 with the launching of vehicles AS-201, AS-202, and AS-203. Manned flight, the second development phase, was not destined to take place until autumn of 1968, when Apollo 7 was launched by Saturn 1B vehicle AS-205. (The AS-204 fire had temporarily slowed flight testing, although the carrier itself was later used in the Apollo 5 mission.)

The third development phase consisted of checking the flight performance of the Lunar module — the one as yet untested element of Apollo. The initial unmanned orbital test of the LM was made on 22 January 1968 as part of the Apollo 5 mission. Its objectives were to verify the operation of LM subsystems and staging and to evaluate the orbital performance of the Saturn 1B's S-4B stage with instrumentation unit. The Lunar module descent stage propulsion system was ignited in orbit, on three separate occasions, followed by two successful ignitions of the ascent stage propulsion motor. The Apollo 5 mission lasted approximately 7 hours and 50 minutes; no attempt at recovery of the orbittested Lunar module was attempted.

Meanwhile, in the fourth development phase, the much larger and more powerful Saturn 5 was being prepared for its initial unmanned flight. The ability of this carrier to bring the command module to a velocity equaling that to be attained on a return trip from the Moon was a key factor in the first Saturn 5 flight test, on 9 November 1967. In this Apollo 4 mission, the huge carrier functioned flawlessly, lifting off from Launch Complex 39 at Cape Kennedy within 1 second of the planned time. It lofted CSM-017 into a 110-mile circular orbit, in what turned out to be a highly successful test of Apollo

hardware. The total weight placed in orbit was 278,699 pounds, a world's record — an almost incredible increase over the 31-pound Explorer 1 satellite orbited a mere decade earlier.

Shortly after entering into its initial orbit, the S-4B stage fired a second time, inserting the CSM into an elliptical orbit with a 10,703-mile apogee. Next, the service module's propulsion system fired for 16 seconds, raising the apogee to 11,232 miles and proving that the motor could ignite and cut off in a vacuum. Later, it re-ignited and burned for a total of 271 seconds, pushing the command module to a re-entry speed of 24,911 miles per hour, to simulate Lunar return re-entry speeds. The CM was recovered near Midway Island, less than five miles from the designated target recovery point, ending a flight that was astonishingly successful from almost every point of view. Not only did it represent a victory for carrier vehicle technology — the Saturn 5 was fired with all stages active on its first flight — but it proved that the vast array of Apollo ground support equipment was capable of almost flawless operation.

The second flight in the Saturn 5 series, designated Apollo 6, was accomplished on 4 April 1968. The payload was CSM-020, which was equipped with a modified hatch, handrails, and a Block II heat shield, plus Lunar module test article LTA-2R. The objectives of the flight were to demonstrate the

The crawler-transporter carries the 363-foot-high Saturn 5 carrier vehicle (right) past the huge vertical assembly building (center) and the launch control center
blockhouse (left) during "rollout" to Launch Pad B of Complex 39 at Cape Kennedy. (NASA)

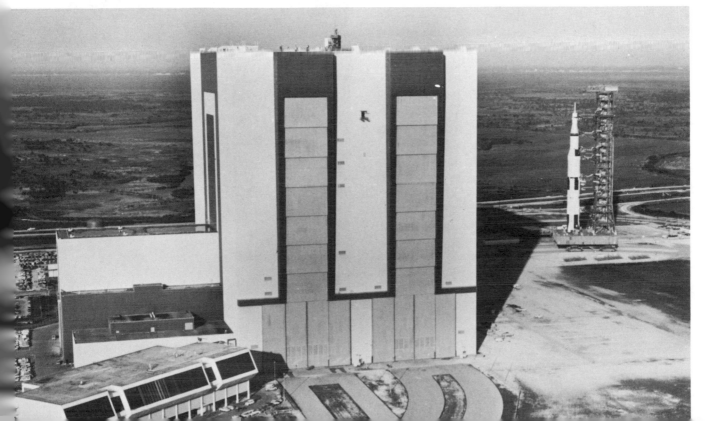

structural and thermal integrity and compatibility of the carrier vehicle and the spacecraft; confirm launch loads and dynamic characteristics; demonstrate all aspects of stage separation; verify the operations of vehicular systems; and, in general, further test mission support facilities and operations.

The S-1C (first) stage of the Saturn 5 fired according to plan, but two engines in the S-2 (second) stage shut down early. Because of the reduced fuel consumption, the total burning time of the remaining three engines increased from 369 to 427 seconds. In its initial burn, the S-4B third-stage engine was fired for 170 seconds instead of the programmed 141, in order to compensate for the less-than-expected velocity at the time the S-2 stage cut off. However, three orbits later, the S-4B engine would not re-start as planned; it was to have fired a second time for slightly more than 5 minutes, sending the vehicle into a trajectory similar to the trans-Lunar path (about 320,000 miles long) but not in the direction of the Moon. The S-4B and the CSM were then to have been separated — the former continuing outward and the latter transferring to a highly elliptical Earth orbit following a retroburn for 4 minutes and 14 seconds of the service module propulsion system. Since the S-4B would not re-start, mission controllers separated the CSM from the S-4B and used the engine on the service module to lift the craft to a 13,831-mile apogee — from where re-entry began. Although the CSM did not achieve the re-entry velocity that had been planned, a velocity considerably in excess of Earth orbital entry was realized, and the capsule's recovery system worked well.

On 11 October 1968, six months after the completion of fourth-phase testing of the unmanned CSM in Saturn 5 flights, the second development phase — manned testing of the CSM with the smaller but proven Saturn 1B carrier — began with the flight of Apollo 7. This first manned Apollo flight was commanded by Navy Captain Walter M. Schirra, Jr., veteran of both the Mercury MA-8 (Sigma 7) mission in October 1962 and the Gemini 6 in mid-December 1965. His companion astronauts were Major Donn F. Eisele of the Air Force and civilian physicist Walter Cunningham. Their command and service vehicle, CSM101, was the first of the re-designed Block II units, incorporating all the improvements made since the AS-204 capsule fire.

The routine was stiff during the 10-day and 20-hour mission, in which the crew logged 780 space man-hours. On a 16-hours-on, 8-hours-off schedule, the astronauts had to perform an impressive, and often exhausting, series of tasks that included manual control of the S-4B stage of the Saturn 5 carrier

before separation; rendezvous with the separated S-4B stage, followed by transposition of the CSM and a simulated docking maneuver with the S-4B stage; optical tracking of the S-4B after separation from the spacecraft; measurement of the performance of the propulsion and propellant gauging systems; navigational exercises using landmarks and stars; checkout of the guidance system's inertial measurement unit in flight; and collection of data on performance of the CM's forward heat shield during re-entry.

The Apollo 7 performed well throughout its complex mission. The initial perigee was 137.9 miles, and the apogee 173.6; but subsequent maneuvering in orbit changed these figures several times. For nearly two hours the spacecraft remained attached to the S-4B stage before the command was given for the separation. Later, employing the 20,500-pound-thrust

Apollo 7 astronauts Schirra (center), Cunningham (left), and Eisele (right) walk through the shower tunnel as they leave the umbilical tower elevator at Launch Complex 34, Cape Kennedy. (NASA)

Astronaut Walter M. Schirra, Jr., Apollo 7 commander, emerges from the command module in Downey, California, following testing. (NORTH AMERICAN ROCKWELL CORP.)

nauts aboard the craft was live — a "first" in the United States manned space program — and the audience numbered in the millions. Among the many experiments assigned to the mission was synoptic terrain photography of land and sea areas. This was done primarily for geoscientists and oceanographers, but also to evaluate various types of film. Global weather patterns were also photographed. In addition, a number of medical tests were conducted, including studies of blood, bone demineralization, and cardiovascular deconditioning resulting from prolonged weightlessness.

Like the orbital flight, the re-entry went smoothly — "a nice, gentle, constant 3G trip," according to Eisele. Splashdown occurred southeast of Bermuda, less than eight miles from the primary recovery ship, at 7:12 A.M. (EDT) on 22 October. In a relatively rough sea, Apollo 7 turned nose down so that its antennas were under water — an event that somewhat delayed recovery. Nevertheless, the command module was located by an SH-3 helicopter, frogmen were lowered, and soon the three astronauts were aboard it — bound for the *Essex*, their recovery ship.

Apollo's fifth development phase called for manned operation of the three modules in orbit around the Earth, this time using the Saturn 5 as the carrier. The sixth phase called for circumnavigation of the Moon, with perhaps a pause to orbit it.

Astronauts Eisele (foreground) and Schirra (right), observed performing in-flight tasks during Apollo 7 in a television transmission received by the manned space flight network. (NASA)

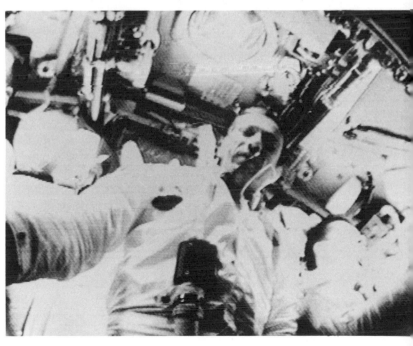

service module rocket engine, the Apollo 7 was brought into position to commence the rendezvous maneuver. From an orbit somewhat higher than that of the S-4B stage, the spacecraft began to catch up with it. When they were about 20 miles behind, the astronauts observed that the stage had begun tumbling in space. The spacecraft then approached to within 5 feet in a simulated docking maneuver.

Apollo 7 was as nearly perfect as one can rightfully expect a development flight to be. Of course, there were some minor problems. Schirra, and then his companions, came down with annoying colds (though their performance was unimpaired, despite their heavy workload during the 163 orbits); and they were bothered by fogging windows, an errant oxygen sensor, and tripping of a couple of circuit breakers due to current overloading.

Television coverage of the activities of the astro-

Lengthy engineering analyses of Saturn 5's performance in the Apollo 6 (AS-502) flight had revealed problems involving longitudinal oscillations and the behavior of the propellant utilization system. Despite the difficulties, studies made during the winter of 1967 and the spring of 1968 led to confidence in the ability of Saturn 5 vehicle AS-503 to perform a manned mission sometime before the end of the year. By the summer of 1968, however, it became apparent that serious delays were developing in the checkout of Lunar module Number 3 at Cape Kennedy, and that it would not be ready for flight until late winter or early spring of 1969. But CSM-103 could be made ready for AS-503. With these facts at hand, it was decided to reverse the fifth and sixth phases and go for the circum-Lunar-orbit shot first.

Apollo 8 went out to the Moon. It went around the Moon. And it returned to the Earth from the Moon. Its virtually unqualified success made it at once a superb monument to human ingenuity, a stunning technological and scientific undertaking, and a thrilling spectacle. In a matter of days, the Solar System seemed to shrink a little as mankind realized that a once impossibly distant frontier had been cracked.

The Saturn 5 performed as expected, boosting Apollo 8 onto the trans-Lunar trajectory four days before Christmas 1968. Colonel Frank Borman, the commander; Lieutenant Colonel William A. Anders; and Captain James A. Lovell, Jr., fully understood that the Lunar mission had inherent risks not present in Earth-orbital flights. The SM's propulsion system had to function to power the spacecraft out of Lunar orbit and back to Earth; and when in orbit around the Moon, the three astronauts would be three *days* rather than an hour or so away — a grave physical and psychological factor.

To reduce risks to a minimum, every possible attention was given to ensure that all systems, subsystems, and components would perform faultlessly. And insofar as feasible, redundant systems were built into the vehicles so that if one failed, the desired function could still be performed by a duplicate system. Moreover, the mission was planned so that it could be terminated at several critical points: at launch, in the temporary parking orbit around the Earth, and prior to entry into Lunar orbit — in the last case, by taking advantage of the "free return" circum-Lunar trajectory.

The trip outward to the Moon was gratifyingly uneventful for the mission planners, for those who were monitoring it, and, of course, for the astronauts themselves. The spacecraft was first placed in an

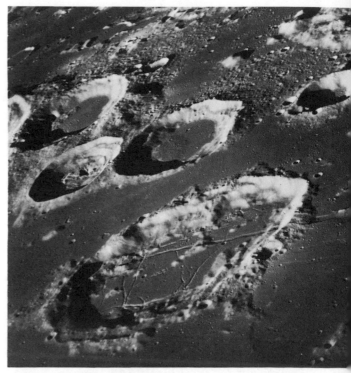

The large crater Goclenius was photographed during Apollo 8 as the spacecraft orbited the Moon. A prominent rille crosses the 35-mile-diameter crater, which is located at 10 degrees south latitude and 45 degrees east longitude. The three-crater grouping at top left consists of Magelhaens, Magelhaens A, and Colombo A. (NASA)

orbit ranging from about 110 miles to 117 miles in altitude. On the second orbit around the Earth, the S-4B stage's J-2 engine was fired for more than 5 minutes, bringing the craft up to escape velocity and onto the trans-Lunar trajectory. At 3 hours and 21 minutes into the mission, the CSM was separated from the S-4B, which then moved off into orbit around the Sun. And at a little more than 55½ hours after liftoff, while traveling 2,200 miles per hour, Apollo 8 passed the neutral point where the gravitational fields of the Earth and Moon balance each other.

After the craft had swung around the rear of the Moon, steps were taken to circularize the orbit to 70 miles above the surface. To accomplish this, the main rocket engine of the service module was fired twice. Almost immediately upon arrival in Lunar orbit, the astronauts commenced photographing the spectacular scene beneath them. They became the first human beings to observe the far side of the Moon, which they reported was more rugged than the near side. Their verbal impressions were invaluable to astronomers, physicists, geologists, and geochemists back on Earth — who learned, for example, that the surface is grayish-white ("like dirty beach sand"); that many of the craters appear to be rounded (which implies that the Moon once might have had an atmosphere); and that the craters look as though they had been made "by meteorites or projectiles of some sort." Observations also were made of potential landing areas for later Apollo crews, one in particular attracting them ("it's a great spot"). Borman philosophized: "The Moon is a different thing to each of us — each one carries his own impression of what he's seen today. I know my own impression is that it's a vast, lonely, forbidding-type existence — a great expanse of nothing that looks rather like clouds and clouds of pumice stone. It certainly would not appear to be a very inviting place to live or work."

A variety of photographic equipment was carried on the Apollo 8 mission, including two 70-mm Hasselblad still cameras, each fitted with 80-mm f/2.8 to f/22 Zeiss Planar lenses, a 250-mm telephoto lens, a 16-mm Maurer motion picture camera with variable frame speed selection, and an assortment of accessories. Lunar stereo strip photography provided invaluable data for later terrain analysis.

The communications links between spacecraft and Earth worked well, with messages from the Lunar orbit being received at the Houston Mission Control Center and placed on the display board in but 6 seconds. More than 50,000 data information bits were received each second by the world-wide tracking network. Live television broadcasts were conducted directly from the astronauts in Lunar orbit. The clarity of communications throughout the mission was excellent.

When it came time to return home, after ten revolutions in the Lunar parking orbit, the service module propulsion system was fired for 3 minutes and 23 seconds. The return journey was completely routine, and re-entry into the Earth's atmosphere was so successful that the command module landed in the Pacific Ocean less than three miles from the predicted point of splashdown, and just eleven minutes behind schedule. Man's first trip out to the Moon — though not yet onto the Moon — was over.

The Apollo 8 flight, wonderful though it was, did not put man in a position to attempt a Lunar landing. The fifth phase in the Apollo development program — manned testing of the Lunar module by simulating in Earth orbit the operations to be undertaken later in Lunar orbit — still had to be carried out. The step was a crucial, and extremely complex, one.

Apollo 9 was as successful as it was difficult. Aside from a brief delay in launching (from 28 Feb-

Firing Room 2 at the Launch Control Center, Cape Kennedy, where the Apollo 9 flight is being monitored. (NASA)

ruary to 3 March) due to an outbreak of colds among the astronauts, everything went as planned. Once in space, Colonel James A. McDivitt, the mission commander, and David R. Scott, pilot of the command module, experienced no further illness; but Russell L. Schweickart, the Lunar module pilot, suffered brief nausea both before and after transferring from the CSM to the LM.

It took about 11 minutes for the Saturn 5 to place Apollo 9 in a circular orbit nearly 112 miles above the Earth. In a mission that was a good 25 percent more difficult than earlier Apollo flights, the astronauts were faced with a heavy work schedule. During the first orbit around the Earth, Scott activated the explosive bolts to separate the spacecraft from the S-4B stage, then spent a quarter of an hour photographing it and the LM tucked into the adapter section. The protective shroud adapter was then removed, followed by docking of the CM with the LM and withdrawal of the latter from the S-4B stage. (For the first time, the S-4B was re-ignited twice in a mission, to test its quick re-start characteristics; on the second re-start, the stage was fired into heliocentric orbit.)

During the second day, the crew fully exercised the service module's propulsion system, moving their craft out toward the optimum orbit for the series of rendezvous maneuvers that were to come. On the third day, McDivitt and Schweickart transferred from the CM to the LM, where they checked out the onboard systems and fired the descent engine over a range of thrust levels. During this time, the service module propulsion system was ignited for the fifth time to circularize the CSM-LM orbit at 155 miles.

Once in this new orbit, Schweickart took a 38-minute space walk, emerging through the LM hatch dressed in a Lunar pressure suit and carrying a portable life support system on his back. This life support unit, tested for later Lunar landings, provided communications, oxygen, and circulating water for cooling the suit. Using minimum cooling settings, Schweickart reported to ground control that "the suit is very comfortable . . . and I haven't had any problem at all — the only things that are warm at all are my hands." Among Schweickart's tasks in space were retrieval of some test objects from outside the LM and photography of the Earth below. Back inside his spacecraft, he told of his adventures in a ten-minute television broadcast.

The fifth day of the mission was at once the most difficult and the most important; upon its successful completion hinged the decision on when to go for the Lunar landing itself. First, the LM and the CSM were separated to a distance of about 3 miles, and later to 15 miles. A third propulsion maneuver separated the LM by about 100 miles from the CSM. The LM then began rendezvous maneuvers that brought it close to the CSM, with which it later docked. McDivitt and Schweickart transferred back into the CM, ending more than 8 hours of exhausting separation, orbit-changing, rendezvous, and docking exercises.

The success of these exercises was complete. Reflecting on the rendezvous and docking after the mission was over, McDivitt reported:

. . . we used our radar throughout the entire maneuver. It [the CSM] was out to about a hundred miles. And the radar performed superbly. We came back into a range of about 35 miles and began our terminal phase of the rendezvous, where we initiate a maneuver that brings us up underneath the Command Module . . . to his altitude . . . the things that had proved to be so difficult in simulations, where [we] had to make decisions between solutions that were considerably apart — that portion of the difficulty just evaporated, because everybody agreed with everybody else. . . . We made this transfer and came right on up to the Command Module. We saw it at about 2½ miles or so, just where we were supposed to see it. There was a very small portion of light that looks somewhat like a moon, except with blunt ends on it, and sort of crescent shape, but not quite. And, as we came in closer, it appears as a nice shiny circle. We then went ahead with the LM active docking.

The nine days remaining in the flight were relatively relaxing for the crew. The LM's ascent engine was fired, pushing the craft into an orbit more than 4,000 miles high. From the CSM, orbiting far below, the astronauts did some landmark tracking and photography, and developed means of orienting their craft for optimum performance of these jobs.

Like the rest of the mission, re-entry and recovery went like clockwork. Because of rough weather in the originally planned landing area, Apollo 9 made an extra orbit and came down 500 miles to the south at 12:01 P.M. (EST) on 13 March — some 300 miles north of Puerto Rico and three miles from the prime recovery ship, the *Guadalcanal*. Splashdown was but ten seconds late.

Apollo 10, in broad terms, was a repeat of Apollo 8, with the Lunar module acrobatics of Apollo 9 added to the excitement. It was the first flight that proved the feasibility of Lunar orbit rendezvous, and the first to take man within 10 miles of the surface of the Moon. Apollo 10 also served as a test of the LM's descent propulsion system not only in the Lunar landing configuration but in the Lunar environment.

Photographed from the CSM, the LM orbits the Earth during the fifth day of the Apollo 9 mission. Astronauts McDivitt and Schweickart are in the LM, while Scott has remained in the CSM. (NASA)

The splashdown of Apollo 9 took place at 12:01 P.M. on 13 March 1969, more than 800 miles southeast of Cape Kennedy. (NASA)

The Apollo 9 command module being lowered by crane from the USS Guadalcanal to the naval station dock at Norfolk, Virginia. (U.S. NAVY)

And the landing radar was employed in conditions where the reflected energy of the surface below was detected. Apollo 10 was a full dress rehearsal for Apollo 11, except for the powered descent from perilune, the actual landing, ground activity, and finally take-off and ascent.

The 6,407,000-pound Saturn 5 vehicle AS-505 went through its countdown uneventfully, except for the discovery of a pressure drop in the helium lines that pressurize the LM's reaction control system propellant tanks. The trouble was soon traced to a loose electrical connection, and the countdown was resumed. Take-off was on schedule, at 12:49 P.M. on 18 May 1969, and soon afterward Air Force Colonel Thomas P. Stafford (commander), Commander John W. Young (CM pilot), and Commander Eugene A. Cernan (LM pilot) were on their way toward the Moon.

As in Apollo 8, they first entered a temporary, or parking, orbit around the Earth. On the second swing around (about 2½ hours after launch), Saturn 5's third stage re-ignited and injected Apollo 10 onto its trans-Lunar trajectory. A couple of hours later, the CSM separated, made the transposition maneuver, docked with the LM, and then withdrew it from the spacecraft–Lunar module adapter on the third stage.

Launching and transposition over, it was time for a well-deserved 10-hour rest and sleep cycle. Upon awakening, Stafford reported that "all three of us feel great." One minor worry was that the small attitude control rockets had been firing too much and might deplete their propellant supply — but ground control said all was well. The crew later complained about their water supply: "The water is absolutely horrible. I got a horrible slug of chlorine; my mouth is still burning. John did, too. I just want to put that on the record." Communications most of the time were so clear, and the news coverage so intense, that these words of Stafford's along with many other conversations involving routine matters were soon known around the world. The three astronauts were awed by the experience of traveling through space. On looking back at the receding Earth, Cernan marveled, "You blink your eyes and look out there . . . and you know it's three dimensional. But it's just sitting out there in the middle of nowhere. It's unbelievable!" Almost as an afterthought, he added, "Just for the record, it looks like a pretty nice place to live!"

During the 73-hour trans-Lunar coast, they prepared for mid-course corrections (so accurate was their path that a second correction planned for the afternoon of 20 May was not needed); chatted with mission control at Houston; made television transmissions to the Goldstone tracking station; and exercised, navigated, rested, and got ready for the strenuous days ahead. As Stafford put it, "We've got a little time to kill here, so we're going over our Lunar activities — just doing our homework so we'll be ahead of the game when we get there."

At 10:19 A.M. (EDT), during a sleep period, Apollo 10 passed within the sphere of influence of the Lunar gravitational field and commenced accelerating. At approximately 75 hours and 45 minutes into the mission (ground elapsed time), the SM's propulsion system ignited and inserted the spacecraft into elliptical orbit—which, after about two trips around the Moon, was circularized at an altitude of 60 miles. Once in this orbit, the astronauts rested for about 8 hours before beginning their crucial Lunar orbit acrobatics.

Instead of referring to the components of their space vehicle as command and service modules and Lunar module, the crew adopted the nicknames "Charlie Brown" and "Snoopy." So, when it came time for Stafford and Cernan to transfer to the LM, they reported leaving Charlie Brown and going over to Snoopy. Once the two astronauts were there, the reaction control-system (RCS) of the SM was fired briefly to separate the CSM from the LM by about 30 feet. As soon as the CM pilot, Young, reported that Snoopy was looking well, the RCS was fired to

further separate the vehicles. The LM's descent propulsion system was then fired, bringing Snoopy into an orbit with a maximum altitude of about 48,000 feet at about 15 degrees from the planned landing site of the Apollo 11 mission.

The close approach was thrilling to behold. "Hello, Houston, Houston, this is Snoopy. We just saw Earth rise, and it's gotta be magnificent!" exclaimed Cernan. The Moon, he said, was beautiful... There's so many things to do in such a short time. Things seem to come over the horizon at you. Okay, we're coming on Apollo Ridge . . . on my right. There's Apollo Rille right in front of my window. It appears to be just a couple of hundred feet. . . . Man, I tell you we are low. We are close, babe." Stafford joined in, observing that "there's enough boulders around here to fill up Galveston Bay. . . . It's a fantastic sight. We have different shades of brown and grays here."

Snoopy's next task was to get back to Charlie Brown by simulating the orbit that the Apollo 11 Lunar module would travel when it actually ascended from the Moon's surface. By firing the descent propulsion system, Snoopy was shifted to a new orbit with a perilune of about 60,000 feet.

Just before arriving at its new perilune, Snoopy's descent stage was jettisoned; and at perilune, the ascent propulsion system took over. At the moment of separation of the descent and the ascent stages, the craft vibrated severely, causing an alarmed Cernan to yell, "This son of a bitch! Hit the AGS! Hit the AGS!" — referring to the abort guidance system. Within seconds, Stafford had Snoopy under control,

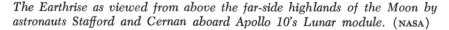

The Earthrise as viewed from above the far-side highlands of the Moon by astronauts Stafford and Cernan aboard Apollo 10's Lunar module. (NASA)

and the maneuver toward rendezvous with Charlie Brown continued. Cernan said later that he didn't "know what the hell that was, baby, but that was something. I thought we were wobbling all over the sky."

Ground control reported at the time that a guidance system switch was not positioned properly — that it was set for "attitude hold," causing the LM to try to orient itself to the CSM, and to tilt off angle and vibrate in the process. Ground control theorized that instructions for the switch had been inadvertently omitted from a revised set of operating procedures given to the astronauts, and that a subsequent voice instruction had not been acted upon because of garbled communications.

After the mission, during their debriefing in Houston, the astronauts explained that when the LM began gyrating, Stafford had manually separated the upper and lower stages and then brought the upper stage under control. Stafford said that the gyration was due to a change-over from one mode of automatic control to another, and not from a faulty switch setting.

The crisis over, Snoopy's ascent stage went through the various sequences remaining for rendezvous and docking. Once the LM and CSM were coupled together, the tired pair of astronauts transferred (with their exposed film and Hasselblad camera) into the mother craft. The remaining fuel for Snoopy's ascent propulsion system was burned, sending the ascent stage into orbit around the Sun. (The descent stage remained in Lunar orbit, in a path ranging from 11 to 218 miles above the surface.) This done, all three astronauts took a well-deserved rest.

Despite the harrowing experience, the trio did not lose their enthusiasm for the mission. For several hours, they took pictures of the Moon and pointed their television cameras down at the surface passing below them so that Earthlings could join in their sense of wonderment. "This satellite of ours," said Cernan, ". . . really had a rough beginning back there somewhere." Later, he added that he had always believed nothing was impossible, and "now I'm convinced of it. I hope that what we're doing here, and what's going to go on in the future is going to be something that's going to be a betterment to all mankind."

At 6:25 A.M. on 24 May, during the thirty-first orbit, the time arrived to ignite the service module's engine to inject Charlie Brown onto the return trajectory back to Earth. "We are returning to Earth," calmly advised Stafford — following a few minutes later with "This burn was absolutely beautiful. And we've got an absolutely beautiful view of the Moon."

So nearly perfect was the firing that ground trackers told the astronauts that only minor mid-course corrections would be required during the 246,283-mile trip home.

The return coast went smoothly, with communications being maintained until atmospheric entry. The drogue parachutes were deployed at about 23,300 feet, and splashdown occurred some 14 minutes after re-entry. The entire trip lasted 8 days and 3 minutes (a minute shorter than expected), including approximately 76 hours on the outward leg, consisting of launch, Earth parking orbit, and trans-Lunar coast; 61½ hours in Lunar orbit; and 54 hours on the return leg. Total length of the voyage was about 700,000 miles. Landing took place within three miles of the recovery ship *Princeton* (a helicopter carrier), about 400 miles east of the Pacific island of Tutuila in American Samoa.

The landing on the Moon, realized during the Apollo 11 mission, was the greatest technological triumph in the long and tortuous chronicle of mankind. The apotheosis of an age-old dream, it represented the highest motives and capabilities of the human mind. For the first time since life was spawned in the primeval "soup," creatures from Earth left their planetary cradle and strode upon an alien world. Man the infant became man the man.

President John F. Kennedy had declared in May 1961:

I believe that this nation should commit itself to achieving the goal, before this decade is out, of landing [a man] on the Moon and returning him safely to Earth. . . .

Apollo 11 was the fulfillment of this pledge. President Kennedy had been able to make the commitment partly because of his faith in the present generation of American scientific, engineering, industrial, and management genius, and partly because he realized the time was right to translate the progress and ambitions of centuries into reality. But when Apollo 11 soared into the heavens, it rode as much on the shoulders of the giants of yesteryear as of those now living. Aristarchus, Copernicus, Newton, Einstein, Tsiolkovsky, Goddard, Oberth, Esnault-Pelterie, and countless others down the corridors of time all contributed to the epochal event.

It will be the task of future historians to assess the full impact on a struggling humanity of the first manned landing on the Moon. It seems clear, however, that man has reached a crossroads in his quest for knowledge—that he can never again be quite the same. The limits of the new era that has dawned will be defined only by man's ultimate intellectual

Apollo 11 Commander Neil A. Armstrong (left) was the first man to set foot on the Moon. Armstrong and the Lunar module pilot, Edwin E. Aldrin, Jr. (right), col- *lected samples on the Lunar surface, deployed scientific instruments, and then rejoined Michael Collins (center) in the command module.* (NASA)

capabilities and by the energy with which he pursues his goals. As Robert H. Goddard wrote in 1922: "There can be no thought of finishing, for aiming at the stars, both literally and figuratively, is the work of generations, but no matter how much progress one makes there is always the thrill of just beginning."

At 9:32 A.M. (EDT) on 16 July 1969, hundreds of thousands of spectators in the Cape Kennedy, Florida, area and hundreds of millions of television viewers all around the world watched spellbound as the beginning passed into history. Saturn 5 performed its AS-506 mission in accordance to plan, placing the S-4B third stage, the instrumentation unit, and the Apollo 11 spacecraft, with astronauts Neil A. Armstrong, Colonel Edwin E. Aldrin, Jr.,

and Lieutenant Colonel Michael Collins aboard, into a temporary parking orbit of from 114.6 to 116.6 miles above the surface of the Earth. (Should anything have gone wrong prior to or during launch, the solid-propellant escape rocket system would have lifted the command module away from the malfunctioning carrier; the CM would have then returned to the ground by parachute.) The instrumentation unit's guidance system computed the exact moment for the S-4B stage to re-ignite in order to insert the spacecraft into its trans-Lunar path. The course was carefully selected so that, should the engine of the service module have later failed to ignite and thus not brought the Apollo 11 into Lunar orbit, the craft would have swung around the Moon and returned

The Apollo Saturn 5 space vehicle carrying Apollo 11 astronauts Neil A. Armstrong, Michael Collins, and Edwin E. Aldrin, Jr., lifted off at 9:32 A.M. (EDT) on 16 July 1969, to begin the first United States manned Lunar landing mission. (NASA)

to Earth along a so-called "free return" circum-Lunar trajectory. After 5.9 minutes of operation, the S-4B stage engine cut off, leaving the spacecraft with an initial velocity of nearly 24,300 miles per hour. Mission commander Armstrong was enthusiastic: "Hey, Houston, this Saturn gave us a magnificent ride. We have no complaints with any of the three stages on that ride. It was beautiful!" Apollo 11 then began its long coast to the Moon. So accurate was the injection onto trans-Lunar trajectory that the first of four planned mid-course corrections was canceled.

Early in the coasting period, while the S-4B was still attached to the spacecraft, the transposition and docking maneuver took place, with propulsion provided by the service module's engine. After the linked command and service modules had turned around and docked with the Lunar module, and the crew was certain that all docking latch and electrical umbilical connections had been made, the LM's four connections to the spacecraft–Lunar module adapter were explosively severed. The LM was then withdrawn from the SLA and the S-4B stage by spring thrusters. The overall maneuver used up more propellant than planned, causing command module pilot Collins to inform mission control: "I expected to be out about 66 feet. My guess would be that I was around 100 or so, and therefore I expect I used a little more gas coming back in." Other than that, everything went according to the book.

At a distance of more than 130,000 miles from Earth, the service module propulsion system was ignited for just under 3 seconds to make a minor trajectory correction. The astronauts staged their first regularly scheduled color television report to the world at approximately 34 hours into the mission (ground elapsed time). They also undertook navigational and housekeeping chores, ate, slept, and reported on the view. As in earlier flights, Apollo 11's crew was inspired by sight of the receding Earth. Said Aldrin, at 12:46 P.M. (EDT) on 17 July:

The view is out of this world. I can see all the islands in the Mediterranean . . . Majorca, Sardinia, Corsica, a little haze over the upper Italian peninsula, a few cumulus clouds out over Greece, Sun setting on the eastern Mediterranean now. . . .

Less than an hour later, Collins added:

I've got the world in my window for a change, and looking at it through the monocular it's really something. I wish I could describe it properly. But the weather is very good. South America is coming around into view. I can see, on what appears to me to be upper horizon, a point that must be just about Seattle, Washington. And

235

Apollo spaceship and escape tower atop the three-stage Saturn 5 prior to launch at Cape Kennedy. The entire launch vehicle stands 363 feet tall.

Command and service modules (foreground) separate from the Lunar module and from the third stage of the Saturn 5 carrier.

CSM turns around and docks with LM. Two astronauts transfer to the LM, a third remains on the CSM. CSM and LM go into orbit around the Moon.

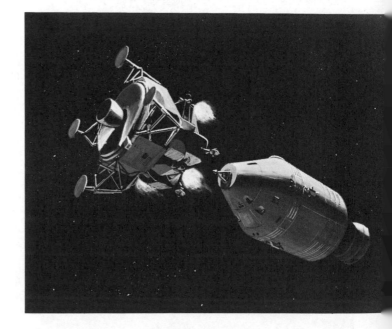

Astronauts detach LM from CSM and direct it downward toward Lunar surface. CSM, with one astronaut, continues in orbit.

Selected events of Apollo's trip to the Moon and return.

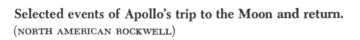

(NORTH AMERICAN ROCKWELL)

236

On the Moon. One astronaut gathers specimens to take back to Earth, while the other watches from the LM.

Using bottom section as launch pad, top section of LM blasts off from Moon to return crew to CSM. LM remains in orbit around Moon; CSM returns to Earth.

Approaching Earth's atmosphere, command module breaks away, leaving service module behind.

The command module, slowed by three parachutes, lands softly in water. Helicopters arrive to pick up crew.

from there I can see all the way down to . . . Tierra del Fuego in the southern tip of the continent.

The astronauts were kept fully informed on the progress of the Soviet Luna 15 probe, which settled into Lunar orbit while Apollo 11 was still en route. Mission control at Houston also informed them that

. . . President Nixon is reported to have declared a Day of Participation on Monday the [21st] for all Federal employees, to enable everybody to follow your activities on the surface. Many state and city governments and businesses throughout the country have also given their employees the day off. So, it looks like you are going to have a pretty large audience for the EVA [extra-vehicular activity].

The trip continued uneventfully, the spacecraft rotating at a few revolutions each hour (the "barbeque" mode) to provide uniform radiation from the Sun on all parts of the hull. The approach to the Moon was so precise that the mid-course correction scheduled for 8:26 A.M. (EDT) on the 19th was canceled. At a distance of 43,495 miles from the Moon, Apollo 11 passed the so-called "neutral" point, beyond which the Lunar gravitational field dominated that of Earth. Consequently, the spacecraft, which had been gradually losing speed on its long coast away from Earth, now began to accelerate.

The world held its collective breath as Apollo 11 neared the Moon and it came time to fire the service module's propulsion system for the 6 minutes and 2 seconds needed to reduce the velocity from approximately 5,600 to 3,700 miles per hour, so as to place the craft into elliptical orbit. The first phase of Lunar orbit insertion occurred on schedule, and Armstrong radioed, "It was like perfect!" The craft was now circling the Moon at a perilune of 70 miles and an apolune of 195. The time was 1:22 P.M. (EDT) on 19 July 1969; the distance covered so far was 244,-930 miles.

After two circuits in this orbit, the propulsion system was re-ignited to bring the craft into a roughly circular orbit of between 62 and 75 miles above the Lunar surface. Gazing down at the Moon below at 2:06 P.M. (EDT), Armstrong described the crew's first view of the landing approach:

This time we're going over that Taruntius crater, and the pictures and maps brought back by Apollos 8 and 10 give us a very good preview of what to look at here. It looks very much like the pictures, but like the difference between watching a real football game and one on TV. There's no substitute for actually being here.

An envious Houston mission controller concurred: "And we certainly wish we could see it first hand also."

Circling of the Moon continued as on-board systems were thoroughly checked out, and both commander Armstrong and the Houston controllers agreed that it was time for the LM descent maneuver to begin. The first step was to undock the Lunar module, code-named "Eagle," from the CSM—which then became "Columbia." Armstrong and Lunar module commander Aldrin pressurized the CM-LM tunnel and Eagle's ascent stage crew compartment, and opened the respective hatches. First Aldrin and then Armstrong transferred into Eagle, where they made extensive reviews of all systems and subsystems. Eagle was uncoupled from Columbia—at approximately 109 hours into the mission, while the spacecraft was in orbit over the Lunar far side—and the LM's reaction control system engines were ignited to effect separation from the mother ship, which remained in orbit with astronaut Collins aboard. Columbia's propulsion system then fired very briefly to place the CSM in a slightly different orbit that would put the two craft a few miles apart at one half revolution after the start of the separation maneuver. As the LM returned to the Lunar near side, Armstrong reported, "The Eagle has wings." The Lunar module was ready. Man was about to descend to the Moon.

Tension rose aboard Eagle, aboard Columbia, at mission control in Houston, and in front of television receivers in homes and public places all over the world. It is estimated that 500 million persons actually watched what was about to occur; and countless millions more either saw delayed tapes or listened to the epochal event over their radios. Only mainland China was kept in enforced ignorance of the imminent conquest of the Moon.

By firing Eagle's descent stage rocket engine, first at 10 percent throttle and then at 40 percent, Armstrong and Aldrin changed their orbit from nearly circular to elliptical, with a perilune of about 50,000 feet above the surface. This was the descent orbit insertion maneuver. When the landing approach corridor had been identified, the engine was again fired, near the perilune point, to permit the craft to descend toward the surface. This was the first phase of the powered descent initiation maneuver.

Everything proceeded under the automatic control of the on-board computer through the point termed "high gate"—at about 7,600 feet altitude and 26,000 feet uprange from the touchdown site, south of the crater Sabine D and northwest of the crater Moltke on the Sea of Tranquillity. During this period, velocity was reduced to approximately 60 miles per hour.

Eagle was in communication with Houston the entire time: "Eagle, Houston, you are go! Take it all at four minutes. Roger, you are go! You are go to continue power descent.... You are looking great at eight minutes." And then: "...you're go for landing! Over." Aldrin answered, "Roger, understand. Go for landing. Three thousand feet."

From high gate, the craft was further braked and lowered to about 500 feet, or "low gate," the crew visually assessing the terrain below to pick the exact point for touchdown. At about 450 feet, the astronauts took over from the computer, having decided against an automatic landing sequence in favor of a semi-automatic mode to enable them to avoid a hazardous, rock-strewn area. The reaction control system thrusters, working under computer control, provided lateral movement over the area.

Getting ever closer, Aldrin reported, "Forward, forward, good. Forty feet. Picking up some dust." And then, "Drifting to the right.... Contact light. Okay. Engine stop!" The contact light on the LM's instrument panel indicated that one of the 68-inch-long probes dangling from Eagle's footpads had touched the surface. Armstrong delayed 1 second after the light went on and then, looking down onto a sheet of Lunar soil blowing away in all directions, turned off the descent engine. Almost as tranquil as the Sea of Tranquillity had been for aeons, Armstrong reported: "Tranquillity Base here. The Eagle has landed." The time was 4:17:41 P.M. (EDT), 20 July 1969—1 minute and 19 seconds ahead of schedule.

Man was on the Moon. More precisely (although they did not know it at the time), the astronauts were at 0 degree 41 minutes North latitude, 23 degrees 26 minutes East longitude. The exact landing spot was not determined until twelve days later.

Up to this point, the millions of television viewers could only hear words being spoken to and from the spacecraft; animation was used to show the descent and landing sequence. Now, once Eagle was on the Moon, the world was to get live television coverage. Ironically, the man who was nearest to the astronauts on the surface could not see what was about to happen: since Columbia was not equipped with a TV receiver, Michael Collins had to be content with listening to his fellow astronauts' words.

Originally, the mission plan had contemplated 2 hours and 4 minutes of post-landing checkout, 35 minutes for a light meal, then a 4-hour rest period and another hour for a main meal before getting ready to step down onto the surface. However, after assuring themselves that their spacecraft was in good shape, Armstrong and Aldrin requested permission to cancel the 4-hour sleep period (or at least post-

pone it) and go out onto the Moon as soon as they could get ready. Houston agreed: "We've thought about it. We will support it." Anyway, Armstrong and Aldrin were unlikely to get much sleep at that stage of their momentous journey.

More than 3 hours were needed to get ready for the Lunar EVA; donning the portable life support system backpacks with their oxygen purge system units proved particularly time-consuming in the cramped quarters of Eagle. Then, with the cabin de-pressurized and the hatch opened, Armstrong slowly descended the nine-rung ladder. At 10:56:20 P.M. (EDT) on 20 July, he made his first step on the Lunar ground. "That's one small step for a man, one giant leap for mankind," he said, realizing that his first words would become immortalized. While testing his footing, Armstrong began to describe what he saw:

The surface appears to be very, very fine grain, like a powder...I can kick it loosely with my toes. Like powdered charcoal. I can see footprints of my boots in the small, fine particles.... No trouble to walk around.... It's quite dark here in the shadow. I can't tell if I've got good footing.

While Armstrong was down on the surface, Aldrin remained in Eagle, monitoring the television camera, taking still photos, obtaining sequence camera coverage, and observing his companion's movements outside. Hardly containing himself, he asked, "Is it okay for me to come out?" Soon, he, too, was on the Moon, at 11:14 P.M. (EDT).

Like tourists visiting a spectacular vacation area, the astronauts took dozens of photographs, and repeated "beautiful, beautiful" several times. One of their first acts was to plant an American flag on the surface. Armstrong focused the TV camera on the flag, and on the plaque attached to Eagle that read:

HERE MEN FROM THE PLANET EARTH
FIRST SET FOOT UPON THE MOON
JULY 1969, A.D.
WE CAME IN PEACE FOR ALL MANKIND

Armstrong and Aldrin had three principal tasks to perform. First, they photographed Eagle from all angles and checked it to determine if any damage had occurred during the flight and landing. Also, they gained information on the surface properties of the Moon by noting the depth (1 to 2 inches) of the depressions made by the LM footpads. Second, the astronauts had to familiarize themselves with the

Summary of Apollo Orbital and Lunar Flights

Launch date	Designation	Carrier vehicle[a]	Mission	Astronauts	Flight time (hr, min)	Total weight injected onto trajectory[b] (lb)	Remarks
26 February 1966	Apollo 1 (AS-201)	Saturn 1B	Suborbital re-entry test of CSM-009	Unmanned	0, 32	33,805	First official Apollo mission test and first Saturn 1B launch. Maximum spacecraft altitude 306 miles; ballistic trajectory 5,400 miles. CM survived high-speed re-entry and was recovered near Ascension Island by helicopter.
5 July 1966	Apollo 2 (AS-203)	Saturn 1B	Earth orbital test of aerodynamic shroud (heat shield)	Unmanned	—[c]	—[d]	Flight verified orbital conditioning characteristics of second-stage propulsion system and performed checkout of shroud. Total orbital weight, including second stage and instrumentation unit, 58,000 pounds. Perigee and apogee 115 and 117.6 miles, respectively; period 88.24 minutes.
25 August 1966	Apollo 3[e] (AS-202)	Saturn 1B	Suborbital re-entry test of CSM-011	Unmanned	1, 33	44,480	Successful test of CM heat shield, and structural integrity and compatibility of stages and spacecraft. SM engine single-burned to raise CSM to 706 miles, followed by repeated re-starts, then final burn to impart 19,900-mph velocity to detached CM. Successful re-entry and recovery in Pacific.
9 November 1967	Apollo 4 (AS-501)	Saturn 5	Earth orbital test of CSM-017	Unmanned	8, 37	85,043	Maiden flight of Saturn 5; first flight from Kennedy Space Center's LC-39. All stages fired successfully. On second orbit, SM propulsion system raised CSM to 11,239 miles altitude; later, it powered CM to a re-entry velocity of about 25,000 mph. Lunar module ground test article LTA-10R also aboard for vibration, acoustics, and structural integrity testing. Successful recovery of CM in Pacific. Total orbital weight 278,-699 pounds, a world record.
22 January 1968	Apollo 5 (AS-204)	Saturn 1B	Earth orbital test of LM-1	Unmanned	—[f]	36,547	First orbital test of Lunar module. Ignition and staging of ascent and descent stages of LM carried out, although trouble in guidance logic caused shutdown of descent engine (later corrected in flight). LM proved ability to abort a Lunar landing and return to CSM. Initial perigee 101 miles, apogee 138 miles; period 89.5 minutes. Performance of instrumentation unit verified.
4 April 1968	Apollo 6 (AS-502)	Saturn 5	Earth orbital test of CSM-020	Unmanned	9, 58	85,050	Flight, intended essentially to repeat Apollo 4, was partially successful, resulting in orbiting of 264,000 pounds at an altitude of from 112 to 226 miles. Lunar module test article LTA-2R also aboard for launch load and environmental testing. Among difficulties experienced: severe vehicular longitudinal vibrations during first-stage flight, premature shutdown of two second-stage J-2 engines, failure of third-stage J-2 engine to re-ignite in space. (Both J-2 engine problems traced to "buzzing" and subsequent fatigue failure of a small liquid-hydrogen line.) As a result, mission was changed. SM engine lifted apogee to 13,831 miles, then powered CM into re-entry trajectory. Recovery near Hawaii.

Date	Spacecraft	Launch vehicle	Mission	Crew			Remarks
11 October 1968	Apollo 7 (AS-205)	Saturn 1B	Earth orbital test of CSM-101	Schirra Cunningham Eisele	260, 9	36,438	Launching of first manned orbital Apollo spacecraft. Flight virtually a complete success. Many in-space experiments conducted, including rendezvous and simulated docking with S-4B stage. Superb photographs taken of Earth and weather patterns; live television coverage. Flight marred to extent that astronauts suffered colds and some consequent disability and discomfort. Initial perigee 142 miles, apogee 177 miles; 163 orbits. Re-entry successful; recovery southeast of Bermuda.
21 December 1968	Apollo 8 (AS-503)	Saturn 5	Lunar orbital test of CSM-103	Borman Lovell Anders	147, 0	87,382	First manned flight to, into orbit around, and returning from Moon. From a total Earth orbital weight of 282,000 pounds (including S-4B stage), the Apollo 8 spacecraft was injected onto trans-Lunar trajectory; went into orbit around Moon (10 revolutions); and returned to Earth for successful recovery. Invaluable photographic and visual observations of both front and rear of Moon, as well as of Earth during trans-Lunar coast and return to Earth. No medical, disorientation, or psychological problems of consequence during flight. Total Saturn Apollo weight on launch pad 6,219,760 pounds.
3 March 1969	Apollo 9 (AS-504)	Saturn 5	Earth orbital test of CSM-104, LM-3	McDivitt Scott Schweickart	241, 1	95,162	Very successful 151-orbit flight around Earth in exercise of CSM and LM systems; third ignition of S-4B stage; CSM-LM separation, rendezvous, and docking; EVA; and Earth resources photography and landmark tracking. Space suit and backpack checked out in space. Flight rating of LM's ascent and descent propulsion systems; reaction control system; guidance, navigation, computer, and display systems; and intervehicular communications. Demonstrated dynamic control of manned, docked spacecraft in orbit. Total space man-hours 725.
18 May 1969	Apollo 10 (AS-505)	Saturn 5	Lunar orbital test of CSM 106, LM-4	Stafford Young Cernan	192, 3	98,264	Almost flawless 8-day flight to and from Moon, including 2½ days in orbit around Moon. First checkout of Lunar rendezvous concept in Lunar space; closest approach by man to Moon (less than 10 miles); and first test of LM near Moon. Minor emergency during LM ascent module staging maneuver when craft tumbled severely but was brought under control by astronauts using abort guidance system. Landmark tracking accomplished in docked condition, and numerous photographs taken. Flight paved way for Apollo 11.
16 July 1969	Apollo 11 (AS-506)	Saturn 5	Lunar landing with LM-5; Lunar orbit of CSM-107	Armstrong Collins Aldrin	195, 18	100,657	Man's first landing on Moon; completely successful flight. Touchdown in Sea of Tranquillity northwest of Molkte and south of Sabine D. Of 21 hours and 22 minutes on Moon, some 2 hours spent by Armstrong and Aldrin on surface, gathering rock and soil samples, emplacing Solar wind, seismic, and laser ranging experiments, and providing television and photographic coverage of landing area. Collins remained in orbit above Moon, in CSM, during period of LM landing, surface activity, and return to orbit. Mission terminated in Pacific on 24 July. Astronauts quarantined 21 days following liftoff from Moon.

a Saturn 1B referred to as Uprated Saturn 1 from June 1966 to mid-January 1968.
b Less S-4B stage with instrumentation unit.
c Stage was exploded during fourth orbit in pressure test of tanks.
d Carried 18,000 lb of hydrogen propellant.
e After successful conclusion of the mission, the Apollo CSM was declared qualified for manned missions. However, the capsule intended for flight AS-204 was destroyed by fire on 27 January 1967 during a pre-launch test, resulting in the deaths of three astronauts and a delay in the man-rating of the Apollo spacecraft due to extensive re-design.
f No recovery planned; LM ascent stage re-entered atmosphere 24 January, descent stage 12 February. Mission itself lasted 7 hr, 50 min.

Apollo Modules and Their Propulsion Systems

Module	Length (feet, inches)	Diameter (feet, inches)	Weight, loaded (pounds)	Weight, empty (pounds)	Propulsion system(s)	Propellants	Thrust (pounds)	Propulsion capabilities
Command	10, 7	12, 10	12,200[a]	11,700	Reaction control engines for CM-SM separation and some abort modes (two redundant systems of six engines each)	Monomethyl hydrazine, nitrogen tetroxide	93 each	Three-axis rotational and attitude control prior to re-entry; roll attitude control during re-entry.
Service	24, 9	12, 10	52,800	10,500	Main single-engine system for trajectory corrections	Hydrazine and unsymmetrical dimethylhydrazine mixture, nitrogen tetroxide	20,500	Upon computer command, fired for pre-calculated period; course correction to and from Moon, injection into Lunar orbit, and escape from Lunar orbit for Earth return.
					Reaction control system for stabilization and control (four clusters of four engines each)	Monomethyl hydrazine, nitrogen tetroxide	100 each	Three-axis stabilization and control in Earth orbit, trans-Lunar trajectory abort, transposition and docking, mid-course corrections, and velocity changes to compensate for propellant settling.
Lunar (overall)	22, 11[b]	31, 0[c]	33,200[a]	9,300	Reaction control engines (sixteen) for stabilization during ascent and descent	Hydrazine and unsymmetrical dimethylhydrazine mixture, nitrogen tetroxide	100 each	Separation of LM from CSM prior to landing; stabilization of LM, three-axis rotational and attitude control during hover, rendezvous, docking.
Lunar descent stage	10, 7	14, 1	22,600	4,500	Pressure-fed, throttlable, highly redundant system; hypergolic ignition; gimbaled for thrust vector control	Hydrazine and unsymmetrical dimethylhydrazine mixture, nitrogen tetroxide	9,870[d]	Employed for maneuvering LM onto Lunar surface. Also can be used (depending on propellant remaining after descent trajectory begun) for emergency abort, to return LM to orbit.
Lunar ascent stage	12, 4	14, 1	10,600	4,800	Pressure-fed, non-throttlable system; fixed thrust, not gimbaled	Hydrazine and unsymmetrical dimethylhydrazine mixture, nitrogen tetroxide	3,500	Used to lift stage from Lunar surface to orbiting CSM. Also available during emergency abort along descent trajectory if descent stage engine cannot be used.

[a] Including crew.
[b] With legs extended.
[c] Diagonally across landing gear.
[d] Nominal full throttle. Also operable within a range of 1,050 to 6,300 pounds.

strange environment by simply walking and working; their evaluations of clothing and equipment were invaluable in helping to plan later explorations. Third, during the couple of hours available to them outside the Eagle, they set up three scientific experiments and collected as many operational and scientific data as possible. In order to provide panoramic coverage, they removed the television camera from the modularized equipment storage assembly (MESA) compartment in the LM descent stage and erected it on the surface. To insure good communications, an S-band erectile antenna was deployed.

The astronauts collected rock and soil samples from the surface and hammered core tubes into the ground to retrieve sub-surface materials. The first "contingency" samples were collected by Armstrong and stowed in the LM's cabin early in the EVA. This precaution was taken to assure that at least some material would be returned to Earth in the event the surface exploration had to be cut off for some reason prior to the collection of the main samples. The contingency samples were placed in sealed bags which were put into metal containers and transferred into the LM ascent stage by an equipment conveyor —a thin, 60-foot, continuous line of 1-inch-wide straps that looped through a support on Eagle's ascent stage and back to the ground. The samples were gathered by the astronauts with a large scoop and by tongs.

Houston was especially interested in the core samples, inquiring, "On the two core tubes which you collected, how did the driving force required to collect these tubes compare? Was there any difference?" From nearly a quarter million miles across space came the answer:

Not significantly. I could get down about the first two inches without much of a problem and then I would pound it in about as hard as I could do it. The second one took two hands on the hammer, and I was putting pretty good dents in the top of the extension rod. And it just wouldn't go much more than—I think the total depth might have been about eight or nine inches. But even there, it—for some reason—didn't seem to want to stand up straight, so that I'd keep driving it in, and it would dig some sort of a hole but it just wouldn't penetrate in a way that would support it and keep it from falling over. If that makes any sense at all. It didn't really to me.

The descriptions of the immediate area around the LM naturally were of great interest to geologists. Aldrin reported "literally thousands" of craters 1 to 2 feet in diameter, and boulders of all shapes up to 2 feet across—and some even larger. Many were above the ground, others partially or almost totally buried. Both astronauts described the ground as being similar to fine sand or silt and "slippery." During their walks around their LM, they left footprints about ⅛ inch deep. Mobility was no problem, as they quickly became accustomed to one-sixth their normal gravity and to their 188-pound (Earth weight) extra-vehicular mobility units (space suits and backpacks). While scooping out samples, Armstrong reported the ground to consist of "a very cohesive material of some sort."

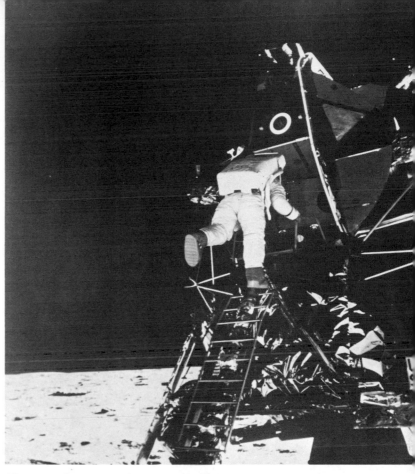

The second man on the Moon, Edwin E. Aldrin, Jr., left the Lunar module and stepped onto the Lunar surface at 11:14 P.M. (EDT) on 20 July 1969. He had remained behind in the LM, taking still pictures and monitoring the television camera, after Neil Armstrong descended to the surface. (NASA)

The Apollo 11 astronauts left a plaque on the Moon commemorating their historic voyage. The plaque was attached to the descent stage of the Lunar module, which remained at the landing site after the astronauts had returned to Earth. (NASA)

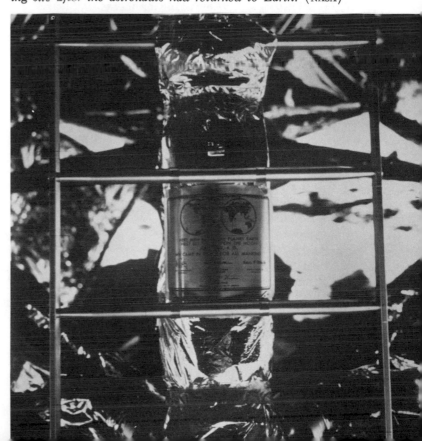

The boots of the Apollo 11 astronauts left imprints about ⅛ inch deep in the layer of fine particles that covers the Moon's surface. The astronauts had no difficulty walking on this powdery substance. (NASA)

The three scientific experiments deployed by Armstrong and Aldrin were the Solar wind composition (SWC) detector and the early Apollo scientific experiments package (EASEP), consisting of a three-axis passive seismic experiments package (PSEP) and a laser ranging retro-reflector (LRRR). The SWC detector was a panel of very thin aluminum foil, which was unrolled so that the foil would be exposed directly to the Sun's rays. In effect, the detector was a trap for the noble-gas constituents of the Solar wind, such as helium, neon, argon, krypton, and xenon. Near the end of EVA, it was folded and placed in one of the sample return containers.

The seismic experiment was deployed to monitor possible "Moonquakes" as well as meteoroid impacts, free oscillations of the Moon, and general signs of internal activity. It might also detect possible surface deformations and variations of external gravitational fields acting on the Lunar mass. The seismic package was powered by a radioisotopic heater developed by the Atomic Energy Commission. Almost imme-

diately, the station went into operation, first reporting tremors—made by the astronauts walking around on the ground nearby—and later what may have been quakes.

The laser reflector, the second part of the EASEP, was actually an array of 100 individual reflectors upon which it was hoped to "bounce" beams emitted from observatories back on Earth. The experiment was designed to provide accurate data on the distance between Earth and the Moon, the nature of Earth's irregular rotation, the motions of the Moon, and the relative motion of Earth and the Moon. After twelve days of searching, Lick Observatory's 120-inch telescope commenced "bouncing" beams off the reflector, thus pinpointing the landing site.

After completing their work on the surface, Armstrong and Aldrin stowed the Solar wind experiment, dusted off their extra-vehicular mobility units, and kicked their boots clean against a footpad. Then they ascended to the platform, swung open the hatch, disconnected the equipment conveyor, and jettisoned equipment and other items no longer needed. Among the "litter" left by Eagle were cameras, the TV unit, hand tools such as tongs and hammer, core bits, the environmental control system canister and bracket, urine bags, and the two portable life support systems. Armstrong and Aldrin took a well-earned rest and then made ready for the return to Columbia, waiting in orbit above.

As preparations were made for the ascent, the cross-talk with Houston increased—and the world heard, but only dimly comprehended, the language of the future. From mission control came such instructions as these:

Call P22 possible program alarm 526 range greater than 400 nautical miles and then use P22 as described on pings 20. Take option one in nouns zero six and use the no-update mode. The rendezvous radar will lock on at about 25 degrees elevation above the horizon. If 503 alarm occurs, designate fail. TA proceed, and allow the rendezvous radar to search for the CSM; and place the range-altitude monitor switch in altitude rate to prevent the tape meter from driving into the stops.

"Roger, I think I have that," reported Tranquillity Base, as Eagle awaited the moment to commence flying. At 1:50 P.M. (EDT) on 21 July, Houston reported: "Eagle, you're looking good to us." Then, from Aldrin: "Roger, understand, we're Number One on the runway." A few minutes later from Tranquillity Base came the countdown: "Nine, eight, seven,

The terrain immediately around the Apollo 11 Lunar module contained thousands of craters like the one shown here. White spots at upper right are caused by reflections from Sunlight on equipment. (NASA)

...three, two, one... first stage engine on ascent. Proceed. Beautiful. Twenty-six, thirty-six feet per second up. Little pitch over, very smooth, very quiet ride." Eagle was flying. Lift off came at 1:54 P.M. (EDT). Man's first sojourn on the Moon had lasted 21 hours and 37 minutes.

The Lunar module's ascent engine burned for more than 7 minutes, providing a total velocity of 4,128 miles per hour. The first phase of the ascent involved a vertical rise to clear terrain features, followed by tipping the craft over a 52-degree angle for insertion into a Lunar orbit with a perilune of about 10 miles. At apolune, the "concentric sequence initiate" occurred, targeted to place Eagle into a circular orbit nearly 17 miles below Columbia's. A terminal phase of engine burn brought Eagle along a line-of-sight path toward Columbia, to station-keeping distance. Eagle then made the terminal rendezvous and docked. Armstrong and Aldrin transferred through the LM-CM tunnel to Columbia, joined Collins, closed the hatches, and jettisoned the "Eagle" that had served them so faithfully. Columbia was Apollo 11 once again, minus its Lunar module. Dock-

ing occurred at 5:35 P.M. (EDT), 3 minutes behind schedule—and 128 hours and 3 minutes into the mission (ground elapsed time).

The journey homeward was essentially a repeat of Apollos 8 and 10. The three-man crew functioned much as they had when Moonbound, making navigational checks, rolling the spacecraft, and so on. Some 3½ hours before the atmospheric re-entry phase began, they turned the CM's heat shield away from the Sun, permitting it to cool to the maximum possible degree. Before re-entry, the SM was explosively separated, after which the engine was fired to increase the module's distance from the CM. At about 400,000 feet above Earth, the CM began to heat up as it met air resistance. As Apollo 11 passed deeper into the atmosphere, the temperature of the heat shield rose to approximately 5,000 degrees F, and the astronauts experienced a deceleration force somewhat greater than 6G at its maximum. At approximately 24,000 feet, the heat shield was jettisoned and the drogue parachutes were deployed. These were severed at 10,700 feet, and pilot chutes pulled out the main parachutes—velocity being reduced first to 125 miles per hour by the drogues and then to 22 miles per hour by the main chutes.

The capsule splashed into the Pacific Ocean at 12:40 P.M. (EDT) on 24 July, some 900 miles southwest of Hawaii and 13 miles from the waiting carrier *Hornet*. A beacon and voice transmissions by automatically deployed antennas led the *Hornet* and its helicopters quickly to the capsule. A recovery frogman swam to the bobbing command module and passed three biological isolation garments with plastic-visored face masks in through the partially, and momentarily, opened hatch.

Donning of the isolation suits was the first step taken here on Earth in a series of rigid quarantine safety measures, developed by the Interagency Committee on Back Contamination. (During the return flight, many other precautionary measures had been taken, such as vacuuming equipment and the spacecraft interior and filtering the cabin atmosphere.) Although most scientists felt the possibility remote that any microorganisms, dangerous or benign, exist on the Moon, the quarantine was necessary to reduce to an absolute minimum the chance of epidemics occurring here on Earth, where the various forms of life might lack natural defenses against alien organisms.

As soon as they emerged in their germ-proof suits, the astronauts were thoroughly washed with a decontaminant, after which they in turn washed the frogman lest he have become contaminated in

Colonel Aldrin prepares to deploy a passive seismic experiments package and a laser ranging retro-reflector. The seismic package will monitor possible "Moonquakes," meteoroid impacts, free oscillations of the Moon, and general signs of internal activity. The laser reflector will "bounce" beams emitted from observatories on Earth. (NASA)

Colonel Aldrin is shown setting up the seismic experiments pac age, which went into operation almost immediately, reportir tremors made by the footsteps of the astronauts on the grour nearby. Indications of what may have been quakes were lat noted by scientists on Earth. (NASA)

the process. The astronauts were then taken by helicopter to the *Hornet* and placed immediately in a quarantine van called the mobile quarantine facility (MQF), which consisted of a lounge area, galley, and sleeping-bathing area. President Richard M. Nixon, who had conversed by phone with Armstrong and Aldrin while they were on the Moon, observed the entire procedure from the deck of the carrier, and later greeted the astronauts through the MQF window. The van was unloaded from the *Hornet* at Ford Island, Hawaii, and then flown to the Manned Spacecraft Center in Houston, where the astronauts with their precious cargo of Lunar rocks and soil transferred into an 83,000-square-foot Lunar receiving laboratory. The quarantine period lasted twenty-one days, starting from the moment that Eagle lifted off from the Moon's surface.

Within the Lunar receiving laboratory, the astro-

nauts and their attendant technicians lived in one crew reception area while physicans, medical technicians, housekeepers, and cooks occupied the other. Meanwhile, the 78 pounds of rock and soil samples gathered on the Moon and the Solar wind experiment were examined in the sample operations area. Protection of these areas from outside Earth contamination, and of the world from possible Lunar contamination, was afforded by "biological barrier systems" —a series of filters that treated both incoming and outgoing air. As an added precaution, air pressure inside the laboratory was somewhat lower than normal, so that flow was always inward.

The area housing Armstrong, Collins, and Aldrin contained 58 rooms, including well-equipped medical and surgical facilities, sleeping quarters, kitchen, and a storage room for the command module. A variety of animal life was exposed to the Lunar samples in

After having deployed the seismic experiment   Colonel Aldrin walks in the direction of the laser reflector and the Lunar module. (NASA)

the biological test laboratory to see if there was any biological cross-reaction. Creatures such as quail, oysters, and mice—all brought up since birth in a sterile environment—were fed and injected with pulverized Lunar rock to determine what effects it might have.

While the crew were thoroughly examined and de-briefed, and biological tests were continuing, the sample return containers from the Moon were brought into the vacuum laboratory for preliminary examination. Among the first group of samples tested were several lava-like rocks, indicating that volcanoes may have existed on the Moon. Another large rock sample appeared to be similar to Earthly basalt. After the initial tests, the samples were re-packaged and sent to the gas analysis laboratory, where the amounts and types of gases they emitted were measured. In other laboratories, the reaction of the sam-

Colonel Aldrin deploys the Solar wind composition detector, a panel of thin aluminum foil rolled and assembled to serve as a trap for the noble-gas constituents of the Solar wind. White spots at upper left are caused by reflections of Sunlight on equipment. (NASA)

ples to atmospheric gases and water vapor was observed, and petrological, geochemical, physical, and mineralogical analyses were conducted. After a long quarantine, the samples were sent to research laboratories in many parts of the United States and to foreign countries for detailed post-quarantine study and analysis.

As landings on the Moon continue, Apollo hardware will gradually be modified and augmented to permit man to spend longer and longer periods there. Removal of the propellant tanks and rocket engine from the ascent portion of an LM would create an LM "shelter" vehicle. It could land a substantial payload on a one-way mission to the Lunar surface and could protect and sustain two astronauts on the Moon for as long as two weeks — a promising sequel to the day-long visits of early Apollo crewmen. An un-

manned LM shelter would be launched by one Saturn 5, while the astronauts in their separate LM "taxi" would be launched by a second Saturn 5. Meanwhile, orbiting versions of Apollo might be developed to provide up to two weeks' observation time for mapping those vast areas on the visible and far sides of the Moon that are not immediately accessible to ground exploration.

Roving vehicles called Molabs would extend the radius of action for ground expeditions operating from early, semi-permanent bases on the Moon. These bases would have their own Solar or nuclear power stations, hydroponic vegetable gardens and chicken farms, and — maybe — facilities to extract water from local rocks. Needless to say, all occupied spaces would be pressurized and air conditioned to provide the same comfort enjoyed today by passengers in a pressurized jetliner. These operations would undoubtedly require heavy logistics support from Earth and a steady increase in personnel. Such a program might require the development of unmanned logistics vehicles and manned spacecraft with greater payload capacities. The more powerful carrier rockets needed for these purposes might be obtained by first adding a nuclear-propelled upper stage to a Saturn 5 that had been uprated by strapping on solid-propellant rockets. And, in the future, completely new carrier rockets may be needed for journeys to the planets.

But before going to the planets, man will want to use his present Saturn and Apollo technology to further his activities in Earth orbit. One program now in development is called the Saturn workshop — an embryonic space station to be built in three steps, using a Saturn S-4B stage, an Apollo CSM, and finally a modified Lunar module.

Prior to launch, the S-4B will be modified so that the crew can readily make it their home during their sojourn in space. The principal modifications are the addition of an aluminum grid-pattern floor in the lower section of the tank, the installation of living quarters and working area partitions, and the emplacement of a fire retardant liner around the inside surface. A cloth ceiling adjacent to the bulkhead containing the hydrogen and oxygen tanks will serve to orient the astronauts during their 28 days in orbit. Ceiling beams will serve as hand rails. Outside, a meteoroid shield will be added to provide protection for the crew, as well as a solar array to furnish electrical power.

Ample room will be provided for living space inside the workshop. For example, one sleeping compartment will have 67 square feet of space, and the other 70 square feet. The food and waste management areas are allotted 30 square feet each. An electrical power distribution system will be installed prior to launch, and lights will be moved about by the astronauts in accordance with their requirements.

The crew will enter and leave the workshop through the airlock, without having to de-pressurize either their ferry spacecraft or the S-4B. A multiple docking adapter attached to the airlock will permit as many as five ferry craft to couple to the S-4B at once. The planned docking adapter is a cylindrical pressure vessel over 17 feet long and 12 feet in diameter at its widest point. At the forward end is a single axial docking port, and at four positions at 90-degree intervals are four radial docking ports. Three of these and the axial port will receive Apollo command and service module configurations. The fourth radial port will accommodate the Lunar module–Apollo telescope mount combination. The planned airlock itself is 16 feet long, including a structural transition section, and is mounted at the forward end of the S-4B stage within the instrumentation unit and the spacecraft adapter structure. The airlock forward end is attached to the multiple docking adapter. The airlock is large enough to accommodate two astronauts at a time, in pressurized suits fitted with portable life support equipment.

In order to undertake the mission, which is part of NASA's Apollo applications program, a two-stage Saturn 5 will loft the S-4B stage workshop and the Apollo telescope mount (ATM) into a 240-mile-high orbit. Earlier, it had been planned to use a Saturn 1B carrier to place the S-4B alone in orbit; but it would have been necessary to send a crew to vent and refurbish the stage before scientist-astronauts could occupy it. With the use of Saturn 5, the S-4B stage can go into space empty of propellant and ready for immediate use. Moreover, with the Saturn 1B mode, a second carrier would have had to orbit the ATM, whereas a single Saturn 5 can place both the workshop and the telescope module in orbit together.

The day after the workshop and ATM have been orbited by the Saturn 5, a Saturn 1B will take off with three astronauts aboard the Apollo CSM payload.

This artist's conception of the Saturn 5 workshop shows (from left to right) the service module with its rocket engine, the command module and the multiple docking adapter, and the main S-4B converted stage with its airlock module and Solar array panels. The Apollo Lunar module telescope mount and its Solar array panels are attached to the multiple docking adapter. (MC DONNELL-DOUGLAS CORP.)

After rendezvous and docking, they will transfer into the workshop and take up residence for 28 days of experimenting in space. When their work comes to an end, they will close up their temporary home and return to Earth in the Apollo CM. If all goes well, between two and three months later a second Saturn 1B will loft a second Apollo CSM, whose crew may remain in the workshop for up to 56 days.

Experiments to be carried out in the Saturn 5 workshop are divided into four groups: (1) scientific, (2) technological, (3) engineering, and (4) medical. Among the candidates for the first group are Earth terrain photography, X-ray astronomy, galactic X-ray mapping, and the study of the zodiacal light. In the technological area, measurements will be made of the effects of crew motions on workshop dynamics, and how they may affect the operation of precision instruments. Another experiment is concerned with the frequency and density of micrometeoroids striking samples of Vycor-glass surface.

Numerous engineering experiments have been proposed. A typical one is evaluation of a hydrostatic gas bearing subjected to extended zero gravity at various gas pressures. One of many medical experiments involves maintaining the astronauts on a programmed mineral diet to determine mineral balance and the rate and amount of material lost by the body during extended orbital flight.

After the orbiting workshop has accomplished its initial objectives and crews have learned to function for extended periods in an orbital environment, preparations will be made to undertake the Apollo telescope mount experiment. Designed to permit a completely free view of the Sun from well outside the Earth's atmosphere, the ATM will incorporate eight instruments to measure the extreme ultraviolet, X-ray, white light, and hydrogen-alpha (6,563 angstroms) portions of the electromagnetic spectrum. A television system will permit the astronauts in the workshop to view Solar images recorded by the telescopes.

The ATM module will be composed of the ascent stage of an Apollo Lunar module and a "rack" (an octagonal truss structure), employed instead of the standard descent stage. The total weight of the ATM payload will be in excess of 30,000 pounds. The telescopes used in the ATM will be mounted to an 82-inch-diameter cruciform structure.

From Saturn workshops and ATMs will come larger, full-fledged space stations where a dozen or more men may remain for months carrying out scientific and applied research. Meanwhile, the problems of mounting manned expeditions to the planets — Mars especially — will be examined carefully. As far back as 1952, Wernher von Braun published a study describing a fleet of ten chemically propelled spaceships making a round trip over a period of 2 years and 269 days, including a stay of 400 days on Mars. In 1961, NASA's Marshall Space Flight Center and its associated contractors commenced studies of the trajectory requirements for manned fly-by and stopover missions to both Venus and Mars. As interest increased, the Empire (early manned planetary-interplanetary round-trip expeditions) study program was inaugurated. Within Empire, investigations were made of both preliminary mission and overall systems requirements for single and dual planet fly-bys and exploration trips, with varying stay times.

Some of the specific objectives of Empire were:

1. To develop an understanding of the basic physical concepts in scheduling interplanetary flights, taking into account flight trajectories in planning such interplanetary missions as (a) non-stop round trips, (b) stopover round trips, (c) launching of spaceships normal to the ecliptic, (d) precise calculations of guidance sensitivities, and (e) non-stop trips passing both Mars and Venus.

2. To investigate the role of electrical and nuclear propulsion for planetary missions, especially for manned Mars travel.

3. To examine problem areas associated with the goal of manned interplanetary exploration in the 1970's; contribute to definitions of requirements for post-Saturn 5 Earth-launched vehicles; furnish potential goals for operational nuclear engines; and investigate the general requirements and lead times for an initial manned mission.

These and other penetrating studies of the possibility of mounting manned expeditions to Mars were conducted in the early 1960's, and became known as Empire Phase 1. Emphasis was on manned exploration in the middle to late 1970's, with principal attention to trajectory studies and the general feasibility of fly-by and planetary orbital missions. In Phase 2 of Empire, investigations were begun to determine if faster trips to Mars would be possible in the same time period, leading to a landing on the planet. Work went on in nuclear and low-thrust electrical propulsion, navigation and guidance, tracking, optical communications, environmental protection and life support systems, and design of a spacecraft permitting descent from orbit around Mars to the surface and return to orbit (the Mars module). One section of the study program became known as Umpire (unfavorable manned planetary-interplanetary round-trip expeditions). The word "unfavorable" was used in the sense that the relative positions of Earth and Mars will not permit the most economical and shortest transit in the 1975-1985 period.

Once the general feasibility of going to Mars had been established, attention was directed to problems facing crews. One study sought to determine the number of kinds of personnel necessary on long-duration space flights, and to identify the basic selection techniques and training required. Another study sought to establish the kinds of environments that would permit the crew to work in an optimum manner. Moreover, scientific tasks for the astronauts during the long interplanetary flight period were spelled out. Other studies sought to define the scientific activities they would perform both in Mars orbit and on the surface.

In the latter half of the 1960's decade, more attention was placed on the Saturn 5 as a support carrier for manned Mars expeditions, although alternative possibilities were being investigated. Standardization of planetary spacecraft also became a goal. For example, the objective of one study was to "determine if a variety of manned space missions to Mars and Venus can be accomplished with a common design concept ... and define that design concept and the missions within its capabilities."

As the Apollo Lunar landing was becoming a reality, America found itself beset with increasing financial obligations in Viet Nam and serious internal problems at home. These have combined to cause a reduction in financial resources applicable to space exploration, particularly that aimed at objectives beyond the initial Lunar landings. Although work has all but ceased on manned Mars travel, many of the vehicular and other tools already exist to make such travel feasible. Saturn 5's primary responsibility is to the Apollo program; but suitably modified, it has the capability of making important contributions to the exploration of the planets. Just when such a mission may be undertaken depends on public and Congressional support. From the scientific and engineering standpoint, it appears to be feasible to begin the first voyage in mid-November 1981, provided that decisions to go ahead on certain elements of the post-Apollo program are made in the near future. If a mission departed at that time, it would arrive at Mars about 9 August 1982 and return to Earth in mid-August 1983.

A typical Mars landing mission, as conceived on the basis of upgraded Saturn 5 technology and refinements of post-Empire studies made following the Apollo 11 mission, would begin with the orbiting of the elements for either one or two identical spaceships by two-stage Saturn 5's and newly developed "space shuttles." These would be re-usable carriers for transporting men and equipment between the ground and Earth orbit. While the mission could be carried out with a single ship, the use of two would provide an additional safety factor, since each would be large enough to accommodate the astronauts of its sister ship in the event of a major failure. Furthermore, with two ships, additional equipment could be carried, enhancing the probability of achieving mission objectives. The nominal crew of each ship would be six men.

The inter-planetary vehicle assembled in Earth orbit would weigh 1.6 million pounds and consist of three nuclear shuttles, or propulsion modules, placed side by side, with the ship (or ships) carrying the astronauts docked to the center module. The two outer modules would be fired to put the vehicle onto trans-Martian trajectory, after which they would be separated and returned to Earth orbit. There, they would be checked out and re-fueled by the Earth-to-orbit shuttles for further use. Meanwhile, the spaceship with the remaining module would continue on its 270-day voyage to Mars.

The spaceship itself would be divided into three major sections. The forward compartment would be an unpressurized area housing the Mars surface exploration module, an airlock to provide for pressurized transfer to this module, and unmanned exploration probes (six for use on Mars, two for Venus on the return leg of the trip). The main mission module, aft of the airlock, would contain living quarters, the control area, experimental laboratories, and a radiation "storm" shelter in which the crew could live during periods of intense Solar activity. To the rear of the mission module, and adjacent to the nuclear propulsion system, would be the biological laboratory for receiving and analyzing surface samples from Mars. This unit would be sterilized and remain sealed until initial analyses of the samples had been performed by remote control.

The entire spaceship would be continuously rotated, if Saturn workshop experiments in the 1970's show it necessary to provide the crew with artificial gravity during the long Earth–Mars coast period. If two ships made the trip simultaneously, they could be docked end to end and rotated in the plane of the longitudinal axis.

On reaching Mars, the spaceship — its weight now down to 675,000 pounds — would be placed in an elliptical orbit. The crew's first task would be to launch the unmanned probes, whose prime purpose would be to return samples from the ground to the biological laboratory. If analysis revealed no significant biological hazards, three of the crew members would then descend to the planet in the surface exploration craft, or Mars excursion module. This 95,000-pound, 22-foot-base-diameter craft would con-

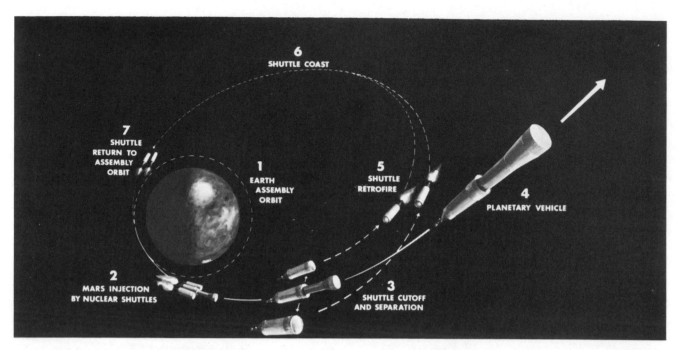

The vehicle used for the first Mars landing mission would be assembled in Earth orbit and would consist of the spaceship(s) plus three nuclear shuttles, or propulsion modules. The two outer modules would be fired to place the spaceship onto trans-Martian trajectory. They would then be returned to Earth orbit for re-fueling. The main vehicle would continue on to Mars. (NASA)

The inter-planetary vehicle would be divided into three main sections. The forward compartment (right) would contain the Mars excursion module, eight unmanned exploration probes, and an airlock. The main mission module (center) would contain the living quarters, control area, laboratories, and radiation shelter. The biological laboratory would be housed in the third section (left). (NASA)

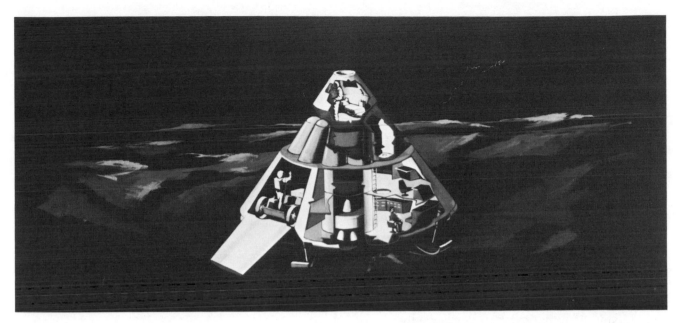

The Mars excursion module would weigh 95,000 pounds and have a 22-foot base diameter. This surface exploration unit would contain living quarters, a laboratory, and a one-man rover unit. Like the Lunar module, it would have an ascent and a descent stage. (NASA)

The Mars excursion module would carry three astronauts to the planet's surface, where they would spend thirty to sixty days collecting scientific information. The astronauts would then return to the mother ship in the module's ascent stage, abandoning the descent stage on the Martian surface. (NASA)

tain living quarters, a laboratory, and a one-man rover unit. The Mars excursion module, like the Lunar module used in the Apollo 11 mission, would have ascent and descent stages. After spending thirty to sixty days on the surface collecting scientific information, the astronauts would return in the ascent stage to the orbiting mother ship, abandoning the descent stage on the planet.

The trip home would begin after the transfer of the three-man exploration party and their scientific payload from the ascent stage of the Mars excursion module to the mission module. Just prior to departure from Mars orbit, the inter-planetary vehicle would weight about 380,000 pounds — the loss in weight being accounted for by consumption of propellant, food, and oxygen and by abandonment of the surface probes and the excursion module.

The profile for a Mars mission in 1981–1983 includes a passage close to Venus on the return voyage. In addition to providing an opportunity for close-up observation of that cloud-shrouded planet, this passage results in lower approach velocities to Earth, and thus greater weight tolerances for the Earth–Mars round trip. When passing Venus, the astronauts would conduct radar mapping of surface features and launch two scientific probes of the planet's atmosphere.

The manned Mars landing mission would conclude with the return to Earth orbit, using the remaining propellant in the nuclear stage for the braking maneuver. This would further reduce the weight of the vehicle to 160,000 pounds. After docking with a space station, the crew would be given medical examinations and, if there were no need for an extended quarantine, promptly returned to Earth via shuttle.

It is far from certain when the public will watch on television the return of a Mars mission. Manned flight to the red planet seemed to be the next logical step after the Lunar landings. During the past few years, however, the resources available to space flight development have been decreasing — in the United States, at least. In the fiscal year 1959, NASA's first year of operation, the space agency had a budget of just under $331 million. By the fiscal year 1965, NASA's appropriations had peaked at $5¼ billion — leading to Federal employment of some 35,000 persons in the summer of 1967. Nationwide, more than 400,000 people were working on the space program in one capacity or another.

In a few short years since then, budgets have decreased drastically, and the highly trained work force has been cut almost in half. Today, NASA spends about $3 billion a year, although the tremendous enthusiasm attending the Apollo 11 Lunar landing may lead to new increases in space funding.

Why, as man was successfully conquering the Moon, should the space program have begun to falter?

Part of the answer lies with Apollo itself. The Kennedy goal committed the United States to send astronauts to the Moon, and bring them safely back, before 1970. In order to pave the way for this stupendous undertaking, such programs as Saturns 1 and 1B, Ranger, Surveyor, Lunar Orbiter, Mercury, and Gemini had to be carried out and completed — all within a rather tight time schedule. This required the application of impressive human and monetary resources to build up enormous industrial and mission support facilities. Unless the nation accepted new and major goals beyond the initial Apollo landings, however, these resources were bound to dwindle as preparatory programs ended and Apollo approached reality. And dwindle they did.

It is still too early to tell how the United States — and Soviet Russia and other nations — will react to the continuing challenge of the space frontier. Landing on the Moon represents a vital step towards the understanding of the Solar System and the universe. The exploration, exploitation, and colonization of the Moon will take generations. But will man content himself with conquering Earth's satellite, or will his insatiable curiosity and boundless energy carry him outward to new worlds? The answer is for us to decide. If man wills it, the Lunar landing will be just the beginning — not the end — of a new era of discovery.

Bibliography

To maintain a bibliography of manageable length is not an easy task when one considers the vast amount of material that must be consulted in writing a history covering several thousand years of intellectual and technological development. Since the 1930's, in the field of rocketry alone, hundreds of engineering books have been published and as many more covering the essentially scientific aspects of astronautics. In addition, literally thousands of journal and magazine articles have appeared in many languages throughout the world.

The following bibliography includes only major works that bear on historical or potentially historical aspects of the subject. Most of the bibliography is limited to book references, but occasionally an important journal article is cited, particularly if it treats pre-1900 events not otherwise recorded, or even cited, in books. Since most post-1900 events in one way or another have been recorded at least superficially in the book literature, and since many of the books listed cite original periodical sources, only an occasional listing of the latter is made.

A comprehensive annotated bibliography of English-language book literature from the 1930's to the early 1960's is Frederick I. Ordway's *Annotated Bibliography of Space Science and Technology* (Washington: Arfor Publishers, 1962). See also H. H. Koelle and H. J. Kaeppeler's *Literature Index of Astronautics* (Tittmaning Oberbayern: Verlag Walter Pustet). In addition, the National Aeronautics and Space Administration and the National Aerospace Education Council, both in Washington, periodically release bibliographies. The United States Department of the Army's library has issued a series of bibliographies on works published in the 1950's and 1960's, and the United States Air Force Academy's Department of Astronautics has released similar material. In addition, the Science and Technology Division of the Library of Congress in Washington maintains very complete bibliographic records in the fields of rocketry and astronautics and publishes many compendiums.

Other useful sources are Bernard M. Fry and Foster E. Mohrhart's edited work *A Guide to Information Sources in Space Science and Technology* (New York: Interscience Publishers, 1963) and such bibliographic publications of the Jet Propulsion Laboratory, California Institute of Technology, as *Open Literature Surveys* and *Astronautics Information Abstracts;* and the American Meteorological Society's *Annotated Bibliography on Rocket Meteorology and Meteorological and Geoastrophysical Abstracts* (Boston). The National Aeronautics and Space Administration in Washington regularly publishes *Scientific and Technical Aerospace Reports,* and the American Institute of Aeronautics and Astronautics in New York, the *International Aerospace Abstracts*—which examines over a thousand books and journal articles each year. In London, the monthly *Index Aeronauticus: Journal of Aeronautical and Astronautical Abstracts* is published by the Ministry of Aviation, while the *Service de Documentation et d'Information Technique de l'Aéronautique* in Paris abstracts a great volume of material on rocketry and astronautics. World journal literature is also abstracted by *Current Contents of Space, Electronic and Physical Sciences,* published by the Institute for Scientific Information in Philadelphia. In Russia, the semimonthly *Referetivnyi Zhurnal* (*Reference Journal* on rocketry and space flight) appears regularly.

In addition to these, abstracts and bibliographies are found in most of the world's rocket and astronautic journals. These include those published by societies in the pioneering nations, such as America, Britain, Germany, and Russia, as well as by dozens of recently formed organizations all over the world. Today most societies have joined the International Astronautical Federation, which, since 1950, has organized the annual International Astronautical Congress. The related International Academy of Astronautics has its own journal, *Astronautica Acta.* Listed below are the major current IAF societies and their addresses; in America, France, Germany, and Russia the present names of the societies are quite different from their original ones but they are either direct or indirect descendants of the pioneer organizations. All publish one or more journals, most containing abstract and bibliographic material.

International Astronautical Federation
250, rue Saint Jacques
Paris 5ᵉ, France

Argentina
Asociación Argentina de Ciencias Aeroespaciales
Rodriguez Peña 1693, Buenos Aires

Austria
Österreichische Gesellschaft für
    Weltraumforschung und Flugkörpertechnik
Theresianumgasse 27, A-1040 Vienna IV

Belgium
Association Belge des Ingénieurs et Techniciens
    de l'Aéronautique et de l'Astronautique
20 Avenue de la Ramée, Brussels 18

Brazil
Sociedade Interplanetaria Brasileira
Caixa Postal 8250, São Paulo

Bulgaria
Bulgarian Astronautical Society
Union of Scientific Workers
18 Boulevard Tolbouhine, Sofia

China (Republic of)
Astronautical Society of the Republic of China
41 Nan Hai Road, Taipei, Taiwan

Cyprus
Cyprus Astronautical Society
P.O. Box 210, Limassol

Czechoslovakia
Commission on Astronautics
Czechoslovak Academy of Sciences
Národní tr. 3, Prague I

Denmark
Dansk Astronautisk Forening
Postbox 31, Copenhagen—K

Finland
Astronauttinen Tutkimus-Seura
Kauppalantie 6, Helsinki

France
Société Française d'Astronautique
47, rue Dumont d'Urville, 75—Paris 16ᵉ

German Democratic Republic
Deutsche Astronautische Gesellschaft
Poststrasse 4—5, 102 Berlin 2

German Federal Republic
Deutsche Gesellschaft für Raketentechnik und
    Raumfahrt e. V.
am Glockenbach 12, 8 Munich 5

Greece
Hellenic Astronautical Society
Voulis Street 14, Athens

Hungary
Magyar Asztronautikai Egyesület
Szabadsag tér 17, Budapest V

India
Indian Rocket Society
P.B. No. 35, Trivandrum

Iran
Iranian Astronautical Society
Institute of Geophysics
Teheran University, Teheran

Israel
Israel Astronautical Society
c/o Dept. of Aeronautical Engineering
Technion, Haifa

Italy
Associazione Italiana Razzi
Via Nazionale 172, Rome

Japan
Japanese Rocket Society
Yomiuri Newspaper Building
1—3 Ginza-Nishi, Chuo-ku, Tokyo

Mexico
Sociedad Mexicana de Estudios Interplanetarios
Apartado 4409, Mexico 12, D.F.

Netherlands
Nederlandse Vereniging voor Ruimtevaart
Camplaan 34, Heemstede (NH)

Norway
Norsk Astronautisk Forening
Postboks 43, Blindern, Oslo

Peru
Instituto Peruano de Relaciones Interplanetarias
Casilla 4877, Lima

Poland
Polskie Towarzystwo Astronautyczne
P.K.i.N.p. 23—18, Warsaw 22

Portugal
Grupo Português de Astronáutica
Instituto Superior Técnico
Avenida Dr. A. José de Almeida, Lisbon

Rumania
Commission d'Astronautique de l'Académie de
    la République Populaire Roumaine
15 rue Constantin Mille, Bucharest

Spain
Agrupación Astronáutica Española
Avenida Gmo. Franco 377, Barcelona

Sweden
Svenska Interplanetariska Sallskapet
Box 5045, Stockholm 5

Switzerland
Swiss Association for Space Technology
Plattenstrasse 28, 8032 Zurich

Union of Soviet Socialist Republics
Commission on Exploration and Use of Outer Space
U.S.S.R. Academy of Sciences
Ulitza Vavilova 32, Moscow V-312

United Kingdom
British Interplanetary Society
12 Bessborough Gardens, London S.W.1

United States
American Institute of Aeronautics and Astronautics
1290 Avenue of the Americas
New York, N.Y. 10019

Yugoslavia
Jugoslovensko Astronauticke i Raketno Drustvo
Bulevar Revolucije 44, Belgrade

In addition, most nations have space research groups attached to their national academy of sciences or similar organization, and many of these issue journals and symposia proceedings. These groups have their IAF equivalent, the Committee on Space Research, which holds annual meetings and issues voluminous proceedings. The names and addresses of these and many other rocket and astronautical organizations are found in such sources as Interavia's *ABC World Directory of Aviation and Astronautics* (Geneva, Switzerland) and American Aviation Publications' *World Space Directory* (Washington, D.C.).

The rocket and astronautical society literature is supplemented by the excellent contemporary trade journals, such as Britain's *Flight International*, Switzerland's *Interavia*, and America's *Aviation Week and Space Technology*, *TRW Space Log*, and *Space/Aeronautics*. There also are such other commercial journals as *Sky and Telescope*, *Space Science Reviews*, *Icarus*, *Planetary and Space Science*, *Space Life Sciences*, and *Ailleurs*, as well as the society-published (but of general interest) *Aeronautics and Astronautics* and *Spaceflight*.

Principal rocket and astronautical events are chronicled each year in NASA's *Astronautics and Aeronautics*, a day-by-day survey of what has happened all over the world. The period from 1915 to 1960 is compiled in one volume by Eugene M. Emme: *Aeronautics and Astronautics*. Much information of a compilatory nature is also published by the United States House of Representatives and the United States Senate space committees (respectively, Science and Astronautics, and Aeronautical and Space Sciences).

Information sources prior to the advent of the Space Age in 1957 are much more scarce than those since. For events from 1900 to Sputnik 1, it is necessary to consult the journals of the early rocket and astronautical societies (*e.g.* the German *Die Rakete* and its successors; the *Bulletin of the American Interplanetary Society* and its successors; and the *Journal of the British Interplanetary Society*), the book literature, and widely scattered articles appearing in technical and nontechnical sources outside the rocket-space field. Prior to 1900 the job becomes even more difficult.

Much of the information in this book has come from interviews and correspondence with persons closely associated with these events and from detailed inspections of their memorabilia. Limitations of space prohibit this sort of material in a bibliography.

1 The Lure of Other Worlds

Selected books on the history of astronomy and of man's ideas of the universe around him are first given:

Abetti, Giorgio. *History of Astronomy*. New York: Abelard-Schuman, 1952.

Bentley, John. *A Historical View of the Hindu Astronomy*. London: Smith, Elder, 1825.

Berry, Arthur. *A Short History of Astronomy; From Earliest Times Through the Nineteenth Century*. New York: Dover, 1961.

Brennand, W. *Hindu Astronomy*. London: Chas. Straker & Sons, 1896.

Brewster, Sir David. *Memoires of the Life, Writings, and Discoveries of Sir Isaac Newton*. 2 vols. Edinburgh: Thomas Constable, 1855.

Carlos, Edward Stafford. *The Sidereal Messenger of Galileo Galilei*. London: Rivingtons, 1880.

Carmody, Francis J. *Arabic Astronomical & Astrological Sources in Latin Translation*. Berkeley: University of California Press, 1956. (Extensive bibliography.)

Clerke, Agnes M. *A Popular History of Astronomy During the Nineteenth Century*. London: A. & C. Black, 1902.

Copernicus, Nicolaus. *De Revolutionibus Orbium Coelestium*. New York: Johnson Reprint, 1965. (Facsimile reprint.)

Delambre, Jean Baptiste Joseph. *Histoire de l'Astronomie Ancienne; Histoire de l'Astronomie du Moyen Age; and Histoire de l'Astronomie Moderne*. Paris: V. Courcier, 1817, 1819, and 1821, respectively.

Derham, William. *Physico-Teology: Or, A Demonstration of the Being and Attributes of God, from his Works of Creation*. London: A. Strahan, 1798. (Critique of Huygens, possibility of habitation of planets, and so on.)

Doig, Peter. *A Concise History of Astronomy*. London: Chapman & Hall, 1950.

Flammarion, Camille. *La Pluralité des Mondes Habités*. Paris: Didier & Cie, 1864.

Fontenelle, Bernard S. Bouvier de. *Conversations on the Plurality of Worlds*. London: A. Bettesworth, 1715. Also: *A Discovery of New Worlds*. London: Will. Canning, 1688. (Translations of the original French *Entretiens sur la Pluralité des Mondes*.)

Galilei, Galileo. *Dialogue Concerning the Two Chief World Systems—Ptolemaic and Copernican*. Berkeley: University of California Press, 1953.

Grant, Robert. *History of Physical Astronomy from the Earliest Ages to the Middle of the Nineteenth Century*. London: Henry & Bohn, 1852.

Heath, Thomas Little. *Aristarchus of Samos*. Oxford: Clarenden Press, 1913.

———. *Greek Astronomy*. London: Dent, 1932.

Huygens, Christian. *The Celestial Worlds Discover'd: Or Conjectures Concerning the Inhabitants, Plants, and Productions of the Worlds in the Planets*. London: Printed for Timothy Childe at the West-end of St. Paul's Church-yard, 1698. (English edition of *Cosmotheoros*.)

Kesten, Hermann. *Copernicus and His World*. London: Secker and Warburg, 1945.

Lewis, George Cornewall. *An Historical Survey of the Astronomy of the Ancients*. London: Parker, Son and Bourn, 1862.

Ley, Willy. *Watchers of the Sky*. New York: Viking, 1963.

Martin, Th. H. *Aristarque de Samos*. Paris: Imprimerie des Sciences Mathématiques et Physiques, 1871.

Neugebauer, Otto Eduard, ed. *Astronomical Cuneiform Texts: Babylonian Ephemerides of the Seleucid Period for the Motion of the Sun, the Moon and the Planets*. London: Lund, Humphries, 1955.

———. *Egyptian Astronomical Texts*. London: Lund, Humphries, 1960.

Orr, Mary Ackworth. *Dante and the Early Astronomers*. London: Gall & Inglis, 1913.

Pannekoek, A. *History of Astronomy*. New York: Interscience Publishers, 1961.

Plutarch. *De Facie in Orbe Lunare*. Cambridge: Harvard University Press, 1957. Found in his *Moralia* as *The Face on the Moon* in Harold Cherniss's translation in the Loeb Classical Library XII.

Rosen, Edward. *Kepler's Conversation with Galileo's Sidereal Messenger*. New York: Johnson Reprint, 1965.

Sambursky, S. *The Physical World of the Greeks*. London: Routledge & Kegan Paul, 1956.

Seyyed Hossein Nasr. *An Introduction to Islamic Cosmological Doctrines*. Cambridge: Harvard University Press, 1964.

Shapley, Harlow, and Howarth, Helen E. *A Source Book in Astronomy*. New York: McGraw-Hill, 1929.

Singer, Charles, ed. *Studies in the History and Method of Science*. 2 vols. Oxford: University Press, 1917 (Vol. 1) and 1921 (Vol. 2).

Singer, Dorothea Waley. *Giordano Bruno*. London: Abelard-Schuman, 1950.

Small, Robert. *An Account of the Astronomical Discoveries of Kepler*. London: J. Mawman, 1804; reprinted: Madison: University of Wisconsin Press, 1963.

Struve, O., and Zeberts, V. *Astronomy of the 20th Century*. New York: Macmillan, 1962.

Swedenborg, Emanuel. *Earths in our Solar System which are Called Planets and Earths in the Starry Heaven, their Inhabitants, and the Spirits and Angels there from Things Heard and Seen*. London: Swedenborg Society, 1962.

Tannery, Paul. *Recherches sur l'Histoire de l'Astronomie Ancienne*. Paris: Gauthier-Villars, 1893.

Thorndike, Lynn. *The Sphere of Sacrobosco and its Commentators*. Chicago: University of Chicago Press, 1949.

Whewell, William. *Of the Plurality of Worlds*. London: John W. Parker & Son, 1859.

Wilkins, John. *The Discovery of a World in the Moone; Or, A Discourse Tending to Prove 'tis Probable there May be Another Habitable World in that Planet*. London: E. G. for Michael Sparke and Edward Forrest, 1638.

Winlock, H. E. *Excavations at Deir el Bahri*. New York: Macmillan, 1942. (Astronomical concepts in ancient Egyptian tomb of Sen-mūt.)

Young, L. B., ed. *Exploring the Universe*. New York: McGraw-Hill, 1963.

A number of surveys of the fictional literature on space have been made, including:

Bailey, J. O. *Pilgrims Through Space and Time*. New York: Argus Books, 1947.

Berneri, Maria Louise. *Journey Through Utopia*. London: Routledge & Kegan Paul, 1950.

Bleiler, E. F., ed. *The Checklist of Fantastic Literature*. Chicago: Shasta, 1948.

Bretnor, Reginald, ed. *Modern Science Fiction, its Meaning and its Future*. New York: Coward-McCann, 1953.

Davenport, Basil. *Inquiry into Science Fiction*. New York: Longmans, 1955.

De Camp, L. Sprague. *Science-Fiction Handbook*. New York: Hermitage House, 1953.

———, and Ley, Willy. *Lands Beyond*. New York: Rinehart, 1952.

Derleth, August, ed. *Beyond Time and Space*. New York: Pellegrini and Cudahy, 1950.

Flammarion, Camille. *Les Mondes Imaginaires et les Mondes Réels*. Paris: Didier & Cie, 1876. (Reviews many fictional works.)

Freedman, R. *2000 Years of Space Travel*. New York: Holiday House, 1963.

Gaul, A. *Complete Book of Space Travel*. New York: World, 1956.

Gibbs-Smith, C. H. *A History of Flying*. London: B. T. Batsford, 1953.

Gove, Philip Babcock. *The Imaginary Voyage in Prose Fiction. A History of its Criticism and a Guide for its Study, with an Annotated Check List of 215 Imaginary Voyages from 1700 to 1800*. New York: Columbia University Press, 1941.

Green, R. L. *Into Other Worlds*. New York: Abelard-Schuman, 1958.

Hodgson, John Edmund. *The History of Aeronautics in Great Britain from the Earliest Times to the Latter Half of the Nineteenth Century*. London: Oxford University Press, 1924.

Lecornu, J. *La Navigation Aérienne*. Paris: Vuibert & Nony, 1909.

Leighton, Peter. *Moon Travellers*. London: Oldbourne Books, 1960.

Moskowitz, Sam. *Explorers of the Infinite*. New York: World, 1963.

Nicholson, Marjorie. *Voyages to the Moon*. New York: Macmillan, 1948.

Tissandier, Gaston. *Bibliographie Aéronautique*. Paris: H. Launette, 1887.

A selection of novels dealing with Lunar and planetary travel from antiquity to the end of the eighteenth century is given below (editions cited are not necessarily the first).

A. Antiquity to 1800

An Account of Count d'Artois and his Friend's Passage to the Moon, in a Flying Machine, Called, An Air Balloon, Which was Constructed in France . . . . Litchfield: Printed for Collier and Copp, 1785.

Furetiriana, ou les bons mots et les remarques d'histoire, de morale, de critique, de plaisanterie, et d'érudition de M. Furetière, Abbé de Chalivoy, de l'Académie Française. Brussels: François Foppens, 1698.

La Relation du Monde de Mercure. Found in Charles G. T. Garnier's *Voyages Imaginaires, Songes, Visions et Romans Cabalistiques*. Vol. 16. Amsterdam and Paris: Rue et Hôtel Serpente, 1777.

Brunt, Samuel. *A Voyage to Cacklogallinia*. London: J. Watson, 1727. See New York: Facsimile Text Society, Columbia University Press, 1940.

Cyrano de Bergerac. *Histoire comique des états et empires de la lune et du soleil*. Paris: Chez Charles le Sercy, 1656. See *Voyages to the Sun and Moon*. London: George Routledge & Sons, 1923, and *Other Worlds*. London: Oxford University Press, 1965.

Danby, William. *The Somnium Scipionis of Cicero*: Rivingtons, 1829.

Daniel, Gabriel P. *Voiage du monde de Descartes*. Paris: Chez la Veuve de S. Bénard, 1691. See *A Voyage to the World of Cartesius*. London: T. Bonnet, 1694.

Defoe, Daniel. *The Consolidator: Or Memoirs of Sundry Transaction from the World in the Moon*. London: Benj. Bragg at the Blue Ball, 1705.

———. *A Journey to the World in the Moon*. Edinburgh: James Watson in Craig's Cross, 1705.

Firdausī. *The Shāh-Nāma of Firdausī*, done into English by A. G. Warner and E. Warner. London: Kegan Paul, 1905.

Gonsales, Domingo (pseud. for Francis Godwin, Bishop of Hereford). *The Man in the Moone: Or a Discourse of a Voyage Thither*. London: John Norton for Ioshua Kirton and Thomas Warren, 1638.

La Folie, Louis Guillaume de. *Le Philosophe Sans Prétention . . . .* Paris: Clusier, 1775.

Kepler, Johannes. See Lear, John. *Kepler's Dream, with Full Text and Notes of Somnium, Sive Astronomia Lunaris*. Berkeley: University of California Press, 1965.

Lodovico, Ariosto. *Orlando Furioso*. London: J. Harington, 1607. George Bell and Sons, 1876. In English heroical verse.

Lucianus, Samosatensis. *The Works of Lucian of Samosata*. Vol. 2. Oxford: Clarendon Press, 1905. (Contains Icaro-Menippus.)

———. *True History*. London: A. H. Bullen, 1902. (Note: the first English edition was entitled *Certaine Select Dialogues of Lucian, Together with his True Historie, translated from the Greeke into English by Mr. Francis Hickes. Whereunto is added the Life of Lucian gathered out of his owne Writings, with briefe Notes and Illustrations upon each Dialogue and Booke. By T. H. Mr. of Arts of Christ-Church in Oxford*. Oxford: 1634.)

Morris, Ralph. *A Narrative of the Life and Astonishing Adventure of John Daniel at Smith at Royston in Herefordshire. For a Course of Seventy Years*. London: Printed for M. Cooper, at the Globe in Paternoster-Row, 1751.

Roumier, Marie-Anne de. *Voyages de Milord Céton dans les sept planettes ou le nouveau mentor*.

In Garnier's *Voyages Imaginaires*, Vols. 17 and 18.

Russen, David. *Iter Lunare: or, A Voyage to the Moon*. London: J. Nutt, 1703.

Vasse, Cornélie (Wouters), Baronne de. *Le Char Volant, ou Voyage dans la Lune*. London and Paris: La Veuve Ballard & Fils, 1783.

Voltaire, François Marie Arouet de. *Le Micromégas*. In Vol. 23 of Garnier's *Voyages Imaginaires*. See also: *Micromégas: A Comic Romance*. London: D. Wilson, 1753.

Wilson, Miles. *The History of Israel Jobson . . . .* London: 1757.

B. *Nineteenth Century*

Astor, John Jacob. *Journey to Other Worlds*. New York: D. Appleton, 1894.

Atterley, Joseph (pseud. for George Tucker). *A Voyage to the Moon with some Account of the Manners and Customs, Science and Philosophy of the People of Morosofia and Other Lunarians*. New York: Elam Bliss, 1827.

Eyraud, Achille. *Voyage à Venus*. Paris: Michel Levy Frères, 1863.

Fowler, George. *A Flight to the Moon; or, the Vision of Randalthus*. Baltimore: Printed and sold by A. Miltenberger, 1813.

Greg, Percy. *Across the Zodiac: The Story of a Wrecked Record*. 2 vols. London: Trubner & Co., Ludgate Hill, 1880.

Hale, Edward Everett. *His Level Best and Other Stories*. Boston: Robert Brothers, 1872. (Contains "The Brick Moon.")

Lasswitz, Kurd. *Auf zwei Planeten*. Donauworth: Verlag Cassianeum, 1948 (originally published: Weimar, 1897).

Locke, Richard Adams. *The Celebrated "Moon Story," its Origin and Incidents*. New York: Bunnell and Price, 1852.

———. *The Moon Hoax: Or A Discovery that the Moon has a Vast Population of Human Beings*. New York: W. Gowans, 1859.

Poe, Edgar Allan. "The Unparalleled Adventure of One Hans Pfaall" from *Works* of Edgar Allan Poe edited by J. H. Ingram. Edinburgh: A. & C. Black, 1875.

Serviss, Garrett P. *Edison's Conquest of Mars*. Los Angeles: Carcosa House, 1947.

Verne, Jules. *Autour de la lune*. Paris: J. Hetzel, 1872. See *From the Earth to the Moon and Round the Moon*. London: Sampson, Low, Marston & Co., 1902.

———. *De la terre à la lune*. Paris: J. Hetzel, 1866.

Wells, H. G. *The First Men in the Moon*. London: George Newnes, 1901.

———. *The War of the Worlds*. London: William Heinemann, 1898.

2 A Thousand Years of Rocketry

General:

Hime, Henry William Lovett. *Gunpowder and Ammunition*. London: Longmans, 1904 (second edition appeared as *The Origin of Artillery* in 1915).

Hoeffer, Ferdinand. *Histoire de la chimie depuis les temps les plus reculées jusqu'a notre époque*. 2 vols. Paris: L. Hachette et Fortin, Masson & Cie, 1842.

Partington, James R. *A History of Greek Fire and Gunpowder*. Cambridge: W. Heffer & Sons, 1960.

Reinaud, Joseph Toussaint, and Favé, Ildephonse. *Histoire de l'Artillerie: feu grégeois, des feux de guerre et des origines de la poudre à canon*. 2 vols. Paris: J. Dumaine, neveu et succ. de G.-Laguione, 1845.

Sarton, George. *Introduction to the History of Science*. 3 vols. Baltimore: Williams and Wilkins, 1927 (Vol. 1) and 1931 (Vols. 2 and 3).

History of Rocketry to the Nineteenth Century:

A. *Chinese, Mongolian, and Arab Developments*

Amiot, Joseph Marie. *Art Militaire des Chinois, ou recueil d'anciens traités sur la guerre . . . .* Paris: Didot l'aîné, 1772.

———. *Memoire concernant l'histoire, les sciences, les arts, etc. des Chinois*. Vol. 8. Paris: Nyons, 1776.

Davis, Tenney L., and Ware, James R. "Early Chinese Military Pyrotechnics." *Journal of Chemical Education* 24, November 1947, pp. 522–537.

Fèng Chia-Shèng. *The Discovery and Westward Transmission of Gunpowder* (in Chinese). Kowloon: Chiao Liu Publication Service, 1962.

Gaubil, Antoine. *Histoire de Gentschiscan et de toute la dinastie de Mongous, ses successeurs, conquérants de la Chine*. Paris: 1739.

Goodrich, L. C., and Fèng Chia-Shèng. "The Early Development of Firearms in China." *Isis*, Vol. 36, No. 104, Pt. 2, 1946, pp. 114–123. Also "Addendum."

d'Incarville, Pierre. "Manière de faire des fleurs dans les feux d'artifices chinois." *Receuil de l'Académie des Sciences,* savants d'étrangers. Vol. 4. Paris: 1763.

Mailla, Joseph Anne-Marie Moriac de. *Histoire générale de la Chine.* Vol. 9. Paris: P. O. Pierres, 1777–1784.

Needham, Joseph, with the assistance of Wang Ling. *Science and Civilization in China.* Vol. 4, part 2, Cambridge: University Press, 1965.

d'Ohsson, Abraham Constantine Mouradgea. *Histoire des Mongols.* 4 vols. La Haye and Amsterdam: 1834–1835.

Pauthier, Jean Pierre Guillaume. *Chine, ou description historique, géographique et littéraire de ce vaste empire, d'après des documents chinois.* Paris: Librairie de Firmin-Didot et Littéraire et Cie, 1821.

Reinaud, Joseph Toussaint. "De l'art militaire chez les Arabes," *Journal Asiatique,* Vol. 12, No. 9, September 1848, pp. 193–237.

———— and Favé, Ildephonse. "Du feu grégeois, des feux de guerre, et des origines de la poudre à canon chez les Arabes, les Persans, et les Chinois." *Journal Asiatique,* Vol. 14, No. 10, October 1849, pp. 257–327.

Wang Ling. "On the Invention and Use of Gunpowder and Firearms in China." *Isis,* Vol. 37, Nos. 109–110, Pts. 3–4, July 1947, pp. 160–178.

B. Indian Developments

Beatson, Alexander. *A View of the Origin and Conduct of the War with Tippoo Sultaun; Comprising a Narrative of the Operations of his Army under the Command of Lieut. General George Harris, and of the Siege of Seringapatam.* London: G. & W. Nicol, Pall-Mall, 1800.

Dirom, Alexander. *A Narrative of the Campaign in India, which Terminated the War with Tippoo Sultaun.* London: W. Bulmer, 1793.

Mackenzie, Lt. Roderick. *A Sketch of the War with Tippoo Sultaun* . . . . 2 vols. London: J. Sewell, Cornhill, T. Egerton, Whitehall, and J. Debrett, Picadilly, 1799.

Mir Hussain, Ali Khan Kirmānī. *The History of the Reign of Tipú Sultán, Being a Continuation of the Neshani Hyduri.* Calcutta: Susil Gupta, 1858. (Translated from the Persian manuscript by Colonel W. Miles.)

C. Early European Developments

Livre de channonerie et artifice de feu. Paris: Vincent Sertenas, 1561. (Includes a "Petit traité contenant plusieurs artifices de feu, très utile pour l'estat de channonerie, recueilly d'un vieil livre escrit à la main, et nouvellement mis en lumière.")

Anderson, Robert. *The Making of Rockets.* London: Printed for Robert Morden, at the Atlas in Cornhill, 1696.

Babington, John. *Pyrotechnia or, A Discovrse of Artificiall Fireworks* . . . . London: Thomas Harper, for Ralph Mab, 1635.

Bate, John. *The Mysteries of Nature and Art.* London: Printed for Andrew Crooke, 1654. See Book 2: *The composing of all manner of Fier-Works for Triumph and Recreation.*

Biringuccio, Vannoccio. *De la pirotechnia.* Venice: Venturino Roffinello, 1540. See: Smith, Cyril S. and Gnudi, Martha T., *The Pirotechnia of Vannoccio Biringuccio.* New York: The American Institute of Mining and Metallurgical Engineers, 1942.

Frezier, Amédée François. *Traité des feux d'artifice.* Paris: D. Jollet, 1706; Hague: 1741; Paris: Nyons, 1747.

Geissler, Christoph Friedrich von. *Neu Curieuse und Vollkommene Artillerie* . . . . Dresden: 1718.

Gellius, Aulus. *Noctes Atticae, or the Attic Nights of Aulus Gellius.* Translated by John C. Rolfe. London: W. Heinemann, 1927; See also: *Attic Nights.* Translated by William Beloe. London: 1795.

Hero of Alexandria. *The Pneumatics.* Translated and edited by Bennet Woodcroft. London: Taylor Walton & Maberly, 1851.

Jones, Robert. *A New Treatise on Artificial Fireworks.* London: J. Millan, T. Lewis and Richardson and Urquart, 1765.

Lorrain, Hanzelet (Jean Appier). *La Pyrotechnie.* Pont-à-Mousson: I. and Gaspard Bernard, 1630.

Nye, Nathaneal. *The Art of Gunnery.* London: printed for William Leak, 1647.

d'Orval, Perinet. *Essay sur les feux d'artifice pour le spectacle et pour la guerre.* Paris: Chez Coustelier, 1745.

Pavelourt, Daniel. *Brieve instructions sur le faict de l'artillerie de France.* Paris: 1597.

Ruggiere, Gaetano and Sarti, Giuseppi. *A Description of the Machine for the Fireworks* . . . . London: W. Bowyer, 1749.

Schmidlap, Johann. *Kustliche und Rechtschaffene Feuerwerck zum Schimpff* . . . . Nuremberg: 1591.

Simienowicz, Casimir (or Kazimierz). *The Great Art of Artillery.* London: printed for S. Tonson at Shakespeare's Head in the Strand, 1729.

Nineteenth-Century Developments:

A. *European Rocketry*

Bem, Jozeph. *Erfahrung über die Congrevschen Brand-Raketen bis zum Jahr 1819* . . . Weimar: Im Verlage des Grossherzoglichen Sächs, priv. Landes-Industrie-Comptoires, 1820.

———. *Notes sur les fusées incendaires.* Warsaw: 1819.

Brock, A. St. H. *Pyrotechnics.* London: Daniel O'Connor, 1922.

———. *A History of Fireworks.* London: George G. Harrap, 1949.

Browne, W. H. *The Art of Pyrotechny: Being a Comprehensive and Practical Instructions for the Manufacture of Fireworks, Specially Designed for the Use of Amateurs.* London: The Bazaar Office, 1883.

Chertier, François-Marie. *Nouvelles recherches sur les feux d'artifice.* Paris: 1854.

Cockburn, James P. *Memoire on the Preparation of Rockets.* London: 1844.

Congreve, Sir William. *A Concise Account of the Origin and Progress of the Rocket System.* Dublin: A. O'Neil, 1817.

———. *A Concise Account of the Origin and Progress of the Rocket System with a View of the Apparent Advantages Both as to the Effect Produced, and the Comparative Saving of Expense, Arising from the Peculiar Facilities of Application which it Possesses as Well for Naval and Military Purposes.* London: J. Whiting, 1807.

———. *The Different Modes of Use and Exercises of Rockets.* London: 1808.

———. *Memoir on the Possibility, the Means and the Importance of the Destruction of the Boulogne Flotilla, in the Present Crisis* . . . . London: J. Whiting, 1806.

———. *A Treatise on the General Principles, Powers, and Facility of Application of the Congreve Rocket System* . . . . London: Longman, Rees, Orme, Brown & Green, 1827.

Corréard, Joseph. *Histoire des Fusées de guerre, ou Recueil de tout ce qui a été publié ou écrit sur ce projectile.* Paris: 1841.

Cutbush, James. *A System of Pyrotechny, Comprehending the Theory and Practice, with the Application of Chemistry; Designed for Exhibition and for War.* Philadelphia: C. F. Cutbush, 1825.

Dennett, John. *A Concise Description of a Powerful Species of War Rockets* . . . . London: 1832. (Relates uses of converted war rockets.)

Dennisse, Amedée. *Feux d'artifices: formules nouvelles* . . . . Paris: 1886.

Dolleczek, Anton. *Geschichte der Österreichschen Artillerie* . . . . Vienna: Druck von Kreisel & Gröger, 1887.

Emin-Pacha, Mahomet. *Mémoire sur un nouveau système de confection des fusées de guerre* . . . . Paris: 1840.

Hale, William. *Treatise on the Comparative Merits of a Rifle Gun and Rotary Rocket* . . . . London: W. Mitchell, 1863.

Hoyer, Johann Gotfried. *System der Brandraketen nach Congreve und Andern.* Leipzig, 1827.

Kentish, Thomas. *The Complete Art of Firework-Making.* London: Chatto & Windus, 1905.

Konstantinov, Konstantin. *Lectures sur les fusées de guerre faites en 1860* . . . . Paris: 1861.

———. *Mémoire sur les fusées de guerre* . . . . 2 vols. Paris: 1858–1861. Note: a Russian edition of this work appeared in 1864.

———. *Nyekotorioy Svedyeniya o Vvyedenii i Oopotyeblenii Boyevih Ratyet (Some Information and Application of War Rockets).* St. Petersburg: 1855.

Meyer, Moritz. *Traité de Pyrotechnie.* Liege: Felix Oudart, 1844.

Mongéry, Merigon de. *Traité des fusées de guerre* . . . . Paris: 1825.

Moore, William. *A Treatise on the Motion of Rockets.* London: 1813.

Morel, A. M. Th. *Traité practique des feux d'artifice.* Paris: Chez Firmin Didot, 1800.

Mori, Giuseppe. *Sul rinculo delle armi da fuoco e movimento de razzi.* Naples: 1839.

Peretsdorf, J. Ravichio de. *Traité de pyrotechnie militaire, contenant tous les artifices de guerre en usage en Autriche.* Strassbourg: 1824.

Pralon, A. *Une page de l'histoire de l'artillerie—les fusées de guerre en France.* Paris: 1883.

Rogier, Charles. *A Treatise on the Utility of a Rocket Armament Assisted by Balloons, where Ships of War Cannot be Accessible; both Defensive and Offensive, to Annoying the Enemy's Harbour, that are Stubborn and Delight in War.* Knutsford: Cheshire, 1818.

Ruggieri, Claude-Fortuné. *Elémens de pyrotechnie.* Paris: Barba Librairie, 1811.

Scoffern, John. *New Resources for Warfare.* London: Longman, Brown, 1859.

———. *Projectile Weapons of War and Explosive Compounds.* London: Cooke & Whitley, 1852.

Solms: see Uhlhor, Friedrich. *Reinhard Graf zu*

Solms, *Herr zu Münzenberg*. Marburg: N. G. Elwert Verlag, 1952.

Thiroux, Charles Victor. *Observations et vues nouvelles sur les fusées de guerre*. Paris: 1849.

Viluma, Marques de. *Noticia sobre el origen, progresos y estado actual de los cohetes de guerra llamados a la Congreve*. Madrid: 1833.

B. War of 1812 in America

Barney, Mary. *Narrative Memoir of the Late Commodore Barney*. Boston: Grey & Bowen, 1832.

Foother, Hulbert. *Sailor of Fortune: The Life and Adventures of Commodore Joshua Barney, U.S.N.* New York: Harper, 1940.

Gleig, G. R. *Narrative of the Campaign of the British Army at Washington and New Orleans*. London: J. Murray, 1826.

Parker, Thomas. *Narrative of the Battle of Bladensburg*. Washington, D. C.: Bailey Pamphlets, Library of Congress, 1814.

Robinson, Ralph. "Use of Rockets by the British." *Maryland Historical Magazine*, Vol. 40, No. 1, March 1945, pp. 1–6.

Stein, Charles Francis, Jr. *Our National Anthem The Star-Spangled Banner*. Baltimore: Wyman Park Federal Savings and Loan Association, 1964.

C. Miscellaneous United States

Military Pyrotechny for the Use of Cadets of the U.S. Military Academy, West Point. West Point, N.Y. U.S. Military Academy, 1839.

3 Pioneers of Space Travel

Deutherty, Charles Michael. *Robert Goddard: Trail Blazer to the Stars*. New York: Macmillan, 1964.

Gartman, Heinz. *The Men Behind the Space Rockets*. New York: David McKay, 1956.

Goddard, Robert H. *Autobiography*. Worcester, Mass.: St. Onge, 1967.

———. *Rocket Development*. Englewood Cliffs, N.J.: Prentice-Hall, 1948.

Kosmodemyansky, A. *Konstantin Tsiolkovsky*. Moscow: Foreign Languages Publishing House, 1956.

Lehman, M. *This High Man*. New York: Farrar, Straus, 1963 (Biography of Goddard.)

Oberth, Hermann. *Die Rakete zu den Planetenräumen*. Munich: R. Oldenbourg, 1923.

———. *Man into Space*. New York: Harper, 1957.

———. *The Moon Car*. New York: Harper, 1959.

———. *Wege zur Raumschiffahrt*. Munich: R. Oldenbourg, 1929.

Thomas, Shirley. *Men of Space*. Vol. 1. Philadelphia: Chilton, 1960. (Contains biographies of Goddard and Tsiolkovsky as well as other individuals.)

Tsiolkovsky, Konstantin Eduardovitch. *Sobranie Sochinenie (Collected Works)*. Moscow: Izd. Akademii Nauk U.S.S.R., 1951, 1954, and 1959. Note: These have been translated and released by the National Aeronautics and Space Administration in Washington, D.C., as Technical Translations F-236, 237, and 238, dated 1965. Also, NASA issued his *Works on Rocket Technology* as TT F-243, 1965, containing the 1903 article "A Rocket into Cosmic Space," the 1911 article "The Investigation of Universal Space by Means of Reactive Devices," and the 1926 "Investigation of Universal Space by Reactive Devices."

Verral, C. S. *Robert Goddard: Father of the Space Age*. Englewood Cliffs, N.J.: Prentice-Hall, 1963.

Walters, H. B. *Hermann Oberth: Father of Space Travel*. New York: Macmillan, 1962.

Williams, B. and Epstein, S. *The Rocket Pioneers*. New York: Julian Messner, 1955.

Winders, G. H. *Robert H. Goddard: Father of Rocketry*. New York: Day, 1963.

4 The Legacy of the Pioneers

Adams, Carsbie C., and others. *Space Flight*. New York: McGraw-Hill, 1958.

Ananoff, Alexandre. *L'Astronautique*. Paris: Librairie Arthème Fayard, 1950.

Barré, J. J. "Des fusées de guerre." *Revue Historique de l'Armée*. Vol. 12, No. 4, 1956, pp. 157–162.

———. "Historique des Etudes Françaises sur les Fusées à Oxygene Liquide." *Memorial de l'Artillerie Française*. 1er fasc. 1961. Reprinted Paris: Imprimerie Nationale, 1961.

Baumgarten-Crusius, Artur von. *Die Rakete als Weltfriedenstaube*. Leipzig: Rossberg'sche Buchdruckerei, 1931.

Bergman, A. "The Use of Rockets and Illuminating Shells in the Present War." *Journal of Acetylene Lighting*. Vol. 20, No. 1, July 1918, pp. 12–14.

Bloom, Ursula. *He Lit the Lamp*. London: Burke, 1958. (Contains details of A. M. Low's missile work.)

Brügel, Werner. *Männer der Rakete*. Leipzig: Hachmeister und Thal, 1933.

Butlerov, A. A., ed., and others. *Reaktivnoe Dvizhenie (Jet Propulsion)*. Leningrad and Moscow: ONTI, Glavnaya Redaksiya Obshcheteknicheskoi Literatury, 1935. (A second volume was released the following year.)

Canby, C. *History of Rockets and Space.* Manhasset, N.Y.: New Illustrated Library of Science and Invention, 1963.

Cleater, P. E. *Rockets Through Space.* New York: Simon & Schuster, 1936.

De Leeuw, H. *From Flying Horse to Man in the Moon.* New York: St. Martin's Press, 1963.

Emme, Eugene. *A History of Space Flight.* New York: Holt, Rinehart & Winston, 1965.

Esnault-Pelterie, Robert. *L'Astronautique.* Paris: A. Lahure, 1930.

———. *L'Astronautique-Complément.* Paris: Société des Ingénieurs Civils de France, 1935.

———. *L'exploration par fusées de la très haute atmosphère et la possibilité des voyages interplanétaires.* Paris: Société Astronomique de France, 1928.

Faber, Henry B. *Military Pyrotechnics.* 3 vols. Washington, D.C.: U.S. Government Printing Office, 1919.

Haley, Andrew G. *Rocketry and Space Exploration.* Princeton, N.J.: Van Nostrand, 1958.

Harper, Harry. *Dawn of the Space Age.* London: Sampson Low, Marson, 1946.

Hohmann, Walter. *Die Erreichbarkeit der Himmelskörper.* Munich: R. Oldenbourg, 1925.

Kaiser, H. K. *Kleine Raketenkunde.* Stuttgart: Mundus-Verlag, 1949.

Kleimenov, I. T., ed., and others. *Raketnaya Tekhnika (Rocket Technology).* Moscow and Leningrad: ONTI, 1936.

Korolov, Sergey Pavlovich. *Raketnyi Polet v Stratosfere (Rocket Flight in the Stratosphere).* Moscow: Voenizdat, 1934.

Kronstein, Max, and Dellenbag, J. *Rocket Mail Catalogue and Historical Survey of First Experiments in Rocketry.* Jamaica, N.Y.: F. Billig, 1955.

Langemak, G. E., and Glushko, V. P. *Rakety, Ikh Ustroistvo i Primeneniye (Rockets, Their Construction and Utilization).* Moscow: ONTI, 1935.

Lasser, David. *Conquest of Space.* New York: Penguin, 1931.

Lehmann, Ernst A. *Zeppelin.* New York: Longmans, 1937. (Contains a description of French use of rockets against German dirigibles during World War I.)

Ley, Willy. *Die Fahrt ins Weltall.* Leipzig: Hachmeister und Thal, 1926.

———. *Die Möglichkeit der Weltraumfahrt.* Leipzig: Hachmeister und Thal, 1928.

———. *Rockets, Missiles and Men in Space.* New York: Viking, 1968.

Moore, Patrick. *Space: The Story of Man's Greatest Feat of Exploration.* New York: Macmillan, 1968.

Noordung, Hermann. *Das Problem der Befahrung des Weltraums.* Berlin: R. C. Schmidt, 1929.

Pendray, G. Edward. *The Coming Age of Rocket Power.* New York: Harper, 1945.

Perelman, Jakov Isidorovich. *Mezhplanetnye Puteshestviya (Interplanetary Travels).* Leningrad and Moscow: ONTI, 1935.

Philp, C. C. *Stratosphere and Rocket Flight.* London: Sir Isaac Pitman & Sons, 1937.

Rynin, Nikolai Aleksevich. *Mezhplanetnye Soobshcheniya (Interplanetary Communications).* This great nine-volume encyclopedic work was released between 1928 and 1932 by several different publishers in Leningrad and in numbers ranging from less than a thousand to fifteen thousand. Vol. 7 is a biography of Tsiolkovsky and Vol. 9 a comprehensive bibliography.

Sänger, Eugen, *Raketenflugtechnik.* Munich: R. Oldenbourg, 1933.

Scherschevsky, Alexander Boris. *Die Rakete für Fahrt und Flug.* Berlin: C. J. E. Volckmann, 1929.

Tikhonravov, M. K. *Raketnaya Tekhniya (Rocket Technology).* Moscow: ONTI, 1935.

Tsander, Fridrikh Arturovich. *Probleme Poleta Pri Pomoshchi Raketnykh Apparatov (Problems of Flight by Jet Propulsion).* Note: this 1932 work has been translated and released in English. Jerusalem: Israel Program for Scientific Translations, 1964.

Valier, Max. *Raketenfahrt.* Munich: R. Oldenbourg, 1930.

Wilcox, A. *Moon Rocket.* London: Thomas Nelson & Sons, 1946.

5 The Rocket Returns to War

In this section of the bibliography only those works primarily concerned with World War II rocketry are recorded; many books listed for Chapter 6 contain information on wartime rocketry, though they generally concentrate on postwar efforts.

U.S. Rocket Ordnance: Development and Use in World War II. Washington, D.C.: Government Printing Office, 1946.

Benecke, Th. and Quick, A. W. *History of German Guided Missile Development.* Brunswick, Germany: Verlag E. Appelhaus, 1957.

Bolster, C. M. *Assisted Take-off of Aircraft.* Northfield, Vt.: Norwich University, 1960.

Bowman, Norman J. *Handbook of Rockets and Guided Missiles.* Chicago: Perastadion Press, 1957.

Boyce, Joseph C., ed. *New Weapons for Air Warfare.* Boston: Little, Brown, 1947. (Covers U.S. guided-missile developments.)

Burchard, John E., ed. *Rockets, Guns and Targets.* Boston: Little, Brown, 1948.

Crow, Sir Alwyn D. "The Rocket as a Weapon of War in the British Forces." *Institution of Mechanical Engineers Journal and Proceedings,* Vol. 158, No. 1, June 1948, pp. 15–21.

Dornberger, Walter. *V-2.* New York: Viking, 1954.

Feist, Uwe, and Maloney, Edward T. *Messerschmitt Me163.* Fallbrook, Calif.: Aero, 1967.

Gatland, Kenneth W. *Development of the Guided Missile.* New York: Philosophical Library, 1952.

Huzel, Dieter K. *Peenemünde to Canaveral.* Englewood Cliffs, N.J.: Prentice-Hall, 1962.

Irving, David. *The Mare's Nest.* London: William Kimber, 1964. (British Intelligence activities in attempting to discover nature and capabilities of German bombardment rocket weapons and countermeasures taken.)

Joubert de la Ferté, Sir Philip B. *Rocket.* New York: Philosophical Library, 1957. (Story of V-1 and V-2 seen from the British side of the fence.)

Klee, Ernst, and Merk, Otto. *The Birth of the Missile.* New York: Dutton, 1965. (Deals with Peenemünde and the V weapons.)

Kooy, J. M. J. and Uytenbogaart, J. W. H. *Ballistics of the Future.* Haarlem, Netherlands: N.V. de Technische Vitgeverij H. Stam, 1946. (Contains information on V-1 and V-2 missiles and their operational use.)

Lusar, Rudolf. *German Secret Weapons of the Second World War.* New York: Philosophical Library, 1959.

McGovern, James. *Crossbow and Overcast.* New York: Morrow, 1964. (Covers Allied intelligence efforts to discover the capabilities of the V weapons and the means by which the Americans rounded up the leading German rocket scientists plus documentation and materiel at the close of hostilities in the spring of 1945.)

Napier, A. F. S. "British Rockets in the World War." *British Royal Artillery Journal,* Vol. 73, No. 1, January 1946, pp. 11–20.

Ordway, Frederick I., III, and Wakeford, Ronald C. *International Missile and Spacecraft Guide.* New York: McGraw-Hill, 1960. (Part 1 contains a detailed survey of World War II rockets and missiles.)

Pile, General Sir Frederick. *Ack-Ack: Britain's Defence Against Air Attack During the Second World War.* London: George C. Harrap, 1949.

Ross, Frank, Jr. *Guided Missiles: Rockets and Torpedoes.* New York: Lothrop, 1951.

Rosser, R. B., Newton, R. R. and Gross, G. L. *Mathematical Theory of Rocket Flight.* New York: McGraw-Hill, 1947. (Official final report on Section H, Division 3 of NDRC on exterior ballistics of fin-stabilized rockets.)

Sänger, Eugen, and Bredt, Irene. *Rocket Drive for Long Range Bombers.* Whittier, Calif.: Robert Cornog, 1952.

Walters, Helen B. *Wernher von Braun: Rocket Engineer.* New York: Macmillan, 1964.

Weyl, A. R. *Guided Missiles.* London: Temple Press, 1949.

Ziegler, M. *Rocket Fighter.* London: MacDonald, 1963. (Covers the Me 163 rocket airplane.)

Zim, H. S. *Rockets and Jets.* New York: Harcourt, 1945.

6 Postwar Military Rocketry

Chapters 6–9 deal with the two decades from the end of World War II to 1966. Many of the hundreds of books dealing with the period are concerned with more than one subject. For ease of reference, therefore, multisubject works are generally not given, with the result that only a relatively few, carefully selected works are cited. The majority of these books contain ample bibliographic material to which the reader can refer for further reading and research.

Guided Missiles—Operations, Design and Theory. New York: McGraw-Hill, 1958.

Abel, Elie. *The Missiles of October: The Cuban Missile Crisis 1962.* London: MacGibbon & Key, 1966.

Akens, David S. *A Pictorial History of Rockets and Rocketry.* Huntsville, Ala.: Strode Publishers, 1966.

Altman, D., and others. *Liquid Propellant Rockets.* Princeton, N.J.: Princeton University Press, 1960.

Baar, J., and Howard, W. E. *Combat Missileman.* New York: Harcourt, 1961.

———. *Polaris: The Concept and Creation of a New and Mighty Weapon.* New York: Harcourt, 1960.

Barrère, M., and others. *Rocket Propulsion.* Amsterdam: Elsevier Publishing, 1960.

Bergaust, Erik. *Reaching for the Stars.* New York: Doubleday, 1960. (Biography of Wernher von Braun; gives considerable attention to events in the 1945–1960 period and the Army ballistic missile program.)

Brodie, B. *Strategy in the Missile Age.* Princeton, N.J.: Princeton University Press, 1959.

Burgess, Erik. *Guided Weapons.* New York: Macmillan, 1957.

————. *Long-range Ballistic Missiles.* New York: Macmillan, 1962.

Caiden, Martin. *Rockets and Missiles—Past and Future.* New York: McBride, 1954.

Chapman, J. L. *Atlas: The Story of a Missile.* New York: Harper, 1960.

Clemow, J. *Short-range Guided Weapons.* London: Temple Press, 1961.

Emme, Eugene M., ed. *History of Rocket Technology.* Detroit: Wayne State University Press, 1964. (Covers not only ballistic missile developments but carrier vehicles and spacecraft.)

Gantz, K. F. *United States Air Force Report on the Ballistic Missile: Its Technology, Logistics, and Strategy.* Garden City, N.Y.: Doubleday, 1958.

Gavin, James M. *War and Peace in the Space Age.* New York: Harper, 1958. (By former Army general; is concerned with tactical and strategic implications of missiles, spacecraft.)

Gröttrup, Irmgard. *Rocket Wife.* London: A. Deutsche, 1959. (The story of the Germans who worked on Russia's missile program under Helmut Gröttrup from the mid-1940's until the early 1950's).

Hartt, J. *Mighty Thor.* New York: Duell, Sloan & Pearce, 1961.

Huggett, C., Bartley, C. E., and Mills, M. M. *Solid Propellant Rockets.* Princeton, N.J.: Princeton University Press, 1960.

Humphries, John. *Rockets and Guided Missiles.* New York: Macmillan, 1956.

Kit, B., and Evered, D. S. *Rocket Propellant Handbook.* New York: Macmillan, 1960.

Lee, A., ed. *Soviet Air and Rocket Forces.* New York: Praeger, 1959.

Medaris, J. B. *Countdown for Decision.* New York: Putnam, 1960. (By the former head of the Army Ballistic Missile Agency.)

Merrill, G., and others, eds. *Dictionary of Guided Missiles and Space Flight.* Princeton, N.J.: Van Nostrand, 1959.

Neal, R. *Ace in the Hole.* New York: Doubleday, 1962. (The story of the Minuteman ICBM.)

Ordway, Frederick I., III, and Wakeford, Ronald C. *International Missile and Spacecraft Guide.* New York: McGraw-Hill, 1960. (Part 2 describes postwar missiles and spacecraft.)

Parry, Albert. *Russia's Rockets and Missiles.* Garden City, N.Y.: Doubleday, 1960.

Schwiebert, Ernest G. *A History of the U.S. Air Force Ballistic Missiles.* New York: Praeger, 1965.

Skelton, W. R. *Countdown: The Story of Cape Canaveral.* Boston: Little, Brown, 1960.

Sutton, George P. *Rocket Propulsion Elements.* New York: Wiley, 1963.

Zucrow, Maurice. *Aircraft and Missile Propulsion.* 2 vols. New York: Wiley, 1958.

7 Probing the Fringe of Space

Relatively few books have been written that treat sounding rockets and carrier vehicles exclusively. Many astronautical works cited for the last two chapters contain much information on carriers.

Berkner, Lloyd V., ed. *Manual of Rockets and Satellites.* New York: Pergamon Press, 1958.

Boyd, R. L. F., and Seaton, M. J., eds. *Rocket Exploration of the Upper Atmosphere.* New York: Pergamon Press, 1954.

Buedeler, Werner. *Operation Vanguard.* London: Burke Publishing, 1957.

Gatland, Kenneth W. *Spacecraft and Boosters.* London: Iliffe Books, 1964.

Holder, W. G. *Saturn Five: The Moon Rocket.* New York: Messner, 1968.

Lange, O. H., and Stein, R. J. *Space Carrier Vehicles: Design, Development and Testing of Launching Rockets.* New York: Academic Press. 1963.

Newell, Homer E., Jr. *High Altitude Rocket Research.* New York: Academic Press, 1953.

————. *Sounding Rockets.* New York: McGraw-Hill, 1959.

Ordway, Frederick I., III, ed. *Advances in Space Science and Technology.* Vols. 6 and 7. New York: Academic Press, 1964 and 1965. (Contain two-part monograph on "Rocket, Missile and Carrier Vehicle Testing, Launching and Tracking Technology" within and outside the United States, by Mitchell R. Sharpe, Jr., and John M. Lowther.)

Rosen, Milton W. *Viking Rocket Story.* New York: Harper, 1955.

Samson, D. R., ed. *Development of the Blue Streak*

Satellite Launcher. New York: Pergamon Press, 1963.

Southall, Ivan. *Woomera.* Sydney: Angus and Robertson, 1962. (Describes the large Australian launching site for sounding rockets, carrier vehicles, and missiles.)

Stehling, Kurt R. *Project Vanguard.* Garden City, N.Y.: Doubleday, 1961.

Vaeth, J. Gordon. *200 Miles Up.* New York: Ronald Press, 1955.

Wexler, H., and Caskey, J. E., Jr., eds. *Rocket and Satellite Meteorology.* Amsterdam: North-Holland Publishing, 1963.

Young, R. E. *Telemetry.* London: Temple Press, 1963. (Describes how information is sent by radio from sounding rockets and probes to receiving stations on the ground.)

8 The Remote Explorers

This section lists books that deal principally with the subject of the chapter and those that cover the general field of astronautics. This has been done to avoid duplicating the bibliography for the next chapter, which deals only with manned space flight.

Above and Beyond: The Encyclopedia of Aviation and Space Sciences. 14 vols. Chicago: New Horizons, 1968.

The McGraw-Hill Encyclopedia of Space. New York: McGraw-Hill, 1968.

Soviet Writings on Earth Satellites and Space Travel. New York: Citadel, 1958.

The Teacher's Handbook of Astronautics. London: British Interplanetary Society, 1963.

Adams, Carsbie C., von Braun, Wernher, and Ordway, Frederick I., III. *Careers in Astronautics and Rocketry.* New York: McGraw-Hill, 1962.

Baar, James, and Howard, William E., *Spacecraft and Missiles of the World.* New York: Harcourt, Brace & World, 1966.

Berkner, Lloyd V., and Odishaw, Hugh, eds. *Science in Space.* New York: McGraw-Hill, 1961.

Berman, A. I. *Physical Principles of Astronautics.* New York: Wiley, 1961.

Bester, Alfred. *The Life and Death of a Satellite.* Boston: Little, Brown, 1966.

Blasingame, B. P. *Astronautics.* New York: McGraw-Hill, 1964.

Boyd, R. L. F. *Space Research by Rocket and Satellite.* New York: Harper, 1960.

Bucheim, R. W., and Rand Corp. staff. *Space Handbook: Astronautics and Its Applications.* New York: Random House, 1959.

Carter, L. J. *Artificial Satellite.* London: British Interplanetary Society, 1951.

Chester, M., and Kramer, S. B. *Discoverer: The Story of a Satellite.* New York: Putnam, 1960.

Clarke, Arthur C. *The Coming of the Space Age.* Des Moines: Meredith, 1967.

——. *Interplanetary Flight.* New York: Harper, 1951.

——. *The Making of a Moon.* New York: Harper, 1957.

——. *Voices from the Sky.* New York: Harper, 1965.

Corliss, William R. *Propulsion Systems for Space Flight.* New York: McGraw-Hill, 1960.

——. *Scientific Satellites.* Washington: NASA, 1967.

——. *Space Probes and Planetary Exploration.* Princeton, N.J.: Van Nostrand, 1965.

De Galiana, T. *Concise Encyclopedia of Astronautics.* London: Collins, 1968.

Deutsch, A. J., and Klemperer, W. B., eds. *Space Age Astronomy.* New York: Academic Press, 1962.

Editors of Fortune. *The Space Industry: America's Newest Giant.* Englewood Cliffs, N.J., Prentice-Hall, 1962.

Ehricke, Krafft A. *Space Flight.* 2 vols. Princeton, N.J.: Van Nostrand, 1960, 1962.

Frye, William E., ed. *Impact of Space Exploration on Society.* Tarzana, Calif.: AAS, 1966.

Gatland, Kenneth W. *Astronautics in the 60s.* New York: Wiley, 1962.

——, ed. *Spaceflight Technology.* New York: Academic Press, 1960.

——. *Spaceflight Today.* Los Angeles: Aero Publishers, 1964.

Gilmer, J. R., and others, eds. *Commercial Utilization of Space.* Tarzana, Calif.: AAS, 1968.

Glasstone, Samuel. *Sourcebook of the Space Sciences.* Princeton, N.J.: Van Nostrand, 1965.

Grey, J., and Grey, V., eds. *Space Flight Report to the Nation.* New York: Basic Books, 1962.

Haber, Heinz. *Space Science.* New York: Golden, 1967.

Haviland, Robert P., and House, C. M., eds. *Handbook of Satellites and Space Vehicles.* Princeton, N.J.: Van Nostrand, 1965.

Hess, H. H., and others, eds. *Review of Space Research.* Washington, D.C.: National Academy of Sciences, 1962.

Hobbs, M. *Basics of Missile Guidance and Space Techniques.* New York: John F. Rider, 1959. (Two volumes on control, guidance, telemetry, tracking, optics, etc.)

Howard, William E., and Barr, James. *Spacecraft and Missiles of the World.* New York: Harcourt, Brace & World, 1966.

Hubert, Lester F., and Lehr, Paul E. *Weather Satellites.* Waltham, Mass.: Blaisdell, 1967.

Hunter, Maxwell W., II. *Thrust into Space.* New York: Holt, Rinehart & Winston, 1966.

Jacobs, H., and Whitney, E. E. *Missile and Space Projects Guide.* New York: Plenum Press, 1962.

Jacobs, Horace, ed. *Exploitation of Space for Experimental Research.* Tarzana, Calif.: AAS, 1968.

Jaffe, Leonard. *Communications in Space.* New York: Holt, Rinehart & Winston, 1966.

King-Hele, D. *Satellites and Scientific Research.* New York: Dover, 1960.

Koelle, H. H., ed. *Handbook of Astronautical Engineering.* New York: McGraw-Hill, 1961.

Krieger, F. J. *Behind the Sputniks: A Survey of Soviet Space Science.* Washington, D.C.: Public Affairs Press, 1958.

LeGalley, Donald P., ed. *Space Science.* New York: Wiley, 1963.

Leondes, C. T., and Vance, R. W. eds. *Lunar Missions and Exploration.* New York: Wiley, 1964.

Ley, Willy, ed. *Harnessing Space.* New York: Macmillan, 1963.

————. *Mariner to Mars.* New York: New American Library, 1966.

————. *Ranger to the Moon.* New York: New American Library, 1965.

Liller, W. *Space Astrophysics.* New York: McGraw-Hill, 1961.

Loosbrock, J. F., and others, eds. *Space Weapons— A Handbook of Military Astronautics.* New York: Praeger, 1959.

Lundquist, Charles A. *Space Science.* New York: McGraw-Hill, 1966.

McCauley, John F. *Moon Probes.* Morristown, N.J.: Silver Burdett, 1969.

Mesmer, G., and Stuhlinger, Ernst, eds. *Space Science and Engineering.* New York: McGraw-Hill, 1964.

Morganthaler, George W., and Morra, Robert G., eds. *Unmanned Exploration of the Solar System.* North Hollywood, Calif.: Western Periodicals, 1965.

Mueller, George E., and Spangler, Eugene R. *Communication Satellites.* New York: Wiley, 1964.

Naugle, John E. *Unmanned Space Flight.* New York: Holt, Rinehart & Winston, 1965.

Naylor, J. L., ed. *Advances in Space Technology.* London: George Newnes, 1962.

Newlan, Irl. *First to Venus: The Story of Mariner II.* New York: McGraw-Hill, 1963.

Ordway, Frederick I., III, ed. *Advances in Space Science and Technology.* New York: Academic Press. (Annual review volumes 1959-1969.)

————, Gardner, James Patrick, and Sharpe, Mitchell R., Jr. *Basic Astronautics.* Englewood Cliffs, N.J.: Prentice-Hall, 1962.

————, and others. *Applied Astronautics.* Englewood Cliffs, N.J.: Prentice-Hall, 1963.

————, and Wakeford, Ronald C. *Conquering the Sun's Empire.* New York: Dutton, 1963.

Ovenden, M. W. *Artificial Satellites.* Harmondsworth: Penguin Books, 1960.

Pardoe, G. K. C. *The Challenge of Space.* London: Chatto and Windus, 1964.

Ramo, S., ed. *Peacetime Uses of Outer Space.* New York: McGraw-Hill, 1961.

Ruppe, Harry O. *Introduction to Astronautics.* (2 vols.) New York: Academic Press, 1966, 1967.

Seifert, Howard S., ed. *Space Technology.* New York: Wiley, 1959.

Sheldon, Charles S., II. *Review of the Soviet Space Program.* New York: McGraw-Hill, 1968.

Shelton, William R. *American Space Exploration.* Boston: Little, Brown, 1967.

Shternfeld, A. *Soviet Space Science.* New York: Basic Books, 1959.

Singer, S. F., ed. *Progress in the Astronautical Sciences.* Amsterdam: North-Holland Publishing, 1962.

Solomon, L. *Telstar.* New York: McGraw-Hill, 1962.

Stuhlinger, Ernst. *Ion Propulsion for Space Flight.* New York: McGraw-Hill, 1964.

————, and others, eds. *Astronautical Engineering and Science.* New York: McGraw-Hill, 1963.

Trinklein, F. E., and Huffer, C. M. *Modern Space Science.* New York: Holt, Rinehart & Winston, 1961.

Vaeth, J. Gordon. *Weather Eyes in the Sky: America's Meteorological Satellites.* New York: Ronald Press, 1965.

Van Allen, James A., ed. *Scientific Uses of Earth Satellites.* Ann Arbor, Mich.: University of Michigan Press, 1956.

Vassiliev, M., and Dobronravov, V. V. *Sputnik into Space.* London: Souvenir Press, 1958.

Vertregt, M. *Principles of Astronautics.* Amsterdam: Elsevier Publishing, 1960.

Wheelock, Harold J., ed. *Mariner Mission to Venus.* New York: McGraw-Hill, 1963.

Widger, William K., Jr. *Meteorological Satellites.* New York: Holt, Rinehart & Winston, 1966.

9 Manned Space Flight

Abbas, A. *Till We Reach the Stars: The Story of Yuri Gagarin.* Bombay: Asia Publishing House, 1961.

Alexander, Tom. *Project Apollo: Man to the Moon.* New York: Harper, 1964.

Badgley, Peter C., ed. *Scientific Experiments for Manned Orbital Flight.* North Hollywood, Calif.: Western Periodicals, 1965.

Bell, J. N. *Seven into Space.* Chicago: Popular Mechanics, 1960. (About the seven original Mercury astronauts.)

Benson, O. O., and Strughold, H., eds. *Physics and Medicine of the Atmosphere and Space.* New York: Wiley, 1960.

Bergman, Jules. *Ninety Seconds to Space: The X-15 Story.* Garden City, N.Y.: Doubleday, 1960.

Bergwin, C. R., and Coleman, W. T. *Animal Astronauts: They Opened the Way to the Stars.* Englewood Cliffs, N.J.: Prentice-Hall, 1963.

Braun, Wernher von. *Mars Project.* Urbana, Ill.: University of Illinois Press, 1953.

Bridgeman, W., and Hazard, J. *The Lonely Sky.* New York: Holt, 1955. (On the D-558-2 rocket airplane.)

Burgess, Eric, ed. *Voyage to the Planets.* Tarzana, Calif.: AAS, 1968.

Cameron, A. G. W., ed. *Interstellar Communication.* New York: W. A. Benjamin, 1963.

Campbell, Paul A. *Earthman, Spaceman, Universal Man?* New York: Pageant, 1965.

———, ed. *Medical and Biological Aspects of the Energies of Space.* New York: Columbia University Press, 1961.

Carpenter, M. S., and others. *We Seven.* New York: Simon & Schuster, 1962. (By the seven original Mercury astronauts.)

Carter, L. J., ed. *Realities of Space Travel.* New York: McGraw-Hill, 1957.

Clarke, Arthur C. *Challenge of the Spaceship.* New York: Harper, 1959.

———. *Exploration of Space.* New York: Harper, 1952.

———. *Exploration of the Moon.* New York: Harper, 1954.

———. *Man and Space.* New York: Time, Inc., 1964.

———. *The Promise of Space.* New York: Harper & Row, 1968.

Coombs, Charles. *Project Apollo Mission to the Moon.* New York: Morrow, 1965.

———. *Skyrocketing into the Unknown.* New York: Morrow, 1954. (About rocket airplanes.)

Crossfield, Alfred S., with Blair, Clay, Jr. *Always Another Dawn.* Cleveland: World Publishing, 1960. (On U.S. rocket-powered airplanes.)

Cummings, Clifford I., and Lawrence, H. R., eds. *Technology of Lunar Exploration.* New York: Academic Press, 1963.

Dole, Stephen H. *Habitable Planets for Man.* New York: Blaisdell Publishing, 1964.

Everest, F. K., Jr. *Fastest Man Alive.* New York: Dutton, 1958. (Story of X-2 rocket airplane.)

Faget, Maxime. *Manned Space Flight.* New York: Holt, Rinehart & Winston, 1965.

Fallaci, Oriana. *If the Sun Dies.* New York: Atheneum, 1966.

Gagarin, Yuri. *Road to the Stars.* Moscow: Foreign Languages Publishing House, 1962.

Gantz, K. F., ed. *Man in Space.* New York: Duell, Sloan & Pearce, 1959.

Gatland, Kenneth. *Manned Spacecraft.* New York: Macmillan, 1967.

———, and Kunesch, A. M. *Space Travel.* New York: Philosophical Library, 1953.

Gerathewohl, S. J. *Principles of Bioastronautics.* Englewood Cliffs, N.J.: Prentice-Hall, 1963.

Grissom, Virgil. *A Personal Account of Man's Venture into Space.* New York: Macmillan, 1968.

Gurney, Gene. *Walk in Space: The Story of Project Gemini.* New York: Random House, 1967.

Hilton, W. F. *Manned Satellites.* London: Hutchinson, 1965.

Lansberg, M. P. *Primer of Space Medicine.* Amsterdam: Elsevier Publishing, 1960.

Lewis, Richard S. *Appointment on the Moon.* New York: Viking, 1968.

Ley, Willy. *Beyond the Solar System.* New York: Viking, 1964.

———. *Conquest of Space.* New York: Viking, 1949.

———, and von Braun, Wernher. *The Exploration of Mars.* New York: Viking, 1956.

Lundgren, William R. *Across the High Frontier.* New York: Morrow, 1955. (About the X-1A and its test pilot.)

MacGowan, Roger A., and Ordway, Frederick I., III. *Intelligence in the Universe.* Englewood Cliffs, N.J.: Prentice-Hall, 1966.

Maisak, Lawrence. *Survival on the Moon*. New York: Macmillan, 1966.

Mallan, Lloyd. *Men, Rockets and Space Rats*. New York: Julian Messner, 1961.

Marbarger, J. P., ed. *Space Medicine*. Urbana, Ill.: University of Illinois Press, 1951.

Olney, Ross. *Americans in Space*. Camden, N.J.; Nelson, 1967.

Ordway, Frederick I., III. *Life in Other Solar Systems*. New York: Dutton, 1965.

Pierce, P. N., and Schuon, Karl. *John H. Glenn: Astronaut*. New York: Franklin Watts, 1962.

Pirie, Norman W., ed. *Biology of Space Travel*. London: Institute of Biology, 1961.

Richardson, Robert S., ed. *Man and the Moon*. Cleveland: World Publishing, 1961.

Ruzic, Neil. *The Case for Going to the Moon*. New York: Putnam, 1965.

Ryan, Cornelius, ed., and others. *Across the Space Frontier*. New York: Viking, 1952.

———. *Conquest of the Moon*. New York: Viking, 1953.

Sharpe, Mitchell R. *Living in Space — The Environment of the Astronaut*. New York: Doubleday, 1969.

———. *Yuri Gagarin, First Man in Space*. Huntsville, Ala.: Strode, 1969.

Shelton, William R. *Flights of the Astronauts*. Boston: Little, Brown, 1963.

Stambler, Irwin. *Project Gemini*. New York: Putnam, 1964.

Sullivan, Walter. *We Are Not Alone*. New York: McGraw-Hill, 1964.

Swenson, Loyd S., Jr., and others. *This New Ocean: A History of Project Mercury*. Washington: NASA, 1966.

Thomas, Shirley. *Men of Space*. Vols. 2 through 10. Philadelphia: Chilton, 1961–1968.

Titov, G., and Caiden, M. *I Am Eagle!* Indianapolis: Bobbs-Merrill, 1962.

Tregaskis, Richard W. *X-15 Diary*. New York: Dutton, 1961.

White, Clayton S., and Benson, O. O., Jr. eds. *Physics and Medicine of the Upper Atmosphere*. Albuquerque, N.M.; University of New Mexico Press, 1952.

Wunder, Charles C. *Life into Space: An Introduction to Space Biology*. Philadelphia: F. A. Davis, 1966.

Index

A-series rockets, 71–73, foll. p. 100, 103, 106, 115, 118 – 119, 126
A-1 satellites, 188, 190
Aberdeen Proving Ground, 94, 95, 122–123
Adams, Michael J., 204
Advanced Research Project Agency (ARPA), 167, 206
Aeolopile, 22, foll. p. 68
Aeolus sounding rockets, 154
Aerobee sounding rockets, 151, 152, 156, 157, 159, 160
Aerojet Engineering Corporation, 94, 101, 103, 151, 160, 177, 220
Aerospace Corporation, 133
Africano, Alfred, 80, 81, 84
Agate sounding rockets, 157
Agena stages, 163, 196, 211, 215, 216
Air Force Museum, 204
airplanes:
  assisted takeoffs for, 54, 56, 73–74, 75, 85, 93, 94, 101–103, 109, 119
  carrier rockets launched from, 156, 158
  pilotless, 37–39
  rocket-powered, 34, 36, 65, 66, 74, 82, 87, 89, 103, 108–109, 203–205
  rockets and missiles fired by, 36, 37, 68, foll. p. 68, 84–91 passim, 95–102 passim, 110, 113, 114, 142–143
  sounding rockets launched from, 153
  supersonic, 122, 203–205
Air Research and Development Command (ARDC), 133, 135, 137
air-to-air weapons, 84, 86, 99, 101, 102, 110, 114, 143, 144
air-to-surface weapons, 86–87, 88, 90–91, 95–96, 98–99, 102, 110, 113, 142–143
Albertus Magnus, 28
Aldrin, Edwin E., Jr., 215, 216, 234, 235, 238–248
al-Hasan al-Rammāh, 27, foll. p. 68
Allegany Ballistics Laboratory, 94, 160
Alouette satellite, 189
altitude:
  infinite, attainment of, 45–46
  for missiles, 87, 98, 104, 111–112, 128–129
  orbital, summarized, 173, 212–214
  for sounding rockets, 153, 156–157
  in V-2 studies, 123, 125
American Institute of Aeronautics and Astronautics, 78
American Interplanetary Society, 60, 63, 78–81
American Rocket Society, 80, 81, 82, 84, 94, foll. p. 100, 151
American Telephone and Telegraph Company, 186

Amiot, Joseph Marie, Father, 25
Ananoff, Alexandre, 17
Anaxagoras, 2, 68
Anders, William A., 228, 241
Anderson, Lowell O., 179
Anglicus, Robertus, 6
animals, space flight by, 129, 155, 156, 164, foll. p. 164, 181, 188–189, 205, 206, 207, 208
Anna satellite, 188
Antipodal Bomber, 119
antitank weapons, 94–95, 110, 112
Apollo program, foll. p. 164, 166–171, 193, 196, foll. p. 196, 217–248, 251
  in the future, 248–254
  spacecraft, foll. p. 196, 217–223, 226–227, 229–230, 236–237, 242, 248
Apollo Review Board, 224
Apollo telescope mount (ATM), 250
Applications Technology Satellites (ATS), 188
Apt, Milburn G., 204
Arabs, 5, 27–28, foll. p. 68
Arcas sounding rockets, 153, 157
Archer sounding rockets, 157
Archytas of Tarentum, 22, foll. p. 68
Arcon sounding rockets, 153, 157
Argo rockets, 157, 163, 172–173
Ariel satellites, 161, 189, 190
Ariosto, Lodovico, 11
Aristarchus of Samos, 3, 6, 68, 233
Aristotle, 3
Armstrong, Neil A., 211, 213, 234, 238–248
Army Ballistic Missile Agency (ABMA), 128, 129, 161–163, 165, 167, 179, 206
Arnold, Henry H., 85
Arnold, Weld, 85
Around the Moon (Verne), 17–18, 56
artificial satellites, see spacecraft
Aspan sounding rockets, 153, 157
Asp sounding rockets, 153, 157
asteroids, 8
Astrobee sounding rockets, 153, 157
astronautical theory, evolution of, 40–44, 100
Astronautics, 81
Astronautique, L' (Esnault-Pelterie), 75
astronomy, 2–9, 68, foll. p. 68
Atlas missiles, 121, 122, 128, 133–135, 139, 178
  as carrier rockets, 159, 161, 162, 163, 172–173, 177, 178, 192, 193, 197, 198, 206, 207, 209
Atlas Scientific Evaluation Committee, 133
atmospheric research, see scientific research, space
Atomic Energy Commission, 129, 130, 132, 244
Atterlay, Joseph, 16

Australia, 154, 156, 189
Austria, 31, 32, 35–36
automatic picture transmission (APT), 184
Aviavnito sounding rocket, 63
Axter, Herbert, 116, 117
Babylonia, 2, 4, 68, foll. p. 68
Bacon, Roger, 28
Ballistic Missile Division, U.S. Air Force, 133, 134
ballistic missiles, see missiles
balloons:
  Echo satellite, 184
  rockets launched from, 153, 156
Barney, Joshua, 33
barrage rockets, 86–87, 95–97, 112
Barré, J. J., 75, 76
Bat missiles, 99, 102
Baum, Werner, 140
Bayrische Motoren Werke, 74
bazooka rockets, 45, 48, 94–95, 110
Becker, Karl, 71
Bélier sounding rockets, 157
Bell, Gordon, 30
Bell Aircraft Company, 203
Bell Telephone Company, 144–145, 184
Belyayev, Pavel I., 209, 212
Beregovoy, Georgi, 217
Bérénice sounding rockets, 155
Bergman, A., 36
Berkner, Lloyd V., 180
Best, Alfred H., 80, 81
Betts, Austin W., 167
Big Horn antenna, 186
biological research, 183, 188–189, 205
Biringuccio, Vannoccio, 29
Black Brant sounding rockets, 156
black powder (see also solid propellants), 23–28
Blagonravov, A. A., 197
Bleymaier, Joseph S., 169
Blohm and Voss missiles, 110, 113
Bloodhound missiles, 149
Blue Scout carrier rocket, 163
Blue Streak missiles, 142, 174, 175
Bode, Hendrik W., 133
Boeing Company, 144, 170, 193
Bölkow-Junkers sounding rockets, 157
Bolster, C. A., 101
Bomarc missiles, 144, 145
Bombrini Parodi Delfino Company, 77
bombs:
  nuclear, 120, 121, 127–128, 164, 187
  rocket-propelled, 86, 87, 97–98, 99, 105, 120–121, 122
Borman, Frank, 211, 213, 228, 241
Boudinot, Truman, 117
Boulogne, rocket attack on, 31
Boushey, Homer A., Jr., 101
Boxer, R. A., 34–35
Boyle, John A., 10
Bradshaw, Granville, 38, 39

Brahe, Tycho, 6–7
Bredt, Irene, 119
Brett, George H., 54
"Brick Moon, The" (Hale), 18–20, 202
British Interplanetary Society, 60, 76
Bruce, C. F., 91
Brucker, Wilber M., 162
Brunt, Samuel, 14–15
Budd Wheel Company, 93
"Bug," the, 37, 38
Bull, Harry W., 82
Bullpup missiles, 142
Bumblebee program, 143
Bumper program, 125, 127
Burke, Arleigh A., 130
Bush, Vannevar, 9
buzz bombs, 105
Bykovsky, Valery, 205, 212
Byzantine Empire, 23

Caddell, W. M., 37
Caleb rockets, 156, 158
California Institute of Technology:
  Galcit Rocket Research Group, 84–85, 94, 101, 176
  Jet Propulsion Laboratory, 103, 126, 129, 163, 165, 192, 199
  National Defense Research Committee (NDRC), 84, 93–99
Camp Devens, Mass., 48
Canada, 156, 188, 189
Cape Kennedy (Canaveral), foll. p. 100, 125, 127, 128, 131, 153, 161, 162, 167, 169–171, foll. p. 196, 199, 200, 215, 224, 225, 228, 229, 234, 236
capsule recovery, 155, 181, 189
Carl, Marion E., 203
Carpenter, M. Scott, 207, 209, 212
carrier rockets, 150, 156–175, 177, 178, 179, 192, 205–207
  for Apollo program, 196, 217–218
cars, rocket-powered, 64–65
Carver, Nathan, 82
Castille, William, 117
Centaure sounding rockets, 157
Centre National d'Études Spatiales, 175
Cernan, Eugene A., foll. p. 196, 215, 231–233, 241
Chaffee, Roger B., 224
Chance-Vought Aircraft, Inc., 132
Chaparral missiles, 145
Charlie Brown, 232
Chen Tsung, 26
Cheranovskii, C. I., 62
Cherwell, Lord (F. A. Lindemann), 92
China, 2, 22, 23–27, 68, foll. p. 68, 148
Chin Dynasty, 23
Ch'ing Haii-Tzu, 23, 25
Chrysler Corporation, 127, 169
Churchill, Sir Winston, 90, 92
Cicero, Marcus Tullius, 9

Civil War, 34, foll. p. 68
Clark, J. E., 130
Clarke, Arthur C., 185
Clark University, Mass., 37, 44–45, 48, 49
Cleator, P. E., 76, 77
Cleaver, A. V., 92
Cleveland Rocket Society, 82
Cockburn, Sir George, 32
Cogswell, W. P., 177
Collins, Michael, 215, 234, 235, 238–248
Columbia, 238–245
Comena, Anna, 23
command module (CM) (see also service module), 218–223, 224, 225–233, 234, 236–238, 240–242, 245, 248
Communications Satellite Corporation (Comsat), 186
communications satellites, 164, 183, 184–186, 187, 189
Complete Compendium of Military Classics, The, 23–25
concurrency policy, 134
Congreve, Sir William, 30–34
Conrad, Charles, Jr., 211, 213, 215
Consolidated Vultee Aircraft Corporation (Convair), 122, 132, 178
Cook, William R., 88
cooling systems, 67, 69, 70, 82
Cooper, L. Gordon, Jr., 196, foll. p. 196, 207, 208, 209, 211, 212, 213
Copenhagen, rocket attack on, 31
Copernicus, Nicolaus, 6, 7, 68, 233
Corelli, Riccardo M., 78
Corporal missiles, 129
cosmonauts, 196, foll. p. 196, 205, 207–210, 212–213, 224
Courier satellites, 184, 189
Cranz, Carl, 71
crawler-transporter, 225
Crocco, G. A., 77–78
Crocco, Luigi, 77
Crossfield, A. Scott, 203
Crow, Sir Alwyn D., 77, 90, 92, 122
Cuba, 148, 149
Cunningham, Walter, foll. p. 196, 226, 241
Cyrano de Bergerac, Savinien de, 13

D-1 satellite, 189, 190
D-558-2 rocket airplane, 203
Dahlgren Proving Ground, 93, 94
Damblanc, Louis, 75
Dana, William H., 204
Dane, P. H., 101
Daniel, Gabriel, 13–14
Daniel Webster, USS, 132
Dan sounding rockets, 153, 157
DAR-3 sounding rockets, 157
Dauphin sounding rockets, 157
Davis, Tenny L., 26–27
Day of Participation, 238
Deacon sounding rockets, 153
death of space fliers, 216, 224
decoys, missile, 145, 146
Defense Communications Agency, 187
Defense Department, 128, 129, 148, 159, 160, 165, 167, 169, 178, 179, 183, 186–187, 189
Defoe, Daniel, 14
De Gaulle, Charles, 142
Degenkolb, Gerhard, 106
De Havilland, Sir Geoffrey, 38, 39
De Havilland Company, 142
Delco Company, 37
Dewar, Bradley, 94
Diamant carrier rockets, 173, 175
Discoverer satellites, 163, 183, 185, 189
Discovery of a New World (Wilkins), 12–13, 78
Dixon, A. E., 176

docking operations, 196, 211, 213, 214, 230, 233, 235, 236, 245
Dornberger, Walter, 70–73, 100, 106, 107–108, 114, 116, 118
Douglas Aircraft Company, 135, 177, 178
Dowdell, William E., 179
Dragon sounding rockets, 157
Dresser Manufacturing Company, 95
Driscoll, John J., 101
Dryden, Hugh L., 99, 165, 199, 218
Dubouloz, Joseph, 76
Dunn, Louis G., 133
Durant, Frederick C., III, 179

Eagle, 238–245
Eagle missiles, 143
Early Bird satellite, 164, 186, 189
Earth:
  artificial satellites in orbit around, 150, 158, 159, 161, 163, 164, foll. p. 164, 167, 175, 177, 180–189
  early views of, 2–9, 68, foll. p. 68
  grouping of, 8
  manned orbital flights around, 196, foll. p. 196, 205–217
  and orbital rendezvous plan, 218
  in science fiction, 15, 20, 21
Earth resources technology satellite (ERTS), 189–190
Earthrise, 232
East German Astronautical Society, 159
Eben, Baron, 31
Echo satellites, 163, 164, 185, 189
Edwards Air Force Base, 139, 204
Egypt, 2, 4, 68, foll. p. 68
Eichstadt, Konrad Kyser von, 28
Einstein, Albert, 233
Eisele, Donn F., foll. p. 196, 226, 227, 241
Eisenhower, Dwight D., 159, 165
Eisfeld, J. F., 65
Elektron satellites, 183, 189
Elles, Sir Hugh, 77
Empire studies, 250
Environmental Science Services Administration, 184
Enzian missiles, 110, 111
Eratosthenes, 5
Erebus, HMS, 32
Éridan sounding rockets, 157
Esnault-Pelterie, Robert, 60, 63, 74–75, 233
ESSA satellites, 184–185, 189
Essex, USS, 227
Ethan Allen, USS, 130
Europa carrier rockets, 173, 174, 175
European carrier vehicles, 173
European Launcher Development Organization (ELDO), 173, 175
European Space Research Organization (ESRO), 189
Exos sounding rockets, 153, 157
Explorer satellites, 163, 164, foll. p. 164, 183, 187, 188–189
extra-vehicular activity (EVA), 215, 216, 238–239, 243, 244
Eyraud, Achille, 17

Faget, Maxime A., 205–206
Falcon missiles, 143
Far Side rockets, 156, 158
Favé, Idelphonse, 25
Federov, E., 180
Feng Chi-shang, 25
Feoktistov, Konstantin P., 209, 212
Feuerlilie missiles, 110, 111
Firdausi of Persia, 10, foll. p. 68
fire-arrows, 22–23, 24, 25–28, foll. p. 68
Firebird missiles, 143

fireworks, 23, 24, 27, 28–29
firing room, 229
First Men in the Moon, The (Wells), 21
Fitch, Clyde J., 78
fleet ballistic missiles (FBM), 130–132
Fleisher, Karl Otto, 118
Fontana, Joanes de, 28, foll. p. 68
Fontenelle, Bernard de, 13
Forman, Edward S., 85
Forrestal, James V., 178
Fort Bliss, Texas, 123, 124, 126, 127
Fortikov, I. P., 61
Fort McHenry, 31–32
Fowler, William, 93
Fr-1 satellite, 189
fractional orbital bombardment system (FOBS), 182
France:
  early rocketry in, 28, 29, 36–37, 60, 74–76
  postwar missile program of, 142, 149
  space research programs in, 155, 156, 157, 174, 175, 188, 189, 190
Frau im Mond (Girl in the Moon), 58, 59, 66, 67
Frog missiles, 140, 141
Froissart, Jean, 28
From the Earth to the Moon (Verne), 17, 44
Funk, Ben I., 169
Funryu missiles, 86–87, 89
Furth, Frederick R., 179

Gaedicke, Wilhelm, 36
Gagarin, Yuri, 196, 205, 212
Galcit Rocket Research Group, 84–85, 94, 101, 176
Galilei, Galileo, 7
Gallery, Daniel V., 125, 152
Ganswindt, Hermann, 40–41, 43, 100, foll. p. 100
Gapa missiles, 144
Gardner, Trevor, 133, 162
Gargoyle missiles, 99
gas generators, tests of, 52
Gatland, K. W., 176
Gaubil, Antonine, Father, 26
Geissler, Friedrich von, 29, 31
Gellius, Aulus, 22
Gemini program, 163, 165, 170, 196, foll. p. 196, 210–216, 224, 226, 254
  spacecraft sections, 210–211
General Dynamics Corporation, 132
General Electric Company, 117, 118, 125–127, 144, 166
General Tire and Rubber Company, 94
geodetic satellites, 187, 188, 189
geophysical research, 153–157, 189
geophysical rockets, 154, 155–156, 157
George Washington, USS, 130, 131
George Washington University, 93
German Research Center for Aeronautic and Automotive Propulsion, 110
German Rocket Collective, 140
Germany:
  early rocketry in, 29, 36, 60, 64–74, 78, 85, 100, foll. p. 100
  scientists of, in U.S., 118, 122–123, 126
  in Russia, 118, 140
  space research programs in, 157, 174, 175
  World War II rocket program in, 100, 104–119
Giardini, William A., 179
Gibson, G. E., 93
Gilruth, Robert R., 206
Givens, Edward G., 224
Gleig, George R., 33
Glenn, John H., Jr., 196, 207, 208, 209, 212

Glennan, T. Keith, 165, 206
gliders, rocket-powered, 65, 66
Glushko, Valentin P., 61, 62, 63
Goclenius (crater), 228
Goddard, Esther C., 46–47, 53, 56
Goddard, Robert H., 37, 40, 43–56, 57, 60, 63, 64, 78, 84, 93, 94, 100, foll. p. 100, 101, 176, 233, 234
Goddard Space Flight Center, 56, 185
Godwin, Francis, Bishop, 11–12, foll. p. 68
Golightly, Charles, 34
Gollin, G. J., 92
Goodlin, Chalmers H., 203
Gordon, Richard, 215
Gorgon program, 102
Grand Central Rocket Company, 160
Grau, Dieter, 166
Gravesande, Jacob Willem, 22, 24
gravity:
  escape from, 42
  Newton's law of, 7–8
  in science fiction, 12–13, 21
Gravity Gradient Stabilization (GGS) satellites, 189
Great Britain:
  early rocketry in, 30–35, 37–39, 60, 76–77
  postwar missile program of, 118, 135, 142, 143, 144, 147, 148, 149
  space research programs in, 155, 156, 157, 158, 161, 174, 175, 187–188, 189, 190
  V-missiles used against, 105, 108
  World War II rocket program in, 87–93
Greb satellites, 187, 189
Greece, 2–5, 22–23, 68
Greg, Percy, 20, 21
grenades, rocket-propelled, 94–95
Grigorov, Naum, 193
Grissom, Virgil I., 207, 208, 209, 211, 212, 224
Gröttrup, Helmut, 118, 140
Grumman Aircraft Engineering Corporation, 132, 218, 221
Guadalcanal, USS, 215, 230
Guam, USS, 215
Guggenheim, Harry G., 53, 54
Guggenheim Aeronautical Laboratory, see Galcit Rocket Research Group
Guggenheim Foundation, 45, 46, 49, 53–54, 56
guidance systems, 37–39, 98, 99, 111–114, 130, 145, 149, 199
guided missiles (see also missiles):
  first development of, 37–39
  and rockets, distinction between, 86
gunpowder, 23–28

HAD sounding rockets, 156
Hagen, John P., 160, 161, 165
Hale, Edward Everett, 18–20, 202
Hale, William, 33
Hall, Edward N., 137
Hall, Harvey, 177
Hamill, James P., 117–118, 122–123, 126, 127
Harbey, G. A., Company, 88
HAT sounding rockets, 156
HATV (High-Altitude Test Vehicle), 177
Häussermann, Walter, 166
Hawk rockets, 145, 153, 157
Hecht missiles, 110, 111
Heinisch, Kurt, 67
Heinkel, Ernst, 74
Heinkel rocket airplanes, 108–109
helicopters, Wasp rockets for, 142
heliocentric theory, 3, 6
Heller, Gerhard, 179
Henschel missiles, 110, 112, 113, 114
Heraclitus, 2

Hercules Powder Company, 93
Hericlides of Pontus, 3, 68
Hermann, Rudolf, 106
Hermes program, 125–127, 151, 178
Hero of Alexander, 22, foll. p. 68
Herschel, Sir John, 17
Herschel, Sir William, 8
Hertel, Heinrich, 108
Hickman, Clarence N., 53, 84, 93–94, 95
Hill, Louis W., Space Transportation Award, 56
Himmler, Heinrich, 108
Hipparchus, 5
Hirsch, André Louis, 75
Hitler, Adolph, 72, 105, 106, 108, 116
Hoefft, Franz von, 35–36
Hohmann, Walter, 64
Holy Moses rockets, 99
Honest John missiles, 129
Hoover, George W., 179
Horstig, Major von, 71
Houbolt, John C., 218
Hound Dog missiles, 122, 143
Houston Mission Control Center, 229, 232, 235, 238, 239, 243, 244, 246
Hsue-shen Tsien, 85
Hückel, Hugo A., 69
Hückel-Winkler rockets, 69
Hughes Aircraft Company, 192
Hull, Edward, 118
Huntsville, Ala., 127–128, 161–170 passim, 179
Huygens, Christian, 15
Huzel, Dieter K., 117, 118
hydyne, 128
Hyland, Lawrence A., 133

Ibn Junis, 5
Ibn Khaldūn, 27
Icaro-Menippus (Lucian), 10
I-go missiles, 87, 88
illumination, rockets for, 34, 36
incendiary rockets, 30–33
India, 30
Initial Defense Communication Satellite Program (IDCSP), 187
Injun satellites, 189
instruments, see payloads
Intelsat, 164, 186
Interagency Committee on Back Contamination, 245
intercontinental ballistic missiles (ICBM's), 120–122, 123, 128, 129, 132–142, 164, foll. p. 164
and anti-ICBM program, 143–148
carrier rockets based on, 156, 162, 163–169, 205–207
satellites to detect, 186, 189
U.S. force of, 139
intermediate-range ballistic missiles (IRBM's), 100, foll. p. 100, 128–132, 135, 139–142, 158
carrier rockets based on, 156, 163
International Council of Scientific Union's Committee on Space Research, 197
International Geophysical Year, 153–155, 159, 179, 180
international launching, 189
International Telecommunications Satellite Consortium, 186
Interplanetary Communications (Rynin), 61, 63
interplanetary exploration:
early predictions of, 43
future plans for, 196, foll. p. 196, 251–254
in science fiction, 15, 20, 21, 202
and space probes, 158, 159, 164, foll. p. 164, 188, 193–201
interplanetary societies, 60, 64, 76, 78
Ionian school of astronomy, 2

Iowa, State University of, 153, 183
Iris sounding rockets, 153, 157
Italy, 29, 60, 77–78, 156, 157, 188, 189, 190
Iter Lunare (Russen), 14

Japan, 27, 86–89, 156, 157, 158
Javelin, 156
JB-series missiles, 120–121, 122
jet-assisted takeoffs (JATO), 54, 56, 73–74, 75, 85, 93, 94, 101–102, 103, 109, 111–112
Jet Propulsion Laboratory, 103, 126, 129, 163, 165, 192, 199
Jewett, Frank B., 84
Johns Hopkins University, 143, 151
Johnson, Alvin M., 203
Johnson, Lyndon B., 166, 170
Joinville, Sire de, 27–28
Jubb, Leonard Walter, 77
Judi Dart sounding rockets, 157
Jungert, Wilhelm, 122
Junkers rocket planes, 109
Juno carrier rockets, 128, 161–163, 164, 172–173
Jupiter (planet), 2, 6, 7, 8, 9, 68
Jupiter missiles, 100, foll. p. 100, 122, 128–130, 135, 139
as carrier rockets, 156, 160, 161–163, 165, 167, 206, 207

K'ai-fung-fu, battle of, 26
Kai-Kā'ūs, 10, foll. p. 68
Kamikaze planes, 87, 89, 90, 98, 143
Kammler, Hans, 107, 115
Kappa sounding rockets, 156, 157, 158
Kapustin Yar, 182
Karlson, P., 109
Katyusha rockets, 63, 86, 88
Koldysh, Mstislav, 182
Kendrick, James B., 179
Kennedy, John F., 149, 166, 170, 185, 196, 218, 233, 254
Kepler, Johannes, 6, 7, 11
Kepler's Dream (Lear), 11
Kerr, Robert, 199
Kessenich, Gregory J., 94
Kessler, F. W., 82
Kettering, Charles, 37
Kettering Grammar School, 159
Key, Francis Scott, 31–32
Khrunov, Yevgeni, 217
Khrushchev, Nikita, 149
Kiang-chin, 26
Kibalchich, Nikolai I., 40, 41, 43, 100, foll. p. 100
Killian, James R., Jr., 128, 165
Kincheloe, Ivan C., 203
Kirk, James T., 34
Kistiakowsky, George B., 133
Knight, William J., 204
Komarov, Vladimir M., 209, 212, 216, 224
Konstantinov, Konstantin I., 31
Korabl Sputnik satellites (see also Sputnik), 205
Korean War, 126, 127, 132
Korolev, Sergei P., 62, 140
Kosmodemyansky, A., 40
Kosmos satellites, 164, 181–182, 185, 189, 199
Kostikov, A. G., 140
Kramer, Max, 114
Krause, Ernst H., 151
Kuers, Werner, 166
Kühnel, Ilse, 60
Kummersdorf project, 70–72, 74
Kunesch, A. M., 176

La Folie, Louis Guillaume, 15
Lagrange, Joseph, 8
Laika, 164, foll. p. 164
Laird, Melvin R., 139, 148
Lambda sounding rockets, 156, 157
Lana missiles, 129
Lang, Fritz, 58
Lange, Oswald, 166

Langley Medal, 56
Langley Research Center, 185, 203, 205, 218, 224
Lani, Corrado, 78
Laplace, Marquis de (Pierre Simon), 8
Lark missiles, 98
Larynx, the, 38, 39
laser ranging retro-reflector (LRRR), 244, 246
Lasser, David, 78, 79
Lasswitz, Kurd, 20, 21
launch escape system, 219
launching, see carrier rockets; rocket launching
Lauritsen, Charles C., 93, 94, 133
Lear, John, 11
Lee, Robert E., 33
LeMay, Curtis, 177
Lemkin, William, 78
Len-GIRD, 61
Leonov, Aleksei A., 196, foll. p. 196, 209, 210, 212
Le Prieur, Y. P. G., 36, 37, foll. p. 68
Leverrier, Urbain, 8
Ley, Willy, 60, 64, 65, 69, 82
Lick Observatory, 244
liftoff, 171, 235
Lindbergh, Charles A., 46
Lindenberg, Hans, 117
Lion, Thomas W., 34
Lippisch, Alexander, 109
Liquid-Propellant Rocket Development (Goddard), 45, 47
liquid propellants:
British, 92–93
first experiments in, 35, 36, 42, 43, 45, 47–53, 60
French, 75, 76
German, 73, 74, 105
Italian, 77–78
Russian, 61, 62, 63
vs. solid, 53, 84, 137, 139
storing of, 118, 135–136
United States, 78–81, 82–83, 85, 101–102, 134–137, 139, 217
Little Joe rockets, 98, 207, 209
Little John rockets, 129
Locke, Richard Adams, 17
Lockheed Aircraft Corporation, 130
Loebell, Ernst, 60, 82
Loki rockets, 179
Long Tom sounding rockets, 156
Loon guided bomb, 120, 122
Lorrain, J. A. Hanzelet, 28, 29
Lovelady, William B., 117
Lovell, James A., Jr., 211, 213, 215, 228, 241
Low, A. M., 37, 39
Lowry Air Force Base, 135
Lubbock, Isaac, 92, 93
Lucian of Samosata, 9, 68, 202
lunar module (LM), 196, foll. p. 196, 218–223, 225, 228–233, 235, 236–238, 240–242, 243, 245, 247, 248, 250
Lunar orbital rendezvous (LOR), 218
Lunar Orbiter spacecraft, 193, 197
Lunar programs, see Moon, the
Lunar spacecraft, 158, 190–192, 193, 195
Lusser, Robert, 105

McConnell Air Force Base, 136
McCormack, James, 133
McDivitt, James A., foll. p. 196, 210, 211, 213, 229–231, 241
McDonnell Aircraft Company, 99, 206, 210
Mace missiles, 121
MacFarlane, Mason, 90
McMorrow, Francis J., 166
McNamara, Robert S., 139, 148, 217
Madelung, George, 111
Magdeburg project, 69–70

magnetic field studies, foll. p. 164, 182, 184, 189, 193, 200–201
mail service, rocket, 69, 72, 82
Malina, Frank J., 85
Malmstrom Air Force Base, 138, 139
maneuvering:
of manned spacecraft, 196, 211, 212, 213
on space walk, foll. p. 196, 211, 213
of unmanned spacecraft, 182, 189
Man in the Moon, The (Godwin), 11–12, foll. p. 68
Man in the Moon (Wilson), 15
manned orbital flights, 212–214, 216
manned orbital laboratory, 169, 217
Manning, Laurence, 78, 79, 80, 81
Marchus Graecus, 28
Mariner spacecraft, 164, foll. p. 164, 197–198, 199, 200, 201
positions of Mariner 4, summarized, 198
Mars (planet):
early views of, 2, 6, 9, 68
grouping of, 8
manned flight plans for, 196, foll. p. 196, 250–254
photographs of, 199
probes toward, 158, 164, foll. p. 164, 193, 197, 198, 200, 201
in science fiction, 20, 21
Mars 1 spacecraft, 197, 201
Mars excursion module, 253, 254
Marshall Space Flight Center, foll. p. 164, 165, 166, 170, 250
Martin, Glenn L., Company, 121, 146, 151, 152, 160, 177
Mason, C. P., 78
Masurca missiles, 149
Matador missiles, 121
Mathematical Principles of Natural Philosophy (Newton), 8
Mathews, Charles W., 206
Mathieson, Charles, 185
Maul, Alfred, 36
Mauler missiles, 145
Mécanique céleste (Laplace), 8
Medaris, John B., 128, 161, 162, 165
medical experiments, 216
Melot, Henri F., 75
Mercury (planet), 2, 3, 6, 8, 9, 68
Mercury program, 196, foll. p. 196, 203, 204, 206–207, 211, 254
summarized, 208–209, 212
meteorological satellites, 164, foll. p. 164, 183–184, 189
Meteo sounding rockets, 155, 157
Method of Attaining Extreme Altitude, A (Goddard), 45–46
Metroc sounding rockets, 153, 157
Mexican War, 33–34
Meyers, W. F., 25
Michigan, University of, Aeronautical Research Center, 144
Micromégas (Voltaire), 15
micrometeoroid studies, 164, 181, 183, 185, 187, 188, 189, 192–193, 200, 201
Midas satellites, 163, 186, 189
Midway, USS, 125
Mielke, Heinz, 159
Mike, nuclear experiment, 132
military rocketry, 23–39, 53–54, 57, 68, foll. p. 68, 70–73, 75, 77, 83–84, 100, foll. p. 100
orbiting laboratory for, 217
vs. peaceful uses, 149
postwar developments in, 120–149, 164
reconnaissance satellites, 178, 181, 186–187, 189

military rocketry (cont.)
  in World War I, 36–39, 45, 48, foll. p. 68
  in World War II, 63, 85, 86–119, 143
Millikan, Clark B., 132, 133, 178
Minneapolis-Honeywell Company, 160
Minuteman missiles, 122, 133, 137–139, foll. p. 164, 165
Mirak rockets, 67, 69, 70, 78
missiles:
  air-to-air, 86, 102, 110, 114, 143, 144
  air-to-surface, 86–87, 88, 98–99, 102, 110, 113, 142–143
  British, 90–92, 142
  carrier rockets based on, 156, 158, 159, 161–169, 175, 179, 205–207, 215
  comparisons of, tables, 129, 135, 139, 141, 145, 149
  cruise, 121–122, 123, 128, 132
  French, 75, 142
  German, 57, 65, 67, 70–73, 100, foll. p. 100, 104–119
  guided, first development of, 37–39
  intercontinental ballistic (ICBM's), 120–122, 123, 128, 129, 132–148, 156, 162–169, 186, 189
  intermediate-range ballistic (IRBM's), 100, foll. p. 100, 128–132, 135, 139–142, 156, 158, 163
  Japanese, 86-87, 88, 89
  multistage systems, 119, 125, 126, 127, 128, 133–139, 142, 144–145, 146, 159
  and rockets, distinction between, 86
  Russian, 120, 139–142, 147, 148–149, 164, foll. p. 164
  short- and medium-range, 127–128, 129, 142
  vs. space exploration program, 156, 159, 160
  surface-to-air (SAM), 86–90, 98, 109–112, 143–149
  surface-to-surface, 91–92, 104–108, 110, 115, 118–119, 123–126, 127, 129, 132–139, 142, foll. p. 164
  test summaries of, 123, 125
  underwater, 112, 114, 130–132, 135
  United States, 98–103 passim, 120–139, 142–148, 164, foll. p. 164
  in World War II, 86–119
Mittelwerke Company, 107, 116–118, 140
modularized equipment storage assembly (MESA), 242
Mohaupt, Henry H., 94
molab, 248
Molniya satellites, 182, 183, 189
Mongolians, 26, 27
Moon, the:
  crater (close up), 245
  early views of, 2–9, 68, foll. p. 68
  exploration of, 158, 159, 162, 163, 164, 181, 190–193, 195, 200
  future use of, 248
  Goddard's report on, 45–46
  landings on, 158, 164, 188, 191–192, 193, 195, 197, 238–244
  photographs of, 190, 191, 193, 194, 197, 200, 228, 234, 243–248
  plaque, 239, 243
  predictions of travel to, 43
  in science fiction, 4, 9–21, 68, 202
  U.S. manned spacecraft program for, foll. p. 164, 166–171 passim, 193, 196, foll. p. 196, 217–248
Moon hoax (1853), 17
Moore, W. T., 94

Morris, Ralph, 15
Mos-GIRD, 61, 62
motion:
  Kepler's planetary laws, 7, 8
  Newton's laws of, 7–8, 22, 41, 44
  rocket, 44–45
  of the spheres, Cicero on, 9
MOUSE (Minimum Orbital Unmanned Satellite of the Earth), 176
Mousetraps, 97
Mrazek, Willy A., 166
Mueller, George E., 168
Muhammad al-Batani, 5
Mulleneux, M., 91
Muratori, 28
Murphey, W. P., 125, 152
MX-324 airplanes, 203
MX-653 airplanes, 203
MX-774 rockets, 122, 132, 151, 178

National Academy of Sciences, 85, 160, 179
National Advisory Committee for Aeronautics (NACA), 165, 181, 203
National Aeronautics and Space Administration (NASA), 56, 165–170, 181, 183–187, 189, 191, 192, 196, 203, 204, 206, 218, 224, 250, 254
National Defense Research Committee (NDRC), 84, 93–99
National Science Foundation, 160, 179
National Security Council, 128
Natter rocket plane, 109, 116
Nautilus, USS, 122
Navaho missiles, 121–122, 123
Naval Research Laboratory (NRL), 151, 160–161, 165, 179
navigation, space, 44
navigation satellites, 182, 186, 189
Nebel, Rudolf, 58, 65, 67, 69
Nebelwerfer rockets, 110
Neptune (planet), 8
Nesmeyanov, A. N., 179, 180
Neu, Edward, 151
Neubert, Erich W., 122, 166
Newton, Sir Isaac, 7–8, 22, 41, 44, 233
Newton, Philippe W., 179
Nicolson, Marjorie, 10
Nike program, 144–149, 153, 154, 156, 157
Nikolaus, F., 114
Nikolayev, Adrian G., 205, 212
Nimbus satellites, 184, 185, 189
Nixon, Richard M., 148, 238, 246
Noctes Atticae (Gellius), 22
Noordung, Hermann, 202
North American Aviation, Inc., 122, 123, 167, 169, 170, 177, 204, 218
North American Rockwell (see also North American Aviation, Inc.), 218
Northrop Aircraft Company, 121, 177
Northrop flying wing, 120
Norton Sound, USS, 152
nosecones:
  Jupiter C tests of, foll. p. 100, 128–129
  re-entry, problems of, 134
nuclear bomb:
  and missile development, 120, 121, 127–128, 164
  satellites for explosion detection, 187, 189
nuclear submarines, 122, 130–132
nuclear warheads, 129, 130, 132, 141, 145, 149, 165
Nye, Nathaneal, 29

Oberth, Hermann, 40, 56–59, 63, 64, 65, 66, 67, 74, 75, 100, foll. p. 100, 176, 202, 233

Ohsson, Constantine Mouradgea d', 27
On the Revolutions of the Celestial Orbs (Copernicus), 6
Opel, Fritz von, 64–65, 66
Opel-Rak cars, 64–65
"Operational Requirements for Guided Missiles," 122
orbital flights, manned, 212–214
orbital velocity:
  and payload launching, 56, 57
  stage principle for, 43
Orbiter Project, 179
Orbiting Astronomical Laboratory, 187, 188
Orbiting Geophysical Observatories, 188
Orbiting Solar Observatories, 187, 188
orbits:
  assembling structures during, 217
  calculation of, 177
  changing of, 182, 211, 212
  for communication satellites, 184–186
  of manned space flights, summarized, 212–214
  planetary, 8, 68
Ordcit project, 103–104
Orlando Furioso (Ariosto), 11, 68
Ostrander, Don R., 167
oxygen, liquid, 85

Paperclip, Operation, 116–118, 122
parallel staging, 159, 169
Parca missiles, 149
Parmenides of Elea, 2–3
Parsons, John W., 85
passive seismic experiments package (PSEP), 244, 246
Patrick Henry, USS, 130
Patton, J. R., Jr., 101
Paulet, Pedro A., 35, 36
Pauthier, Joseph P. G., 25
Pavelourt, Daniel, 28
payloads, scientific:
  nature of, 158
  recovery of, 155, 181, 205
  for unmanned spacecraft, 150–158 passim, 176, 180–200 passim
Peenemünde Experimental Center, 72–73, 74, 100, foll. p. 100, 104–109, 112, 114, 115
Pegasus satellites, 167, 187, 188, 189
Pendray, G. Edward, 60, 78, 79–80, 81
Perelman, Jakov I., 60, 61
Pershing missiles, 129
Petri, George W., 179
Pfaall, Hans, 16–17
Philolaus, 3
Phoenix rockets, 143, 157
photographic missions:
  early attempts, 36
  in interplanetary probes, 199, 200
  by manned space flights, foll. p. 196, 207, 213
  in Moon probes, 190–193, 200
  by unmanned satellites, 182, 183, 197
Pickering, William H., 165
Pierce, H. Franklin, 78, 84
Pile, Sir Frederick, 88
Pinkney, William, 33
Pioneer spacecraft, 163, 190, 197, 199, 201
Pirquet, Guido von, 60, 202
planetary motion, 6–8, 9, 68
planets (see also interplanetary exploration), 2–8, 68, foll. p. 68
Plato, 3
Plutarch, 9
Pluto (planet), 8
Pobeda missiles, 140
Poe, Edgar Allan, 16, 17
Poggensee, Karl, 69
Poland, 157

Polaris program, 122, 129, 130–132, 135, 137, 139
Polyot satellites, 182, 189
Popovich, Pavel R., 205, 206, 212
Poppel, Theodor A., 122
Porter, Richard, 117, 180
Poseidon program, 132
Post, Kenneth, 88
Powers, Francis Gary, 148–149
Pratt, Fletcher, 78
Princeton, USS, 233
Private rockets, 103
Project Reichenberg, 105
propellants (see also liquid propellants; solid propellants):
  for carrier rockets, summarized, 172
  liquid vs. solid, 53, 84, 137, 139
  for missiles, summarized, 62, 87, 88, 98, 111–112, 129, 135, 141, 145, 149
  pumps, Goddard's tests for, 51–52
  for sounding rockets, 151, 156–157
Proton satellites, 159, 164, 182, 183, 189
Ptolemy, 5, 6, 7
Puckett, Allen E., 133
pump-driven rockets, tests of, 51–52, 55
Pushover, Operation, 125
Putt, Donald L., 162
Putze, Erich, 140
Pythagoras of Samos, 2–3, 5, 68

Quail decoy missiles, 143
Quarles, Donald A., 159, 161–162, 179
Queen Bee, 39
Queen Wasp, 39

Raborn, William F., 128, 130
radiation studies, 150, 155, 164, foll. p. 164, 181–189 passim, 201, 216
radio (see also guidance systems):
  and artificial satellites, 186, 187, 188, 189
  in guided missile development, 37–39
Radio Corporation of America, 184
radio telemetry, 176
Rakete, Die, 64, 65, 76
Raketenflugplatz, 65, 67, 69, 70, 72, 78
ramjet propulsion system, 126
Ramo, Simon, 133
Rand Corporation, 133, 135, 177, 178
Rand Project, 177–178
Ranger spacecraft, 162, 164, 191, 193, 194, 195
Rasko sounding rockets, 157
Raven sounding rockets, 157
Reach Project, 152
reaction control system (RCS), 218, 232
Reaction Motors, Inc., 94, 101, 151, 203, 204
reaction principle, 17, 21, 22, 24, 41–44, 56, foll. p. 68
reconnaissance satellites, 177, 178, 182, 186, 189
Redeye missiles, 145
red fuming nitric acid (RFNA), 85, 101
Redstone Arsenal, 127–128, 161–163, 165
Redstone missiles, 100, 127–128, 129
  as carrier rockets, 156, 159, 160, 167, 179, 206, 207, 209
Red Top missiles, 144
Rees, Eberhard, 106, 118, 122, 168
Regent missiles, 142
Regulus missiles, 132
Reinaud, Joseph Toussaint, 25
Reitsch, Hanna, 105

Relay satellites, 164, 185, 186, 189
rendezvous techniques, 196, foll. p. 196, 211, 213, 218, 236
Reno, Jesse Lee, 33
REP Hirsch prize, 75
Repulsor rockets, 69, 70
Rheinmetall-Borsig Company, 74, 105, 111
Rheintochter missiles, 110, 111–112
Richthofen, Major von, 74
Riedel, Klaus, 65
Riedel, Walter, 106, 118
Rigel program, 132
Ritland, Osmond J., 185
Road to Space Travel, The (Oberth), 57
Rockaire sounding rockets, 153
Rocket and Satellite Research Panel, 123
rocket airplanes, *see* airplanes
rocket-assisted takeoffs (*see also* JATO), 73–74, 93, 119
Rocket Development (Goddard), 45, 47
Rocketdyne Division, 122, 167, 169
Rocket into Planetary Space, The (Oberth), 56, 57, 64, 202
rocket launching:
 for anti-ICBM missiles, 146
 in Civil War, 34, foll. p. 68
 from ships, 112, 114, 125, 130
 turntable for, 47, 48
 from underground silos, 135, 136–139
 in World War II, 86, 88, 89, 91, 92, 96, 97, 108, 110, 112, 114
Rocket Propulsion Establishment, 149
rocketry (*see also* military rocketry):
 attitudes toward, 36, 60, 76
 military vs. peaceful uses of, 149
 pioneers of, 40–58, 74, 100
 and scientific research, 102–104, 150 ff.
 as space travel key, 21, 40–46, 60, 68, 100, 119, 202 ff.
 World War II effect on, 86 ff.
rockets (*see also* carrier rockets; missiles; sounding rockets):
 distinctions between types of, 86, 150
 invention and early development of, 22 ff., 68, foll. p. 68
 medieval, 28, foll. p. 68
 multistage systems in, 42–43, 44, 45, 100, 119, 125, 126, 127, 128, 133–146 *passim*, 156, 159, 160–179 *passim*
 reaction principle in, 17, 21, 22, 24, 41–44, 56, foll. p. 68
 in science fiction, 14, 17–21
 tables of, 48–52, 62, 87, 88, 98, 103, 104, 111–114, 123, 125, 129, 135, 139, 141, 145, 149, 153, 157, 172–173, 195, 201, 208–209, 212–214, 240–242
rocket societies, 60, 64, 70, 76, 78, 82, 84, 94
Rocket-Sonde Research Branch, 151
Rockets Through Space (Cleator), 77
Rockoon sounding rockets, 153
Roland missiles, 149
Romick, Darrell, 202
Roosevelt, Franklin D., 93
Rosen, Milton W., 151, 160, 179
Ross, H. E., 202
Roswell, N. Mex., 46–47, 49–52, 54, 100, foll. p. 100
Ruggieri brothers, 29
Russen, David, 14
Russia:
 early rocketry in, 31, 40–43, 60–63, 100
 and German rocket scientists, 114, 118, 140

Russia (cont.)
 postwar missile program of, 120, 121–122, 127–128, 139–142, 147–149
 space exploration program in, 154–159, 164, foll. p. 164, 179, 180–183, 188–195, 196, foll. p. 196, 198, 200, 201, 205, 207–210, 212–214, 215, 216, 222, 224, 254
 World War II rocket program in, 86, 88
Rynin, Nikolai A., 60, 61, 63

SA-2 missiles, 148–149
Saab missiles, 142
Sacrobosco, Johannes, 5
SAM's, *see* missiles, surface-to-air
Samos satellites, 186, 189
Sander, Friedrich Wilhelm, 64–65, 66
Sandy, Operation, 125
Sandys, Duncan, 88–89
Sänger, Eugen, 73, 82, 119
San Marco satellite, 189, 190
satellites, artificial, *see* spacecraft
satellites, planetary, 7, 8
Satin, Alexander, 179
Saturn (planet), 2, 6, 8, 9, 15, 68
Saturn carrier rockets, foll. p. 164, 166–175, 188, 196, foll. p. 196, 218, 224, 225, 226, 227, 228, 231, 234, 235, 236, 240, 242, 248, 249, 251
Saturn 5 workshop, 248–250
Schachner, Nathan, 78
Schaefer, Herbert, 69
Scherschevsky, Alexander B., 35, 58, 63
Schimmelfennig, Alexander, 34
Schirra, Walter M., Jr., foll. p. 196, 207, 208, 209, 211, 212, 213, 226, 227, 241
Schlidt, Rudolf, 179
Schmetterling missiles, 110, 112
Schmidding und Dynamit A. G., 74
Schmidt, Paul, 105
Schmiedl, Friedrich, 69
Schneider, Fred P., 116
Schriever, Bernard A., 133, 185
Schubert, W., 101
Schultze, August, 122
Schweickart, Russell L., foll. p. 196, 292–231, 241
Schwidetzky, Walter, 123
science fiction, 8–21, 44, 56, 68, 100, 202
scientific research, space:
 artificial satellites for, 156, 159, 163, 164, foll. p. 164, 177, 180–189
 interplanetary probes for, 195, 197–198, 200–201
 in manned space flight program, foll. p. 196, 207, 216, 242–244
 moon probes for, 188, 190–193, 200
 sounding rockets for, 150–156, 181
 in V-2 program, 123, 125
Scott, David R., 211, 213, 229–231, 241
Scott, Sir James, 32
Scott, Winfield, 33
Scout carrier rockets, 161, 163, 172–173
Seacat missiles, 148, 149
Sea Dart missiles, 149
sea-rescue rockets, 34–35, 39
Seaslug missiles, 149
Secor satellite, 187, 189
Sedov, Leonid I., 180
seismic detector, 244, 246
Sejó, battle of, 27
Seleucus of Seleucia, 3
Senate Foreign Relations Committee, 139
SEREB, 142, 175
Sergeant rockets, 129, 179
Seringapatam, battles of, 30

service module (SM) (*see also* command module), 218–223, 225–233, 236–242
Serviss, Garrett P., 21
Shāh-Nāma (Firdausi), 10–11, 68, foll. p. 68
Shatalov, Vladimir, 217
Shell Petroleum Company, Ltd., 92
Shepard, Alan B., Jr., 160, 207, 208, 209, 224
Shesta, John, 80, 81, 84, 151
Ship Inertial Guidance System, 130
ships:
 missile-carrying, 112, 114, 125, 128, 129, 130–132, 143–144, 148, 149
 sounding rockets launched from, 96–97, 152
shower tunnel, 226
Shyster missiles, 140, 141
Sidereus nuncius (Galileo), 7
Sidewinder missiles, 143
Sidewinder-Raven sounding rockets, 157
Siemienowicz, Kazimierz, 29
Sigma sounding rockets, 156
signal rockets, 34–35, 36
Singer, S. Fred, 176, 179
Sirius, 15
Skate, USS, 122
Skean missiles, 140, 141
Skinner, Leslie A., 83–84, 94–96
Skua sounding rockets, 155, 156, 157
Skybolt missiles, 142
Skylark sounding rockets, 156, 157, 158
Slayton, Donald K., 209
sleds, rocket-powered, 65–66
Smith, A. M. O., 85
Smith, Bernard, 80, 81
Smithsonian Institution, 45, 46, 49, 56, 204
Snare project, 89–90
Snark missiles, 121, 122
Snoopy, 232
Société pour l'Étude et la Réalisation d'Engins Balistiques (SEREB), 142, 175
Solar System:
 and early astronomers, 2–8, 68, foll. p. 68
 future travel in, 201, 254
 modern view of, 8
 in space-travel fiction, 15
Solar wind detector, 244, 248
solid propellants:
 British research in, 77, 93
 early black-powder rockets, 23–28, 45
 German use of, 69, 71
 vs. liquid, 53, 84, 137, 139
 Russian, 86
 for submarine program, 130, 131, 135
 U.S. research in, 83–84, 85, 93, 101, 137, 139
Solrad satellites, 187, 189
Somnium (Kepler), 11
Somnium scipionis (Cicero), 9
sounding rockets, 150–158, 160, 181
 carrier rockets based on, 156, 159–161
Soviet Union, *see* Russia
Soyuz program, 196, 216, 217
spacecraft, manned, 160, 163, 196, foll. p. 196, 202–254
 for Apollo project, 217–248
 construction research for, 182, 189
 design problems of, 203–204
 Gemini sections, 210–216
 orbiting laboratory design, 217
 proposed, for Mars flight, foll. p. 196, 248–250
 of science fiction, 13, 14, 15–16, 17–21
 summarized, 208–209, 212–214
spacecraft, unmanned, 164, foll. p. 164, 176–201

spacecraft, unmanned (cont.)
 carrier rockets for, foll. p. 100, 150, 156–163, 166–175, 177, 178, 179
 instrumentation in, 176, 183
 for manned space flight development, 203
 for Moon exploration, 158, 162, 164, 166, 168, 188–193
 orbital, 158, 163, 164, foll. p. 164, 176–190
 for planetary probes, 158, 164, 195–201
 success rates in launchings, 183, 186–187
 types and purposes of, 188–189
spacecraft–Lunar module adapter (SLA), 220–221, 235
space exploration, 150–222
 in Goddard's rocketry monographs, 45–46, 100
 manned space flight programs, 196, foll. p. 196, 202–254
 NASA established for, 165
 Oberth's theories of, 56–58, foll. p. 100
 Plato on, 3
 publications on, 40–43, 45–46, 57–58, 61, 63–64, 76–77, 78
 rocket as key to, 21, 40–46, 60, 68, 100, 119, 202 ff.
 and Russian carrier rockets, 141, 158–159
 in science fiction, 4, 8–21, 68, foll. p. 68, 202
 with sounding rockets, 150–158, 160
 theoretical development of, 40–43, 100, foll. p. 100
 and unmanned spacecraft, 150, 156–163, 164, 167–175, 176–201
 U.S. vs. Russian attitudes toward, 156, 159, 164
space stations:
 proposals for, 169, 202
 in science fiction, 18–20
space surveillance tracking systems, 187, 189
Space Technology Laboratories, 133
space walks, 196, foll. p. 196, 209–210, 211, 212–214
Spadeadam Rocket Establishment, 174, 175
Spanish Civil War, 39
Sparrow missiles, 143
Spencer, H., 89
Sperry Gyroscope Company, 37
splashdown, 231, 237
Sprint missiles, 146, 148
Sputnik satellites, 158, 164, foll. p. 164, 205
stabilization:
 Goddard's work on, 46, 47, 49–51
 for sounding rockets, 151
 spin introduced for, 33
Stafford, Thomas P., foll. p. 196, 213, 215, 231–233, 241
Stalin, Joseph, 61
Stanton, Austin W., 179
stars, 2–8, 68, 187
Staver, Robert, 116–118
Steinhoff, Ernst, 106, 112, 114
Steinhoff, Fritz, 112, 114
Steuding, Hermann, 106
Stever, H. Guyford, 181
Stewart, Charles L., 116, 117
Stewart, Homer J., 159, 161
Stiff, R. C., 101
Stooge missile, 90
Strategic Missiles Evaluation Committee, 133
Stuart, Jeb, 34
Stuhlinger, Ernst, foll. p. 196
submarines:
 missile-carrying, 112, 114, 120, 122, 129, 130–132, 135, 137, 139
 rocket bombs against, 97–98

Sun, the, 2–8, 9, 68, foll. p. 68
  satellite orbits around, 158, 163
  and scientific research programs, 150, 187, 189, 200–201
Sun-clock, 2, 4, 68
Sung Dynasty, 23, 25–26
Sun Saumiso, 23
Surcal satellites, 187, 189
Surveyor spacecraft, 192–193, 197
Sweden, 142
Swedenborg, Emanuel, 15
Switzerland, 33, 149
Syncom satellites, 164, 186, 189
systems development, study of, 182, 189

tactical satellite communications system (Tacsatcom), 187
Tactite sounding rockets, 155
Taifun missiles, 110, 112
Takeuchi, Ryuji, 185
Talbott, Harold E., 132
Talcott, George H., 33
Talos missiles, 144. 145
tandem staging, 159, 169
Tartar missiles, 143–144, 145
Tatum, Liston, 179
telemetry, 176
telescope:
  of Galileo, 7
  orbiting, 220
television:
  of Moon photographs, 191, 193
  via satellite, 184–186, 189, 205
Telstar satellites, 164, 185, 189, 205
Tereshkova, Valentina V., 205, 212
Terrapin sounding rockets, 153
Terrier missiles, 143, 145
Tessman, Bernard, 118
Thales of Miletus, 2, 68, foll. p. 68
Theodore Roosevelt, USS, 131
Thiel, Walter, 105
Thiokol Chemical Company, 94, 126
Thomas, Charles S., 130
Thompson, Floyd L., 224
Thompson, L. T. E., 53, 93
Thor missiles, 122, 133, 135, 139
  as carrier rockets, 156, 161, 163, 172–173, 187–188
Thunderbird missiles, 147, 149
Tigercat missiles, 147
Tikhonravov, M. K., 62, 63, 179
Tiling, Reinhold, 69, 71
Tiny Tim rockets, 99
Tippoo Sultaun, 30
Tiros satellites, 164, foll. p. 164, 183–184, 189
Titan missiles, 133, 135–136, 139
  as carrier rockets, 163, 165, 167, 169, 170, 172–173
Titov, Gherman, 158–159, 205, 212
Tizard, Sir Henry, 93
Toftoy, Holger N., 116–118, 124
Tokaty, G. A., 61
Tolman, Richard C., 93
Tomahawk sounding rockets, 157
Tombaugh, Clyde, 8
Topaze missiles, 142
Torré, Morel, 29
TOS System, 184
Townsend, John W., Jr., 165

Tractatus de sphaera (Sacrobosco), 5–6
Trailblazer sounding rockets, 153
Tranquillity Base, 239, 244
Transit satellites, 186, 189
Treatise on Horsemanship and War Strategems, 27, foll. p. 68
Trichel, Gervais W., 116
Truax, Robert C., 82–83, 101, 102, 179
TRW Space Log, 189
Tsander, Fridrikh A., 61, 62, 63
Tsiolkovsky, Konstantin E., 40–43, 58, 60, 63, 74, 100, foll. p. 100, 176, 233
Tucker, George, 16
Twiggs, David, 33
Twining, Nathan F., 133
Tyura Tam, 182

Ufa Film Company, 58, 59, 65, 66
Uhl, Edward G., 94–95
United Aircraft Corporation, 167, 169
United States:
  British rocket attacks on, 31–33
  early rocketry in, 33–34, 43–56, 60, 78–85, 100, foll. p. 100
  and German rocket scientists, 100, 104, 114–119
  postwar missile program in, 100, foll. p. 100, 120–139, 142–148
  space exploration programs in, 151–173, 176–181, 183–189, 191–200, 203–254
  World War II rocket programs in, 93–104
United States Air Force, 99, 101, 120–121, 177
  and postwar missile program, 120–122, 123, 128, 129, 132–139, 142–144
  and space research program, foll. p. 100, 151, 152, 167, 169, 178, 179, 186–187, 203–205
United States Army, 53–54, 83–84
  and postwar missile program, 100, foll. p. 100, 120, 122–130, 144–148
  and space research program, 151, 152, 161–163, 165, 167, 178, 179
  World War II rocket program in, 93, 94–95, 97, 103–104
United States Army Air Corps, 53–54, 85, 95, 97
United States Navy, 46, 48, 53, 56, 82, 84
  and postwar missile program, 120, 125, 128–132, 143–144
  and space research program, foll. p. 100, 151–153, 160–161, 176–178, 179, 186–187, 203, 204
  World War II rocket program in, 93, 94, 96–99, 101, 102, 143
UP-3 missiles, 88–89
Uranus (planet), 8

V-1 missiles, 104–105, 120–121, 122

V-2 missiles, 65, 71, 72–73, 100, foll. p. 100, 105, 106–108, 115–119
  Russian versions of, 140
  as sounding rockets, 150–151
  U.S. versions of, 123–126, 127
Valier, Max, 64, 65, 66
Valturio, Robert, 23
Van Allen, James A., foll. p. 164, 183
Vance, Cyrus R., 127, 215
Vandenberg, Hoyt S., 178
Vandenberg Air Force Base, 134, 138, 139, 189
Van Devander, C. W., 78
Van Dresser, Peter, 84
Van Evera, Dr., 93
Vanguard carrier rockets, 159–161, 162, 163, 172–173, 179, 180
Vanguard satellites, 164, 183, 184, 189
variable-thrust rockets, 56
Vela satellites, 187
velocity:
  in Mariner 4 flight, 198
  of missiles, tables, 87, 88, 98, 104, 111–114, 123, 125
  orbital, 43, 56, 57
  of Viking sounding rockets, 153
Venus (planet):
  early views of, 2, 3, 6, 7, 9, 68, foll. p. 68
  grouping of, 8
  probes toward, 158, 164, foll. p. 164, 193, 196, 197–201, 250–254
  Soviet spacecraft impacted on, 198–200, 201
Venus spacecraft, 197, 198–200, 201
Vera Historia (Lucian), 9–10
Verein für Raumschiffahrt (VfR), 64–70, 72
Verne, Jules, 9, 17–18, 41, 44, 56, 100, 202
Véronique sounding rockets, 157
Vesta sounding rockets, 156, 157
Viet Nam, 148, 149, 250
Vigilante airplanes, 122
Viking sounding rockets, 151–153
  as carrier rockets, 156, 159–161
Vincent, Thomas, 127
Viper sounding rockets, 153
Volkhart, Kurt C., 64, 65
Voltaire, 15
Volynov, Boris, 217
Von Braun, Magnus, 116, 117
Von Braun, Wernher, 58, 65, 67, 70–73, 74, 100, 106–109, 114–118, 119, 122, 124, 126, 127, 161, 165, 166, 168, 178, 179, 202, 250
Von Kármán, Theodore, 85
Von Neumann, John, 133, 135
Voskhod spacecraft, 196, foll. p. 196, 207, 209–210, 212
Vostok spacecraft, 158–159, 181, 196, 205
Voyage à Venus (Eyraud), 17
Voyage to Cacklogallinia (Brunt), 14–15
Voyage to the Moon, A (Atterlay), 16
Voyage to the Moon (Cyrano de Bergerac), 13
Voyages to the Moon (Nicolson), 10

Wac Corporal rockets, 104, 125, 127, 151, 152
Walker, Joseph A., 204
Walter, Hellmuth, 73–74, 108–109
Wang Ling, 23
Wardell, Michael, 92
Ware, James R., 24, 26–27
War of 1812, 31–33
War of the Worlds (Wells), 21
Warren Air Force Base, 139
Wasp rockets, 142, 153, 157
Wasserfall missiles, 110, 112
weather satellites, 164, foll. p. 164, 183–184, 189
Webb, James E., 185, 199
Webster, A. G., 93
Welborn, John C., 117
Welles, Orson, 21
Wells, H. G., 21, 44
Welsh, Edward C., 183
Western Electric Company, 144–145
Whipple, Fred L., 179
White, Edward H., II, 196, foll. p. 196, 210, 211, 213, 215, 224
White, Robert M., 204
White, Thomas D., 185
White Sands, N.M., 104, 123–126, 127, 145, 146, 151–152
Wiesner, Jerome B., 133
Wilkins, John, 12–13, 78
Wilkins, Sir Hubert, 78
Williams, Clifton C., 224
Wilson, Charles E., 128, 129, 133
Wilson, Miles, 15
Winkler, Johannes, 69
Woolams, Jack, 203
Wooldridge, Dean E., 133
Woolwich Royal Arsenal, 30, 77
Worcester, Mass., 44, 45, 47, 48, 49, 100
World War I, 36–39, 45, 48, foll. p. 68
World War II, 63, 85–119, 143
Worth, William Scott, 33
Wright Air Development Center, 137
Wyld, James H., 82, 84

X-1 rocket airplanes, 203, 204
X-2 rocket airplanes, 203-204
X-15 rocket airplanes, 122, 204, 205
X-20 Dynasoar program, 205
XB-70 airplanes, 122

Yaeger, Charles E., 203
Yates, Donald M., 133
Yegorov, Boris B., 209, 212
Yeliseyev, Alexei, 217
Yo I-Fang, 25
York, Herbert F., 167
Young, David, 179
Young, John W., 211, 212, 215, 231–233, 241
Younger, Allan, 77
Youngquist, Robertson, 101

Zanssen, Leo, 107
Zasyadko, Alexander, 31
Zborowsky, Helmut von, 74
Zond spacecraft, 193, 198, 201
Zucker, Gerhard, 69, 72